ABOVE and BEYOND

THE ENCYCLOPEDIA OF AVIATION and SPACE SCIENCES

VOLUME 14
WINGS – ZULU TIME
INDEX

ABOVE and BEYOND

THE ENCYCLOPEDIA OF AVIATION and SPACE SCIENCES

NEW HORIZONS PUBLISHERS, INC.
CHICAGO

COVER PHOTO:

The cockpit of a DC-8 commercial
transport simulator at the United
Air Lines training facilities
in Denver, Colorado.
United Air Lines, Inc.

Library of Congress Catalog Card Number 68–14013
Published simultaneously in Canada
Printed in the United States of America

Printed by Kingsport Press, Inc., Kingsport, Tennessee
Typesetting by American Typesetting Company, Chicago
Color separations and preparatory by Schawk Graphics, Inc.,
Litho Color Separators, Chicago
Paper, New Horizons Text, by Oxford Paper Company

The cantilever wing of the Boeing 727 is an exceptionally strong structure.

Wings

Lighter-than-air vehicles ascend and remain aloft through their own buoyancy. Heavier-than-air vehicles, whether they are tethered kites, gliders, airplanes, or helicopters, depend upon the dynamic action of air against all or part of the aircraft's surface to provide lift (*see*). Wings of heavier-than-air vehicles are airfoils (*see*) designed to produce the required lift. While many components of an aircraft may serve as airfoils and contribute to lift, such as the surface of the fuselage, only the wing is designed primarily for this purpose.

The rotary wing of a helicopter (*see*) is, in fact, a rotating airfoil which produces lift by rotating through the air. Wings of airplanes and gliders (*see*) are fixed in position, and lift is produced by the dynamic action of the air against the wing surfaces. As the machine moves forward through the air mass, the wing overcomes the forces of gravity and permits the airplane or glider to rise into the air and remain aloft.

A wing is one of the major components of an airplane (*see*), along with the fuselage (*see*), empen-

nage (*see*), landing gear (*see*), and powerplant. Although the fuselage may represent more volume, the wing is normally the largest surface. Its components include the leading edge, trailing edge, ailerons (*see*), wing flaps, tip, structural members, skins, and attachments. Wings extend outward perpendicularly from the fuselage or main body of the airplane, with the amount of sweepback depending upon the type of vehicle and its design. In cross-section, the wing takes on the appearance of a tear drop, being thicker toward the leading edge and tapering off toward the rear or trailing edge. The lower surface is relatively flat, while the upper surface is curved or contoured.

Wings come in varied shapes and sizes. The materials used for fabrication range from wood (*see*) and fabrics (*see*) to heat-resistant metal alloys. The function, however, is the same—to provide the force of lift by obtaining the desired reaction from the air through which it moves.

Lift Factors

The lift created results from a combination of wing size, shape, angle at which it moves through

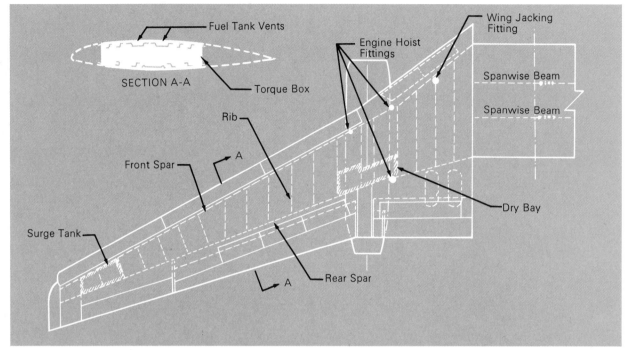

The Boeing 737 wing is an aluminum alloy, two-spar structure. The main wing loads are carried by front and rear spars (shear loads) and upper and lower panel assemblies (bending loads).

the air, air density, and airspeed. It is measured in terms of lift expressed in pounds and stated in equation form reads:

$$L = C_L \times \tfrac{1}{2}p \times SV^2$$

in which L is the lift in pounds and C_L is the lift coefficient (wing shape and angle of attack). Density, p, is expressed in slugs per cubic foot; S represents the wing area in square feet, and V is the airspeed in feet per second. Air passing over the upper curved part of the wing must travel farther than air passing below the flatter, lower surface, yet the air reunites at the trailing edge at the same time. This means the air passing over the top of the wing must move faster than air passing below the wing, resulting in a negative pressure on top and a positive pressure below. The differential results in the element of lift, permitting the airplane to overcome the forces of gravity.

Considering the cross-section again, a line drawn from the center of the leading edge to the center of the trailing edge would represent the *chord*, or the longitudinal dimension of the airfoil section. The rise in the curve of the airfoil from its chord is the *camber*. The upper camber is the upper part of the airfoil, and the lower camber is the lower part.

The wing is placed on the fuselage so that the center of gravity (*see*) falls within the main aerodynamic chord of the wing. The main aerodynamic chord is simply a range within which the center of

gravity must fall to provide proper weight and balance (*see*).

If shape and size are so important to the amount of lift, it might be concluded that all wings should be large and thick to provide maximum lift. This conclusion might be correct if overcoming gravity were the only concern, but there are other forces. Increased size and thickness increase the force of drag (*see*), and drag has an adverse effect on speed and performance.

Drag is a force opposite to the direction of the motion of the aircraft. This force includes profile drag or drag caused by the skin friction. There is also an induced drag, which is the result of the force from the downward velocity imparted to the air. The induced drag actually increases as the lift increases.

If speed were the only concern, all wings would be thin and small, but they would operate to the prejudice of lift. Between the extremes are multiple possibilities, requiring a compromise to provide the proper size and shape for desired performance of the specific airplane.

The main structural member of the wing is the *wing spar* or beam which runs the length of the wing from the fuselage to the tip of the wing. Some designs have one spar and some have two. Depending upon the construction, these can be either metal or wood. *Former ribs*, which have the

shape of the profile of the wing in cross-section, are attached to the spar. Some are strictly former ribs, providing shape, while others are compression ribs designed to handle load factors. Wings that are covered with fabric are internally trussed, but wings covered with metal or plywood are not, because the stresses are transferred to the metal or wooden skins. For high-speed transport and military aircraft, box beams using extruded and machined components are commonly used.

Regulations specify that the strength of stressed-skin wings must be proved by load tests or by combined structural analysis and load tests. Rib tests must simulate the conditions in the airplane relative to torsional rigidity of spars, fixity conditions, lateral supports, and attachment to spars. All parts of the surface must be suitably protected against deterioration or loss of strength in service due to weathering, corrosion, and abrasion.

The outer end of the wing is called the *wing tip* and has more to do with stability (*see*) than with structural integrity or strength. The inner end of the wing that affixes to the fuselage is the *wing root*. The *butt rib* is the innermost rib between the wing structure and the main body of the airplane.

Wing Shape

The easiest shape to visualize would be a flat wing which when viewed from above appeared to be a rectangle. In order to provide the differential between negative pressure on top and positive pressure below, this flat rectangular plane or wing cannot be used. Wings must taper toward the tip, meaning that the wing is not as wide at the tip end as at the root end.

Most wings also taper in the other dimensions, meaning that they become thinner toward the tip than at the root. To say that fixed wings are perpendicular to the fuselage is an oversimplification. Most wings sweep back to some degree. This degree of sweepback is known as the *angle of incidence*. High-speed jet aircraft have a greater angle of incidence than lighter, slow-speed equipment. Furthermore, wings vary as to the amount of upward slope between the root and the tip. This upward sweep is known as *positive dihedral* and is measured in degrees. There are some isolated cases of negative dihedral in use.

Increasing the *angle of attack* (*see*) increases lift. This angle is the amount of variance from a horizontal plane with which the wing moves through the air. Basically, the pilot changes the angle of attack by changing the attitudes of the aircraft. The classic example is the placing of one's hand out of the window of a fast moving automobile. If the hand remains level, it does not move from the plane in which it is placed. If the leading edge of the hand is tilted upward, the angle of attack is increased, and the hand tends to move upward in the air stream. The point at which a wing is affixed to the fuselage has an established angle of attack, compatible with the overall design of the wing.

The number of wings determines whether the airplane is a biplane or a monoplane. The monoplane may have a high wing, midwing, or low wing.

Externally Braced, Cantilever, and Semicantilever

The airplane may be externally braced, or it may be a cantilever or semicantilever. A biplane is externally braced, having the wings attached to the

The framework of a 1928 Cessna Model AW is seen before the fabric has been applied. Note the cantilever type of wing construction.

Wings

top and bottom of the main structure and then braced with wires and rods. The biplane provides an excellent strength-to-weight ratio, is simple, and permits inexpensive construction compared with other types. The biplane has fine lift characteristics and is capable of slow flight. The drag caused by external bracing, however, and the susceptibility to ice collection constitute disadvantages. Some monoplanes are externally braced, transmitting the flight and landing loads through struts (*see*) and other external braces to the main fuselage structure.

A full cantilever wing requires no external bracing since one end is rigidly fixed to the fuselage and the other end is free. The wing root can withstand the loads imposed in flight or in landing. This wing is highly efficient but expensive, and it requires heavy materials. Drag is minimal.

Between the two extremes is the semicantilever wing. It is basically a cantilever, but depends on supplemental strength from a limited number of external braces, which take the form of one or two wing struts which run from the fuselage to a point on the wing. The strut reduces the requirement for heavy materials yet is small enough to produce the minimum of drag.

High, Low, and Midwings

In monoplane designs, the wing may be on the top, on the bottom, or at the middle of the fuselage. Proponents of the high-wing design praise the inherent stability induced by having the capsule or cabin hanging below the lift-producing wing. Obvious advantages are found in the downward visibility and ease of entry into the cabin area. Protection from the sun is a plus factor. High-wing monoplanes have the strut attached to the bottom of the wing and running to the lower part of the fuselage.

Low-wing monoplanes provide upward visibility.

The Travelair 4000 was a typical example of a biplane requiring drag-producing struts and bracing wires to maintain structural strength.

They are normally cantilevers, but those which are not have the strut attached to the top of the wing running to a point high on the fuselage of the aircraft. Examples of these would be the various low-wing agricultural airplanes in production.

Some planes are built with the midwing configuration. Although they have enjoyed military acceptance, very few have found wide acceptance in general aviation (*see*). Attempts at producing other wing configurations, such as the inverted gull wing, have met some military success. They permit shorter landing gear and use of long propellers to absorb the full benefits of the powerplants installed.

A problem inherent in designing efficient wings is the loss of lift as a result of failure of the air to move smoothly over the surface. A thin layer of air adheres to the surface of the wing and has its own circulatory action known as the *boundary layer* (*see*). Efforts are made through use of spoilers (*see*), slots, and other devices to minimize the separation of the main flow of air from the surface and thus delay the moment of burbling and stall (*see*). Most airplanes increase lift by changing the contour through the use of wing flaps, which are located between the aileron and the

In 1927 the cantilever wing was an innovation that had not been entirely accepted. This photograph was used by Clyde Cessna to illustrate the structural integrity of this type of wing.

fuselage and attached to the trailing edge of the wing structure. In retracted or trailing position they are, in fact, a part of the main wing surface. Other efforts to increase lift have been made through use of induced air into the boundary layer and slotted leading edges.

With breakthroughs in supersonic and subsonic speeds, aviation looks forward to increased use of variable pitched wings which move backward into a delta configuration for flight and to the more conventional wing position for takeoffs and landings.

Leslie L. Thomason

See also: Aerodynamics, Variable geometry

Winnie Mae, Lockheed Vega

The Lockheed Vega was a single-engine, high-wing monoplane which first appeared in 1927 and was produced until 1933. It was the first aircraft ever produced by Lockheed, and the Vega was to bring much fame to the name of Lockheed. Of the 131 Vegas built, one in particular was to become truly famous. This was the one purchased by F. C. Hall, an oil man from Oklahoma City, in 1930. Hall named the craft *Winnie Mae* after his daughter. A private pilot, Wiley Post (*see*), was retained to fly the aircraft for Mr. Hall in business trips.

Wiley Post, however, had other ideas. He was fascinated by the idea of setting new long-distance records with this aircraft, and persuaded his employer to fly it in the 1930 National Air Races, which he won.

Then, in June of 1931, Post and navigator Harold Gatty left New York in an attempt to set a round-the-world record. They returned to New York 8 days 15 hours 51 minutes later, having achieved their goal.

Then in July, 1933, Post set out alone to attempt to lower the record. The *Winnie Mae* was equipped with revolutionary new gadgets such as a Sperry automatic pilot and a radio direction finder. Post brought the *Winnie Mae* back in 7 days 18 hours 49 minutes, again establishing a new record.   Claude G. Luisada

See also: World records and round-the-world flights

Wise, John

American balloonist; inventor
Born: February 24, 1808;
    Lancaster, Pennsylvania
Died: September 29, 1879;
    Lake Michigan

One of America's foremost contributors in the history of ballooning was John Wise, a Pennsylvania farm youth. At age 14 he read a German newspaper account of a balloon flight from Germany to Italy, and from then on he devoted his life to the study and practice of aerostatics.

In 1835 Wise made his first ascent over Philadelphia, Pennsylvania, in a balloon of his own design. He had never seen another balloon or manned ascension at that time, but his experiment was a complete success. In subsequent experiments he was the first to advance the theory that a steady wind blew from west to east at an altitude of two to three miles. He believed that such air currents could be beneficially used by balloonists to fly from America to Europe.

Wise tested his theory on July 1, 1859, when he ascended at St. Louis, Missouri, with three passengers, bound for New York City. The balloon came safely to the ground near Henderson, New York, more than 800 miles from its starting point.

On another flight Wise's balloon was caught in the updraft of a thunderstorm. The hydrogen balloon expanded so rapidly that it exploded and Wise was injured. Remnants of the balloon acted like a makeshift parachute to bring him to the ground. The experience led him to invent a rip panel by which he could turn the balloon into a parachute.

On a second attempt to reach New York City from the Midwest, Wise and a companion went down over Lake Michigan and were drowned.

Robert L. Parrish

See also: Balloons, History of aviation

Women in aerospace

The story of aviation from the development of lighter-than-air craft to the exploration of space beyond the Earth's atmosphere cannot be fully told without including the contributions made by many dedicated women.

The advent of powered flight in 1903 eliminated

Women in aerospace

a measure of the previous requirement of great physical strength, and the opportunity to fly opened up for women. However, flying was not considered a proper activity for "ladies" of that period, but those who were impervious to public opinion and had enthusiasm, dedication, and the willingness to risk injury or death made a place for themselves in what was primarily a man's world. In 1908 a Frenchwoman, Baroness de la Roche, was the first woman to solo. In 1910 Blanche Stuart Scott, a student of Glenn Curtiss (see), was practicing taxiing and "accidentally" soloed, thereby earning a first for an American woman. Soon after this, the Aero Club of America, which was then authorized to issue pilots' licenses, enrolled the name of the first woman to get a pilot's license—Harriet Quimby, who in her short career of 15 months became the first woman in the world to fly the English Channel.

During the years before World War I, more and more women joined the ranks of daredevils, exhibition flyers, and aerial record breakers. Among the most famous of these were Katherine Stinson, her sister Marjorie, and Ruth Law Oliver (see). Katherine was noted for her aerobatic skill and cross-country flying, and for her aircraft-designing ability. She is believed to be the first woman to fly the mail. Marjorie Stinson learned to fly when she was 18 years old and established her reputation as a flight instructor at the family's Texas flying school. The girls' brother Eddie Stinson was taught to fly by his sisters, and he went on to become a famous aircraft manufacturer. Ruth Law Oliver soloed in 1912 and later became famous as an aerobatic and exhibition pilot.

In World War I when flying became a military activity, most of the exhibition and stunting events were restricted. Women were not permitted to enter the military flying ranks, though several did serve as flight instructors.

Women Set Records

During the 1920's and 1930's, growing numbers of pilots were turning to racing and record-setting, and contributed to better designs of airplanes and better flying techniques. It required precision, cool judgment, and imagination—qualities possessed by such women as Ruth Nichols, Phoebe Fairgrave Omlie, Viola Gentry, Louise Thaden, and Blanche Noyes in the United States; Lady Mary Heath, Lady Mary Bailey, and Amy Johnson in England.

Among their credits: Ruth Nichols set a cross-country record for women in 1930 flying from east to west in less than 17 hours; in 1931 she set a women's altitude record of 28,743 feet; also in 1931 she set the women's speed record at 215.65 mph. Her

British aviatrix Amy Johnson (*left*) vanished on a flight in 1941. American Amelia Earhart, also lost, shown in a 1935 photo (*right*).

attempt to make a solo transatlantic flight in 1931 was thwarted by a takeoff accident in Newfoundland.

Phoebe Omlie was an exhibition stunt flyer who turned to racing for a while, winning three times in the 1930 National Air Races, and winning the National Sweepstakes Race in 1931 from California to Cleveland over a field of 80 men and women.

Viola Gentry set a solo endurance record in 1928 by flying for eight hours.

Louise Thaden set altitude, speed, and distance records, but her greatest achievement was winning the 1936 Bendix Transcontinental Air Race with copilot Blanche Noyes. She was awarded the Harmon Trophy for outstanding pilot in 1936.

Blanche Noyes became active in air-marking (signs on roofs or on the ground 10-20 ft. high for guidance), and is chief of the Airmarking Division of the Federal Aviation Administration. She was given the Lady Hay Drummond Trophy in 1959 for her many years as an outstanding woman pilot.

Lady Mary Heath and Lady Mary Bailey competed in the distance flight in 1928 from London to Cape Town, South Africa. Hardships plagued both women, but Lady Mary Bailey became the first woman to fly the route solo in the same year.

Amy Johnson (*see*) ranks among the top two or three women in aviation achievement, and her greatest accomplishment was flying solo from England to Australia in 19½ days in 1930.

The most famous of all women pilots was Amelia Earhart (*see*), still held in esteem by all in aviation. She started flying in 1920 and established many records for women. Her greatest interest was trailblazing, flying long distances, and she was the first woman to make a solo flight across the Atlantic in 1932.

The Ninety-Nines and Whirly Girls

Licensed women pilots in the U.S. in 1929 only numbered 117, though not all of them were actively

Space programs attract women in all nations. Jerrie Cobb *(left)* underwent the examinations of the Mercury program in an attempt to become the first U.S. female astronaut. Dr. Nancy Roman *(center)* is a top space scientist. U.S.S.R.'s Valentina Tereshkova *(right)* was first woman in space.

flying. Tough competitors among themselves, the women who flew in the 1920's and 1930's nevertheless were bound together in a spirit of comraderie, realizing an obligation to the field of aviation. Out of this spirit was formed the Ninety-Nines *(see)*, organized in 1929 with Amelia Earhart as president.

After World War II the Ninety-Nines concentrated on their original aims, and in recent years have focused on education in the space age with the Amelia Earhart Scholarship Fund, air-marking, and numerous air races including the famous All-Women's Transcontinental Air Race (AWTAR). This Powder Puff Derby *(see)* as it is popularly called, was first flown in 1947 with the aim of stimulating interest in private aviation. A new organization formed by and for women—the Whirly Girls *(see)*—is composed of licensed helicopter pilots. Begun in 1955 with 13 members, it has grown to over 100 members, and one of this group, Dr. Dora Daugherty, holds the women's altitude and distance records in helicopters.

Women Pilots in World War II

Two women leaders to emerge in World War II were Nancy Harkness Love and Jacqueline Cochran *(see)*. Nancy Love organized and headed the Women's Auxiliary Ferrying Squadron (WAFS) in 1942 with 25 of the best pilots selected from dozens of applicants. To be selected, a woman had to have at least 500 hours flying time and had to be qualified in planes of 200 hp or more. Jacqueline Cochran led a group of women pilots to Britain to join the women's division of the Air Transport Auxiliary (ATA), formed to ferry planes wherever they were needed by the military. Over 100 women pilots from Allied countries served with the ATA under Miss Pauline Gower. While in England, Jacqueline Cochran studied the ATA ferrying command, and upon her return to the United States in 1942 was appointed director of the Women's Air Force Service Pilots (WASP).

Jacqueline Cochran's flying career has extended from 1932 until the present, and she has broken more records than any other pilot in the world. In 1953 she flew a Sabre-Jet F-86 faster than the speed of sound—a momentous first for women. (The first woman to fly a jet was Ann Baumgartner Carl, a WASP, in 1944.) In 1960 she flew at Mach 2 and in 1962 she set 49 records in one international flight of 5,120 miles from New Orleans, Louisiana, to Hanover, Germany. Miss Cochran's competitors during these years were Elizabeth Boselli and Jacqueline Auriol of France. Both women set formidable records, but Miss Cochran consistently set new ones, and her present speed record is 1,429.346 mph in a Lockheed 104G.

Aside from setting jet records, the women have made an effort to increase their ranks since World War II, seeking to contribute on an equal basis to the growth of aviation. Since the infancy of U.S. airlines, women have been denied cockpit positions as pilots on scheduled passenger lines, though they have flown cargo planes and nonscheduled lines. A Russian woman astounded ground personnel at London Airport on September 28, 1965, when she climbed from behind the controls of a big four-engine Soviet Ilyushin 18 airliner. Miss Maria Atanassova at 35 was a 17-year veteran pilot with the Bulgarian airline, TABSO.

Thousands of women have flown with airlines as stewardesses and have performed many acts of heroism. The first stewardess was Ellen Church who was hired by United Air Lines in 1930 to care for passengers. Miss Church was a registered nurse who loved to fly, and she convinced airline officials that stewardesses were needed.

New Records

In the 1960's women continue to break records in the tradition of the early years of flight. In Columbus, Ohio, in 1964 a housewife weary of

routine household duties decided to fly around the world in the family plane. After careful planning and preparation, Jerrie Mock (*see*) made the first women's solo flight around the world in a ten-year-old single-engine airplane which she dubbed *The Spirit of Columbus*. Shortly afterward Joan Merriam Smith repeated the flight in a small twin-engine plane. Then in 1967 two other women made similar flights: Miss Sheila Scott (*see*), an English pilot and actress, broke Mrs. Mock's speed record; and Ann Pellegrino, in a sister ship of Amelia Earhart's, duplicated the Earhart route exactly 30 years after Miss Earhart was lost.

Women have roles in aviation other than flying airplanes. Representative of these are: Mrs. Olive Ann Beech, who has been president of the Beech Aircraft Company since 1950; Laurel Ronneau, who is one of four managers of the Los Angeles International Airport; Mrs. Donald Quarles, special assistant for women's aviation activities in the office of General Aviation Affairs, Federal Aviation Administration, a post created to help coordinate the contributions women make to U.S. aviation.

Women and Space

In June, 1963, a 26-year-old Russian woman, Valentina Tereshkova (*see*), became the first woman to orbit the Earth. She logged 48 orbits. Miss Tereshkova was not a pilot and had no aviation background aside from a recreational activity of parachute jumping. In 1961 Jerrie Cobb had undergone the same difficult physical examination given to the Mercury astronauts. In 1961 several other women followed who were eager to be the first female astronaut. The opposition they met to women participating in the program still prevails in the U.S. space program.

Among women known to have made other contributions to space exploration are Nan Glennon, an engineer who has helped design rockets; Edith Olson, a miniaturization expert; Nancy Roman, whom NASA placed in charge of developing astronomical observatories in 1959; and Franki van der Wal, who helped develop nose cones.

The real story of women in aviation today is being written by the thousands of women who either fly for recreation or earn their living by flying. The latter include Mrs. Tracy Pilurs, an aerobatic pilot, who built her own Smith Mini-plane; Miss Berne Studer, Canadian bush pilot in the lake country of Canada; and June B. Edwards, owner of the Agri-Business Information Agency which provides services to agricultural aviation.   Mary Jo Janey

See also: Astronauts, Flight, Stewards and stewardesses

Wood

Wood is a combination of long, intertwined chains of cellulose impregnated with an extremely complex substance called *lignin*. It is the primary product of an amazingly complicated chemical factory known as a tree.

Wood was extensively used in early airplane construction. Spruce, Douglas fir, oak, mahogany, walnut, and birch lumber were used in various airframe and propeller applications. It was soon discovered that plain wood had many drawbacks and the best way to avoid these was to laminate sheets of wood together, using various glues, to build the different parts of aircraft.

Although metals were primarily used for aircraft construction by World War II, the shortages of aluminum and other aircraft metals early in the war led to some use of wood. Bomb-bay doors, wing flaps, and other aircraft parts were made from a phenol-glued plywood during this time. Wood was used extensively in basic and primary training aircraft, light cargo planes, and all gliders.

Lightweight metals have all but replaced wood in modern aircraft, although propellers of some light aircraft are still made of wood. The largest application of wood in a modern aircraft factory is in the mock-up of a new aircraft. The versatile material may have even penetrated space, since it has been reported that early U.S.S.R. re-entry vehicles were made of wood.   John F. Judge

See also: First World War aircraft, Lamination, Materials, World War I

Woomera rocket range

A woomera is a hand-held aboriginal wooden stick used to launch a spear and is the name given to the town and aerospace vehicle launching range set up in South Australia as part of a joint U.K.-Australia venture in 1947. Now designated the Weapons Research Establishment (WRE) of the Australian Department of Supply, it lies in the desert 320 miles north-northwest of Adelaide, the state capital. Over 5,000 people work there and a complete town has been built. The Woomera range was first used to test the ballistics of bombs dropped from aircraft, then major U.K. guided weapon trials were held there in the 1950's and high-altitude research rockets, notably the U.K. Skylark, have been fired during and since the International Geophysical Year (*see*). Woomera has excellent optical and radar tracking facilities, a digital computer (WREDAC), and there is an engineering support facility at Salisbury, near Adelaide,

where there is also a large airfield, Edinburgh Field. The Woomera range head area is as large as England and Scotland, and an impact area on the northwest coast, 1,250 miles away, is the size of France.

Aerospace activities include the Baker-Nunn satellite tracking cameras, testing of the Australian drone Jindivik, a Minitrack station, deep space radar antennas, and radio communication equipment used in conjunction with the NASA manned spaceflights. The 107-lb. satellite WRESAT-1 (Weapons Research Establishment Satellite) was launched on November 29, 1967, by a modified three-stage U.S. Redstone rocket. In its 20 years of operation Woomera has become a major space facility vital to both European and U.S. programs and the wide areas of desert will undoubtedly prove of great use.   Paul M. Danforth

See also: Australia's aviation, United Kingdom aerospace activities, WRESAT

Worden, Alfred M.

Astronaut
Born: February 7, 1932;
Jackson, Michigan
Service: Major, USAF

Major Alfred M. Worden was an instructor at the Aerospace Research Pilot School from which he was graduated in 1965 when he was notified of his selection to the fifth group of astronauts (*see*) in April, 1966.

Worden earned a bachelor of military science degree from the U.S. Military Academy in 1955. In 1963 he earned M.S. degrees in aeronautical engineering and instrumentation engineering from the University of Michigan.

After being commissioned in the USAF, Worden served as a pilot and armament officer with the 95th Fighter Interceptor Squadron at Andrews Air Force Base from 1957 to 1961.

Worden has logged more than 2,327 hours flying time including 1,875 hours in jets. He is currently training for future space missions and is engaged in support activities for Apollo (*see*). Worden and his wife, the former Pamela Vander Beek, have two children.   J. W. Kroehnke

See also: Astronauts

World Aeronautical Chart, *see* Charts

World records and round-the-world flights

Since the advent of the air age in 1783 when man first ascended in a balloon, he has constantly strived to better his performance in the air. With the phenomenal progress that has been made in aviation since the first powered flight in 1903, records have been made and broken many times. Aviation has always been highly competitive, with nations and representative people continually trying to fly higher, faster, and farther.

Air-minded pioneers recognized early the desirability of standardizing procedures for certifying records. It has been well shown that record achievements have value in accelerating aeronautical progress. Pioneering flights and the attainment of new marks of speed, distance, and altitude have been an active stimulus to greater performances.

Such activity has served particularly to center public attention on flying, a fact which may be best exemplified by the tremendous increase in public interest which followed Charles Lindbergh's historic flight. Regardless of whether a record has the widespread effect of that transatlantic solo crossing, or is an accomplishment of principally technical interest, each flight that exceeds previous performances is a forward step.

Round-the-World Flights

Some of the early attempts at flying around the world also helped to promote aviation and stimulate flyers to greater achievements. The first successful U.S. attempt on April 6, 1924, began at Seattle, Washington, with four Douglas World Cruisers (*see*). After some difficulty, two of the planes completed the flight and returned to the U.S.

The first airship (*see*) to fly around the world was Germany's *Graf Zeppelin* in 1929. On June 23, 1931, Wiley Post (*see*) and Harold Gatty flew around the world in the *Winnie Mae* (*see*). In 1933, Post became the first man to make a solo round-the-world flight.

Howard Hughes (*see*) in 1938 adopted a multiple-crew system and set up a network of radio stations for weather reports around the world. His successful round-the-world flight was important because it proved the possibility of circling the globe by air without undue hardship because of advances in navigation, communications, and engineering.

FAI Rules

The Federation Aeronautique Internationale (FAI) (*see*) establishes the rules governing world record trials and aeronautic competitions. Rules for official world aircraft and spacecraft records are proposed

initially by various national aero clubs (*see*) that are members of the FAI. They are then evaluated by the FAI International Sporting Aviation Commission and submitted for final approval to the delegates of the aero clubs attending the annual conferences.

Each record has been established in accordance with official rules of procedure designed to insure the authenticity of the performance. Record flights are supervised and observed by qualified officials, and conducted in accordance with the FAI Sporting Code. Instruments used for recording performances are required to meet rigid accuracy standards. All attempts to establish official records must meet identical FAI standards. The FAI rules have these goals: 1) an equal opportunity to every competitor; 2) competent, unbiased judging; and 3) scientifically accurate recording.

To establish uniformity in the recognition of the many possible aircraft performances, a standard record classification has been adopted by the FAI for world and world class records.

World Records

World records are defined as maximum performances regardless of the class or type of aircraft used. The following are recognized: 1) *Aircraft*: Distance in a straight line; Distance over a straight line; Altitude; Altitude in horizontal flight; and Speed over a straight course; and 2) *Nonairbreathing Manned Rockets:* Duration with Earth orbit; Altitude with Earth orbit; Distance with Earth orbit; Greatest mass lifted with Earth orbit; Duration without Earth orbit; Altitude without Earth orbit; Distance without Earth orbit; and Greatest mass lifted without Earth orbit.

World Class Records

All other records which are international in scope and represent the best world performances for a particular type of aircraft are termed world class records to differentiate from world records.

World class records are defined as the best national performances for the classes and categories of aircraft recognized by the FAI. The aircraft classes which have been adopted by the FAI for the purpose of providing standard classification are: Free Balloons—Class A; Airships—Class B; Landplanes—Class C-1; Seaplanes—Class C-2; Amphibians—Class C-3; Gliders—Class D; and Rotorplanes—Class E. Powered aircraft are also subdivided into the following: Piston engines—Group I; Turboprop engines—Group II; Jet engines—Group III; and Rocket engines—Group IV.

In the case of landplanes, seaplanes, amphibians, and rotorplanes, there is a further subdivision by gross weight. For landplanes, amphibians, and rotorplanes, the world class records are:

Without payload:
1. Greatest distance in a straight line without landing or refueling
2. Greatest distance in a closed circuit without landing or refueling
3. Greatest altitude or height above sea level
4. Greatest altitude in a horizontal sustained flight
5. Greatest speed over a straight course (3 km and 15/25 km)
6. Greatest speed in a closed circuit over an established course for each of the following distances: 100 km (62.137 miles), 500 km (310.685 miles), 1,000 km (621.369 miles), 2,000 km (1,242.739 miles), 5,000 km (3,106.849 miles), and 10,000 km (6,213.698 miles)
7. Speed around-the-world
8. Time-to-climb to 3,000, 6,000, 9,000, 12,000, and 15,000 m or additional 5,000 m consecutively (light aircraft excluded)

With payload of 1,000 kg (2,204.6 lbs), 2,000 kg (4,409.2 lbs), 5,000 kg (11,023 lbs), 10,000 kg (22,046 lbs), or additional 5,000 kg consecutively (light aircraft excluded):
1. Greatest altitude or height
2. Greatest speed in a closed circuit over an established course for each of the following distances: 1,000 km (621.369 miles), 2,000 km (1,242.739 miles), 5,000 km (3,106.849 miles), and 10,000 km (6,213.698 miles)
3. Greatest payload lifted to a height of 2,000 m (6,561 feet)

World class records recognized for gliders are:
Greatest distance to a fixed point and return
Greatest distance in a straight line
Greatest distance to a fixed point
Greatest height or altitude above sea level
Greatest gain in height
Speed for 100 km over a triangular course
Speed over 300 km over a triangular course
Speed for 500 km over a triangular course

World Class Records for Airships and Free Balloons

For each of these classes of aircraft, world records are recognized by the FAI and as in the case of landplanes, seaplanes, amphibians, rotorplanes, and gliders, types of performances have been selected for recognition which it is believed are of greatest importance to performance development in each class.

Speed Over a Recognized Course

The FAI recognizes maximum speed performances between selected national capitals and internationally important cities. These performances are termed

World Records: Manned Spaceflight

Record Holder	Country	Date	Spacecraft	Record
Distance with Earth Orbit				
Maj. G. S. Titov	U.S.S.R.	8/6-7/61	Vostok II	436,912 mi.
Cdt. A. G. Nikolayev	U.S.S.R.	8/6-7/61	Vostok III	1,640,168 mi.
Lt. Col. V. F. Bykovsky	U.S.S.R.	6/14-19/63	Vostok V	2,066,654 mi.
Lt. Col. L. G. Cooper & Lt. Cdr. C. Conrad	U.S.	8/21-29/65	Gemini V	3,312,997 mi.
Lt. Col. F. Borman & Cdr. J. A. Lovell, Jr.	U.S.	12/4-18/65	Gemini VII	5,719,457 mi.
Endurance with Earth Orbit				
Maj. G. S. Titov	U.S.S.R.	8/6-7/61	Vostok II	25:11:00
Cdr. A. G. Nikolayev	U.S.S.R.	8/11-15/62	Vostok III	94:09:59
Lt. Col. V. F. Bykovsky	U.S.S.R.	6/14-19/63	Vostok V	118:56:41
Lt. Col. L. G. Cooper & Lt. Cdr. C. Conrad	U.S.	8/21-29/65	Gemini V	190:55:14
Lt. Col. F. Borman & Cdr. J. A. Lovell, Jr.	U.S.	12/4-18/65	Gemini VII	330:35:00
Greatest Altitude with Earth Orbit				
Maj. Y. A. Gagarin	U.S.S.R.	4/12/61	Vostok	203.19 mi.
Col. P. I. Belyayev & Lt. Col. A. A. Leonov	U.S.S.R.	3/18/65	Voskhod II	309.25 mi.
Lt. Cdr. C. Conrad & R. F. Gordon, Jr.	U.S.	9/13-15/66	Gemini XI	850.65 mi.
Endurance in Group Flight				
Capt. W. M. Shirra & Maj. T. P. Stafford	U.S.	12/15-16/65	Gemini VI	
Lt. Col. F. Borman & Cdr. J. A. Lovell, Jr.	U.S.	12/15-16/65	Gemini VII	20:02:39
Total Time in Space				
Capt. J. A. Lovell, Jr.	U.S.	11/11-15/66	Gemini VII & XII	425:09:34

Source: *National Aeronautic Association*

Significant Round-the-world Flights

Flight	Date	Time Elapsed[1]	Flt. Time[2]	Pilot(s)	Aircraft	Country
First successful round-the-world flight. Takeoff point, Seattle, Washington.	4/6/24	5 mo. 22 da.	363:	Capt. L. Smith & Lts. L. Arnold, E. Nelson & J. Harding	Douglas biplane	U.S.
Graf Zeppelin, first airship to fly round-the-world	8/7-29/29	21:07:34	—	Dr. Eckener	dirigible	Germany
First round-the-world solo flight	7/15-22/33	7:18:00	—	Wiley Post	Lockheed Vega	U.S.
Round-the-world flight demonstrates new equipment with multiple crews	7/14/38	3:19:17	—	Howard Hughes et al	Lockheed Super Electra	U.S.
First nonstop flight with inflight refueling by loop-hose method	3/2/49	—	94:01	USAF Capt. James Gallagher	Boeing B-29	U.S.
Rolls-Royce Avon jet engines used for first time	12/28/55	—	—	John Cunningham	deHavilland Comet III	England
First round-the-world jet passenger service inaugurated	3/3/59	—	—	BOAC	—	England
First flight over Poles in north-south direction	/ /65	2:22:00	—	Capts. J. Martin, F. Austin, & H. Finch	Boeing 707	U.S.

[1]Days:hours:minutes   [2]Minutes:seconds

course records and must be made over bases between previously designated cities.

Speed On a Commercial Route

In addition to speed records over a recognized course, the FAI recognizes the best performances in speed accomplished by aircraft with normal certificates of airworthiness belonging to regular airlines flying over regular air routes.

Feminine Records

Feminine records are recognized in all classes except those with payloads and light aircraft classified according to weight.

For a new record to be recognized, a performance must better the existing record by the following required margin:

Speed records   1 per cent

Altitude records	3 per cent
Distance records	1 per cent
Duration records (balloons)	1 per cent
Time-to-climb records	3 per cent
Maximum payload records	500 km (1,100 lbs.)

Until recently, the achievements in world records involved various types of aircraft only. The advent of the space age has brought about a new classification for manned spacecraft in world record attempts. On October 7, 1960, in a meeting at Barcelona, Spain, the FAI adopted the first rules to govern official world records for manned spacecraft.

Gordon Gregg and Helen Olian

See also: Altitude and altitude records, Distance and distance records, Endurance and endurance records, Polar flights, Speed and speed records

A Cockburn-Lange photograph said to be taken in actual aerial combat.

World War I

Airplane becomes an instrument of war

The airplane was not quite 11 years old when it was called for active duty in what some historians have called The Great War. From meager reconnaissance service in 1914 as a frail spruce and linen machine barely able to sustain itself in flight, the craft had developed into a truly great fighting machine when the end came late in 1918.

While most of the recorded aerial action of WWI took place on the Western, and to some extent on the Eastern Front, airplanes were actually serving military men over many land areas. Veteran naval officers of the major powers also begrudgingly accepted the machine for sea duty. During the course of the war, planes of the various nations made appearances, if only briefly, over the Atlantic and Indian oceans; the Mediterranean, Baltic, and Black seas; the Dardanelles; the Alps and the Balkans; and faraway places

like Africa, China, Japan, and the Sinai Peninsula and Palestine (now Israel).

For many years military experts had known the value of "seeing over the next hill" and of spotting enemy movements and gun emplacements. Earlier wars, including the U.S. Civil War, demonstrated the value of aerial platforms for such purposes. Of course, in that conflict the generals were limited to balloons (see) and, while partially effective, a balloon and its basket run up on a cable had limited mobility with the resultant limited success.

At the outbreak of WWI, it is estimated that the Allies and the Central Powers had several hundred airplanes, none of which had been constructed as war machines. They were 50-to-75-horsepower machines, built by such famous pioneers as Louis Bleriot (see) and Henri Farman (see) in France; Igo Etrich in

Austria; and others. Some resembled birds in their construction and the German *Taube*, or "Dove", achieved early success as a reconnaissance machine. The *Five O'Clock Taube*, called that because a German aviator in 1914 flew one over Paris every day at that time to drop two 4-pound bombs and leaflets demanding that the city surrender, achieved early fame. The Taube was so punctual that Frenchmen set their clocks by its 5 p.m. appearance. This dropping of leaflets is believed to be the first use of the airplane for psychological warfare.

Looked upon by many as a toy of no real military value in the years just preceding WWI, the airplane quickly proved its worth as a mobile observation post in the sky. For the first time in a great armed conflict, the generals were able to receive firsthand knowledge and accurate information of what the enemy was up to behind his lines. Planes bearing the red, white, and blue cockades (insignia) of the Allies and the black crosses of the Central Powers took to the air to observe enemy movements, shoot aerial photographs, and direct cannon fire. This was still the age of chivalry in the air, and opposing pilots would salute or wave to each other as they passed in the sky.

One day one of the pilots, probably irked by some action of an opposing pilot on the previous day, loaded his pockets with rocks and instead of waving to his adversary, tried to knock him out of the sky by throwing rocks at his machine. Rusty chains were also hurled across the sky in a further attempt to down an enemy aircraft. One Russian aviator, Alexander A. Kazakov, flying a French-built airplane, even tried to down his adversary's machine by trailing an anchor on a chain. Flying over his opponent, he would endeavor to hook the anchor to some part of the other airplane. He too was only moderately successful. This led to shotguns and pistols and finally to automatic rifles and machine guns. The day of chivalry even in the air was drawing to a close. Now it became a case of better machines, more armament, and better trained pilots. The first war in the air was underway.

The War Begins

The first so-called military airplanes (or aeroplanes as the word was commonly spelled in the early years) left much to be desired as fighting machines. In most cases, they were capable of carrying a pilot and aerial observer up to about 3,000 feet, but not much more. Their 50-to-75-horsepower engines provided speeds of about the same number of miles per hour. Flight duration was often limited to short hops. One notable exception was the flight of three English Avro's that took off from a base in France on November 21,

German Taubes were flown over Paris and dropped leaflets with a demand that the city surrender. The Taube was one of a number of aircraft designs that imitated bird forms.

The German Parabellum pistol fitted with a shoulder stock was used in early air combat prior to the incorporation of armament into aircraft.

The Spandau machine gun on a Fokker Eindecker being loaded. The gun, equipped with an interrupter gear, was mounted on the aircraft to fire through the propeller.

A typical Lewis machine gun installation in a Handley Page 0/004. The bag was used to collect the empty cartridges.

German camouflage on a Gotha bomber with a multicolored pattern typical of the Central Powers' aircraft camouflage.

The observer in a Rumpler observation airplane operates a radio signal key while checking troop movements on the ground.

1914. The three tiny machines, each carrying four 20-pound bombs, made a 250-mile roundtrip flight and successfully bombed the Zeppelin (dirigible) sheds at Friedrichshafen, Germany.

A popular powerplant used in many WWI machines was the *rotary engine*. This engine differed from *radial engines* of today in that the cylinders revolved around the stationary crankshaft with the propeller mounted on an extension of the crankcase. The engine was not equipped with a conventional throttle and it normally ran at only two speeds—full power or none. Speed was controlled by a button that permitted the pilot to cut the engine in and out. With the entire engine revolving, a terrific torque was generated and it took a lot of skill for the pilot to control the machine both on the ground and in the air. The most popular rotary engines of WWI were the French Gnome and Le Rhone, the English Bentley, and the German Oberursel.

Attempts were made to stow small bombs or grenades aboard which observers could drop over the side. *Flichettes*, small steel arrows with weighted tips, were also tossed out by the handfuls as anti-personnel weapons. None of these early attempts proved to be successful from a military standpoint.

During the first year, however, aircraft such as the German Taube, the French Morane and Bleriot, along with the English British Experimental, provided "eyes in the sky" for military tacticians. It is generally conceded that the early German craft were superior to those flown by the Allies. This was due in part to a greater interest in the aircraft as a military machine and to the inventive genius of early Austrian and German aerial pioneers. German craftsmen, with typical Teutonic thoroughness, played a major role too in the actual construction of the better-designed machine.

Following the rock-throwing days things moved fast, but pilots and observers found it difficult to be very effective with a pistol, a rifle, or a shotgun from a fluttering airplane. Special mounting devices were then used to mount army rifles for the observers' use. It is interesting to note here that less than two months after the start of the war, France recorded the first aerial victory. One of their pilots brought down a German plane with rifle fire early in October, 1914. Others were not so fortunate, and cases are on record where observers shot off their propellers and damaged their own aircraft rather than the enemy. A bit more successful were the machines that had a .30 caliber machine gun mounted on the top wing, firing over the propeller. However, this too had limitations since the gun was difficult to aim and it was

Rockets attached to the outer struts of a
French Nieuport were used for balloon strafing.

difficult to replace ammunition drums in flight. A few inventive pilots tried to install light cannons on their planes with some success. This innovation, however, did not reach a fully developed stage until WWII.

Innovations

Late in 1914 and early 1915, still another method was tried to make the airplane a more effective sky fighter. Pusher-type airplanes with propellers at the rear of the fuselage permitted observers or gunners to be placed at the front of the machine. This allowed aircraft such as the English Vickers Gunbus and the French Farman to carry a front-firing Lewis machine gun on a movable mount. Theoretically, this gave gunners a marked advantage since they now had an unobstructed range of fire forward and to some extent a wider field of fire.

Other machines followed suit and soon there were more Allied planes, some with forward fuselages looking like bathtubs, that could fire automatic weapons in the direction of flight. Although Allied planes had the advantage of forward-firing weapons, German aircraft of the period were superior in speed and maneuverability. They could elect to stay and fight or use their speed to outmaneuver the French and English pilots. These same machines were also used for early attempts at ground support for the infantry. Not only did they spot troops moving up to the front, but they were often able to lend a hand by diving on the enemy with small arms and rifle fire. Although only partially effective, the psychological effects were great. These operations gave comrades in the trenches a real lift. The airplane was now on its way to becoming an offensive weapon, but the day of real air-to-air combat and effective ground strafing had to await development of the synchronized machine gun.

About the same time, advancements were taking place in related fields. The English pioneered wireless telegraphy from the airplane to artillery posts for directing effective gunfire on specific targets. New cameras and camera mounts were developed that permitted the taking of reasonably good aerial photos.

The navies of the warring powers also took a new interest in the flying machine. Aircraft were fitted with pontoons (*see*) to permit operations from the water. Like their ground-based counterparts, these machines served in several theaters of operations as scouts to check on and report enemy fleet movements, direct shipboard fire from the surface fleet, and detect activities of submarines. Later, along with the Zeppelins (*see*), they became very effective as destroyers of the underwater craft. Experiments were also conducted using the catapult method of launch-

ing seaplanes (*see*) from the decks of battleships. The English were the leaders in this work and were successful in launching small observation-type planes. After returning from a scouting mission, the plane landed alongside the vessel and was hoisted aboard with block and tackle. Near the end of the war, the English converted the battlecruiser H.M.S. *Furious* into the first aircraft carrier and began conducting experiments on launching and retrieving fighter-type aircraft—a prelude to the giant carriers operated so successfully by the United States in World War II.

The German Navy also pioneered in the field of naval aviation. Her converted cargo steamer *Wolf*, with a Friedrichshafen seaplane aboard, cruised the Indian, South Pacific, and South Atlantic oceans in 1917. With the help of the seaplane, nicknamed *Wolfchen* ("wolf cub"), she sank or captured 28 Allied vessels.

Armament

The first attempt to mate aerial rockets with the airplane also came about in WWI. The French in 1917 attached five or ten small rockets, not unlike the kind used for Fourth of July celebrations, to the outer wing struts. Aircraft equipped in this manner were used effectively against German observation balloons that went down in flames when rockets ignited the inflammable hydrogen gas. Many of the balloon observers saved their lives by jumping from the basket when the attack occurred, using another new military development, parachutes (*see*). Early parachutes were too clumsy to be worn on the body. Instead, they were attached in a tube to the side of the balloon basket. When the jumper left the basket after hooking on a harness, the parachute trailed out behind him and lowered him safely to the Earth. Later, in 1918, the compact parachute was developed by the Germans, but few were produced. The Allied airmen of WWI, except for balloon observers, flew the entire war without parachutes.

Aircraft armament improved greatly during the war. Early tests for the use of machine guns involved the heavy, water-cooled type used by the infantry. These were modified to air-cooled, lightweight weap-

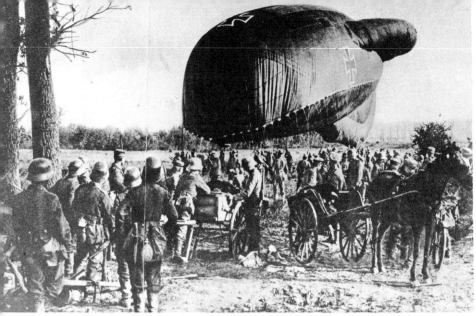

An observation balloon used to direct the fire of artillery batteries (*left*) is prepared for launching. The observer in a balloon under attack abandons the gondola (*right*) using a parachute.

ons and most fighter aircraft carried two guns, as did the Vickers (Allies) or the Spandau (German). Rate of fire and accuracy also improved. During the course of the war, the rate of fire of the standard guns increased from 500 to 1,000 rounds a minute.

In observation-type aircraft, the heavier machine-gun, like the Lewis, continued to be employed by the observer in the rear cockpit. The Lewis gun was used with or without its air-cooled jacket and was the standard Allied gun. It was fed from a top-mounted revolving drum containing 50 to 100 rounds. It weighed several pounds, was hard to handle in the plane's slipstream (*see*), and changing ammunition drums was difficult. German observers and gunners used the Parabellum machine gun, an air-cooled weapon fed by belts of ammunition

Attempts were made to install cannons aboard aircraft. The most notable was the installation of a 37mm cannon that fired through the propeller hub of a French Spad (*see*), flown by their great ace, Guynemer. Reports vary as to its success. Still another attempt to use heavier armament was a French airplane, the Voisin Cannon, which made its appearance in 1917. It sported the largest piece of ordnance of WWI, a 47mm cannon carried in the nose of this big pusher biplane. Again, it was not very successful, but it was the forerunner of things to come in WWII.

An earlier French Voisin (1915) was designed as one of the first light bombers. It was an odd looking pusher powered by a 140-hp engine that gave it a top speed of 65 mph. A slow but steady ship, it could carry a large load of small bombs. It was flown by such great French airmen as Charles Nungesser, who went on to score 45 aerial victories. Precision bomb sights like those used in WWII were, of course, unknown and results depended to a great extent on

the observer's ability to direct his bomb drops by hand and by chance. The few crude navigation instruments aboard the craft left much to be desired in pinpointing exact locations for bombing missions—a far cry from the radar (*see*) and other precision instruments of WWII.

Camouflage and Marking

The art of aircraft camouflage and aircraft marking was still another WWI innovation. Early military machines, like their civilian brothers, were constructed of wood (*see*) and covered with a linen or cotton fabric. The fabric (*see*) was shrunk to the frame with a clear dope (*see*) giving the airplane a varnished look. It soon became apparent that the early slow-flying machines made fairly good targets for riflemen on the ground or in the air. Many patterns were devised to camouflage the machines. This was particularly important to those machines engaged in low-level bombing and observation work. When night flying came into being, many machines took advantage of darker colors to go unseen. Later, the trend was to paint aircraft in many different loud and colorful hues, prompting writers to refer to the squadrons as "Flying Circuses."

For identification purposes, aircraft insignia (*see*) became very important. Machines on both sides looked a lot alike and mistaken identity resulted in unfortunate accidents. The English Union Jack flag, used on early British planes, is a case in point. This emblem had a cross in its design that was mistaken for similar German markings. It was quickly changed, similar to the deletion of the red center of the U.S. insignia during WWII, when it was mistaken for Japan's Rising Sun.

The nations finally settled on standard markings, many of which are still used. The Allied Cockade consisted of several circles of various color combina-

tions of red, white, and blue. These appeared on the top and bottom surfaces of the wings and on the side of the fuselage. Stripes of the same color were often used on the rudder. The Central Powers' insignia was the Iron Cross or the Latin Cross, applied in the same manner.

Individual markings were also permitted and just about as many combinations appeared as there were pilots to apply them. Insignias like *Hat-in-Ring* that showed Uncle Sam's hat being tossed into the ring, were made famous by Capt. Edward Rickenbacker (*see*) and his squadron. Members of the Lafayette Escadrille (*see*) flew machines bearing a screaming Indian head. The plane flown by the French ace, Guynemer, featured a flying stork and the words *Vieux Charles* (*Old Charley*).

The Germans flew the most colorful ships and devised many personal markings. Ernst Udet, for example, flew a red Fokker D8 emblazoned with a red and white candy stripe design on the top wing. On the tail were the words *Du Doch Nicht* (*No, Not You*), meaning that no enemy flier was going to get on his tail and shoot him down.

Additional markings included registration or manufacturers' numbers and symbols. Squadron numbers and letters were also painted on the machines for additional identification.

Breakthrough

The real breakthrough in aerial warfare came with adoption of the machine gun timed to fire through the propeller. Credit for the first crude attempt at this innovation is given to the French pilot Roland Garros (*see*). Flying alone in a Morane Bullet on the morning of April 1, 1915, Garros overtook a German two-seater Albatros out on an observation mission. Maneuvering to a position slightly above and behind the German machine, Garros fired a burst from his Hotchkiss machine gun through his propeller to down the first aircraft to be so destroyed. So amazing was this new innovation that Garros quickly scored five victories in five days and received the Legion of Honor and the plaudits of every Frenchman. He was given the title of ace (*see*), an honor accorded by the Parisians of that day for the performance of some outstanding feat. This was quickly interpreted as referring to a pilot who had scored five aerial victories and actually was the start of the ace rating.

Garros' invention was a crude arrangement consisting of metal plates attached to the base of the propeller blades. Those bullets from the machine gun which did not pass through the propeller arc would usually bounce harmlessly off the metal plates. However, stories persist that on more than one occasion

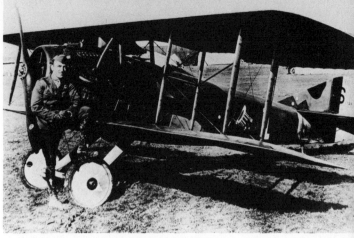

Capt. Eddie Rickenbacker, America's Ace of Aces, and his French Spad XIII. The *Hat-in-the-ring* and *Number One* were his personal insignia.

The famed *Flying Circus* squadron at its base. Baron von Richthofen stands with his cane at the right of the aircraft.

something went wrong and the pilot shot off his own propeller.

It was, however, to be left to others to develop the real aerial combat weapon, the synchronized machine gun. Later in April, Garros' machine was forced down behind enemy lines and captured before he could destroy his "mystery" weapon. The great German aircraft designer Anthony Fokker (*see*) quickly improved the system by developing a cam and lever system, known as an *interrupter gear*, which permitted the gun to fire only when there was no propeller blade in front of the gun barrel. Mounting a Parabellum machine gun on one of his successful monoplanes, the Eindecker, Fokker started many of Germany's aerial war heroes on the road to lasting fame as aces of the war. Fortunately, the Allies were soon able to capture a German machine and further advanced the idea by developing the *Constantinesco gear* to fully synchronize the guns with the propeller. This gun gear was the invention of George Constantinesco, a Rumanian working for a British aeroplane company. Fluid under pressure was used to transmit impulses through tubing to the firing mechanism of

the gun. It could be adapted for use with any type of aircraft and became the standard of the day. A similar gear system was also used by the Central Powers on their aircraft.

Aces Up

This all-important development led to the rise of the fighter pilot, for now he had a truly offensive weapon and could engage the enemy in air-to-air combat with an excellent gun platform. From this moment until the end of the holocaust late in 1918, the dashing WWI aviators were probably the most publicized figures of the war. Blazing daily trails across the sky they brought fame and glory to themselves and their countries as they earned the title of ace, many of them many times over.

High above the muddy trenches where thousands died to win or lose a few feet of shell-torn earth, the WWI pilot lived out the last remaining days of individual military combat. He was likened to the knights of old who charged forth to fight for an ideal or right a wrong. Daily action in the sky was a real challenge to one's ability to outfly, outguess, outmaneuver, and outfight an adversary in personal combat. While dogfights (*see*) of 25 or 30 planes were not uncommon, individual engagements usually resulted.

Pilots soon learned the value of developing fighter techniques that went far beyond simple turns and shallow dives that a few years before had been considered daring maneuvers. Terms like *wingover*, *split S*, *falling leaf*, and *Immelmann*, common to all pilots today, were added to the airman's vocabulary. They were aerobatic maneuvers (*see*) and tactics used to throw the enemy off a pilot's tail or get one's machine into an attack position. Pilots soon learned that every aircraft had a blind spot. Approaching a machine from the proper angle, the enemy could now bring his guns to bear and it was possible to deliver a mortal blow without undue risk.

During WWI, two older military terms—strategy and tactics—were added to the language of the airmen. *Strategy* is what you do in the way of outthinking the enemy before the air battle begins. *Tactics* is what you do after the battle is joined to outfight your opponent. The strategic concept was evident almost at once as the early machines endeavored to spot enemy movements and knock out ammunition dumps before an attack. Tactical concepts came later with faster and better-armed airplanes that could outfight the enemy.

Double Wings and Dashing Aviators

As 1916 turned into '17 and then into '18, the machines grew in stature, too. Airplanes such as the

French Spad and Nieuport, the English Sopwith Camel (*see*), the S.E. 5a (*see*), and the German Fokkers and Albatros could range far afield to seek out and destroy the enemy in the air and on the ground. By now, the fighter-type machine that started out as a fragile monoplane gave way to the more sturdy biplane—an aeronautical change that was to last for the next 20 years. Speeds had been upped to 110 to 130 mph.

Triplanes were also introduced, as evidenced by such popular craft as the Sopwith Tripe, flown by the English Ace Collinshaw, and the Fokker Tripe, made famous by the Germans Werner Voss and Baron Manfred von Richthofen (*see*). Certain triplanes had the weakness of losing the center wing in steep dives and many pilots were a bit leery of flying them.

Biplanes continued to dominate the air and were built as both single- and two-place machines. While the Allies favored the single-seat fighter as their top pursuit plane (*see*), the Germans continued to build a number of successful two-place fighters.

War correspondents were quick to exploit the derring-do of the sky fighters. Many stories, some probably colored and exaggerated, have been handed down about aerial engagements between such fighter groups as the French *Cigognes Escadrille* ("Stork Squadron"), or the American volunteer group, Lafayette Escadrille, and the German *Jagdstaffels* ("Squadrons"), including those known as the Flying Circus (*see*). These names and the names of the pilots and the planes they flew became well known by 1918. Many of the aces who survived the war were to achieve even greater and more lasting fame in the postwar era of aviation. From the French Air Force came such greats as Rene Fonck (*see*) (73 confirmed victories), George Guynemer (53), and Charles Nungesser (45). The Royal English Flying Corps had champions like Edward Mannock (73), William Bishop (*see*) (72), and Raymond Collinshaw (68). The German aces, led by the war's top scorer, "The Red Baron," Manfred von Richthofen (80), Ernst Udet (62), and Oswald Boelke (40), the "father of pursuit aviation" and "creator of the Flying Circus."

The Americans had their heroes too, but since the United States did not enter the war until 1917, their scores were not as great. The first Americans in combat were members of a volunteer group, the Lafayette Escadrille, formed in 1916. They flew French airplanes and started such aces as Raoul Lufbery (17) and Edwin Parsons (8) on their way. Later, most of the Lafayette pilots transferred to the American Air Service, although some stayed with French units. A

Top Aces of World War I					
Flyer	Rank	Victories	Flyer	Rank	Victories
Allied Powers			*Belgium*		
United States			Willy Coppens	Major	34
Edward Rickenbacker	Captain	26	Edmond Thieffry	Lieutenant	10
Frank Luke	2nd. Lt.	21	Andre de Meulemeester	Adjutant	10
Alan M. Wilinson	Captain	19	F. Jacquet	Captain	7
Raoul Lufberry	Major	17	Jan Olieslagers	Lieutenant	6
George Vaughn	1st. Lt.	13			
Field Kindley	Captain	12	**Central Powers**		
British Empire			*Germany*		
Edward Mannock	Major	73	Manfred von Richtofen	Captain	80
William Bishop	Lt. Col.	72	Ernst Udet	Lieutenant	62
Raymond Collishaw	Major	60	Erich Lowenhardt	Lieutenant	56
James T. B. McCudden	Major	57	Werner Voss	Lieutenant	48
			Bruno Loerzer	Captain	45
France			*Austro-Hungary*		
Rene Fonck	Captain	75			
Georges Guynemer	Captain	53	Godwin Brumowski	Captain	40
Charles Nungesser	Lieutenant	45	Julius Arigi	Lieutenant	32
Georges Madon	Lieutenant	41	Frank Linke-Crawford	Lieutenant	30
Maurice Boyeau	Lieutenant	35	Benno Fiala	Lieutenant	29
			Josef Kiss	Lieutenant	19
Italy					
Francesco Baracca	Major	36	First U.S. flyer to down five enemy aircraft in World War I:		
Silvio Scaroni	Lieutenant	26	Captain Frederick Libby 10		
Pier Ruggiero Piccio	Major	24	First U.S. ace of World War I:		
Flavio Barracchini	Lieutenant	21	Captain Alan M. Wilinson 19		
Fulco Ruffo di Calabria	Captain	20	First U.S. ace to serve with the American Expeditionary Forces (AEF):		
Russia (List refers to those records available)			Captain Raoul G. Lufbery 17		
Alexander Kazakov	Captain	17	First U.S. AEF ace of World War I:		
P. D'Argueff	Captain	15	Captain Douglas Campbell 6		
Alexander de Seversky	Lt. Cdr.	13	Top U.S. ace of World War I:		
I. Smirnoff	Lieutenant	12	Captain Edward V. Rickenbacker 26		
M. Safonov	Lietuenant	11			

Primary source of information: *Colonel Leonard W. Lilley, USAF (ret.)*

number of American pilots who joined the Royal Flying Corps before the U.S. declared war spent their entire WWI flying career with the British. By war's end, more than 100 American pilots had earned the title of ace. They continued to fly in French and English machines since no U.S.-designed airplane ever saw combat in WWI.

The greatest mechanical contribution of the United States was development of the Liberty engine, a 400-hp, lightweight, 12-cylinder, V-type which was produced in great numbers. Early use of the Liberty engine was with the American-built English airplane,

the de Havilland (DH-4), known as the Liberty DH-4. Several U.S. squadrons operated these machines with great success during 1918. The DH-4 and the Liberty engine were used for many years by many nations in the postwar period.

Using airplanes purchased from France and England, U.S. squadrons were credited with destroying almost 800 enemy planes and some 70 balloons. The Americans lost 289 planes in combat. The leading American ace was Eddie Rickenbacker, who scored 26 confirmed victories. Frank Luke, known as the "Arizona Balloon Buster," downed 19 enemy planes

The Fokker Triplane was used by several of the great German flyers. This aircraft *(left)* was the personal plane of Werner Voss. A flight of English S.E.5a's *(right)* showing the Allied Cockade.

A Nieuport Scout, with the insignia used by the French ace Nungesser, carried a Vickers machine gun that was fired through the propeller.

The German Albatros D.III was used by the Central Powers during *Bloody April*. It carried twin Spandau machine guns.

and balloons in only 17 days at the front. American observation squadrons flew 35,000 hours and took 18,000 photographs.

A lesser-known, but equally effective, unit was the U.S. Balloon Squadron which provided an observation service during 1918. They made more than 5,800 ascensions and were aloft for some 6,800 hours. More than 100 U.S. observers were forced to parachute when their balloons were attacked by enemy aircraft.

Several of the other nations also had their share of heroes. The top Italian ace was Francesco Baracca who scored 34 times before his death in June, 1918. On the opposing side over the Italian Front were the Austrian leaders, Godwin Brumowsky (40) and Link Crawford (30).

Tiny Belgium's top pilot was Willy Coppens, who downed 26 enemy balloons along with 11 aircraft for a total of 37. Most of his victories came while he was flying the French-built Hanroit HD-1.

Farther to the east, Alexander Kasakov led the Russian fighters with 17. He was closely followed by Alexander de Seversky (*see*) (13), who later became one of the leading aircraft designers in the U.S.

The Fortunes of War

Air supremacy changed hands many times during the four-year conflict, most notably during a period early in 1917. It was the Germans' turn first and it started with the formation of Baron Von Richthofen's Jagdstaffel 11 on January 1, 1917. The group was issued one of the war's top fighting machines, the Albatros D-III. Following another successful Albatros, the D-2, the Albatros D-III was noted for its fast climb and ease of handling. It was powered by a 160-hp Mercedes engine that gave it a top speed of 110 mph. It was armed with twin Spandau machine guns.

Between January 1 and April 22, 1917, the Baron and his "Gentlemen" brought down 100 British aircraft. In the fourth month of that year, German squadrons on the Western Front were unusually successful. In what came to be known to the English as "Bloody April," German aces downed 75 British planes (105 men) in one five-day period. On April 6 alone (the day the U.S. declared war on Germany), 44 British pilots went down. By the end of the month, the British had lost 315 pilots and observers.

Individuals scored heavily during this period, too. By month's end, Richthofen's silver loving cup collection (he had one made for each victory) totaled 52. Another German pilot, Hermann Goering, who later earned acehood and still later, in WWII, was to head the *Luftwaffe* organization, scored several victories during this period.

In May, the Allies were able to reverse the situation and to hold the advantage. New high-performance aircraft such as the Sopwith Camel and the S.E.5a allowed English pilots to boost their scores. During May, British pilots shot down 255 German machines. The French, flying souped-up Spads and Nieuports, added 95 to bring the month's total to 350.

British Naval Ace Raymond Collinshaw, whose all-black Sopwith Triplane was called *Black Maria*, ran his string to 16 during the same period. Many of William Bishop's 72 victories were also scored at this time. As the second-ranking English ace, Bishop was the only military man in British history to receive his country's three highest honors, the Victoria Cross, Distinguished Service Order, and the Military Cross, at one ceremony.

Bombers

Closely following development of the fighter airplane were the bombers that were to carry the war directly to the enemy cities. Early machines had insufficient power to carry a sizable bomb load; the

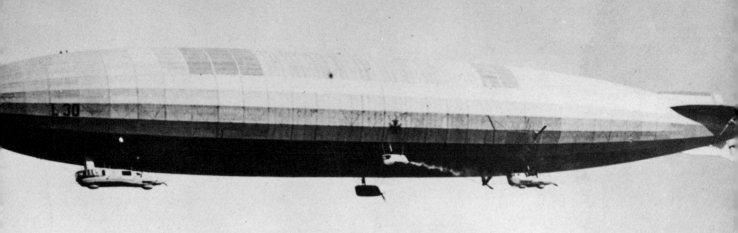

A German Zeppelin flying over the Western Front, probably en route to a bombing target.

Germans were the first to overcome this deficiency by using the Zeppelin for bombing raids. With speeds of 60 mph, the ability to fly higher than defending aircraft, and without fear of antiaircraft fire from the ground, the airships struck at many targets in France and England during 1914 and 1915.

An early Zeppelin attack on England was flown on March 17, 1915, but was forced to turn back due to bad weather and fog. Over Calais, France, the weather cleared and the commander, Ernst Lehmann, lowered his famous *Cloud Car* for the first time on a bombing mission. The target: Calais. The Cloud Car was a small plywood, streamlined tub with a cockpit for an observer and his telephone. Staying in the clouds high over the target, with engines turned off for silent operation, and out of range of the pursuit aircraft, the Zeppelin would lower the car on a cable. The observer would use his phone to order dropping of the bombs, watch the strikes, and make corrections for speed and drift. When all bombs were dropped (usually over 8,000 pounds), the car was winched aboard and the Zeppelin returned to base.

While Zeppelins did little actual damage, they did create panic in the streets and protective measures had to be devised. These included development of antiaircraft guns, powerful searchlights, and, of course, higher-climbing pursuit airplanes. Since the airships used highly inflammable hydrogen gas, and were subject to destruction when hit by *ack-ack* (antiaircraft fire) or explosive and incendiary ammunition from aircraft machine guns, German losses mounted, forcing diversion of the Zeppelins to patrol and scouting service with the German Navy.

Their place was taken by larger bombardment-type aircraft capable of long-range, heavy-load missions. The Germans produced such aircraft as the Friedrichshafen, a twin-engine bomber with a crew of four. Powered with two 260-hp Mercedes engines, it could carry a ton of bombs and fly above 10,000 feet. The Gotha bomber (*see*), another twin-engine bomber,

could carry an even greater load and had a ceiling of over 20,000 feet. The Zeppelin-Stakken, largest of German bombers, was powered by four 260-hp engines, had a wingspan of 135 feet, and was 72 feet long. These machines were used for day and night operations and completed 52 attacks on England, dropping 2,772 bombs. They killed 857 people, injured another 2,000, and inflicted great property damage. Aeronautically speaking, these machines were well ahead of their time and it is remarkable that they were designed and built by the same companies which had been turning out the tiny, fragile Taube only three years before.

The English countered with giants of their own. The Handley Page 0/400 was a twin-engine biplane with 275-hp engines, a ceiling of 10,000 feet, flying at 80 mph, and carrying eight 200-pound bombs and eight 112-pounders. The bombs were contained in a special compartment with an electrically operated release mechanism. It was followed by the Handley-Page V/1500 with a span of 126 feet, powered by four 350-hp Rolls-Royce engines, and carrying over three tons of bombs. It could fly at 100 mph, climb to 10,000 feet in 21 minutes, and stay in the air for 12 hours. These large English bombers carried the war to many German cities, including Frankfort, Koblenz, Cologne, Mainz, and Stuttgart, with ever-increasing bomb loads. Before the war was over, the British had developed 1,650- and 3,000-pound bombs and were ready to bomb Berlin.

A quick look at war maps of the period will show why the Allies were most interested in developing long-range bombers. They had farther to go. French bombers often flew up to 250 miles to reach targets in Germany. Since the German armies had occupied so much of France, their targets were relatively close except, of course, for strikes across the Channel to England.

Although less well known, the Italians also produced a giant bomber—the Caproni. Designed to fly

An experimental Royal Flying Corps oxygen mask being fitted to an observer.

over the mountain barriers between Italy and Austria, they were three- and four-engine machines of about the same specifications as the German and English giants.

Operating at high altitudes for sustained periods of time, the crews of the big bombers needed another assist—oxygen (see). Early oxygen systems consisted of a tube and mouthpiece connected to an oxygen container in the cockpit. The crew members sucked the mouthpiece like a pipe; the oxygen mask (see) was to come later.

Large airplane development had advanced so far by the end of the war that the English had a bomber, the Vickers-Vimy, they said could cross the Atlantic. In 1919 it did, carrying John Alcock and Arthur Brown (see) on the first successful transatlantic flight in history.

Development of the smaller two-man bombers also advanced rapidly. They served many purposes including light-bombing missions and support of ground troops. From early attempts with 80-hp engines, bombers like the French Salmson (1918) featured a 270-hp radial, air-cooled engine, a ceiling of 20,000 feet, self-sealing gas tanks, and both forward and rearward-firing machine guns. Almost 600 Salmsons were flown by U.S. squadrons in addition to the French squadrons so equipped.

Another was the English DH-4 of comparable size that was to use the famous American Liberty engine, already described. This plane earned fame as the searcher which found the "Lost Battalion" and made the first successful airdrops to supply a beleaguered infantry company cut off from help.

In this same class, the French Caudron-G-4 was the first twin-engine plane on the Western Front. It was powered by two 80-hp LeRhone engines and had a top speed of 85 mph.

German entries in this field included the Hannover CL-3, a two-place bomber with a 180-hp engine. It could fly above 17,000 feet or "on the deck" for ground support, and was one of the first airplanes to carry armor around the cockpits to protect crews.

It also featured a "belly gun" which the observer could fire through the bottom of the fuselage. This innovation was designed to discourage the fighter pilot's typical attack plan of coming up underneath the unprotected belly of the enemy.

Another German machine in this class, one designed especially for ground support, was the Junkers J.1. This aircraft was the world's first all-metal plane. It was covered with corrugated dural sheets in place of the standard doped fabric. It was powered with a 200-hp engine which, like the cockpit and fuel tank, was armored with 5mm chrome-nickel sheet steel. Several later versions of the Junkers were purchased for use with the U.S. Air Mail Service following the war.

The great advances made in aviation during WWI were due in large measure to the mating of the pilot to his machine. As a fighting team they were superb, but their contributions went far beyond that.

Conclusion

It has been said, and rightly so, that WWI advanced aviation far beyond the few years that the holocaust lasted. Under the pressure of war, many things were accomplished in days rather than months. For example, the Liberty engine was conceived in 36 hours starting on May 29, 1917. It passed its first 50-hour test on August 25, 1917, and by October it was installed in an airplane. In the spring of 1918 it was flying in France. This was typical of the rapid development of all aviation. The war produced most of the leaders who advanced the science later.

Fighter aces like Fonck and Nungesser, who attempted early transatlantic flights; Ernst Udet, who as an aerobatic champion thrilled air show lovers the world over as he developed new aircraft in his role as a test pilot; Eddie Rickenbacker, who founded one of the great U.S. commercial airlines (see); Billy Mitchell (see), who went on to prove the value of aerial bombardment by sinking "unsinkable" battleships, though it cost him his reputation; Billy Bishop, who served his native Canada for years as an aviation expert and consultant, and the many, many others who continued in aviation as a career led us through the 20's and the years of the barnstormers (see); the doldrums of the 30's; the Second World War; and to the threshold of man's greatest aerial accomplishment—the conquest of space.

The aerospace world of the sixties owes a real debt of gratitude to all the airmen of World War I. As they pass in review, we, like the sky knights of 1914, salute them. Gene Kropf

See also: First World War aircraft, Second World War aircraft, World War II

French and British Spitfires fly from a captured German airfield.

World War II

The war that was won by airpower

Air power played a leading role in World War II from the opening campaign, the German invasion of Poland, through the final act, the atomic bomb attacks on Japan. The vital importance of airpower throughout this conflict is best illustrated by the fact that no nation was successful in any major campaign without first winning air superiority. Control of the air was an essential element in military operations on both land and sea.

Extremely rapid technical progress was made in the two decades following World War I and the aircraft of 1939 were far advanced over those of 1917. When war finally came the role of aviation became more important and far more devastating than anyone had predicted. Technical progress was accelerated and the military aircraft of 1945 were substantially superior to those of 1939. Production boomed and all the warring nations expanded their air forces

to a completely unexpected degree. Five thousand airplanes were considered a staggering force in 1939, but by the end of the war many tens of thousands were operating in all the major theaters. The United States was the leader and produced some 296,000 airplanes in the five years from July, 1940 to July, 1945, but the other major powers also had remarkable production records.

Conceptually, the proper military employment of aircraft was a matter of heated debate around the world in 1939. One of the primary schools of thought held that aircraft were most effective if used in the support of ground troops, in operations of "combined arms." The other popular concept concerned the idea of independent air operations which struck far behind the front lines into the industrial heartland of an enemy. Giulio Douhet (*see*) in Italy, H. M. Trenchard in England, and "Billy" Mitchell (*see*) in the U.S. were advocates of this concept, but it was widely held in almost all air forces.

Only two nations, however, Great Britain and the United States, equipped their air forces properly to assume this role of independent air operations. Over the long run this proved of great importance, and Germany and Japan suffered far more from aerial bombardment than did any of the belligerents.

In retrospect it is clear that the Allies made better use of aviation than did the Axis powers. Allied tactics generally were more flexible, and their air formations became expert in close support of ground and naval forces as well as independent operations. Once the initial Axis superiority in aircraft was overcome, the Allies pressed their aerial offensive in a manner that Hitler never dreamed of in 1939. For example, during 3½ years of war the United States Army Air Forces alone flew more than 2,360,000 combat sorties against Germany and Japan, dropping approximately 2 million tons of bombs and destroying about 40,000 enemy planes, compared with a loss of some 23,000 of its own from enemy action.

German Blitzkrieg

Poland was the first victim of the German *Blitzkrieg* and it fell in approximately one month, during September, 1939. The *Luftwaffe* (*see*) demonstrated for the first time the potency of a well-coordinated attack, with aircraft supporting columns of tanks and armored vehicles (*Panzer*) by protecting their flanks and bombarding the enemy directly in their path.

Next objectives of Hitler's conquest were Denmark and Norway. Less than 50,000 troops were employed in these actions, with the units moving against Norway traveling in large numbers of transport aircraft as well as ships. The operation began on April 9, 1940, and met little resistance except in the extreme northern part of Norway near the port of Narvik, out of reach of the *Luftwaffe's* initial assault.

The German attack on Scandinavia was the first of its combined army, navy, and air force operations and it was emminently successful, even though hastily planned. It was triggered by Allied preparations to occupy Norway in an attempt to outflank Germany. A British-French force was ready to embark from Britain when the Germans struck.

On May 10, 1939, the German attack against the Low Countries and France was launched. The *Luftwaffe* used its full strength to support two army groups which wheeled through Holland and Belgium and into France, bypassing the Maginot Line, the strongest part of the French defenses. Almost immediately, the *Luftwaffe* won air supremacy over the battlefield and allowed the outnumbered German army to win a stunning victory.

In Holland, the attack was carried by ground units that were substantially smaller than the Dutch Army. The German force, however, was aided by small numbers of parachute troops which were dropped behind Dutch lines at key points and supported by *Luftwaffe* air strikes and parachute-dropped supplies until the ground troops advanced.

The main thrust of the German armored units was directed at Belgium, but key points in its defenses, such as the Fort Eben Emael were breached quickly by the *Luftwaffe* airborne troops using unorthodox tactics. Resistance in Belgium was quickly silenced and the main *Panzer* elements of the German army poured through the Ardennes Forest onto the plains of Northern France. The *Panzer* units and Junkers Ju-87 Stuka dive-bombers presented an almost perfect lesson in modern armored warfare to the British and French armies, which were unprepared for such rapid movement by ground forces and for the difficulties of fighting without air cover.

The one flaw in the German victory was the escape of nearly 250,000 Allied troops from Dunkirk, across the channel to England. Hitler ordered his armored formations to swing westward away from this pocket of resistance near Dunkirk, and to leave its elimination to the *Luftwaffe*. However, the British mustered an armada of some 1,000 small craft and protected it with a strong cover of fighter planes from bases in England so that almost all of the troops in the pocket were saved from May 26 through June 3. This was the only time during the fall of France that the Allies wrested local air superiority from the *Luftwaffe*. Substantial numbers of aircraft were lost on each side in the air battle over Dunkirk.

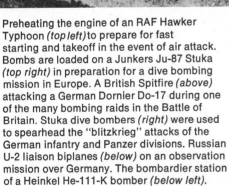

Preheating the engine of an RAF Hawker Typhoon *(top left)* to prepare for fast starting and takeoff in the event of air attack. Bombs are loaded on a Junkers Ju-87 Stuka *(top right)* in preparation for a dive bombing mission in Europe. A British Spitfire *(above)* attacking a German Dornier Do-17 during one of the many bombing raids in the Battle of Britain. Stuka dive bombers *(right)* were used to spearhead the "blitzkrieg" attacks of the German infantry and Panzer divisions. Russian U-2 liaison biplanes *(below)* on an observation mission over Germany. The bombardier station of a Heinkel He-111-K bomber *(below left)*.

The German advance continued without letup toward Paris, however, and the French capitulated on June 20.

Battle of Britain

The Battle of Britain (*see*) was the first independent air campaign of World War II. The *Luftwaffe* lost this battle primarily because it was designed for close support of an army and it did not have the heavy bombers and long-range aircraft needed to carry out a strategic bombing campaign. Despite its deficiencies, the *Luftwaffe* came perilously close to subduing the Royal Air Force (RAF) (*see*).

Early in the attacks, which became heavy in August, 1939, certain weaknesses of the German equipment became evident and these led to substantial losses. The Stuka dive bomber and the Me-110, which had never been used when the Germans did not hold air superiority, did not have adequate speed and were shot down in large numbers by the aggressive English pilots and had to be withdrawn. Also, the short range and endurance of the Me-109 gave it a very short time for combat over southern England. In many cases German bombers did not have fighter escort, and when they did, they were forced to use the shortest routes of approach and could only stay in the target area for a brief period.

The first element in the German plan called for the destruction of the Royal Air Force, especially the 700 fighters it had scattered through southern England at the beginning of the battle. This portion of the plan nearly succeeded before the *Luftwaffe* high command ordered the effort concentrated on the cities. A strange factor in these attacks on the RAF and its facilities was the small interest shown in the 18 or so radar stations along the English coast, even though

the Germans knew their purpose. One station was destroyed and five damaged before the focus of the *Luftwaffe* offensive was shifted. However, these radar stations were vital in that they warned of the speed, direction, and size of attacking formations so that the few defending fighters could be efficiently dispatched without being wasted in widespread patrolling.

Mass attacks on London began early in September with nearly 1,000 aircraft appearing over the city on some days. The RAF fighters took a steady toll and *Luftwaffe* losses reached a peak on September 15 when some 56 of its aircraft were downed in one day. By the middle of October, it had become clear that the English had won the Battle of Britain and that it would be impossible for the *Luftwaffe* to protect an invading army trying to cross the channel.

Between July 10 and the end of October, the Germans lost some 1,800 aircraft over England while the RAF lost less than 1,000. *Luftwaffe* loss rate during the battle was about 5 per cent; that is, 1 out of every 20 aircraft flying over England was shot down. This was one of the most successful air defense operations of the war.

Even this relatively low loss rate was too heavy for the Germans to bear on a sustained basis, despite the fact that most of the 1,800 aircraft had been replaced by new production by the end of October. Operations were suspended in the daytime for the most part, and shifted to the night to reduce losses. Heavy night attacks on the capital city continued for several months, well into 1941 in a bombing campaign that became known as the "Blitz of London."

During the fall of 1940 the *Luftwaffe* was called upon to maintain a reconnaissance of North Atlantic shipping in the support of U-boat operations, and

Bomb craters are visible from a British Lancaster bomber on a raid over Germany.

also to attack merchant ships. A small number of four-engine Focke-Wulf Kurrier aircraft bore the brunt of this mission, which continued with marked success until 1943. During 1940, 1941, and 1942, the Germans sank more than 16,000 Allied ships, and aircraft played an important role in this success.

In the spring of 1941, Hitler made a new *Blitzkrieg* thrust into the Balkans. The *Luftwaffe* and armored columns again were the spearhead, and they overran Yugoslavia and Greece during about two weeks in April.

A second opportunity for an independent aerial operation presented itself in May. The British had managed to move about 40,000 of their own and Greek troops back to the island of Crete during the final days of the Greek campaign, and there was no way to eliminate this force except by an air assault. Following heavy bombing for several days, Crete was invaded by parachute and glider troops and subdued quickly, but the Germans were reported to have lost another 5,000 men. The RAF threw strong forces into the battle and provided air cover so that some 15,000 troops could be evacuated from Crete.

Air War in Russia

During the first months of *Operation Barbarossa* in 1941, the German attack on the U.S.S.R., the Soviet Air Force was overrun and all but annihilated, but it survived to be reorganized, reequipped, and retrained. By the end of the war it was a powerful force which played an important role in the Soviet victory.

Hitler's divisions began their attack along a 2,000-mile front on the morning of June 22, 1941, and they were supported by approximately 2,000 aircraft. Tactical surprise was achieved, and the Soviet Air Force was not ready for the *Luftwaffe* attacks against its airfields and facilities, some of which were more than 100 miles behind the border. Many Russian airplanes were destroyed on the ground, and the supply and maintenance organization was thoroughly disrupted. During the summer and fall, the Germans drove to within sight of Moscow and overran much of the Ukraine while they enjoyed complete air superiority. Soviet aircraft losses from June through November, 1941, are placed at 6,400 by Russian sources and nearly 16,000 by German sources.

The major Russian achievement of this period was the removal of more than half of its aircraft and aircraft engine manufacturing plants from the area around Moscow and the Ukraine to safety behind the Ural Mountains. This rescue of the aircraft industry was responsible in large part for the successful development of Soviet airpower later in the war.

Russian production involved small aircraft primar-ily, the fighters and small twin-engine bombers used for support of the ground forces. In 1941 and 1942 fighter production was concentrated on the YAK-1, MiG-3, and Lagg-3. These were substantially inferior to the most numerous German fighter on the Russian front, the Me-109. The Soviets continued to improve their fighters and later in the war had evolved the YAK-9 and La-7 which generally were regarded as the equal of any German design except the jet Me-262.

A Russian favorite was the Il-2 Stormavik, a single-engine, two-place, ground attack aircraft equipped with a heavy cannon to combat tanks. This was one of the few aircraft of the war in which speed, range, and maneuverability were sacrificed to a major degree by adding very heavy armor plate to protect the engine and crew from ground fire. Consequently, Stormavik was able to fly right down on the deck in the midst of major battles in the support of Soviet ground units.

Following its major defeat in the summer of 1941, the Soviet Air Force underwent an extensive reorganization. This reorganization was dictated largely by practical military necessity as the Communist Party was forced to relax its influence on military affairs. Most important of the changes was to place more authority over air operations in the hands of air commanders. Air units formerly had been under the direction of the lower echelons of the Soviet Army, but this command was raised to a much higher level, and the top ground officers, while still in command, gave more responsibility to their Air Force subordinates.

The reorganization left the major air elements (approximately 75 per cent of the total aircraft strength) attached to the Soviet Army, but it also brought into existence the first Soviet independent bombing force. This organization, known as ADD (for Long-Range Aviation), was allowed to select the best flyers, to create its own training schools and ground organization, and generally was considered an elite force. The ADD, along with the antiaircraft defense forces and fighter defense groups, was subordinate to the supreme command in Moscow.

The avowed Soviet purpose in creating the ADD was to be ready with a proficient bomber and transport force in the event that the opportunity for independent air operations presented itself. Western observers estimated that by the end of the war, more than 1,500 long-range aircraft were operational in the ADD. It had a substantial record of operations in the support of major ground offensives, but its bombing offensive into Germany was insignificant compared to the British and American efforts. In

addition, the Soviet unit displayed a woeful lack of expertise on these long-range missions. Many aircraft became lost, the wrong targets were bombed, and the German defenses downed a large percentage of the planes. Stalin made many attempts to bolster ADD by obtaining heavy bombers from the United States or Great Britain under lend-lease, but he was never successful. Finally the Soviets seized a B-29 in Asia, refused to return it to the United States, and produced a copy of this bomber in substantial numbers for ADD.

German air operations in Russia generally followed their classic pattern of close support for front-line infantry and armor units, plus disruptive attacks on communications and reserves immediately behind the front. During the first year of the invasion, however, a limited strategic bombing offensive was undertaken against Moscow, but the numbers of bombers remained quite small, usually less than 100 and never more than 200. The Germans never had the resources nor apparently the desire to attack Soviet industry in an air campaign.

The rapid reorganization and reequipment of the Soviet Air Force in the winter of 1941–42 was aided by some 3,000 lend-lease aircraft from the U.S. and England. This group, plus new Russian production and the remnants of the original air units, gave the Soviets a force of around 12,000 aircraft for operations that summer. However, the *Luftwaffe* with a strength that never exceeded 2,500 aircraft maintained air control over most of the major battles and the German army renewed its advances.

By 1943, the Soviet advantage in aircraft was much larger and the *Luftwaffe* was never again able to hold air superiority over any given area for a significant length of time. At the end of the war, the Russians were estimated to have more than 50,000 aircraft in operational units in Europe and Asia.

North Africa and Italy

The first major offensive of the war in the North African desert was made in November, 1940, by an Italian Army under Marshall Rodolfo Graziani which moved out of Libya into Egypt. This attack moved slowly, unlike the later campaigns in this area that seesawed rapidly back and forth over hundreds of miles. By December the Italians had moved about halfway to Cairo when the vastly outnumbered British Army and Air Force counterattacked. Hundreds of thousands of prisoners and large quantities of supplies were taken in an advance that drove the Italians out of central Libya.

Small elements of the *Luftwaffe* were sent to Africa and were instrumental in stemming this British advance through attacks on their extended supply lines. Later in March, 1941, sizable German armored units under General (later Field Marshal) Erwin Rommel landed and almost immediately attacked with great success. For the next 14 months, the British Eighth Army and the Afrika Corps fought back and forth across Libya and Egypt. Tanks were the key to this highly mobile warfare as the area had no natural defense lines and only one road that hugged the coast. Control of the air also was an important element and neither side was successful when it could not hold air superiority over its tanks.

A constant air battle raged over most of the eastern Mediterranean during this period, with each side attempting to disrupt the other's supply lines. The island of Malta, which lay astride the Axis shipping lanes from Italy to Libya, suffered terribly from aerial bombardment. However, it never fell and it became known as England's "unsinkable aircraft carrier."

Highwater mark of the German campaign in Africa came in mid-1942 when Rommel advanced to El Alamein, some 60 miles to the west of Cairo. The German effort fell short of driving the English out of Egypt, and from that point on the Allies enjoyed a sizable edge in men and materiel. General (later Field Marshal) Bernard Montgomery assumed command of the Eighth Army and his first offensive objective was for the Royal Air Force to secure control of the air over the desert and permanently disrupt the Afrika Corps supply lines. Finally, after a careful buildup, Montgomery began the final offensive in the desert.

Operation Torch, the Allied landings in Algeria and Morocco, came at the same time and caught the Germans between two strong forces. Immediately following Torch, the Germans occupied Tunisia to shorten their supply lines, but this action delayed the final outcome only briefly for the campaign was over within six months. More than 250,000 Axis prisoners were captured along with huge quantities of war materiel.

Airpower played a prominent role in this defeat for it effectively cut the supply line from Sicily to Tunisia more than a month before the end. Both the British Eighth Army advancing from the east and the Americans moving in from the west enjoyed virtually complete air superiority during the last half of the campaign, and they maintained a steady bombardment of German positions in Tunisia and their facilities in the Tunisian ports.

Two months after the victory in Africa the Allies had assembled enough vessels for the invasion of Sicily. An air offensive during these months drove the bulk of the *Luftwaffe* off the island. The Allies

Top Aces of World War II

Flyer	Rank	Victories	Flyer	Rank	Victories
United States			*Germany*		
Richard Bong	Major	40	Erich Hartmann	Major	352
Thomas McGuire	Major	38	Gerhard Barkhorn	Major	301
David McCampbell	Captain	34	Gunther Rall	Major	275
Francis Gabreski	Colonel	31	*Japan*		
Robert Johnson	Lt. Col.	28	Hiroyashi Nishizawa	C.W.O.	104
Gregory Boyington	Lt. Col.	28	Shaichi Sugita	C.W.O.	80
Charles MacDonald	Colonel	27	Saburo Sakai	Lieutenant	64
Joseph Foss	Major	26	*Canada*		
George Preddy	Major	25.83	G. F. Beurling	Flt. Lt.	31
Robert Hanson	1st. Lt.	25	V. C. Woodard	Sq. Ldr.	20
Lance Wade	Wing Cdr.	25	*Belgium*		
Cecil Harris	Lieutenant	24	R. deHemricourt deGrunne	Lieutenant	13
John Meyer	Colonel	24	V. Ortmans	S/Lieutenant	11
Eugene Valencia	Cdr.	23	I. DuMonceau deBergandal	—	7.5
Ray Wetmore	Captain	22.59	*New Zealand*		
United Kingdom			Colin Gray	Wing Cdr.	27.5
James Johnson	Gp. Captain	38	Edgar Kain	Flt. Off.	25
Marmaduke St.J. Pattle	Sq. Ldr.	34	E. D. Mackie	Wing Cdr.	25
Brendan Finucane	Wing Cdr.	32	*South Africa*		
			M. S. Osler	Major	12
France			Cornelius Van Vliet	Major	11
Pierre Clostermann	Lieutenant	33	K. W. Driver	Captain	10
Marcel Albert	Captain	23	*Finland*		
Jean DeMozay	Cdt.	23	Hans Wind	Captain	75
			Eino Juutilainen	Lieutenant	74
U.S.S.R.			Eino Luukkanen	Major	54
I. N. Kozhedub	Maj. Gen.	62	*Poland*		
A. L. Pokryshkin	Gds. Col.	59	S. Skalski	Major	22.25
G. A. Rechkalov	Gds. Capt.	56	W. Urbanowicz	Lt. Col.	17
K. A. Yevstigneev	Gds. Capt.	56	E. Horbaczewski	Captain	16.5

Primary source of information: *Colonel Leonard W. Lilley, USAF* (ret.)

enjoyed at least a two to one superiority in aircraft and pressed this advantage. The assault on Sicily included the first large U.S. airborne troop operation, but this was relatively ineffective because of bad weather, and poor coordination and inexperience on the part of the transport aircraft units. Overall the offensive in Sicily was a success, for it fell within a month and resulted in less than 165,000 Allied casualties.

Almost immediately following the loss of Sicily in mid-August, the Fascist government in Italy surrendered without consulting its German partner. The Germans, however, prevented the collapse of the country by occupying it and reinforcing the defenses it already was preparing in Southern Italy against an Allied landing from Sicily.

Heavy air strikes were initiated against railroad yards and military installations of all types all over Italy. This interdiction campaign continued to harass the Germans during the remainder of their stay in Italy. Landings on the Italian peninsula were made early in September, 1943, after an intensive air bombardment. This ground offensive moved slowly ahead for another 18 months and had driven to the Alps by the time of Germany's complete collapse in the spring of 1945.

Air-Ground Invasion of Germany and France

In June, 1944, the Allies invaded German-occupied France with the most powerful and effective air support ever provided for any army. Nearly 5,000 fighters and 6,000 bombers were assembled for the specific task of softening up German defenses on the French coast, disrupting their supply and communication system, and then providing close air support for the Allied armies. The Allied ground forces were arrayed in some 47 divisions plus heavy auxiliary elements, and they had more than 5,000 ships to move them across the Channel.

The air units pounded the Germans for many weeks ahead of the crossing and then went into an all-out effort with round-the-clock bombing just prior to the landing. Major U.S. and British paratroop and glider units were dropped behind the German lines the morning of the landing, and were supplied by air until a front was stabilized around the landing area. Following a brief period to buildup forces in this pocket, British and American armored units broke through the German lines. The U.S. breakout at Saint-Lo was accompanied by an unprecedented air bombardment. Hundreds of heavy bombers were used in an attack that lasted hours and wiped out German resistance in a gap several miles wide.

General George Patton, moving the Third Army in a swift armored thrust toward Paris, relied almost completely on USAAF fighters to cover his flanks. He used less artillery and infantry support than any previous armored force commander and moved with a speed that surprised the Germans.

As the Allied armies approached Germany, the fighter forces were employed in a massive offensive

U.S. B-26 Marauders attacked the occupied
Amsterdam airport in January, 1944.

against the transportation system inside the Third
Reich and the Low Countries. These continuous
fighter sweeps virtually ended daylight movement of
people and materiel in Western Germany and resulted in the destruction of many thousands of
trucks, railroad cars, locomotives, and bridges.

One of the best indicators of the value of the air
operations is the opinion of the German commanders
who opposed the Allies in France. The reaction of
Field Marshal Karl von Rundstedt, commander in
France during the invasion, was typical. He said,
"Three factors defeated us in the West . . . First was
the unheard-of superiority of your air force, which
made all movement in the daytime impossible.
Second was the lack of motor fuel . . . Third, the
systematic destruction of all railway communications
so that it was impossible to bring a single railroad
train across the Rhine."

Strategic Bombing of Germany

Almost from the beginning of the war, German
cities and industry were subjected to bombings that
were independent of any ground action. The British
government called for them in retaliation for the
bombing of England, and the Royal Air Force
strongly supported them as a means of shortening
the war.

At first, the RAF Bomber Command was relatively
weak and lacked large bombers with the bomb load
and range necessary to make truly damaging attacks.
During this period, Hermann Goering, number two
man to Hitler and chief of the *Luftwaffe*, boasted that
English bombers could never reach Berlin or seri-
ously damage German cities. However, it was not
long before the British built the Short Stirling and
Handley Page Halifax bombers. These four-engine
aircraft could carry a substantially bigger bomb load
than the U.S. B-17 and B-24 and they made an independent bombing campaign effective. By May,
1942, the British had produced enough new bombers
so that they could begin 1,000 plane raids, the first
of which hit Cologne.

The British also quickly developed a rigid theory
about the best tactics for reducing aircraft losses and
getting the maximum effect from such raids. They
abandoned daylight attacks because the German defenses proved very strong, and to insure that the
target was hit at night they "area bombed," with all
the aircraft in a large formation releasing a salvo
of bombs in unison.

The U.S. strategic bombing of Germany proved
very difficult to start, but once in progress it equaled
the British effort. A continuous shortage of heavy
bombers in England was the primary reason for the
delayed start. This was not due to U.S. production
problems with the large four-engine aircraft as much
as to a constant shifting of plans. The first build-up of
B-17 Flying Fortresses in England shortly after Pearl
Harbor was stopped and most of the force diverted
to support Operation Torch in North Africa. In late
1943, a second build-up was slowed down to support
the invasion of France.

Finally, in mid-1944, the 8th Air Force in England
and the 15th Air Force in Italy received enough aircraft so that on most days during the last year of the
war well over 1,000 U.S. heavy bombers raided Germany and its occupied territories. The targets were
primarily heavy industry, aircraft plants, factories
making precision equipment, and oil refineries. Their
locations ranged from the Ploesti oil fields of Rumania in extreme southeastern Europe to the large cities
on the North Sea, such as Hamburg.

U.S. tactics changed substantially with combat experience. The major adjustment came in 1943 on the
first big B-17 raids into Germany when the *Luftwaffe*

Heavy armor flak suits *(left)* were developed to protect Allied bomber crews from shrapnel. Only two crewmembers bailed out of a B-24 Liberator hit by flak *(right)* over northern Italy. The force of the explosion crumpled the wing and the aircraft caught fire and plunged to the ground.

shot down as many as 10 per cent of the attackers. It became clear that the Flying Fortresses could not protect themselves and needed escort fighters, or the raids would have to be made at night as the British had warned. This problem was solved by equipping P-51 Mustang fighters with drop tanks under the wings to give them approximately the same range as the bombers.

High-altitude bombing accuracy also was not as good as predicted and the U.S. was forced to use area bombing to take out many targets.

Final statistics for the air war in Europe showed that the U.S. and British had flown a total of almost 1.5 million bomber sorties, more than 2.5 million fighter sorties, and had dropped about 2.7 million tons of bombs.

V-Weapons and Jet Aircraft

As the war ended the Germans were setting a blistering pace in advanced technology. They were substantially ahead of the Allies with several revolutionary weapons, including jet aircraft *(see)*, rocket-powered aircraft, and guided missiles.

Well over 1,000 Messerschmitt Me-262 twin-jet fighters were produced and a substantial number of these were used in the defenses against Allied bombers. The rocket-powered Me-163 also was operational for a considerable period. If large numbers of these aircraft, which were nearly 100 mph faster than Allied fighters, had been brought into service a year earlier, it is very possible that they could have stopped the Allied bombing offensive.

The first mass-produced missile was the V-1 missile *(see)* (V for Vengeance weapon), which was essentially a pilotless bomber powered by a lightweight and inexpensive pulsejet engine. More than 15,000 V-1's were launched with some 7,800 aimed at London and most of the others at Allied supply points in France and Belgium. Allied fighters and antiaircraft guns shot down nearly half of these missiles which cruised at about 400 mph.

Defense against the V-2 rocket missile *(see)* was impossible however, as it traveled at several times the speed of sound. It was the first long-range ballistic missile, the direct forerunner of the ICBM. About 3,000 V-2's were launched at London and Antwerp. The accuracy of the V-1 and V-2 was poor but they caused more than 30,000 casualties in London alone and did substantial damage.

The Japanese Kawasaki Ki-45 was developed in 1939 and patterned after the U.S. A-18.

An advanced Japanese fighter on display in Washington, D.C., after World War II.

The most sobering point about all of these weapons is that the Germans had the capacity to build them at least a year before they actually did. Hitler and his top advisors became so overconfident after the fall of France in 1940 that they ordered development of advanced weapons stopped for more than a year.

Flying Tigers

Undoubtedly the most unusual and successful air unit in World War II was the American Volunteer Group (AVG) in China, the famous Flying Tigers (*see*) which were organized by Claire Chennault (*see*), a retired U.S. Army Air Corps officer.

Chennault went to China in 1937 to assist in the building of a Chinese Air Force. He had become familiar with the area and was ready with a plan in 1941 when help arrived from the United States in the form of 100 Curtiss-Wright P-40B Tomahawk fighter planes and the volunteer pilots to fly them. In six months of combat, the AVG shot down 297 Japanese aircraft at the cost of only 12 American pilots. The

Parachute fragmentation bombs dropped at low altitudes onto Japanese-held railroad installation in the Philippines. Parachutes permitted the bomber to escape bomb blast and shrapnel.

Flying Tigers ran up their amazing score while flying obsolescent fighter planes in the face of overwhelming numerical odds and against some well-seasoned Japanese pilots.

The Flying Tigers flew against the Japanese in both Burma and China before they were inducted into the Army Air Forces as the 14th Air Force in July, 1942. Chennault was recalled to active duty and promoted to the rank of Brigadier General and early in 1943 given command of the 14th Air Force. It never reached a strength of more than 500 fighters and 190 bombers and its area of operations was as large as western Europe, but in three years of operations the entire 14th Air Force destroyed 2,300 enemy aircraft and probably destroyed another 775 at a cost of 500 aircraft lost from all causes. Allied officers generally credited this lopsided victory to the inflexibility of Japanese plans and tactics, the poor eyesight of their pilots, and the fact that they seldom had a deputy leader for their formations. In air battle, if the Japanese leader was shot down, the other aircraft usually became ineffective.

Gen. Chennault has written extensively of the events that helped form his philosophy of aerial combat and the flexible tactics which are credited with bringing overwhelming victory to American air units in China. During 1937 to 1939 he had an excellent opportunity to observe the air operations of the Japanese and of the Russian air task force fighting the Japanese in China. He was impressed by the fact that these air forces had two characteristics in common: iron-hard discipline and complete denial of an initiative to a subordinate. Chennault wrote, "I remember how on one occasion a group of Russian fighters scrambled from an air field in central China to meet a mixed force of Japanese fighters and bombers. The Japanese fighters were about five minutes ahead of the bombers and contacted the Russian fighters over the field. The engines of the Russian group leader was shot out on the first pass, and he spiraled down to a landing on the field followed one by one by all of the other Russian pilots. The Japanese bombers plastered the field thoroughly while the Russians were landing, and damaged or destroyed all the Russian airplanes. When I inquired why all the planes landed with the group leader, I was told, matter-of-factly, that the Russian pilots had orders to follow the leader under any and all circumstances."

Japanese Conquests

Japanese conquests in the Pacific area outside the Chinese mainland began with an air attack on Pearl Harbor (*see*) shortly after dawn on December 7, 1941. This attack was made by less than 500 aircraft operat-

ing from six carriers steaming some 230 miles north of Hawaii. The Japanese expected to lose a substantial portion of this force, including some carriers, but they achieved complete tactical surprise and caused heavy damage to U.S. forces while losing only 29 of their own airplanes.

The main battleline of the U.S. Pacific fleet was decimated with its eight battleships sunk or badly damaged. A number of smaller ships were damaged along with shore facilities. Some 200 U.S. aircraft were destroyed on the ground, and more than 2,000 men died. The one bright spot was that the Pacific Fleet's three carriers were not in the base at the time. Shortly after Pearl Harbor, Japanese forces made simultaneous attacks on the Philippines, Hong Kong, and Malaya. In the Philippines, the invasion began with an almost inexcusable air defeat at Clark Field near Manila. Despite the fact that news of Pearl Harbor had been received, the aircraft at this installation still were in vulnerable positions when the first Japanese formations appeared. They destroyed more than 115 aircraft while losing 7 and effectively eliminated U.S. airpower in the area. U.S. forces held out briefly on Bataan, Corregidor, and in the southern Philippines, but resistance ended early in May, 1942.

A devastating air attack that knocked out all British aircraft proceeded the ground assault upon Hong Kong. Resistance in this tiny colony lasted less than a month.

Japanese operations against the keystone British base of Singapore began with the landing of troops about halfway down the Malayan peninsula. These troops were provided with substantial air support from bases in French Indochina. Despite the close proximity of this land-based aviation the English sent their two largest naval vessels in the Far East, the battleships *Prince of Wales* and *Repulse*, north from Singapore without air cover in an attempt to disrupt the Japanese shipping supporting the landings. Just three days after Pearl Harbor these ships were attacked by less than 100 Japanese bombers and quickly sunk. Only three aircraft were lost. This action ended most of the remaining speculation about the capital ship being a match for aircraft. Aircraft carriers were quickly acknowledged as the new "queen of the seas."

Singapore fell by the middle of February, but by then it had been bypassed and the Japanese had secured a large portion of the Dutch East Indies. By March, the island of Java had been taken and Allied naval vessels driven from the Java Sea. Darwin, Australia, was hit in a surprise air raid which resulted in substantial casualties and the loss of more than 20 aircraft and 10 ships.

In the Central Pacific, Japanese forces also moved swiftly capturing Wake Island and Guam from the United States and Rabaul, New Britain, from Australian forces.

The Japanese immediately began erecting defenses for the new territories, putting in large air and naval installations at Guam and Rabaul to supplement

U.S. C-47's drop airborne troops over southern France somewhere between Nice and Marseilles after the initial amphibious and airborne invasions in Normandy in June, 1944.

their bases in the Carolines. Plans also were made to cut Australia off from its lifelines to the United States and Europe, and to deliver a final blow to U.S. naval power in the Pacific. A thrust was prepared through the Solomon Islands with the objective of capturing Port Moresby on the southeastern tip of New Guinea, and New Caledonia and Samoa. Another thrust was aimed at Midway Island lying at the extreme western end of the Hawaiian chain in the central Pacific.

In April, a tactically ineffective air raid was made against Japanese cities by 16 Army B-25 bombers led by Lt. Col. James H. Doolittle (*see*). These bombers flew from the deck of the carrier *Hornet* less than 600 miles off the Japanese coast and then crash-landed in Japanese-occupied China. Psychologically, however, this small raid had a very important effect on the war. It raised morale in the U.S. and caused Japanese military leaders to lose face at home. It also convinced the Japanese that the Allies planned to fight back, so that internal arguments against further military thrusts in the South and Central Pacific were effectively stilled.

Battles of the Coral Sea and Midway

The Battle of the Coral Sea occurred early in May, 1942, as a U.S. Navy task force moved to block the Japanese invasion force heading for Port Moresby. It is significant because it was the first major naval engagement in which surface ships never exchanged a shot. Aircraft carried the action completely.

Tactically, the U.S. lost the battle since the carrier *Lexington* was sunk and the only other one in the task force, the *Yorktown*, was severely damaged, while the Japanese had one carrier damaged, The U.S. strategic purpose was achieved, however, as the Japanese transports were harrassed by both carrier and land-based aviation and forced to turn back to Rabaul.

The naval action in the Coral Sea was small, however, compared to that occurring about one month later southeast of Midway. An armada consisting of the bulk of the Japanese fleet was sent to cover a landing on Midway and to force a final showdown with the U.S. Navy. This armada consisted of 4 heavy carriers, 3 light carriers, 11 battleships, more than 50 cruisers and destroyers, and sizable numbers of submarines and auxiliary ships.

Admiral Isoroku Yamamoto, a leading advocate of naval air power in Japan and architect of the Pearl Harbor attack, was in charge of this force, yet his battle plan relegated the carriers to a secondary role. He wanted to land on Midway and force the remnants of the U.S. Pacific fleet out from Pearl Harbor, and then sink them in a classic naval battle using his surface ships. This seemed to be a relatively minor task since Japanese intelligence reported that only 5 U.S. heavy cruisers and a few destroyers were fit for sea. Their intelligence also had reported that the *Yorktown* had been sunk rather than damaged in the Coral Sea, so the Japanese believed that only two U.S. carriers had to be reckoned with, the *Enterprise* and the *Hornet*, and the latest reports placed them in the South Pacific.

U.S. good fortune in this battle began with the breaking of the Japanese naval code so that Admiral Chester W. Nimitz in Honolulu was able to decipher many secret communications and was privy to the basic Japanese plan. Next, the damaged *Yorktown* made it back to Pearl Harbor where repairs which normally would have taken 90 days were completed in two days, and the carrier put back out to sea. This gave the Navy three sizable carriers, the presence of which the Japanese were unaware.

In two days of heavy fighting the U.S. force, which was distinctly inferior, won a crushing victory. The four Japanese heavy carriers were defeated together with more than 250 aircraft and experienced pilots, and the Americans successfully avoided an encounter with the superior force of Japanese surface vessels. Without adequate air cover this surface force was compelled to abandon the Midway landing and withdraw behind Wake Island in the protection of its land-based aircraft. U.S. losses were acceptably light even though the carrier *Yorktown* finally was sunk.

The Battle of Midway generally is considered to be one of the turning points of the war, for the Japanese never recovered their offensive naval capacity. Their heavy losses essentially equalized naval strength in the Pacific as concerned the carriers, the element which had been shown to be the key to success. The war then settled down to be largely a race between U.S. and Japanese industry in the production of carriers and aircraft; the outcome here was never in doubt.

Victory at Midway, some six months after Pearl Harbor, enabled the United States to start planning major offensives. There were many conflicts of opinion at the highest levels about the best plan because the U.S. was in a two-front war, and had agreed with its Allies that Hitler was the main enemy so that Europe had top priority. However, enough resources were allocated for a two-pronged thrust in the Pacific. One was under Admiral Nimitz in the so-called Pacific Ocean Areas, and the other was an "island-hopping" campaign under General Douglas MacArthur.

Bristol Beau fighter of the RAF fires rockets from under its wing rails. These weapons were widely employed in ground support, air-to-air missions, and anti-shipping activities.

The Philippines, Okinawa, and then Japan itself were the main objectives of both of these offensives. By 1944, both had carried to the shores of the Philippines, and despite tenacious Japanese resistance had resulted in a long string of Allied victories. The U.S. Navy had become the largest naval power in history with nearly 5,000 vessels of all types, including nearly 100 heavy and light carriers and more than 18,000 airplanes.

Two naval battles of major consequence were fought. One was an all-out attempt by the Imperial Japanese fleet to stop the U.S. seizure of the Marianas Islands east of the Philippines in June of 1944. This resulted in the biggest carrier battle of the war and a lopsided U.S. victory, which quickly became known as the "Marianas Turkey Shoot." The Japanese lost 7 carriers, 1 battleship, and 1 cruiser either sunk or severely damaged, in addition to some 450 planes destroyed. U.S. losses were minor.

The second key engagement was the Battle of Leyte Gulf and it occurred after the Japanese decided to make their main stand in the defense of the Philippines on the island of Leyte. Virtually the complete Imperial Fleet, strongly supported by land-based aircraft from Leyte, was committed in this battle, and the major ships were all destroyed or severely damaged. Japanese losses included 4 battleships, 3 carriers, and 10 cruisers, compared to U.S. losses of 3 small carriers and 2 destroyers sunk. After this battle the Japanese Navy was not able to have any substantial effect on the course of the war.

A new Japanese tactic, *Kamikaze* (*see*) or suicide air attack, was used for the first time on a major scale in the Leyte Gulf, where it resulted in the sinking of a small carrier. As the U.S. fleet neared Japan Kamikaze attacks became a more important part of the defense strategy. In the battle for Okinawa, more than 30 ships were sunk and 300 severely damaged.

U.S. carrier and land-based aircraft subjected Japan to one of the most devastating bombing assaults on record, before the dropping of the atomic bombs at Hiroshima and Nagasaki which ended the war. The most important element of this aerial assault was delivered by the 20th Air Force which began its operations with very-long-range B-29 Superfortress bombers from the Marianas Islands in November, 1944. The 20th Air Force was placed directly under General H. H. Arnold (*see*), the Air Forces chief, and the Joint Chiefs of Staff in Washington. It was not subject to the orders of the theater commander and it mounted an independent aerial offensive in the truest sense.

During the first five months of operations the 20th Air Force had relatively little success with high-level bombing, for the Japanese defenses were sound, and B-29 losses were relatively high. In March of 1945, Major General Curtis LeMay (*see*) instituted a tactic of low-level fire-bombing from the B-29's with great success. Tokyo and some 65 other Japanese cities were burned out before the atomic bombs were dropped. After the war the Strategic Bombing Survey reported that this devastation would have brought surrender within a few months, even without the A-bombs.

In conclusion, not only did aviation shape the tactical nature of World War II, but the exigencies of the war itself spawned the science, technology, and industry which laid the foundations for present aerospace practice.   Sam Butz

See also: Aircraft Carriers, First World War aircraft, Second World War aircraft

WRESAT

Australia's first space vehicle, Weapons Research Establishment Satellite (WRESAT), was successfully launched from the Woomera rocket range (*see*) in South Australia, on November 29, 1967. WRESAT placed Australia fourth among the nations to orbit its own satellite from its own soil.

The 100-pound, 30-inch by 5-foot conical spacecraft was launched by a modified Redstone booster supplied by the U.S., at 2:18 p.m. Australian time and entered a nearly polar elliptical orbit measuring 100 by 700 nautical miles. Orbital life of the vehicle was a little over a month. As planned, scientific data was transmitted to Earth for the first five days of orbit.

WRESAT was a further step in an intensive program of measurements in the upper atmosphere carried on for some time by Australia using sounding rockets (*see*) and other experimental equipment. In 1966-67 the U.S. and Australia entered into a joint venture called *Project Sparta* involving the study of physical phenomena associated with the re-entry of objects at high velocities into the Earth's atmosphere. A series of re-entry test vehicles were launched at the Woomera range using the U.S. Redstone. This led to the logical choice of the Redstone to launch the Australian satellite project.

WRESAT was fabricated from light-alloy frames and skin. The external surfaces of the cone were treated with a special high-temperature black paint. This was done in order to achieve a satisfactory temperature within the cone during orbit and to withstand the aerodynamic heating encountered during launch and exit from the Earth's atmosphere. The inside of the cone was painted white in order to provide temperature equilibrium of the internal equipment. All instrumentation units were thermally isolated from the flight structure. Equipment included sensors, a Lyman telescope, a neon/argon gas-filled X-ray counter, and a magnetometer.

Measurements of the sun's effect on the Earth's atmosphere were made in three basic areas—a sunset/sunrise experiment, orbital measurements in sunlight, and orbital measurements toward the antisolar point.

Midway in WRESAT'S orbital lifetime, a sounding rocket was launched to coincide with the satellite's passage on its 29th revolution, when it was approaching perigee. The rocket carried instrumentation and experimental equipment similar to that of WRESAT to allow correlation between its data and that collected by the satellite.   Frank A. Burnham

See also: Australia's aviation

Wright brothers

American aviation pioneers; inventors
of the airplane
Born: Wilbur, April 16, 1867;   Died: Wilbur, May 30, 1912;
        Millville, Indiana   Dayton, Ohio
      Orville, August 19, 1871;   Orville, January 30, 1948;
        Dayton, Ohio   Dayton, Ohio

The first successful powered flights in 1903 by Orville and Wilbur Wright marked the beginning of the conquest of the air and ultimately lifted man to dimensions beyond the Earth. The Wright brothers' achievement was the culmination of several years of their own experiments with large kites and gliders and climaxed years of effort by other men to learn the secrets of flight.

Interested in aviation from boyhood, the Wright brothers followed the accounts of the glider experiments of Otto Lilienthal (*see*) in Germany and the pioneering work of American aeronauticists Octave Chanute (*see*) and Samuel Pierpont Langley (*see*). Lilienthal had achieved a minimum of flight control by shifting the weight of his body. The Wright brothers rejected this method as impractical. They discovered that balance, elevation, and steering could be controlled by moving various aircraft surfaces in flight. They devised a hinged rudder and crude aileron-like devices that could be linked together. Then two widely separated surfaces could be moved simultaneously. Thus the center of gravity could be kept constant and an equilibrium maintained. At first, the system used a forerunner of the aileron, a device consisting of a cable arrangement whereby the wing tips could be twisted or *warped* so as to achieve different lifts on the opposite wings.

Wind Tunnel and Glider Testing

Between 1899 and 1902 the Wrights built several kites and gliders which were tested over the sand dunes of Kitty Hawk, North Carolina (*see*), a location chosen for its steady constant winds and soft sand that minimized the effects of hard landings.

In their gliding experiments they got less lifting power from the wings than existing tables of air pressures on curved surfaces had led them to expect.

The launching of the Wright No. 3 glider (modified) at Kitty Hawk with Orville piloting.

In 1901 they set up a small wind tunnel in their workshop at Dayton. Through thousands of experiments with various wing shapes, they corrected the inaccuracies of the tables.

The Wrights designed and built two other parts which contributed to their success: a lightweight engine and a new kind of propeller.

The Wrights began the design of a powered airplane in October, 1902. The machine was a biplane on a skid undercarriage; it had a wingspan of 40 feet 4 inches, a wing area of 510 square feet, and a camber of 1 in 20. It had a biplane elevator in front and a double rudder behind with control cables linked to the warp-cradle. The 12-hp engine drove two geared-down pusher propellers through a cycle-chain transmission in tubes, one being crossed to produce counter-rotation.

Flyer I was launched along a 60-foot wooden rail, laid down into the wind. The engine was revved up while the craft was being held back and then released. When its speed produced sufficient lift, the craft rose from the yoke and flew. The design required the pilot to lie face downward to fly the aircraft which had an empty weight of 605 pounds.

The first attempt at flight was made on December 14, 1903, with Wilbur, who had won a coin-toss, at the controls. Because of an overcorrection with the elevator, *Flyer I* ploughed into the sand just after takeoff. Two days were required for repairs.

The First Successful Flights

Four successful flights were made on the morning of Thursday, December 17, 1903, between 10:30 a.m. and noon. Orville, whose turn it was then, took off first at 10:35 a.m. into a headwind of about 25 mph and flew for 12 seconds, covering 120 feet of ground and over 500 feet in air distance. Despite its short duration, the flight was the first in history in which a machine carrying a man raised itself by its own power into the air in full flight, sailed forward without a reduction in speed, and finally landed at a point on the same level as that from which it had started.

The brothers alternated in making three more flights that morning, each longer than the previous one. On the fourth flight, Wilbur flew 852 feet in 59 seconds. However, while the Wrights were discussing the flights with spectators, a gust of wind rolled *Flyer I* over and damaged the craft so badly that it never flew again.

The First Practical Airplane—1905

The Wrights' next series of powered flights took place in the summers of 1904 and 1905 at the Huffman Prairie near Dayton where an airfield had been set up. From those flights evolved the first fully practical powered airplane, *Flyer III*, which could be banked, turned, and circled and which had a flying time of over half an hour.

Flyer III was of the same general arrangement as the others, but noticeable differences appeared in the placing of the elevator farther forward and the rudder farther back to improve longitudinal control. The wingspan was 40 feet 6 inches; the wing area was slightly reduced, to 503 square feet; the camber was increased slightly; new sets of propellers were used; but the excellent 1904 engine was retained.

The prone pilot position was retained and also, for the start of the season, the warp and rudder linkage. Its speed was approximately 35 mph. Like all the Wright aircraft, it was built inherently unstable and had to be "flown" all the time by the pilot. The rudder outrigger was sprung to allow it to hinge upward if it dragged on the track or the ground.

About 50 flights were made in the 1905 season, but now the Wrights were concerned with reliability and endurance. In September, the trouble they were having in tight turns was diagnosed as a tendency of the lowered wings to slow up and stall, and the cure seemed to be in putting down the nose to gain speed while turning. It was while seeking this cause and cure that they took the important step of unlinking the warp and rudder controls and providing for their separate, or combined, operation in any desired degree.

The Wrights made many excellent flights with the perfected *Flyer*, including durations of 18 minutes 9 seconds; 25 minutes 5 seconds; 33 minutes 17 sec-

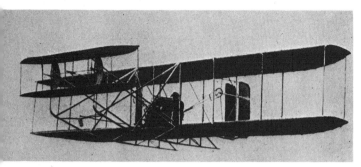

Wilbur taking a passenger at Pau in February or March of 1909.

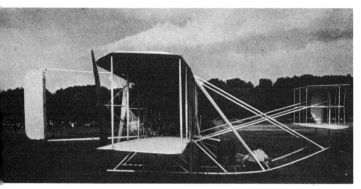

Orville's *Signal Corps* machine at Fort Myer for the second army trials in July, 1909.

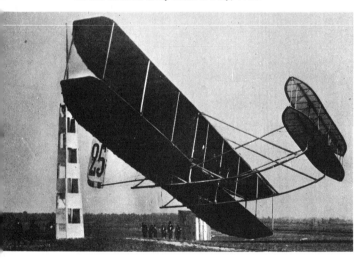

Lefebvre *(above)* in his Wright machine at Rheims, August, 1909, and the Wright machine wheeling out *(below)* at Templehof, Berlin.

onds; and, on October 5th, their record of 38 minutes 3 seconds, during which they covered over 24 miles.

The Developed Wright Flyer—1907-1909

In 1905 the Wrights first offered their invention to the U.S. and British governments. It was turned down, however, largely because the governments assumed that the Wrights were seeking financial assistance, whereas they had made it quite clear that they were offering a finished product. Although the basic patent was granted in 1906, the brothers thought their invention should be guarded until a purchaser was in sight.

The Wrights did not once leave the ground between October 16, 1905, and May 6, 1908, a period of 2½ years, nor did they allow anyone to view their machine. This interruption was due basically to the continued thwarting of the Wrights' legitimate demand that any client guarantee to purchase the aircraft provided it performed as agreed.

During this time, the Wrights built several improved engines and two or three new *Flyers*. The approximate specifications were wing area, about 510 square feet; wingspan, 41 feet; empty weight, 800 pounds; engine, 4 cylinder, 30-40 hp; and speed, 35-40 mph. This type was a two-seater and still retained the derrick-and-rail launching, although it could take off from the rail on engine power alone.

Acclaim at Home and Abroad

In 1909 the U.S. government purchased a Wright biplane for $30,000. In the same year the brothers organized the American Wright Company for the manufacture of airplanes. A trip to France by Wilbur in 1908 created great excitement and interest in Europe. He made many long flights of up to 2¼ hours duration and carried passengers on some 60 occasions.

Meanwhile other companies began to build similar planes, and the Wrights brought suit for infringement of their patent rights. After a long, bitter struggle, the courts upheld them.

In 1912, at the height of his career, Wilbur died of typhoid fever. Three years later Orville sold his interest in the Wright company but continued to work as a consulting engineer.

The Wright brothers received many honors and prizes, including an award by the U.S. Congress in 1909. Orville was awarded the Distinguished Flying Cross in 1929. The original Wright biplane is on exhibition at the National Air and Space Museum *(see)* in Washington, D.C., and the Wright Brothers National Memorial is at the site of their first sustained flight at Kitty Hawk.　　　Charles Gibbs-Smith

See also: History of aviation, Wright Flyer

Wright Flyer

Because the Wright 1903 *Flyer* first flew at Kitty Hawk, North Carolina (*see*), it came to be called the *Kitty Hawk Machine* or just the *Kitty Hawk*. It was the result of years of painstaking observation and experimentation by two brothers, Orville and Wilbur Wright, who thought together and worked together. The Wright brothers (*see*) were, in fact, natural scientists, and their descriptions of the preparations and records of the first successful flights at Kill Devil Hill are testimony to their meticulous preparation.

himself in position in the hip saddle and grasped the elevator lever firmly. The engine was started, and with the propellers whirling, the airplane moved forward slowly, with Wilbur steadying the wingtip. After a run of about 40 feet, the *Flyer* lifted from the track and rose into the air. Orville then flew it for 12 seconds, covering about 120 feet. This flight and the three following, the longest of which was 852 feet, were the first flights by man in a heavier-than-air powered and controlled aircraft. Louis S. Casey

See also: History of aviation

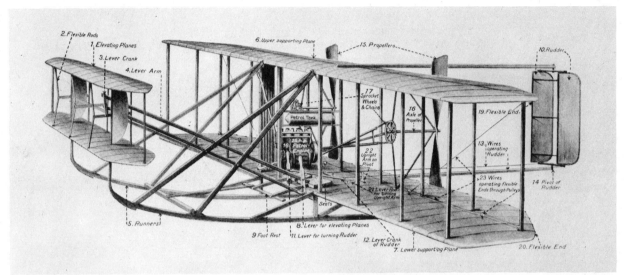

After reading all the published accounts of aeronautical experimenters of their day, the brothers proceeded to construct a glider-kite with which they tried out some of their first ideas of lift and control of an aircraft. Between 1900 and 1902, they constructed and tested three successful gliders.

After the 1902 season, they decided to construct a powered model, but they were hampered by lack of a suitable engine and propeller. To solve the problem, they built their own engine, a four-cylinder, horizontal, water-cooled engine which weighed about 180 pounds and produced 12 to 16 hp. They also designed a new propeller which was to influence propeller design thereafter. To enable them to make soft landings in the sands at Kitty Hawk, they constructed a landing gear similar to sled runners. A track was used for takeoff assist.

During the preliminary tests, numerous difficulties were encountered, and it was not until December 14, 1903, that they were overcome.

Thursday, December 17, dawned cold and windy. It was Orville's turn to try the machine. He settled

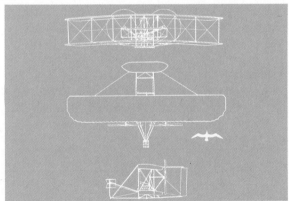

Wright Flyer
Specifications and Performance Data

Engine	designed by the Wrights, 12-16 hp
Wingspan	40 ft. 4 in.
Length	21 ft.
Height	8 ft.
Chord (wind width fore and aft)	6 ft. 6 in.
Aspect ratio (relation of span to chord)	6:2
Camber (wing bow)	1:20
Wing area	510 sq. ft.
Power loading	62 lbs./hp.
Wing loading	1.46 lbs./sq. ft.
Empty weight	605 lbs.
Gross weight with pilot	750 lbs. (approximate)

XB-70, North American Valkyrie

The XB-70 was designed by North American Rockwell as a strategic bomber capable of carrying out its entire mission at a speed of Mach 3. The requirements for the XB-70 were formulated in 1954 when it was planned as a replacement for the Boeing B-52. However, after the flight of the prototype on September 21, 1964, military and congressional controversy over the bomber resulted in policy changes and the decision to build only two of the aircraft to be used for aerodynamic research. The second XB-70 made its first flight in July, 1965, and was destroyed in June, 1966, in an air collision.

The XB-70 is a delta wing aircraft, distinguished by its tail-first design which utilizes a horizontal "foreplane" or canard just behind the cockpit of its needle-nosed fuselage. The foreplane is equipped with trailing-edge flaps and is adjustable for trim control. Another distinguishing feature is the huge ducts at the midship section of the aircraft which feed air to six turbojet engines under the wings. The extremely thin delta wings are constructed of welded stainless steel honeycomb panels and have a total of 11 "elevons" for flight control. The wings also have tips which can be folded downward for

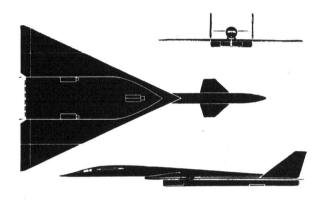

XB-70 North American
Specifications and Performance Data

Engine	Six General Electric YJ93-GE-3 turbojets, approximately 19,500 lbs. static thrust each
Wingspan	105 ft. (with tips extended)
Length	185 ft.
Gross weight	520,000 lbs. (approximate)
Maximum speed	1,980 mph (Mach 3)
Range	7,500 miles

increased stability and maneuverability in supersonic flight (*see*). The wingtips are moved hydraulically to an angle of 25° for low altitude flight and to 65° for high altitude cruising at Mach 3.

The aerodynamic research program for which the XB-70 is used is administered by NASA with mission support provided by Edwards Air Force Base. The program includes support for the National Supersonic Transport Program as well as projects and research for the Department of Defense. Flights of the XB-70 with a crew of two cost about $800,000 each and are made on a schedule of one or two times per month.   Sanford Sasser, Jr.

X-15 research program

The X-15 is a small rocket-powered aircraft that has flown faster and higher than any other winged aircraft in the world. Its flight program has provided important knowledge applicable to the design and development of future spacecraft and high-performance aircraft.

Conceived in the early 1950's, the X-15 is a continuation of the Research Airplane Program first approved by the U.S. government in 1944. Its predecessors were the rocket-powered X-1, X-1A, X-1B, X-1E, D-558 II, X-2, and the jet-powered X-3, X-4, and X-5. Prior to its first flight in 1959, manned flight had been restricted to altitudes below 130,000 feet and speeds under 2,100 mph.

Based upon earlier studies in its laboratories and wind tunnels, the National Advisory Committee for Aeronautics (*see*), predecessor of the National Aeronautics and Space Administration (NASA) (*see*), recommended in 1954 to the USAF and the U.S. Navy the development of an aircraft capable of flying at altitudes of 250,000 feet (50 miles) and 4,000 mph (Mach 6). The purpose of the committee was strictly research. It was agreed then that NASA would accept technical responsibility and the USAF administer the design and construction phases.

The initial airframe contract, calling for the construction of three airplanes, was awarded to North American Rockwell in late 1955. A contract for the rocket engine capable of thrust in excess of 57,000 lbs. was awarded to the Reaction Motors Division of Thiokol Chemical Corp. in September, 1956.

The first of the three aircraft was completed in 1958 and was transported to Edwards Air Force Base (*see*). Under the terms of the contract, North American was responsible for demonstrating the flight-worthiness of the craft, and therefore it conducted the initial flight tests.

The X-15 research rocket plane igniting its engines as it leaves the Boeing B-52 mother plane near Edwards AFB, California, on February 21, 1961.

Early Test Flights

After several planned captive flights to check out the various aircraft systems, Albert Scott Crossfield, Jr. (*see*) was air-launched from a B-52 in a planned powerless glide-flight of the X-15 on June 8, 1959. The first flight of the X-15 lasted about five minutes. Three months later, on September 17, 1959, Crossfield was again launched in the X-15 for free flight. This time he ignited the two interim XLR-11 rocket engines, which were being used until completion of the originally designed XLR-11. The X-15 reached a top speed of 1,393 mph on its first powered flight.

After completion of the contractor tests, the first X-15 was accepted by the USAF and turned over to NASA. Joseph A. Walker (*see*), NASA's chief research pilot, made the first government flight in March, 1960. Meanwhile the third X-15 was being equipped with the larger XRL-99 engine. After several months of ground tests, this craft made its first flight in November, 1960, reaching a top speed of just under Mach 3.

The X-15 flight program continued to increase the speed and altitude capabilities of the craft by small increments. The X-15 reached its design speed on November 9, 1961: USAF Maj. Robert M. White flew the first X-15 to a speed of 4,093 mph, a little over Mach 6. On April, 30 1962, Joseph Walker of NASA piloted the X-15 to 243,700 ft., almost to its design altitude.

However, the X-15 proved to be more successful than its designers thought. On August 22, 1963, Joe Walker flew the third X-15 to a peak altitude of over 67 miles high. Carrying two external tanks with extra fuel for the rocket engine, Maj. William J. Knight piloted the second X-15 to a speed of Mach 6.7 on October 3, 1967.

Research Contributions

Although primarily an airplane with wings and aerodynamic controls, the X-15 travels above the effective atmosphere and must depend upon small peroxide-rocket controls, the forerunners of those used in spacecraft. The pilot is weightless for short periods of time, and the X-15 must make a more severe re-entry than space capsules. Thus the research contributions of the X-15 encompass flights in air and space.

The most important contribution of the X-15 has been the collection of actual inflight data on aerodynamics (*see*), heating, structures, stability and control, bioastronautics (*see*), and man's ability to fly a vehicle of this type. This information is being used to verify wind-tunnel data and other theoretical ground-based studies.

The investigation of the heating caused by air friction at high speeds has been a prime example of discovering significant differences from predicted results of earlier wind-tunnel tests. Future aircraft, such as the supersonic transport (SST) (*see*) and Mach 5 hypersonic transport will depend upon the knowledge acquired by the X-15, whose outside skin routinely reaches temperatures of 1,000°F and sometimes reaches more than 2,000°F.

The adaptive control system used in the third X-15 automatically senses the surrounding atmospheric conditions and aids in the control of the aircraft. A newer version of the control system in now being used in the F-111 (*see*) and the proposed SST.

Energy management techniques, developed to assist the X-15 in precise maneuvering to a landing at a predetermined location, are being studied for use by future manned orbital spacecraft. Simplified versions of the X-15's inertial guidance system (*see*) are being installed on modern aircraft.

The X-15 flight program has demonstrated that Earth exit and re-entry are well within the capabilities of a pilot. Each time the X-15 returns from altitudes higher than 125,000 feet, the pilot must perform precise control maneuvers that allow the X-15 to recover from its steep descent. An error or miscalculation during this time can cause the aircraft to break apart. The pilot must carefully guide the X-15 to its planned landing area and make a 225-mph powerless-glide landing.

In recent years, the X-15 has carried a wide variety of nonaerodynamic scientific experiments because of its ability to fly to and return from the edge of space. Included among these experiments are cameras used to photograph various stars from high altitudes. A scanner is carried that measures the Earth's horizon in various seasons for use as a navigational reference for Apollo (*see*). Equipment carried in a wing-tip pod is used to collect micrometeorites for examination. Measurements of solar energy and sky brightness are also recorded.

Specifications of the X-15

The X-15 airplane is relatively small, about 50 feet long with a 22-foot wingspan. It stands 13 feet high at the tail. Side fairings extend along each side of the X-15 and house the control cables and electrical wiring. The wings are thin, have blunt edges, and are swept back at an angle of about 25°. The vertical tail is wedge-shaped with blunt leading edges and extends above and below the fuselage. The upper two-thirds of the vertical tail is movable for yaw control in the atmosphere. The bottom two-thirds of the lower tail, which was not carried after the first 70 flights, was

Six men who have flown the X-15 *(above)* are Capt. J. Engle, Maj. R. A. Rushworth, J. B. McKay, Maj. W. J. Knight, M. O. Thompson, and W. H. Dana. Knight *(below)* inspects the Number Two X-15 which he piloted to a record speed of 4,500 mph.

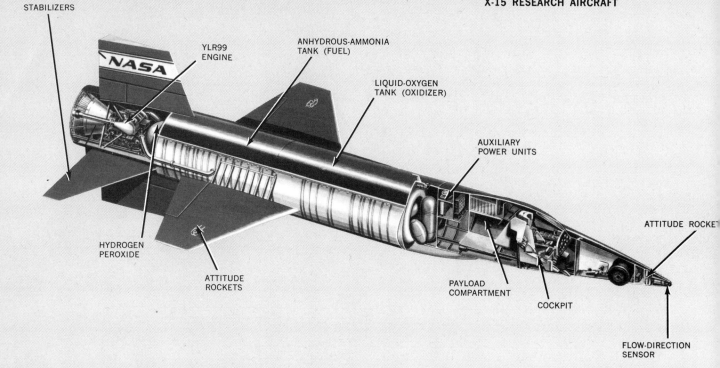

jettisoned for parachute recovery prior to landing. Speed brakes are located on the upper and lower fixed portion of the ventrails.

The complete horizontal tail surfaces are movable. Moving simultaneously, they provide pitch control;

Two stainless steel skids are extended for a landing of the X-15. They are stowed against the side of the fuselage while in flight.

moving differentially, they provide roll control. The X-15 has no wing ailerons but does have wing flaps for landing.

The outer skin of the X-15 is made of Inconel X, a nickel alloy designed to withstand temperatures of 1,200°F. To protect the X-15's skin from high temperatures, the aircraft is covered with a white ablative coating similar to the heat shields (*see*) on re-entry vehicles (*see*). Inside the X-15, titanium (*see*) and stainless steel are used to save weight.

Although a conventional dual-tire nose landing gear is utilized, because of weight and temperature considerations the aircraft has two stainless steel skids that are stowed in flight against the side of the fuselage and are extended just prior to landing.

For flight above approximately 125,000 feet, the X-15 has a reaction control system (*see*) consisting of 12 small peroxide rockets located on the nose and wings. The pilot regulates these rockets, which develop 40 to 100 lbs. of thrust each and are capable of controlling the attitude of the aircraft at the higher altitudes.

The X-15 weighs about 15,000 lbs. empty. Launch weight is approximately 34,000 lbs. Depending on the particular engine, thrust of the XLR-99 is 57,000 to 60,000 lbs. It can be run between idle and full thrust and can be shut down in flight and restarted. The X-15 normally carries 8,500 lbs. of anhydrous ammonia and 10,500 lbs. of propellant. After the propellant is used, the tanks are jettisoned for recovery

and reuse. The design speed of the X-15 with the longer engine burn-time is approximately 5,000 mph.

The third X-15 was destroyed in an accident on November 15, 1967, and the pilot, Maj. Michael J. Adams, was fatally injured. Two other nonfatal accidents have occurred during the almost 200 flights of the three X-15's.

Twelve men have flown the X-15. In chronological order they are: A. Scott Crossfield, North American Rockwell; Joseph A. Walker, NASA; Maj. Robert A. White, USAF; Cmdr. Forrest S. Peterson, USN; John B. McKay, NASA; Maj. Robert A. Rushworth, USAF; Neil A. Armstrong (*see*), NASA; Capt. Joe Henry Engle (*see*), USAF; Milton O. Thompson, NASA; Maj. William J. Knight, USAF; William H. Dana, NASA; and Maj. Michael J. Adams, USAF.

Due to financial considerations, the X-15 flight research program will not be funded beyond the fiscal year 1968. Remaining funds will be used to continue the flight program through the calendar year 1968.   Ralph B. Jackson

See also: History of aviation, Test pilots and test flying, X-series aerospace vehicles

X-rays

X-rays are high-energy electromagnetic radiations of very short wavelength. The range of electromagnetic radiations is represented by a spectrum according to the size of their wavelengths. In order of decreasing wavelength the spectrum includes: radio waves, heat radiation, infrared radiation, visible light, ultraviolet light, X-rays, and gamma rays.

X-rays were first discovered in 1895 by the German scientist Wilhelm Konrad Roentgen. Because of their energy (*see*), X-rays have the ability to penetrate all matter and to be differentially absorbed by different types of matter. As a result, X-rays can be used to take a picture of the inside of an object by making the X-rays that penetrate the object strike a photographic plate. Since X-rays do not pass through all material equally well, those portions of the object that offer the greatest resistance to the rays appear lighter in the photograph. For example, bone is more resistant than other bodily tissue and readily shows up on X-ray photographs used by doctors and dentists.

X-rays occur when electrons traveling at velocities approaching the speed of light collide with the atoms of any material, although materials with high atomic numbers increase the efficiency of X-ray production. When a collision occurs, it produces a loss in the kinetic energy of the electron. Most of this energy is transformed into heat. A very small portion, however, is converted into high-energy X-ray particles.

To produce X-rays, a source of electrons, a method for accelerating them to high energy levels and a target for them to bombard are required. A special gas tube, called an *X-ray tube*, is used for this purpose. In most cases the electron source (cathode) is a tungsten filament, which is heated to a high temperature by passing a current through it. The electrons are then accelerated by applying a high voltage across the tube between the cathode and the target (anode). In this way, the electrons are made to strike the anode to produce X-rays. Some of the stars (*see*), including the sun (*see*), also give off copious amounts of X-rays. Most of these X-rays are trapped in the atmosphere and do not reach the Earth.   Mary-Louise Tally

See also: Electromagnetism, Radiation

X-ray stars

Special devices flown above the Earth's atmosphere in rockets and satellites since 1962 have unexpectedly detected several strong localized objects emitting X-rays (*see*). Difficulties of finding the accurate positions of these objects in the short time rockets are above the atmosphere delayed identification of these "X-ray" stars with optical telescopes until 1966.

The first, known as *Scorpius X-1* (the first source to be found in the constellation Scorpius), is thought to be a 13th magnitude (*see*) object which resembles an old nova (*see*). Its spectrum contains emission lines of hydrogen, helium, and highly excited carbon and nitrogen, but no absorption lines. The intensity of the optical radiation varies irregularly.

The identification excited astronomers, who immediately began deducing the mechanisms that might produce this radiation and what it would mean for theories of the structure of stars and nebulae.

The second source, known as *Cygnus X-2*, is identified with a 15th-magnitude star-like object that fluctuates in brightness. Both emission and absorption lines are visible and fluctuate in radial velocity. The third source, known as *Centaurus XR-2*, may be a peculiar 14th-magnitude star. Its X-ray emission has been found to vary. X-ray sources are apparently correlated with the spiral arms of the Milky Way Galaxy (see).

Other celestial objects also emit X-rays. The Crab nebula was identified as a source by noticing that the X-rays were no longer received when the nebula was occulted, or hidden, by the moon. An experiment on Orbiting Solar Observatory IV (OSO-IV), a satellite launched in 1967, observed X-rays from flares on the sun.   Jay M. Pasachoff

See also: Orbiting observatories, Stars, Sun

The X-24 PILOT lifting body, the latest of the X-series research aircraft.

X-series aerospace vehicles

Research in advanced high-performance craft

In early 1946 high over the runway at Pinecastle Army Air Base, Florida, a B-29 labored skyward. In its specially modified bomb bay it carried a strange looking craft similar in shape to a 50-caliber bullet with straight, stubby, and incredibly thin wings. In the tiny cockpit of the unusual craft sat Jack Woolams, test pilot for the Bell Aircraft Corporation.

Arriving at a predetermined altitude, the B-29 pilot lined up with the 10,000-foot runway below and on receiving the "go" signal from Woolams tripped the latches that held the small craft in the bomb bay. He watched it drop away from the mother ship and hurtle toward Earth.

Woolams made 11 more glide tests of the X-1, first in the U.S. series of pure research aircraft, the

Heavy armor flak suits *(left)* were developed to protect Allied bomber crews from shrapnel.
Only two crewmembers bailed out of a B-24 Liberator hit by flak *(right)* over northern Italy. The
force of the explosion crumpled the wing and the aircraft caught fire and plunged to the ground.

shot down as many as 10 per cent of the attackers. It became clear that the Flying Fortresses could not protect themselves and needed escort fighters, or the raids would have to be made at night as the British had warned. This problem was solved by equipping P-51 Mustang fighters with drop tanks under the wings to give them approximately the same range as the bombers.

High-altitude bombing accuracy also was not as good as predicted and the U.S. was forced to use area bombing to take out many targets.

Final statistics for the air war in Europe showed that the U.S. and British had flown a total of almost 1.5 million bomber sorties, more than 2.5 million fighter sorties, and had dropped about 2.7 million tons of bombs.

V-Weapons and Jet Aircraft

As the war ended the Germans were setting a blistering pace in advanced technology. They were substantially ahead of the Allies with several revolutionary weapons, including jet aircraft *(see)*, rocket-powered aircraft, and guided missiles.

Well over 1,000 Messerschmitt Me-262 twin-jet fighters were produced and a substantial number of these were used in the defenses against Allied bombers. The rocket-powered Me-163 also was operational for a considerable period. If large numbers of these aircraft, which were nearly 100 mph faster than Allied fighters, had been brought into service a year earlier, it is very possible that they could have stopped the Allied bombing offensive.

The first mass-produced missile was the V-1 missile *(see)* (V for Vengeance weapon), which was essentially a pilotless bomber powered by a lightweight and inexpensive pulsejet engine. More than 15,000 V-1's were launched with some 7,800 aimed at London and most of the others at Allied supply points in France and Belgium. Allied fighters and antiaircraft guns shot down nearly half of these missiles which cruised at about 400 mph.

Defense against the V-2 rocket missile *(see)* was impossible however, as it traveled at several times the speed of sound. It was the first long-range ballistic missile, the direct forerunner of the ICBM. About 3,000 V-2's were launched at London and Antwerp. The accuracy of the V-1 and V-2 was poor but they caused more than 30,000 casualties in London alone and did substantial damage.

The Japanese Kawasaki Ki-45 was developed in 1939 and patterned after the U.S. A-18.

An advanced Japanese fighter on display in Washington, D.C., after World War II.

The most sobering point about all of these weapons is that the Germans had the capacity to build them at least a year before they actually did. Hitler and his top advisors became so overconfident after the fall of France in 1940 that they ordered development of advanced weapons stopped for more than a year.

Flying Tigers

Undoubtedly the most unusual and successful air unit in World War II was the American Volunteer Group (AVG) in China, the famous Flying Tigers (*see*) which were organized by Claire Chennault (*see*), a retired U.S. Army Air Corps officer.

Chennault went to China in 1937 to assist in the building of a Chinese Air Force. He had become familiar with the area and was ready with a plan in 1941 when help arrived from the United States in the form of 100 Curtiss-Wright P-40B Tomahawk fighter planes and the volunteer pilots to fly them. In six months of combat, the AVG shot down 297 Japanese aircraft at the cost of only 12 American pilots. The

Parachute fragmentation bombs dropped at low altitudes onto Japanese-held railroad installation in the Philippines. Parachutes permitted the bomber to escape bomb blast and shrapnel.

Flying Tigers ran up their amazing score while flying obsolescent fighter planes in the face of overwhelming numerical odds and against some well-seasoned Japanese pilots.

The Flying Tigers flew against the Japanese in both Burma and China before they were inducted into the Army Air Forces as the 14th Air Force in July, 1942. Chennault was recalled to active duty and promoted to the rank of Brigadier General and early in 1943 given command of the 14th Air Force. It never reached a strength of more than 500 fighters and 190 bombers and its area of operations was as large as western Europe, but in three years of operations the entire 14th Air Force destroyed 2,300 enemy aircraft and probably destroyed another 775 at a cost of 500 aircraft lost from all causes. Allied officers generally credited this lopsided victory to the inflexibility of Japanese plans and tactics, the poor eyesight of their pilots, and the fact that they seldom had a deputy leader for their formations. In air battle, if the Japanese leader was shot down, the other aircraft usually became ineffective.

Gen. Chennault has written extensively of the events that helped form his philosophy of aerial combat and the flexible tactics which are credited with bringing overwhelming victory to American air units in China. During 1937 to 1939 he had an excellent opportunity to observe the air operations of the Japanese and of the Russian air task force fighting the Japanese in China. He was impressed by the fact that these air forces had two characteristics in common: iron-hard discipline and complete denial of an initiative to a subordinate. Chennault wrote, "I remember how on one occasion a group of Russian fighters scrambled from an air field in central China to meet a mixed force of Japanese fighters and bombers. The Japanese fighters were about five minutes ahead of the bombers and contacted the Russian fighters over the field. The engines of the Russian group leader was shot out on the first pass, and he spiraled down to a landing on the field followed one by one by all of the other Russian pilots. The Japanese bombers plastered the field thoroughly while the Russians were landing, and damaged or destroyed all the Russian airplanes. When I inquired why all the planes landed with the group leader, I was told, matter-of-factly, that the Russian pilots had orders to follow the leader under any and all circumstances."

Japanese Conquests

Japanese conquests in the Pacific area outside the Chinese mainland began with an air attack on Pearl Harbor (*see*) shortly after dawn on December 7, 1941. This attack was made by less than 500 aircraft operat-

ing from six carriers steaming some 230 miles north of Hawaii. The Japanese expected to lose a substantial portion of this force, including some carriers, but they achieved complete tactical surprise and caused heavy damage to U.S. forces while losing only 29 of their own airplanes.

The main battleline of the U.S. Pacific fleet was decimated with its eight battleships sunk or badly damaged. A number of smaller ships were damaged along with shore facilities. Some 200 U.S. aircraft were destroyed on the ground, and more than 2,000 men died. The one bright spot was that the Pacific Fleet's three carriers were not in the base at the time. Shortly after Pearl Harbor, Japanese forces made simultaneous attacks on the Philippines, Hong Kong, and Malaya. In the Philippines, the invasion began with an almost inexcusable air defeat at Clark Field near Manila. Despite the fact that news of Pearl Harbor had been received, the aircraft at this installation still were in vulnerable positions when the first Japanese formations appeared. They destroyed more than 115 aircraft while losing 7 and effectively eliminated U.S. airpower in the area. U.S. forces held out briefly on Bataan, Corregidor, and in the southern Philippines, but resistance ended early in May, 1942.

A devastating air attack that knocked out all British aircraft proceeded the ground assault upon Hong Kong. Resistance in this tiny colony lasted less than a month.

Japanese operations against the keystone British base of Singapore began with the landing of troops about halfway down the Malayan peninsula. These troops were provided with substantial air support from bases in French Indochina. Despite the close proximity of this land-based aviation the English sent their two largest naval vessels in the Far East, the battleships *Prince of Wales* and *Repulse*, north from Singapore without air cover in an attempt to disrupt the Japanese shipping supporting the landings. Just three days after Pearl Harbor these ships were attacked by less than 100 Japanese bombers and quickly sunk. Only three aircraft were lost. This action ended most of the remaining speculation about the capital ship being a match for aircraft. Aircraft carriers were quickly acknowledged as the new "queen of the seas."

Singapore fell by the middle of February, but by then it had been bypassed and the Japanese had secured a large portion of the Dutch East Indies. By March, the island of Java had been taken and Allied naval vessels driven from the Java Sea. Darwin, Australia, was hit in a surprise air raid which resulted in substantial casualties and the loss of more than 20 aircraft and 10 ships.

In the Central Pacific, Japanese forces also moved swiftly capturing Wake Island and Guam from the United States and Rabaul, New Britain, from Australian forces.

The Japanese immediately began erecting defenses for the new territories, putting in large air and naval installations at Guam and Rabaul to supplement

U.S. C-47's drop airborne troops over southern France somewhere between Nice and Marseilles after the initial amphibious and airborne invasions in Normandy in June, 1944.

their bases in the Carolines. Plans also were made to cut Australia off from its lifelines to the United States and Europe, and to deliver a final blow to U.S. naval power in the Pacific. A thrust was prepared through the Solomon Islands with the objective of capturing Port Moresby on the southeastern tip of New Guinea, and New Caledonia and Samoa. Another thrust was aimed at Midway Island lying at the extreme western end of the Hawaiian chain in the central Pacific.

In April, a tactically ineffective air raid was made against Japanese cities by 16 Army B-25 bombers led by Lt. Col. James H. Doolittle (see). These bombers flew from the deck of the carrier *Hornet* less than 600 miles off the Japanese coast and then crash-landed in Japanese-occupied China. Psychologically, however, this small raid had a very important effect on the war. It raised morale in the U.S. and caused Japanese military leaders to lose face at home. It also convinced the Japanese that the Allies planned to fight back, so that internal arguments against further military thrusts in the South and Central Pacific were effectively stilled.

Battles of the Coral Sea and Midway

The Battle of the Coral Sea occurred early in May, 1942, as a U.S. Navy task force moved to block the Japanese invasion force heading for Port Moresby. It is significant because it was the first major naval engagement in which surface ships never exchanged a shot. Aircraft carried the action completely.

Tactically, the U.S. lost the battle since the carrier *Lexington* was sunk and the only other one in the task force, the *Yorktown*, was severely damaged, while the Japanese had one carrier damaged, The U.S. strategic purpose was achieved, however, as the Japanese transports were harrassed by both carrier and land-based aviation and forced to turn back to Rabaul.

The naval action in the Coral Sea was small, however, compared to that occurring about one month later southeast of Midway. An armada consisting of the bulk of the Japanese fleet was sent to cover a landing on Midway and to force a final showdown with the U.S. Navy. This armada consisted of 4 heavy carriers, 3 light carriers, 11 battleships, more than 50 cruisers and destroyers, and sizable numbers of submarines and auxiliary ships.

Admiral Isoroku Yamamoto, a leading advocate of naval air power in Japan and architect of the Pearl Harbor attack, was in charge of this force, yet his battle plan relegated the carriers to a secondary role. He wanted to land on Midway and force the remnants of the U.S. Pacific fleet out from Pearl Harbor, and then sink them in a classic naval battle using his surface ships. This seemed to be a relatively minor task since Japanese intelligence reported that only 5 U.S. heavy cruisers and a few destroyers were fit for sea. Their intelligence also had reported that the *Yorktown* had been sunk rather than damaged in the Coral Sea, so the Japanese believed that only two U.S. carriers had to be reckoned with, the *Enterprise* and the *Hornet*, and the latest reports placed them in the South Pacific.

U.S. good fortune in this battle began with the breaking of the Japanese naval code so that Admiral Chester W. Nimitz in Honolulu was able to decipher many secret communications and was privy to the basic Japanese plan. Next, the damaged *Yorktown* made it back to Pearl Harbor where repairs which normally would have taken 90 days were completed in two days, and the carrier put back out to sea. This gave the Navy three sizable carriers, the presence of which the Japanese were unaware.

In two days of heavy fighting the U.S. force, which was distinctly inferior, won a crushing victory. The four Japanese heavy carriers were defeated together with more than 250 aircraft and experienced pilots, and the Americans successfully avoided an encounter with the superior force of Japanese surface vessels. Without adequate air cover this surface force was compelled to abandon the Midway landing and withdraw behind Wake Island in the protection of its land-based aircraft. U.S. losses were acceptably light even though the carrier *Yorktown* finally was sunk.

The Battle of Midway generally is considered to be one of the turning points of the war, for the Japanese never recovered their offensive naval capacity. Their heavy losses essentially equalized naval strength in the Pacific as concerned the carriers, the element which had been shown to be the key to success. The war then settled down to be largely a race between U.S. and Japanese industry in the production of carriers and aircraft; the outcome here was never in doubt.

Victory at Midway, some six months after Pearl Harbor, enabled the United States to start planning major offensives. There were many conflicts of opinion at the highest levels about the best plan because the U.S. was in a two-front war, and had agreed with its Allies that Hitler was the main enemy so that Europe had top priority. However, enough resources were allocated for a two-pronged thrust in the Pacific. One was under Admiral Nimitz in the so-called Pacific Ocean Areas, and the other was an "island-hopping" campaign under General Douglas MacArthur.

Bristol Beau fighter of the RAF fires rockets from under its wing rails. These weapons were widely employed in ground support, air-to-air missions, and anti-shipping activities.

The Philippines, Okinawa, and then Japan itself were the main objectives of both of these offensives. By 1944, both had carried to the shores of the Philippines, and despite tenacious Japanese resistance had resulted in a long string of Allied victories. The U.S. Navy had become the largest naval power in history with nearly 5,000 vessels of all types, including nearly 100 heavy and light carriers and more than 18,000 airplanes.

Two naval battles of major consequence were fought. One was an all-out attempt by the Imperial Japanese fleet to stop the U.S. seizure of the Marianas Islands east of the Philippines in June of 1944. This resulted in the biggest carrier battle of the war and a lopsided U.S. victory, which quickly became known as the "Marianas Turkey Shoot." The Japanese lost 7 carriers, 1 battleship, and 1 cruiser either sunk or severely damaged, in addition to some 450 planes destroyed. U.S. losses were minor.

The second key engagement was the Battle of Leyte Gulf and it occurred after the Japanese decided to make their main stand in the defense of the Philippines on the island of Leyte. Virtually the complete Imperial Fleet, strongly supported by land-based aircraft from Leyte, was committed in this battle, and the major ships were all destroyed or severely damaged. Japanese losses included 4 battleships, 3 carriers, and 10 cruisers, compared to U.S. losses of 3 small carriers and 2 destroyers sunk. After this battle the Japanese Navy was not able to have any substantial effect on the course of the war.

A new Japanese tactic, *Kamikaze* (*see*) or suicide air attack, was used for the first time on a major scale in the Leyte Gulf, where it resulted in the sinking of a small carrier. As the U.S. fleet neared Japan Kamikaze attacks became a more important part of the defense strategy. In the battle for Okinawa, more than 30 ships were sunk and 300 severely damaged.

U.S. carrier and land-based aircraft subjected Japan to one of the most devastating bombing assaults on record, before the dropping of the atomic bombs at Hiroshima and Nagasaki which ended the war. The most important element of this aerial assault was delivered by the 20th Air Force which began its operations with very-long-range B-29 Superfortress bombers from the Marianas Islands in November, 1944. The 20th Air Force was placed directly under General H. H. Arnold (*see*), the Air Forces chief, and the Joint Chiefs of Staff in Washington. It was not subject to the orders of the theater commander and it mounted an independent aerial offensive in the truest sense.

During the first five months of operations the 20th Air Force had relatively little success with high-level bombing, for the Japanese defenses were sound, and B-29 losses were relatively high. In March of 1945, Major General Curtis LeMay (*see*) instituted a tactic of low-level fire-bombing from the B-29's with great success. Tokyo and some 65 other Japanese cities were burned out before the atomic bombs were dropped. After the war the Strategic Bombing Survey reported that this devastation would have brought surrender within a few months, even without the A-bombs.

In conclusion, not only did aviation shape the tactical nature of World War II, but the exigencies of the war itself spawned the science, technology, and industry which laid the foundations for present aerospace practice.   Sam Butz

See also: Aircraft Carriers, First World War aircraft, Second World War aircraft

WRESAT

Australia's first space vehicle, Weapons Research Establishment Satellite (WRESAT), was successfully launched from the Woomera rocket range (*see*) in South Australia, on November 29, 1967. WRESAT placed Australia fourth among the nations to orbit its own satellite from its own soil.

The 100-pound, 30-inch by 5-foot conical spacecraft was launched by a modified Redstone booster supplied by the U.S., at 2:18 p.m. Australian time and entered a nearly polar elliptical orbit measuring 100 by 700 nautical miles. Orbital life of the vehicle was a little over a month. As planned, scientific data was transmitted to Earth for the first five days of orbit.

WRESAT was a further step in an intensive program of measurements in the upper atmosphere carried on for some time by Australia using sounding rockets (*see*) and other experimental equipment. In 1966-67 the U.S. and Australia entered into a joint venture called *Project Sparta* involving the study of physical phenomena associated with the re-entry of objects at high velocities into the Earth's atmosphere. A series of re-entry test vehicles were launched at the Woomera range using the U.S. Redstone. This led to the logical choice of the Redstone to launch the Australian satellite project.

WRESAT was fabricated from light-alloy frames and skin. The external surfaces of the cone were treated with a special high-temperature black paint. This was done in order to achieve a satisfactory temperature within the cone during orbit and to withstand the aerodynamic heating encountered during launch and exit from the Earth's atmosphere. The inside of the cone was painted white in order to provide temperature equilibrium of the internal equipment. All instrumentation units were thermally isolated from the flight structure. Equipment included sensors, a Lyman telescope, a neon/argon gas-filled X-ray counter, and a magnetometer.

Measurements of the sun's effect on the Earth's atmosphere were made in three basic areas—a sunset/sunrise experiment, orbital measurements in sunlight, and orbital measurements toward the antisolar point.

Midway in WRESAT'S orbital lifetime, a sounding rocket was launched to coincide with the satellite's passage on its 29th revolution, when it was approaching perigee. The rocket carried instrumentation and experimental equipment similar to that of WRESAT to allow correlation between its data and that collected by the satellite.　　　Frank A. Burnham

See also: Australia's aviation

Wright brothers

American aviation pioneers; inventors
of the airplane
Born: Wilbur, April 16, 1867;　　Died: Wilbur, May 30, 1912;
　　　　Millville, Indiana　　　　　　　　Dayton, Ohio
　　　　Orville, August 19, 1871;　　　　Orville, January 30, 1948;
　　　　Dayton, Ohio　　　　　　　　　　Dayton, Ohio

The first successful powered flights in 1903 by Orville and Wilbur Wright marked the beginning of the conquest of the air and ultimately lifted man to dimensions beyond the Earth. The Wright brothers' achievement was the culmination of several years of their own experiments with large kites and gliders and climaxed years of effort by other men to learn the secrets of flight.

Interested in aviation from boyhood, the Wright brothers followed the accounts of the glider experiments of Otto Lilienthal (*see*) in Germany and the pioneering work of American aeronauticists Octave Chanute (*see*) and Samuel Pierpont Langley (*see*). Lilienthal had achieved a minimum of flight control by shifting the weight of his body. The Wright brothers rejected this method as impractical. They discovered that balance, elevation, and steering could be controlled by moving various aircraft surfaces in flight. They devised a hinged rudder and crude aileron-like devices that could be linked together. Then two widely separated surfaces could be moved simultaneously. Thus the center of gravity could be kept constant and an equilibrium maintained. At first, the system used a forerunner of the aileron, a device consisting of a cable arrangement whereby the wing tips could be twisted or *warped* so as to achieve different lifts on the opposite wings.

Wind Tunnel and Glider Testing

Between 1899 and 1902 the Wrights built several kites and gliders which were tested over the sand dunes of Kitty Hawk, North Carolina (*see*), a location chosen for its steady constant winds and soft sand that minimized the effects of hard landings.

In their gliding experiments they got less lifting power from the wings than existing tables of air pressures on curved surfaces had led them to expect.

The launching of the Wright No. 3 glider (modified) at Kitty Hawk with Orville piloting.

In 1901 they set up a small wind tunnel in their workshop at Dayton. Through thousands of experiments with various wing shapes, they corrected the inaccuracies of the tables.

The Wrights designed and built two other parts which contributed to their success: a lightweight engine and a new kind of propeller.

The Wrights began the design of a powered airplane in October, 1902. The machine was a biplane on a skid undercarriage; it had a wingspan of 40 feet 4 inches, a wing area of 510 square feet, and a camber of 1 in 20. It had a biplane elevator in front and a double rudder behind with control cables linked to the warp-cradle. The 12-hp engine drove two geared-down pusher propellers through a cycle-chain transmission in tubes, one being crossed to produce counter-rotation.

Flyer I was launched along a 60-foot wooden rail, laid down into the wind. The engine was revved up while the craft was being held back and then released. When its speed produced sufficient lift, the craft rose from the yoke and flew. The design required the pilot to lie face downward to fly the aircraft which had an empty weight of 605 pounds.

The first attempt at flight was made on December 14, 1903, with Wilbur, who had won a coin-toss, at the controls. Because of an overcorrection with the elevator, *Flyer I* ploughed into the sand just after takeoff. Two days were required for repairs.

The First Successful Flights

Four successful flights were made on the morning of Thursday, December 17, 1903, between 10:30 a.m. and noon. Orville, whose turn it was then, took off first at 10:35 a.m. into a headwind of about 25 mph and flew for 12 seconds, covering 120 feet of ground and over 500 feet in air distance. Despite its short duration, the flight was the first in history in which a machine carrying a man raised itself by its own power into the air in full flight, sailed forward without a reduction in speed, and finally landed at a point on the same level as that from which it had started.

The brothers alternated in making three more flights that morning, each longer than the previous one. On the fourth flight, Wilbur flew 852 feet in 59 seconds. However, while the Wrights were discussing the flights with spectators, a gust of wind rolled *Flyer I* over and damaged the craft so badly that it never flew again.

The First Practical Airplane—1905

The Wrights' next series of powered flights took place in the summers of 1904 and 1905 at the Huffman Prairie near Dayton where an airfield had been set up. From those flights evolved the first fully practical powered airplane, *Flyer III*, which could be banked, turned, and circled and which had a flying time of over half an hour.

Flyer III was of the same general arrangement as the others, but noticeable differences appeared in the placing of the elevator farther forward and the rudder farther back to improve longitudinal control. The wingspan was 40 feet 6 inches; the wing area was slightly reduced, to 503 square feet; the camber was increased slightly; new sets of propellers were used; but the excellent 1904 engine was retained.

The prone pilot position was retained and also, for the start of the season, the warp and rudder linkage. Its speed was approximately 35 mph. Like all the Wright aircraft, it was built inherently unstable and had to be "flown" all the time by the pilot. The rudder outrigger was sprung to allow it to hinge upward if it dragged on the track or the ground.

About 50 flights were made in the 1905 season, but now the Wrights were concerned with reliability and endurance. In September, the trouble they were having in tight turns was diagnosed as a tendency of the lowered wings to slow up and stall, and the cure seemed to be in putting down the nose to gain speed while turning. It was while seeking this cause and cure that they took the important step of unlinking the warp and rudder controls and providing for their separate, or combined, operation in any desired degree.

The Wrights made many excellent flights with the perfected *Flyer*, including durations of 18 minutes 9 seconds; 25 minutes 5 seconds; 33 minutes 17 sec-

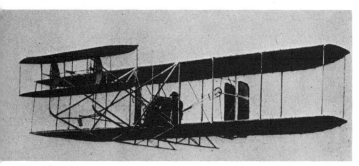

Wilbur taking a passenger at Pau in February or March of 1909.

Orville's *Signal Corps* machine at Fort Myer for the second army trials in July, 1909.

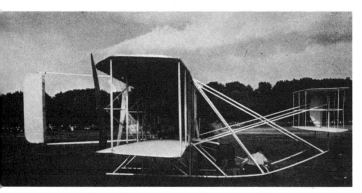

Lefebvre *(above)* in his Wright machine at Rheims, August, 1909, and the Wright machine wheeling out *(below)* at Templehof, Berlin.

onds; and, on October 5th, their record of 38 minutes 3 seconds, during which they covered over 24 miles.

The Developed Wright Flyer—1907-1909

In 1905 the Wrights first offered their invention to the U.S. and British governments. It was turned down, however, largely because the governments assumed that the Wrights were seeking financial assistance, whereas they had made it quite clear that they were offering a finished product. Although the basic patent was granted in 1906, the brothers thought their invention should be guarded until a purchaser was in sight.

The Wrights did not once leave the ground between October 16, 1905, and May 6, 1908, a period of 2½ years, nor did they allow anyone to view their machine. This interruption was due basically to the continued thwarting of the Wrights' legitimate demand that any client guarantee to purchase the aircraft provided it performed as agreed.

During this time, the Wrights built several improved engines and two or three new *Flyers*. The approximate specifications were wing area, about 510 square feet; wingspan, 41 feet; empty weight, 800 pounds; engine, 4 cylinder, 30-40 hp; and speed, 35-40 mph. This type was a two-seater and still retained the derrick-and-rail launching, although it could take off from the rail on engine power alone.

Acclaim at Home and Abroad

In 1909 the U.S. government purchased a Wright biplane for $30,000. In the same year the brothers organized the American Wright Company for the manufacture of airplanes. A trip to France by Wilbur in 1908 created great excitement and interest in Europe. He made many long flights of up to 2¼ hours duration and carried passengers on some 60 occasions.

Meanwhile other companies began to build similar planes, and the Wrights brought suit for infringement of their patent rights. After a long, bitter struggle, the courts upheld them.

In 1912, at the height of his career, Wilbur died of typhoid fever. Three years later Orville sold his interest in the Wright company but continued to work as a consulting engineer.

The Wright brothers received many honors and prizes, including an award by the U.S. Congress in 1909. Orville was awarded the Distinguished Flying Cross in 1929. The original Wright biplane is on exhibition at the National Air and Space Museum (*see*) in Washington, D.C., and the Wright Brothers National Memorial is at the site of their first sustained flight at Kitty Hawk.   Charles Gibbs-Smith

See also: History of aviation, Wright Flyer

Wright Flyer

Because the Wright 1903 *Flyer* first flew at Kitty Hawk, North Carolina (*see*), it came to be called the *Kitty Hawk Machine* or just the *Kitty Hawk*. It was the result of years of painstaking observation and experimentation by two brothers, Orville and Wilbur Wright, who thought together and worked together. The Wright brothers (*see*) were, in fact, natural scientists, and their descriptions of the preparations and records of the first successful flights at Kill Devil Hill are testimony to their meticulous preparation.

himself in position in the hip saddle and grasped the elevator lever firmly. The engine was started, and with the propellers whirling, the airplane moved forward slowly, with Wilbur steadying the wingtip. After a run of about 40 feet, the *Flyer* lifted from the track and rose into the air. Orville then flew it for 12 seconds, covering about 120 feet. This flight and the three following, the longest of which was 852 feet, were the first flights by man in a heavier-than-air powered and controlled aircraft.   Louis S. Casey

See also: History of aviation

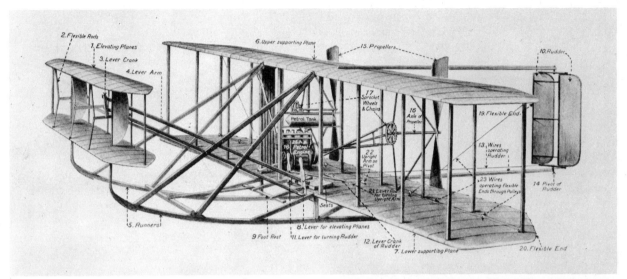

After reading all the published accounts of aeronautical experimenters of their day, the brothers proceeded to construct a glider-kite with which they tried out some of their first ideas of lift and control of an aircraft. Between 1900 and 1902, they constructed and tested three successful gliders.

After the 1902 season, they decided to construct a powered model, but they were hampered by lack of a suitable engine and propeller. To solve the problem, they built their own engine, a four-cylinder, horizontal, water-cooled engine which weighed about 180 pounds and produced 12 to 16 hp. They also designed a new propeller which was to influence propeller design thereafter. To enable them to make soft landings in the sands at Kitty Hawk, they constructed a landing gear similar to sled runners. A track was used for takeoff assist.

During the preliminary tests, numerous difficulties were encountered, and it was not until December 14, 1903, that they were overcome.

Thursday, December 17, dawned cold and windy. It was Orville's turn to try the machine. He settled

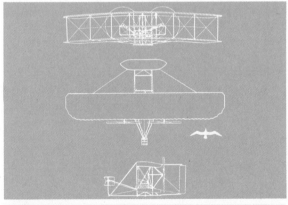

Wright Flyer
Specifications and Performance Data

Engine	designed by the Wrights, 12-16 hp
Wingspan	40 ft. 4 in.
Length	21 ft.
Height	8 ft.
Chord (wind width fore and aft)	6 ft. 6 in.
Aspect ratio (relation of span to chord)	6:2
Camber (wing bow)	1:20
Wing area	510 sq. ft.
Power loading	62 lbs./hp.
Wing loading	1.46 lbs./sq. ft.
Empty weight	605 lbs.
Gross weight with pilot	750 lbs. (approximate)

XB-70, North American Valkyrie

The XB-70 was designed by North American Rockwell as a strategic bomber capable of carrying out its entire mission at a speed of Mach 3. The requirements for the XB-70 were formulated in 1954 when it was planned as a replacement for the Boeing B-52. However, after the flight of the prototype on September 21, 1964, military and congressional controversy over the bomber resulted in policy changes and the decision to build only two of the aircraft to be used for aerodynamic research. The second XB-70 made its first flight in July, 1965, and was destroyed in June, 1966, in an air collision.

The XB-70 is a delta wing aircraft, distinguished by its tail-first design which utilizes a horizontal "foreplane" or canard just behind the cockpit of its needle-nosed fuselage. The foreplane is equipped with trailing-edge flaps and is adjustable for trim control. Another distinguishing feature is the huge ducts at the midship section of the aircraft which feed air to six turbojet engines under the wings. The extremely thin delta wings are constructed of welded stainless steel honeycomb panels and have a total of 11 "elevons" for flight control. The wings also have tips which can be folded downward for

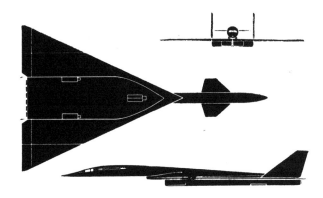

XB-70 North American
Specifications and Performance Data

Engine	Six General Electric YJ93-GE-3 turbojets, approximately 19,500 lbs. static thrust each
Wingspan	105 ft. (with tips extended)
Length	185 ft.
Gross weight	520,000 lbs. (approximate)
Maximum speed	1,980 mph (Mach 3)
Range	7,500 miles

increased stability and maneuverability in supersonic flight (*see*). The wingtips are moved hydraulically to an angle of 25° for low altitude flight and to 65° for high altitude cruising at Mach 3.

The aerodynamic research program for which the XB-70 is used is administered by NASA with mission support provided by Edwards Air Force Base. The program includes support for the National Supersonic Transport Program as well as projects and research for the Department of Defense. Flights of the XB-70 with a crew of two cost about $800,000 each and are made on a schedule of one or two times per month.   Sanford Sasser, Jr.

X-15 research program

The X-15 is a small rocket-powered aircraft that has flown faster and higher than any other winged aircraft in the world. Its flight program has provided important knowledge applicable to the design and development of future spacecraft and high-performance aircraft.

Conceived in the early 1950's, the X-15 is a continuation of the Research Airplane Program first approved by the U.S. government in 1944. Its predecessors were the rocket-powered X-1, X-1A, X-1B, X-1E, D-558 II, X-2, and the jet-powered

X-3, X-4, and X-5. Prior to its first flight in 1959, manned flight had been restricted to altitudes below 130,000 feet and speeds under 2,100 mph.

Based upon earlier studies in its laboratories and wind tunnels, the National Advisory Committee for Aeronautics (*see*), predecessor of the National Aeronautics and Space Administration (NASA) (*see*), recommended in 1954 to the USAF and the U.S. Navy the development of an aircraft capable of flying at altitudes of 250,000 feet (50 miles) and 4,000 mph (Mach 6). The purpose of the committee was strictly research. It was agreed then that NASA would accept technical responsibility and the USAF administer the design and construction phases.

The initial airframe contract, calling for the construction of three airplanes, was awarded to North American Rockwell in late 1955. A contract for the rocket engine capable of thrust in excess of 57,000 lbs. was awarded to the Reaction Motors Division of Thiokol Chemical Corp. in September, 1956.

The first of the three aircraft was completed in 1958 and was transported to Edwards Air Force Base (*see*). Under the terms of the contract, North American was responsible for demonstrating the flight-worthiness of the craft, and therefore it conducted the initial flight tests.

The X-15 research rocket plane igniting its engines as it leaves the Boeing B-52 mother plane near Edwards AFB, California, on February 21, 1961.

Early Test Flights

After several planned captive flights to check out the various aircraft systems, Albert Scott Crossfield, Jr. (*see*) was air-launched from a B-52 in a planned powerless glide-flight of the X-15 on June 8, 1959. The first flight of the X-15 lasted about five minutes. Three months later, on September 17, 1959, Crossfield was again launched in the X-15 for free flight. This time he ignited the two interim XLR-11 rocket engines, which were being used until completion of the originally designed XLR-11. The X-15 reached a top speed of 1,393 mph on its first powered flight.

After completion of the contractor tests, the first X-15 was accepted by the USAF and turned over to NASA. Joseph A. Walker (*see*), NASA's chief research pilot, made the first government flight in March, 1960. Meanwhile the third X-15 was being equipped with the larger XRL-99 engine. After several months of ground tests, this craft made its first flight in November, 1960, reaching a top speed of just under Mach 3.

The X-15 flight program continued to increase the speed and altitude capabilities of the craft by small increments. The X-15 reached its design speed on November 9, 1961: USAF Maj. Robert M. White flew the first X-15 to a speed of 4,093 mph, a little over Mach 6. On April, 30 1962, Joseph Walker of NASA piloted the X-15 to 243,700 ft., almost to its design altitude.

However, the X-15 proved to be more successful than its designers thought. On August 22, 1963, Joe Walker flew the third X-15 to a peak altitude of over 67 miles high. Carrying two external tanks with extra fuel for the rocket engine, Maj. William J. Knight piloted the second X-15 to a speed of Mach 6.7 on October 3, 1967.

Research Contributions

Although primarily an airplane with wings and aerodynamic controls, the X-15 travels above the effective atmosphere and must depend upon small peroxide-rocket controls, the forerunners of those used in spacecraft. The pilot is weightless for short periods of time, and the X-15 must make a more severe re-entry than space capsules. Thus the research contributions of the X-15 encompass flights in air and space.

The most important contribution of the X-15 has been the collection of actual inflight data on aerodynamics (*see*), heating, structures, stability and control, bioastronautics (*see*), and man's ability to fly a vehicle of this type. This information is being used to verify wind-tunnel data and other theoretical ground-based studies.

The investigation of the heating caused by air friction at high speeds has been a prime example of discovering significant differences from predicted results of earlier wind-tunnel tests. Future aircraft, such as the supersonic transport (SST) (*see*) and Mach 5 hypersonic transport will depend upon the knowledge acquired by the X-15, whose outside skin routinely reaches temperatures of 1,000°F and sometimes reaches more than 2,000°F.

The adaptive control system used in the third X-15 automatically senses the surrounding atmospheric conditions and aids in the control of the aircraft. A newer version of the control system in now being used in the F-111 (*see*) and the proposed SST.

Energy management techniques, developed to assist the X-15 in precise maneuvering to a landing at a predetermined location, are being studied for use by future manned orbital spacecraft. Simplified versions of the X-15's inertial guidance system (*see*) are being installed on modern aircraft.

The X-15 flight program has demonstrated that Earth exit and re-entry are well within the capabilities of a pilot. Each time the X-15 returns from altitudes higher than 125,000 feet, the pilot must perform precise control maneuvers that allow the X-15 to recover from its steep descent. An error or miscalculation during this time can cause the aircraft to break apart. The pilot must carefully guide the X-15 to its planned landing area and make a 225-mph powerless-glide landing.

In recent years, the X-15 has carried a wide variety of nonaerodynamic scientific experiments because of its ability to fly to and return from the edge of space. Included among these experiments are cameras used to photograph various stars from high altitudes. A scanner is carried that measures the Earth's horizon in various seasons for use as a navigational reference for Apollo (*see*). Equipment carried in a wing-tip pod is used to collect micrometeorites for examination. Measurements of solar energy and sky brightness are also recorded.

Specifications of the X-15

The X-15 airplane is relatively small, about 50 feet long with a 22-foot wingspan. It stands 13 feet high at the tail. Side fairings extend along each side of the X-15 and house the control cables and electrical wiring. The wings are thin, have blunt edges, and are swept back at an angle of about 25°. The vertical tail is wedge-shaped with blunt leading edges and extends above and below the fuselage. The upper two-thirds of the vertical tail is movable for yaw control in the atmosphere. The bottom two-thirds of the lower tail, which was not carried after the first 70 flights, was

Six men who have flown the X-15 *(above)* are Capt. J. Engle, Maj. R. A. Rushworth, J. B. McKay, Maj. W. J. Knight, M. O. Thompson, and W. H. Dana. Knight *(below)* inspects the Number Two X-15 which he piloted to a record speed of 4,500 mph.

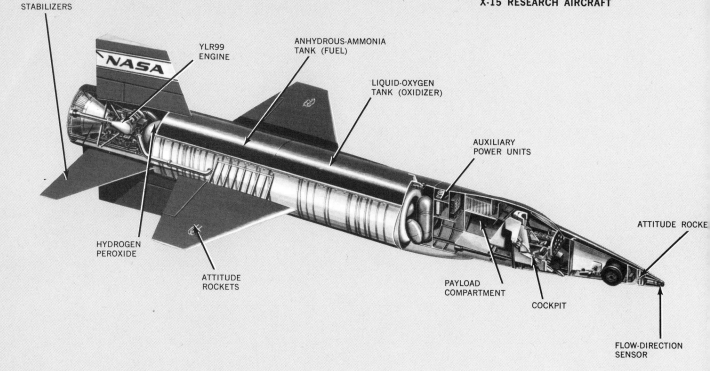

STABILIZERS

YLR99 ENGINE

ANHYDROUS-AMMONIA TANK (FUEL)

LIQUID-OXYGEN TANK (OXIDIZER)

AUXILIARY POWER UNITS

ATTITUDE ROCKE

HYDROGEN PEROXIDE

ATTITUDE ROCKETS

PAYLOAD COMPARTMENT

COCKPIT

FLOW-DIRECTION SENSOR

jettisoned for parachute recovery prior to landing. Speed brakes are located on the upper and lower fixed portion of the ventrails.

The complete horizontal tail surfaces are movable. Moving simultaneously, they provide pitch control; moving differentially, they provide roll control. The X-15 has no wing ailerons but does have wing flaps for landing.

The outer skin of the X-15 is made of Inconel X, a nickel alloy designed to withstand temperatures of 1,200°F. To protect the X-15's skin from high temperatures, the aircraft is covered with a white ablative coating similar to the heat shields (*see*) on re-entry vehicles (*see*). Inside the X-15, titanium (*see*) and stainless steel are used to save weight.

Although a conventional dual-tire nose landing gear is utilized, because of weight and temperature considerations the aircraft has two stainless steel skids that are stowed in flight against the side of the fuselage and are extended just prior to landing.

For flight above approximately 125,000 feet, the X-15 has a reaction control system (*see*) consisting of 12 small peroxide rockets located on the nose and wings. The pilot regulates these rockets, which develop 40 to 100 lbs. of thrust each and are capable of controlling the attitude of the aircraft at the higher altitudes.

The X-15 weighs about 15,000 lbs. empty. Launch weight is approximately 34,000 lbs. Depending on the particular engine, thrust of the XLR-99 is 57,000 to 60,000 lbs. It can be run between idle and full thrust and can be shut down in flight and restarted. The X-15 normally carries 8,500 lbs. of anhydrous ammonia and 10,500 lbs. of propellant. After the propellant is used, the tanks are jettisoned for recovery

Two stainless steel skids are extended for a landing of the X-15. They are stowed against the side of the fuselage while in flight.

and reuse. The design speed of the X-15 with the longer engine burn-time is approximately 5,000 mph.

The third X-15 was destroyed in an accident on November 15, 1967, and the pilot, Maj. Michael J. Adams, was fatally injured. Two other nonfatal accidents have occurred during the almost 200 flights of the three X-15's.

Twelve men have flown the X-15. In chronological order they are: A. Scott Crossfield, North American Rockwell; Joseph A. Walker, NASA; Maj. Robert A. White, USAF; Cmdr. Forrest S. Peterson, USN; John B. McKay, NASA; Maj. Robert A. Rushworth, USAF; Neil A. Armstrong (*see*), NASA; Capt. Joe Henry Engle (*see*), USAF; Milton O. Thompson, NASA; Maj. William J. Knight, USAF; William H. Dana, NASA; and Maj. Michael J. Adams, USAF.

Due to financial considerations, the X-15 flight research program will not be funded beyond the fiscal year 1968. Remaining funds will be used to continue the flight program through the calendar year 1968.   Ralph B. Jackson

See also: History of aviation, Test pilots and test flying, X-series aerospace vehicles

X-rays

X-rays are high-energy electromagnetic radiations of very short wavelength. The range of electromagnetic radiations is represented by a spectrum according to the size of their wavelengths. In order of decreasing wavelength the spectrum includes: radio waves, heat radiation, infrared radiation, visible light, ultraviolet light, X-rays, and gamma rays.

X-rays were first discovered in 1895 by the German scientist Wilhelm Konrad Roentgen. Because of their energy (*see*), X-rays have the ability to penetrate all matter and to be differentially absorbed by different types of matter. As a result, X-rays can be used to take a picture of the inside of an object by making the X-rays that penetrate the object strike a photographic plate. Since X-rays do not pass through all material equally well, those portions of the object that offer the greatest resistance to the rays appear lighter in the photograph. For example, bone is more resistant than other bodily tissue and readily shows up on X-ray photographs used by doctors and dentists.

X-rays occur when electrons traveling at velocities approaching the speed of light collide with the atoms of any material, although materials with high atomic numbers increase the efficiency of X-ray production. When a collision occurs, it produces a loss in the kinetic energy of the electron. Most of this energy is transformed into heat. A very small portion, how-ever, is converted into high-energy X-ray particles.

To produce X-rays, a source of electrons, a method for accelerating them to high energy levels and a target for them to bombard are required. A special gas tube, called an *X-ray tube*, is used for this purpose. In most cases the electron source (cathode) is a tungsten filament, which is heated to a high temperature by passing a current through it. The electrons are then accelerated by applying a high voltage across the tube between the cathode and the target (anode). In this way, the electrons are made to strike the anode to produce X-rays. Some of the stars (*see*), including the sun (*see*), also give off copious amounts of X-rays. Most of these X-rays are trapped in the atmosphere and do not reach the Earth.   Mary-Louise Tally

See also: Electromagnetism, Radiation

X-ray stars

Special devices flown above the Earth's atmosphere in rockets and satellites since 1962 have unexpectedly detected several strong localized objects emitting X-rays (*see*). Difficulties of finding the accurate positions of these objects in the short time rockets are above the atmosphere delayed identification of these "X-ray" stars with optical telescopes until 1966.

The first, known as *Scorpius X-1* (the first source to be found in the constellation Scorpius), is thought to be a 13th magnitude (*see*) object which resembles an old nova (*see*). Its spectrum contains emission lines of hydrogen, helium, and highly excited carbon and nitrogen, but no absorption lines. The intensity of the optical radiation varies irregularly.

The identification excited astronomers, who immediately began deducing the mechanisms that might produce this radiation and what it would mean for theories of the structure of stars and nebulae.

The second source, known as *Cygnus X-2*, is identified with a 15th-magnitude star-like object that fluctuates in brightness. Both emission and absorption lines are visible and fluctuate in radial velocity. The third source, known as *Centaurus XR-2*, may be a peculiar 14th-magnitude star. Its X-ray emission has been found to vary. X-ray sources are apparently correlated with the spiral arms of the Milky Way Galaxy (see).

Other celestial objects also emit X-rays. The Crab nebula was identified as a source by noticing that the X-rays were no longer received when the nebula was occulted, or hidden, by the moon. An experiment on Orbiting Solar Observatory IV (OSO-IV), a satellite launched in 1967, observed X-rays from flares on the sun.   Jay M. Pasachoff

See also: Orbiting observatories, Stars, Sun

The X-24 PILOT lifting body, the latest of the X-series research aircraft.

X-series aerospace vehicles

Research in advanced high-performance craft

In early 1946 high over the runway at Pinecastle Army Air Base, Florida, a B-29 labored skyward. In its specially modified bomb bay it carried a strange looking craft similar in shape to a 50-caliber bullet with straight, stubby, and incredibly thin wings. In the tiny cockpit of the unusual craft sat Jack Woolams, test pilot for the Bell Aircraft Corporation.

Arriving at a predetermined altitude, the B-29 pilot lined up with the 10,000-foot runway below and on receiving the "go" signal from Woolams tripped the latches that held the small craft in the bomb bay. He watched it drop away from the mother ship and hurtle toward Earth.

Woolams made 11 more glide tests of the X-1, first in the U.S. series of pure research aircraft, the

X standing for *experimental*, before he reported it ready for powered flight. He did not get to make the first powered flight, however. Woolams was killed the Friday before Labor Day, 1946, as he checked out a plane he was to pilot in an air race.

Another Bell pilot, Chalmers "Slick" Goodlin, first flew the X-1 under rocket power on December 9, 1946, over Muroc Dry Lake (now Edwards Air Force Base) in California. He and "Tex" Johnston, also a Bell pilot, made 21 acceptance flights in the plane during the next year, but it remained for Air Force Maj. Charles "Chuck" Yeager (*see*) to establish a new world speed record and surpass the speed of sound. This historic flight was made on October 14, 1947, but the achievement was kept secret until eight months later.

Bell Aircraft had been given the go-ahead by the U.S. Army Air Corps during December, 1944, for the development of the X-1, an 800-mph rocket-powered airplane. This secret project was designated MX-524. The X-1, forerunner of the X-15, X-24, and other research aircraft, was the first rocket-powered airplane built specifically to collect information about high-speed aerodynamics.

The First U.S. Rocket Aircraft

In June, 1944, a Spitfire pilot over Germany had an encounter with a rocket-powered Messerschmitt Me.163B. Encounters after that were frequent and U.S. military interest in rocket-propelled aircraft, begun as early as 1938, increased.

A U.S. rocket airplane, the first specifically built to operate with a rocket powerplant, made its initial flight between the first and second sightings of an Me.163B. This was the MX-324, a subscale prototype of what was intended to be the XP-79 interceptor fighter designed by John Northrup. It had a delta-wing platform and provisions for a pilot to lie in a prone position.

The MX-324 incorporated many features of the larger XP-79 design, although it was intended to fly at speeds below 320 knots. Its power source was a lightweight acid-analine rocket motor built by Aerojet. Thrust output was 200 pounds. The first flight, on July 5, 1944, began at the end of a towline attached to a P-38. At an altitude of about 10,000 feet, the MX-324 pilot, Harry Crosby, dropped the tow cable and opened the pressurized lines that fed fuel and oxidizer to the combustion chamber. Powered flight lasted four minutes. The landing, on Harper's Dry Lake, California, was uneventful. A full-size, high-speed version of the MX-324 aircraft was not forthcoming, however, and little progress was made until the X-1 project got under way.

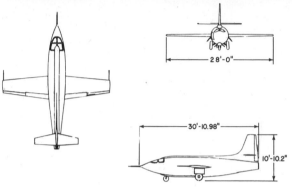

Bell Aerosystems' X-1 and silhouettes.

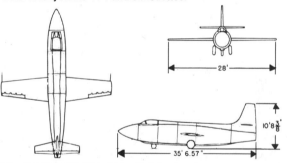

The X-1A and X-1B built by Bell Aerosystems and silhouettes for the X-1A.

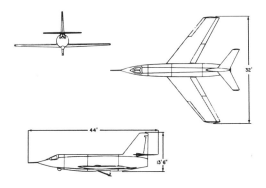

The X-2, built by Bell Aerosystems, while in flight and silhouettes.

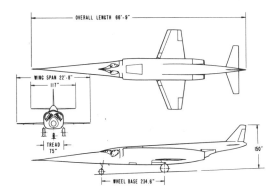

The X-3, built by Douglas Aircraft Co., and silhouettes.

MX-524

Conferences were held in January, 1945, at the Aberdeen Proving Grounds to discuss drag characteristics of various three-dimensional bodies and behavior of shock waves from the standpoint of ballistic information.

Information was gathered from all available sources on the subject of rockets, including conferences where rocket research projects were in progress. Jet engine manufacturers were visited, and conferences were held to discuss various engine designs and their suitability for the MX-524 airplane.

At a conference on January 15, at which the Bell Aircraft researchers gathered to acquaint each other with progress being made, it was agreed that a project for developing a supersonic research aircraft was highly desirable, and that such a flying laboratory would be in great demand by research and development groups. But there was no source book that would reveal the secrets of supersonic flight.

By March, the project number had been changed to MX-653, and the decision was made to use the Reaction Motors (R-M) rocket. The 6,000-pound-thrust rocket engine first considered was to use acid aniline, but the Reaction Motors project utilized liquid oxygen (see) and a combination of alcohol and water. This R-M rocket was to have been equipped with a turbopump, but waiting for this

pump to be completed would have held up the program, so it was decided to use a pressure system incorporating liquid nitrogen. This cut down by approximately half the amount of fuel that the craft could carry, but permitted the project to move ahead.

X-1

The R-M rocket engine originally was developed under sponsorship of the Navy for ultimate use in a high-speed research airplane to be manufactured by a company other than Bell. Inasmuch as the first phase of this airplane called for use of a jet engine, with the rocket installation to be made at a later date, the Navy agreed to permit use of the Reaction Motors product in the X-1, which the Army Air Force was sponsoring.

By mid-March, the preliminary design of the X-1 had been agreed upon, detail engineering was pushed forward, and actual construction of the aircraft followed close behind.

Three X-1 aircraft were built. All were 31 feet long, 11 feet high, and had 28-foot wingspans. All were powered by an R-M 6,000-pound-thrust liquid-propellant rocket motor using liquid oxygen, alcohol, and water. The first two vehicles each had a gross weight of 13,500 pounds. The third in the series, which had a low-pressure propellant system and a hydrogen peroxide steam-turbine-driven propellant pump, weighed 15,000 pounds. High-pressure

inert gas was used in the first two to force propellants from the tanks into the combustion chamber. The second X-1 subsequently was redesigned by the National Advisory Committee for Aeronautics (NACA) (*see*) into the X-1E by revising the cockpit, installing a thinner wing, and including the low-pressure propellant system used in the third X-1.

Four additional X-1 aircraft were authorized for construction: A, B, C, and D. The X-1C never was built. One each of the other three was delivered. All three were identical: 36 feet long, 11 feet high, 28-foot wingspan, gross weight of 17,000 pounds.

Collectively the X-1 series made substantial contributions to aerospace from 1947 until the early 1960's. The first X-1 was the first aircraft to fly faster than sound, and in 1949 it established a world altitude record of 73,000 feet. Before it was retired to the National Air and Space Museum (*see*) of the Smithsonian Institution, it flew 967 mph. The second X-1, or the X-1E, now is on display at Edwards Air Force Base (*see*). The third X-1 was destroyed on the ground by an explosion in 1951 prior to its first powered flight.

On December 12, 1953, Chuck Yeager flew the X-1A to another new world speed record of 1,650 mph, or Mach 2.42. The following year Maj. Arthur "Kit" Murray flew it to a new world altitude record of 94,000 feet. It subsequently was destroyed by fire. The X-1B established still another world record of Mach 2.3 on December 2, 1954, with Lt. Col. Frank K. "Pete" Everest, Jr. (*see*) at the controls. The X-1D was destroyed by fire a month after its first flight in July, 1951.

Skystreak and Skyrocket

Although never assigned an X designation, two Douglas aircraft, the D-558-1 Skystreak and the D-558-2 Skyrocket, share credit in helping the United States to gain the lead in the development of high-performance aircraft.

While the X-1 program essentially was an Army Air Force effort (prior to 1947 when the Air Force became a separate service) with assistance from NACA, the D-558 program was initiated by the Navy with NACA and Douglas as partners.

The Skystreak was powered by a conventional turbojet engine, the TG-180, most powerful jet engine of its day. The craft was 35.8 feet long, stood 12.1 feet high, and had a wingspan of 25 feet. It was unique in that it probably had the first cockpit that could be jettisoned in an emergency. Drag on the main fuselage would slow it down, and the nose section with the cockpit would travel faster and thus separate. As the nose section slowed down, a second release mechanism would allow the pilot's seat to separate, and the pilot could perform a normal bailout.

Piloted by Navy Cmdr. Turner Caldwell over Muroc Dry Lake, the Skystreak established a world speed record of 640.7 mph on August 20, 1947. Five days later, with Marine Maj. Marion Carl flying the aircraft, it pushed that record to 650.6 mph.

The Skyrocket originally was powered by both a J-34 turbojet and a rocket motor for high-speed operations. The jet engine was removed for later flights and the rocket fuel capacity was almost doubled. In its later version, the D-558-2 was carried aloft by a B-29 like the X-1.

The Skyrocket was 10 feet longer than its predecessor, but it had the same wingspan and was approximately as high. Its wings, however, were swept back about 40 degrees. After its modification to full rocket power, Douglas test pilot Bill Bridgeman took over flying the craft and gradually nursed the plane higher and faster until on August 7, 1951, he hit a record altitude of 79,494 feet; eight days later he hit 1,238 mph.

X-2

The Bell X-2, second in the X-series of research aircraft made aviation history in 1956–57 over Edwards AFB, flying at greater speeds and to higher altitudes than ever before attained by piloted aircraft. USAF Capt. Milburn G. Apt flew the X-2 to a record 2,148 mph on September 27, 1957, during a flight in which Apt lost his life. Earlier, USAF Capt. Iven Kinchoeloe piloted the aircraft to an altitude of 126,200 feet and for the record-setting mission was awarded the McKay Trophy for 1956. Also in 1956, Pete Everest pushed the plane to a record of 1,900 mph and for his work was awarded the 1957 Octave Chanute Award and the 1957 Harmon International Aviation Award.

From a drag and power standpoint, the X-2 was designed to surpass the speed of the X-1A. The X-2 incorporated several innovations, including the use of stainless steel and K-monel in fuselage and wings. Both metals have a much higher melting point than aluminum, which loses its strength at high temperatures. The landing gear consisted of a flat skid rather than retractable wheels, which saved weight and allowed more space for fuel.

The Curtiss-Wright rocket engine that propelled the X-2 was capable of developing power equal to that of a modern navy cruiser. A comparison of the small airplane and a giant cruiser illustrates the tremendous power needed to drive the X-2 as it explored the flight problems in the thermal area.

Special provisions were made in the X-2 for the pilot's safety. The cabin was heavily insulated and pressurized and was detachable. The entire cabin structure could be separated from the rest of the airplane by an explosive charge. A ribbon-type parachute was designed to carry the capsule to a low altitude where the pilot could then parachute to the ground. The windshield of the X-2 was made of highly tempered glass capable of withstanding a temperature of almost 1,000° F. The windshield also was tinted to filter infrared rays.

A converted Boeing B-50 was adapted to carry the X-2 to the altitude from which it began its flights. This allowed the plane to start high-speed flight at high altitude with a full fuel load, thereby permitting flights of longer duration.

X-3

The X-3 was designed by Douglas under joint sponsorship of the Air Force, NACA, and the Navy. It began flight tests in October, 1952, with test pilot Bill Bridgeman at the controls. The X-3 had a striking appearance—a slender fuselage, long tapered nose, and short wings located toward the tail. Viewed from above, the X-3 resembled a huge stiletto.

Length of the X-3 was 66 feet 9 inches, nearly three times its span of 22 feet 8 inches. The top of its tail, rising on a boom over the twin-jet exhausts, measured 12.5 feet from the ground. The airplane stood on a retractable tricycle landing gear (see). The gross weight and length slightly exceeded those of the familiar DC-3 transport, yet the X-3 wingspan was less then the span of the DC-3 tail.

Before the X-3 was built, more than 60 designs were considered. Ultimate selection was a midwing monoplane of unique proportions, powered by the two axial-flow turbojet engines. This combination provided the best basis for eventual development into practical, operational aircraft.

The problems solved in the X-3 design involved both aerodynamics (see) and uses of new materials (see) and construction methods. One important contribution was the development of construction techniques with titanium (see) used extensively throughout the X-3. The aircraft also had a cooling system of tremendous capacity. Insulation was provided to protect the pilot and equipment from blistering temperatures of sustained, high-speed flight.

The X-3 carried a payload of 1,200 pounds of special research instruments. Comprehensive instrumentation included more than 850 pinhole orifices to record pressures over various portions of the airplane. Temperature readings were registered at 150 points, while stresses and air loads were indicated by 185 electric strain gauges.

X-4

Next vehicle in the X-series of research vehicles was the X-4, a miniature flying laboratory with sweptback wing surfaces and tail surfaces consisting of a vertical fin and rudder. The X-4 was designed to explore the stability of aircraft of the sweptback, all-wing configuration at sonic-range speeds. It had no horizontal stabilizer, and elevons on the trailing edge of the wing acted both as elevators and ailerons. The plane was equipped with a pilot ejection seat, a tricycle landing gear, and was powered by two gas turbines.

Two X-4 aircraft were built by Northrup in 1948 under contract to the Air Force. The X-4 was 20 feet long, 15 feet high, and had a wingspan of approximately 25 feet. Gross weight was 7,000 pounds.

X-5

The Bell X-5 was the first aircraft to feature wings whose degree of sweepback could be varied in flight. Unlike the rocket-powered X-1, the X-5 was jet-propelled and was capable of longer sustained flights. It took off from the ground under its own power instead of being launched from a mother aircraft.

The X-5 was used by NACA to investigate aerodynamic effects of changing the degree of wing sweepback during flight. It had all the advantages of conventional-wing aircraft in takeoff, climb, maneuvering, and endurance, and was capable of very high speeds.

Viewed in profile, the X-5 had a "flying guppy" configuration because its Allison J-35 turbojet engine was under the cockpit rather than behind the pilot. The powerplant extended through the second and third quarter of the craft's length, the tailpipe protruding beneath the fuselage and not from the rear.

The X-5 was 33 feet 4 inches long and measured 12 feet in height from ground to fin tip. Wingspan was 32 feet 9 inches, and weight was approximately 10,000 pounds. A slender, spear-like boom extending an additional 8 feet from the nose housed yaw-measuring devices and a Pitot tube used in registering indicated airspeed.

A major development in designing the X-5 was a mechanism for changing wing sweepback in flight while simultaneously compensating for the resulting shift of the center of gravity (see). Each wing had a specially designed fairing (see) to insure that its leading edge presented a smooth airfoil regardless of sweepback angle. The leading edges of the wings

The X-4 *(top left)* explored unknown factors of sonic range flight. The X-5 *(above),* next in the series of research aircraft, was used as a flying laboratory by NACA (now NASA) to investigate the aerodynamic effects of wing degree changes in flight. The X-7 *(top center)* which followed an unsuccessful X-6, was designed to support studies leading to the development of the Bomarc antiaircraft missile. The X-10 *(center right)* was designed to further studies for missile development by providing a flying test bed for components of the USAF surface-to-surface guided Navaho. The X-13 *(top right)* was the world's first vertical takeoff and landing plane. The X-14 *(right)* was the first VTOL to employ jet vectored thrust and the X-15 *(below),* now in its ninth year of flight, is the only U.S. manned hypersonic aircraft.

were fitted with slats that were part of the upper surface when not extended. When extended, they increased aerodynamic lift, appreciably reducing stalling speed.

Two dive brakes were located in the sides of the fuselage forward of the cockpit. These were metal door-like protuberances that could be opened hydraulically until they were at nearly right angles to the fuselage. Protruding, they provided rapid deceleration. The axial flow turbojet engine developed 4,900 pounds of thrust.

The cockpit was a few feet behind the plane's nose. Its sliding Plexiglas canopy conformed almost perfectly with the smooth contour of the fuselage. Visibility was excellent. The cockpit was pressurized and air-conditioned to maintain safe and comfortable conditions for the pilot at high altitudes. Both the cockpit canopy and the seat could be jettisoned in an emergency.

X-6

X-6 was the designation given a version of the huge Convair B-36 intercontinental bomber which was to have been powered entirely by nuclear engines. However, the X-6 never got beyond the drawing board stage.

X-7

Lockheed built the X-7, a test vehicle designed to support studies leading to the USAF Bomarc antiaircraft missile. It also served as a flying testbed for the Bomarc ramjet engines. A total of 28 X-7's were built. The X-7's first flight was in April, 1951, from Holloman Air Force Base, New Mexico. The X-7 was recoverable, and some of them flew as many as ten missions. In all, the X-7 flew more than 100 times and was in service for more than ten years. It provided ground engineers with 140 channels of telemetry (see) and thus proved a significant research tool.

X-8

The X-8, a product of Aerojet General Corp. is flying today, although it is now known as the Aerobee (see). The vehicle, a high-altitude research rocket, has grown in size and capability and has been used by the Navy, Army, Air Force, and NASA. It still is produced in two versions, the Aerobee 150 and the 350. Another version, the Aerobee-Hi, also was produced. Early Aerobee flights were made over the White Sands Missile Range (see) except for five flights made from shipboard. Aerobee launch facilities since have been constructed in Canada, Virginia, Florida, the Grand Bahamas, and Brazil. In 1956 a Navy Aerobee-Hi set a record for U.S.-built rockets

The X-17 was used in the Polaris development program to test re-entry shapes and materials and launched nuclear devices over the Pacific.

by reaching 164 miles into space with a 145-pound payload.

X-9

Bell Aircraft Corp. designed and built the X-9. It was known as the Shrike (not to be confused with the Navy *Shrike* missile) and was a scaled-down test vehicle for the GAM-63 Rascal air-to-ground missile. The purpose of the program was to solve aerodynamic, propulsion, and guidance problems encountered in development of the Rascal. The first

Although it never flew, the X-20, or *Dyna-Soar*, was to have gathered data on hypersonic flight and to have been a manned orbital spacecraft.

X-9 flight was made in May, 1950. The program was terminated in 1953. A total of 31 of the 23-foot-long X-9 vehicles were built.

X-10

The X-10 was an unmanned aircraft in the true sense having twin J-40-1 turbojet powerplants, canard-type airfoils, and retractable tricycle landing gear. The craft was designed to test components of the Air Force SM-64 Navaho surface-to-surface guided missile. The vehicle operated at supersonic speeds over long distances under automatic control and could return to launch base for a runway landing.

The X-10 was also designed to gather data at supersonic velocities on aerodynamic design, control, and automatic guidance equipment. It succeeded an earlier Navaho test vehicle called the MATIV.

X-11 and X-12

Both the X-11 and X-12, built by Convair for the Air Force, were test vehicles to support development of the Atlas intercontinental ballistic missile (ICBM). The X-11 and X-12 were to serve as the first two steps in the development of the first U.S. ICBM. The X-11 was a single-rocket engine test vehicle, and the X-12, a three-engine vehicle. Both were preliminary to a five-engine version. Ultimately, this approach as well as the five-engine Atlas was dropped.

X-13 (VTOL)

The X-13 was the world's first Vertijet (vertical takeoff and landing jet airplane). In 1951 it demonstrated successfully its remarkable ability to take off straight up, make the transition to high-speed horizontal flight, then back to vertical hovering for a zero-speed landing.

The X-13 was a revolutionary VTOL research craft, first of an entirely new class of high-performance jets. It flew for more than a year at the Air Force Flight Test Center before it was publicly unveiled. The first flight was made December 10, 1955, by Peter F. "Pete" Girard, chief engineering test pilot for Ryan Aeronautical Co., builders of the X-13. The first complete VTOL flight in full operational sequence was made by Girard on April 11, 1956.

The stubby fuselage of the X-13 was little larger than the plane's engine. Its shoulder-high delta wing had small fins at the tips. The vertical tail surface was sweptback, appearing very large in proportion to the wing. Length of the plane was approximately 24 feet, wingspan was about 21 feet, and its height was 15 feet.

The X-13 in contrast to previous flying testbeds was a complete, full-scale, piloted airplane. It was designed on radical new principles specifically as a jet VTOL airplane. Rising and descending on a column of exhaust gases, it depended solely upon thrust from its jet engine for both direct lift and high-speed flight.

The most unusual feature of the X-13 was its jet reaction control system, developed to provide complete control of the airplane during hovering and near-zero-speed flight. This system was necessary because of the lack of normal airflow over the aerodynamic control surfaces at these extremely low speeds. Necessary control forces were developed by jet-engine exhaust deflection and thrust variations. In addition to jet reaction controls, the plane was equipped with a conventional aerodynamic control system for conventional flight. The pilot operated both systems from stick-and-rudder cockpit controls.

Another unique feature of the X-13 was the method of takeoff and landing. The plane did not have conventional landing gear, but a single hook mounted beneath the forward fuselage, which engaged a trapeze mechanism in the bed of a ground service trailer. Like a dump truck, the bed of the trailer was hydraulically lifted into the vertical posi-

The problem of drag was solved with the X-21 which achieved laminar flow in the boundary layer by using row upon row of tiny slots running spanwise over the wings. Without laminar flow, an aircraft is robbed of higher speed, range, and engine power.

The X-22A uses its ducts for horizontal thrust *(above)* and vertical thrust *(below)*. Each of the ducts can be rotated for helicopter liftoff or for flight similar to a conventional aircraft.

tion to receive the airplane, then lowered to transport it away in the horizontal position.

For a jet plane, the X-13 was relatively light. To fly straight up, the weight of the plane during vertical takeoff had to be less than the thrust provided by the jet engine. The plane was designed purely for VTOL research and was operated at moderate altitudes and speeds.

X-14

The Bell X-14 was the first VTOL to employ the jet-vectored thrust principle. Powered originally by twin, nose-mounted turbojet engines, the X-14 achieved flight by means of rotating cascade thrust diverters mounted at the tailpipe exit. The pilot directed thrust vertically for hovering flight, horizontally for conventional flight, or at an intermediate angle for transition.

During hovering and low-speed flights, control of the aircraft is maintained by reaction controls. Aerodynamic surfaces serve this function during conventional flight. A two-place, midwing, all-metal monoplane, the X-14 has fixed landing gear.

The aircraft was delivered to the National Aero-

nautics and Space Administration (NASA) Ames Research Center, California, in October, 1959. NASA replaced the original engines with J85 turbojets for increased thrust and redesignated the vehicle the X-14A.

The primary purpose of the X-14A program was to study the stability and control system requirements of V/STOL aircraft (*see*). In addition, the X-14A has been used to investigate and simulate the approach phase of lunar landings for Apollo.

The X-14 is 25 feet long, 8 feet high, and has a wingspan of 34 feet. Its gross weight is 4,000 pounds. Two 2,850-pound-thrust engines give it an operational speed of 160 knots and a maximum speed of 180 knots.

X-15

The X-15 research program (*see*) provided a wealth of information about re-entry from extreme altitudes, physiological behavior of pilots at supersonic speeds, and aerodynamic heating and skin friction.

X-16

Little is known about the X-16 except that it was built by Bell and was associated with the military designation WS-118M. In the military numbering system, *WS* stands for *weapon system*. The X-16, proposed by Bell in 1955, represented the winning design in a competition for a long-range, high-altitude reconnaissance aircraft. The vehicle never was flown as the X-16, but the Air Force says that it "led to significant developments for reconnaissance planes." It still is shrouded in military secrecy, but it can be assumed that it was a stepping stone to the U-2 (*see*) of the late 1950's and the early 1960's and today's RB-57F and SR-71 (*see*) reconnaissance planes.

X-17

The X-17 was a three-stage, solid-fuel, high-altitude rocket built by Lockheed for an early Air Force program to develop re-entry vehicles for its intercontinental and intermediate range ballistic missile. It also was the launch vehicle in the first series of high-altitude nuclear tests, lofting nuclear devices 300 miles into space over the Pacific where they were detonated to gather radiation information. The X-17 first was launched from Cape Canaveral in September, 1956. A total of 26 were built.

X-18

Hiller Aircraft designed and built the X-18, a twin turboprop tilt-wing vertical takeoff and landing (VTOL) testbed for gathering data on VTOL characteristics. As such, it served as the forerunner of today's XC-142 (prototype tilt-wing military

cargo plane built by Ling-Temco-Vought Corp.).
The X-18 was a low-budget experimental craft and
used the fuselage and stabilizer section from the
YC-122, a powered glider. First flight of the X-18
was November 24, 1959.

X-19

The X-19 was designed and built by Curtiss-
Wright Corp. as a triservice VTOL research aircraft.
It featured a tilt-engine configuration rather than
tilt-wing. The X-19 was powered by two turboprop
engines and was identified by its pair of stubby
wings. It flew for the first time in June, 1964.

X-20

Although it never flew, the USAF X-20 (Dyna-
Soar) was perhaps one of the best known vehicles
in the X-series. Its first mission was to gather flight
data in the hypersonic regime (beyond Mach 6),
and prove the concept of piloted boost-glide aircraft.
It also was to have been a manned orbital spacecraft.

Combining the controlled and accurate flight of
an airplane with the high speed of a ballistic missile,
the delta-wing craft ultimately was designed to be
rocketed into space by a Titan III booster and to
orbit the Earth at satellite speeds.

The name *Dyna-Soar* was a contraction of
dynamic soaring (*see*). Essentially, it meant the craft
would use both centrifugal force, as does an orbiting
satellite, and aerodynamic lift, as does an airplane.
Centrifugal force could sustain the X-20 when it
attained orbital speed. At this velocity (about 18,000
miles an hour), it would be flying just fast enough to
offset the pull of the Earth's gravity, but slow enough
to avoid "escaping" deeper into space.

The pilot could control the craft's attitude in
space by firing small gas jets mounted on the glider.
He then would use retrorockets to direct the X-20
out of its orbit and back into the atmosphere where
the craft's wings and controls would permit it to be
maneuvered like an airplane.

The X-20 represented a new approach in the
development of spacecraft. Even though its wings
would add weight to the vehicle, they would provide
much greater lift and maneuverability than ballistic
capsules. Thus when the pilot flew his craft back
into the atmosphere, he would be able to shorten or
lengthen his range by thousands of miles and
maneuver far to the left or right of his flight path to
reach his choice of landing fields.

The Dyna-Soar program (*see*) loomed as a very
expensive project, and it finally was dropped in
favor of the longer range but more conservative
approach represented by the START (Spacecraft
Technology and Reentry Tests) program (*see*).

The X-23, or SV-5D, after it was recovered from
space. It was used in the Precision Recovery
Including Maneuvering Entry (PRIME) program
conducted by the Air Force.

X-21

In April, 1963, a strange aircraft that "inhaled
boundry layer air" passing over and under its wing
was flown for the first time. The plane, designated
the X-21, was a WB-66 modified by Northrop to
study the problem of the buildup of high drag
turbulence over wing surfaces.

Aerodynamicists have been in constant battle
with drag in its various forms. *Induced drag*, which
is the resistance of air to the motion of the wing,
must occur to achieve and maintain flight. *Parasitic
drag* is the resistance of all elements of an airplane
other than the wing that face the airstream but provide no lift. *Friction drag*, the pull exerted by air
particles on the skin surfaces of a moving airplane,
is the most persistent troublemaker. Much of it can
be minimized by improvements, but one type of
friction drag, that resulting from turbulence in the
boundary layer, continues to defy aerodynamicists.

The X-21 was the result of 12 years of Air Force
research into this problem area. Experiments were
conducted through 1967 with the result that aerodynamicists now believe they can extend the range,
endurance, or payload capability of large aircraft

by 50 per cent or more without extra fuel consumption. Final data was not available, however, for application to today's first generation of jumbo jets (*see*).

The X-21 achieved laminar flow (*see*) in the boundary layer (*see*) by the use of row upon row of tiny slots running spanwise along the upper and lower surfaces of the wing. Suction pumps mounted in nacelles beneath the wings "inhale" a thin film of air from the surfaces and expel it rearward. This process prevents the buildup of high-drag turbulence in the boundary layer and allows a smooth airflow over the wing surfaces.

Slots were flush with the surface and ranged in width from 0.003 to 0.010 of a inch. Slot spacing varied from 0.4 to 3.4 inches, depending upon wing chord locations.

The X-21's wings were sweptback at an angle of 30 degrees, and had a 93.5-foot span and an area of 1,250 square feet. There were approximately 16,986 linear feet of slots in the upper and lower wing surfaces. The X-21 was 75.5 feet long and stood 23.6 feet high. With a gross weight of 83,000 pounds at takeoff, the X-21 had a service ceiling of 50,000 feet. Powerplants were J79-GE-13's, pylon-mounted on the aft fuselage just ahead of the tail surfaces. The aircraft operated at subsonic speeds.

X-22

The X-22A research aircraft, built by Bell Aerosystems Co., has completed more than 100 successful test flights, and research is continuing. A V/STOL airplane, the X-22 was designed and is being tested under the Tri-Service V/STOL program.

The first flight of the present X-22A was made on January 26, 1967, when the airplane made a vertical takeoff and a hover flight. Since then, it has made hundreds of vertical and short takeoffs and landings. Flight testing is done at Niagara Falls, New York, International Airport, adjacent to the manufacturer's plant.

Current flights have been made at speeds in the 200-knot range. In addition, more than 50 transitions from vertical to horizontal flight have been carried out.

One of the important phases in the X-22 development program began in spring of 1968. A variable stability system (VSS) designed and built by Cornell Aeronautical Laboratory, went into operation. The VSS will enable the X-22 to automatically change flight characteristics while airborne and thus simulate a wide range of V/STOL configurations.

The VSS is centered around a compact sensing and computing unit and a power-operated flight control system. When combined, these systems modify the way the airplane responds to the pilot's control inputs and cause it to fly as if it had wings and fuselage of different size or shape.

Bell's chief test pilot, Stanley J. Kakol, says the X-22A is "easier to fly than a helicopter." The X-22A, a pure research aircraft, has duct-housed propellers driven by four GE YT-58-8D turboshaft engines rated at 1,250 horsepower each. Twin-mounted on each side of the aft and foreward fuselage, the engines turn an interconnected system of gears and shafts to drive the propellers. Each of the ducts can be rotated from vertical thrust for helicopter liftoff to horizontal thrust for flight similar to a conventional airplane.

The X-22A can also perform short takeoff using about 300 feet of runway with the ducts set at about 30°. A short landing is accomplished in much the same way with the ducts at about 30°. The X-22A can be landed in about 600 feet.

The craft can turn 360° by manipulating the four ducts. The same method is used to make the X-22A move backward, forward, and sideways while hovering. The aircraft has no rudder and needs none because of the versatility given it by the movable ducts.

The overall mission of the X-22A is to explore the characteristics of the dual-tandem ducted propeller V/STOL concept and to evaluate the military potential of this revolutionary concept.

X-23 and X-24

The designation X-23 was reserved for the Air Force unmanned lifting body research craft, the SV-5D, used in the PRIME (Precision Recovery Including Maneuvering Entry) program (*see*), but no administrative action had been taken in the late 1960's to formalize the action.

Action was taken, however, to designate the PRIME vehicle's sister ship, the X-24. The X-24 is a manned lifting body craft used in the PILOT (*see*) program.

While PRIME investigated the hypersonic maneuvering capabilities of the lifting body shape from near-orbital speeds down to Mach 2, the X-24, dropped from a B-52 at 45,000 feet and propelled by a rocket motor to Mach 2 and altitudes up to 100,000 feet, will provide information on the transsonic and subsonic regimes.   Frank A. Burnham

See also: Guidance and control systems, History of aviation, Propellants, Reaction control systems, Speed and speed records, Supersonic flight, Temperature control systems, Testing, Test pilots and test flying, Variable geometry, Wings

YAK aircraft

The versatile Russian aircraft designer, General Aleksander Yakovlev (*see*), heads a design team that has produced a series of piston-engine and jet-engine military aircraft, mostly fighters, since before World War II. Recent products of his bureau have ranged from supersonic long-range fighters to the YAK-24 tandem-rotor helicopter and a variety of training and light general-purpose aircraft.

Yakovlev is one of a small elite group of designers in the U.S.S.R. who control, direct, and manage large complexes of aircraft factories and laboratories.

Yakovlev, born in 1906, began to design aircraft in 1931. Early in his career, he produced a number of training and passenger aircraft. Just before the beginning of World War II, he designed the YAK-1 piston-engine fighter which appeared early in 1940. It was powered by a M-105P engine with a hollow propeller shaft for firing cannon.

The YAK-2, YAK-3, YAK-7, and YAK-9 piston-engine fighters were widely employed between 1941 and 1945. During that time, the Soviet aircraft industry produced more than 30,000 YAK aircraft.

The YAK-3 was the lightest, fastest, and most maneuverable fighter of the time, weighing about 5,800 pounds and with a wing area of about 156 square feet. It was, in many ways, superior to the Focke Wulf-190 and Messerschmitts of any modification and was among the chief fighters of the war.

Between 1946 and 1949, the Yakovlev design office developed and launched into mass production the following planes: the jets YAK-15 and YAK-17; YAK-14, a heavy glider for airborne units; YAK-11, a trainer fighter; YAK-18, a primary trainer; and the YAK-23 fighter. A developmental program started in 1946 has since led to current production of vertical takeoff and landing (VTOL) jets and the swing-wing aircraft in the U.S.S.R.

Current Models

Current production models of U.S.S.R. aircraft are generally known in western countries by code names assigned them by NATO (*see*).

The YAK-18 (code name Max) series (six versions) of the standard primary trainer of the Soviet Air Force and civil flying clubs since 1946 is highly esteemed by Soviet and foreign flyers. The initial production version was powered with a 160-hp M-11FR engine and had tail-wheel landing gear; the YAK-18U has tricycle landing gear and a 260-hp 9-cylinder radial engine; the YAK-18A is a cleaned-up development of YAK-18U with a more powerful engine; the YAK-18P is especially designed for aerobatics (*see*) and has been clocked at about 192 mph; the YAK-18T is an extensively redesigned version of the YAK-18 first shown at the 1967 Paris Air Show and is a cabin version suitable for such various uses as cargo-carrying and ambulance service.

The YAK-25 (Flashlight) is a series (five versions) of tactical fighters introduced at the Tushino air displays near Moscow in 1955 and 1956; they have since become standard equipment in the Soviet Air Force. The Flashlight-A and Flashlight-C are similar twin-jet, all-weather, two-seaters with provisions for an under-fuselage pack of unguided air-to-air missiles (*see*). The Flashlight-B and Flashlight-D are similar multipurpose tactical fighters adaptable for tactical reconnaissance. A trainer version of Flashlight, coded Mangrove, is a tactical reconnaissance aircraft.

Russian YAK-9 piston-engine fighters appeared late in 1942 and carried 12.7mm machine guns.

YAK aircraft

The YAK-28 series (Brewer, Firebar, and Maestro) were seen in considerable numbers in the 1961 Soviet Aviation Day flyby. The three are developments from the YAK-25 and were described by the commentator at the flyby as supersonic multipurpose aircraft. A major change is that these aircraft are shoulder-wing monoplanes, whereas all versions of Flashlight are midwing. The series reportedly consists of a tandem two-seat all-weather fighter, a two-seat tactical multi-purpose reconnaissance craft, and a trainer.

The YAK-12 light-engine aircraft is a passenger version of the YAK series; it is also used for postal service and agricultural purposes.

The YAK-40 (Codling) is a short-haul jet transport designed to operate from Class 5 (grass) airfields and other types of short unsurfaced runways. Although comparatively small, it is powered by three turbofan engines mounted at the tail. It is a cantilever, low-wing monoplane and can accommodate 24 seats in the basic version and 31 seats tourist. The length of the YAK-40 is about 65 feet; span about 82 feet; range about 1,000 miles; top speed about 375 mph.

A number of other aircraft thought to be products of Yakovlev's design bureau have recently been seen.

Two examples of a single-seat, jet-lift VTOL aircraft were seen at a U.S.S.R. air display in July, 1967. The aircraft appears to be of a purely experimental design; it has a wide fuselage of elliptical cross-section, probably with two turbojets mounted side-by-side in the forward section. The entire trailing edge of the cropped delta wings is hinged, forming slotted flaps and ailerons; the tail section appears to be conventional. At the display, one of these aircraft took off vertically, performed a transition at a height of about 160 feet, made a circuit of the airfield including a high-speed flyby, and ended with a 180° hovering turn before making a vertical landing.

Two payload-to-height records were established by a Russian pilot flying an aircraft designated the RV in July, 1959. The RV was described as a swept mid-wing monoplane with two 8,818-pound-thrust turbojets. A payload of about 2,200 pounds was lifted to 67,113 feet, and about 4,400 pounds was lifted to 66,188 feet. The records have since been surpassed.

Sources outside the U.S.S.R. have given the NATO code name of Mandrake to what is believed to be their counterpart to the U-2 (*see*) high-altitude reconnaissance aircraft. Mandrake appears to be a development of the YAK-25 Flashlight. The turbojet engines are probably a variant of the Klimov VK-7/VK-9 series.

Don Radcliffe

See also: Air forces of the world, U.S.S.R. aerospace activities

The YAK-32 one-seat trainer *(above)* held the international altitude record in 1961. The YAK-18P primary trainers in formation *(below)* are especially designed for aerobatics.

Yakovlev, Aleksander Sergeevich

Russian aircraft designer
Born: 1906; Moscow, U.S.S.R.

Aleksander Yakovlev is the leading designer of military aircraft in the U.S.S.R., and he is the man who produced the first Russian jet fighter plane in 1945. For the past 30 years he has been responsible for a flow of designs for sport, training, passenger, fighter, and bomber planes, as well as helicopters. His main efforts, however, were devoted to the design of piston and jet engine fighters and bombers.

Yakovlev served in the Red Army as an automobile mechanic for two years before being transferred to the air service as an aircraft mechanic in 1925. His mechanical aptitude earned him an appointment to the Zhukovsky Air Academy in Moscow where he was graduated with honors in 1931. He then served as an instructor in airframe construction training shops at the academy and with the Main Air Force Board's Department of Experimental Aircraft Construction until 1934.

He is a high-ranking Communist party official who has served his country's aviation interests by providing various types of aircraft including the jet fighter, the YAK (or MiG)-15, and a series of supersonic jet aircraft. Among the latest of his designs is the YAK-24, a heavy helicopter. He has written many articles and technical papers on aeronautics and aerodynamics.   Robert L. Parrish

See also: Air forces of the world, U.S.S.R. aerospace activities, YAK aircraft

Yaw

Yaw is the rotational movement of an aircraft, rocket, or spacecraft about its vertical axis. The *vertical axis* is a line extending through the aircraft or spacecraft from top to bottom which passes through the center of gravity (*see*). The vertical axis is also sometimes referred to as the *yaw axis*.

See also: Aerodynamics, Attitude and attitude control, Axes of rotation

Yaw damper

An undesirable inherent characteristic of some jet aircraft with highly swept wings is known as the *Dutch roll*. A jet in flight, disturbed by a vertical or horizontal air current, yaws slightly to the left or right. This thrusts one wing forward and its lift increases slightly, raising that wing. The yaw motion reverses due to the side load on the fin and the increased drag of the rising wing. Unless stopped at this point, the yaw will continue in the other direction raising the other wing. Normal corrective measures taken by the pilot may actually increase the problem due to the fact that lateral control action quite often is by spoiler action more than aileron action and causes an increase in drag on the rising wing. Pilot correction can also be slightly out-of-phase, which may increase the extent of the roll.

In the motion that follows, the nose swings from side to side and the wings (*see*) bank from side to side with the wing tips describing a circle. To prevent a Dutch roll from beginning, a yaw damper system is installed. The heart of this system is a gyro which

The rudders on a Boeing 727 are controlled by electrical signals sent from the gyroscope in the yaw damper system.

detects the slightest yaw and sends electrical signals to control a hydraulic power unit on the rudder. This signal moves the rudder just enough to stop the yaw (*see*) immediately.   Capt. B. G. Baldwin

See also: Ailerons, Pitch, Roll, Spoilers

Yeager, Charles Elwood

American air force officer; fighter and test pilot
Born: February 13, 1923; Myra, West Virginia
Service: Colonel, USAF (TAC)

Colonel Charles E. "Chuck" Yeager earned worldwide fame as the world's first man to break the sound barrier. On October 14, 1947, he piloted the Bell X-1 rocket research vehicle to a level flight speed of more than 670 mph at Edwards AFB (*see*), California.

Yeager enlisted in the Air Force in 1941, and was trained as an aircraft mechanic. In 1943 he graduated as a fighter pilot. He went to England and flew P-39's with the 8th Air Force.

Yeager downed two enemy aircraft on his first few missions but was shot down over Germany. The French underground helped him evade capture, and he rejoined his unit about three months later. He flew 55 more combat missions and destroyed ten more enemy planes to become a double ace.

Following his record-setting flight, Yeager made 40 more flights in the Bell X-1 eventually achieving a speed of more than 1,000 mph and an altitude of over 70,000 feet. He flew more than 2½ times the speed of sound in the Bell X-1A. He spent nine years as a test pilot and earned numerous honors and

awards. Yeager served as commander of the USAF Aerospace Research Pilot School and is now commander of the noted 4th Fighter Bomber Wing that achieved fame during the Korean war as the "Wing of Jet Aces." Robert L. Parrish

See also: Speed and speed records, Test pilots and test flying, X-series aerospace vehicles

Yegorov, Boris

Cosmonaut; space physician
Born: 1937; Moscow, U.S.S.R.

Boris Yegorov was the medical man in the three-man team aboard the Russian spacecraft Voskhod 1. Colonel Vladimir Komarov (*see*) served as pilot and commander, Konstantin Feoktistov (*see*) was the scientist, and Yegorov was the physician. Yegorov's first-hand observations brought to light the individual reactions of man in flight (*see*).

A 1961 graduate of the Moscow Medical Institute, Yegorov showed an interest in aerospace medicine (*see*) while still in college. He worked part-time at a space research center even before the first manned spaceflight. His master's thesis concerned the functional state of the vestibular apparatus' receptors. He has since published over ten papers.

Before his spaceflight Dr. Yegorov was a member of the parachutist physicians, the doctors who examine cosmonauts (*see*) at their landing places. During that time he made 11 parachute jumps.

Voskhod 1 orbited the Earth October 12 to 13, 1964. Yegorov studied the conditions of the cardiovascular, central nervous, and muscle systems; the measurement of arterial pressure; and other physical effects. He placed particular attention on the vestibular apparatus of the middle ear, a major concern in aerospace medicine. Novosti Press Agency (APN)

See also: Cosmonauts, U.S.S.R. aerospace activities, Voskhod

Yellow alert

A yellow alert is a signal given to warn of an impending air attack. In the United States, the system of alerts is classified by colors which indicate the nearness of an expected attack and the degree of readiness required to meet the situation. A yellow

alert is given when hostile or apparently hostile aircraft are detected enroute to, or over the United States or a country which is an ally.

See also: Blue alert, Civil Defense, Red alert

Young, John W.

Astronaut
Born: September 24, 1930;
San Francisco, California
Service: Commander, USN

Commander John W. Young flew in space twice during the Gemini program, and is a member of one of the three-man Apollo crews. As a test pilot at the Naval Air Test Center prior to his 1962 assignment as an astronaut, Young set the time-to-climb world altitude records of 3,000 and 25,000 meters.

Upon graduation from the Georgia Institute of Technology in 1952 with a B.S. degree in aeronautical engineering, he entered the U.S. Navy. He holds two NASA Exceptional Service Medals, the Navy Astronaut Wings, and the Distinguished Flying Cross.

As a test pilot he was attached to test projects which included evaluations of the F8D and F4B fighter weapons systems. He was also maintenance officer of All-Weather-Fighter Squadron 143 at the Naval Air Station, Miramar, California.

As pilot on Gemini 3, Young was the first member of the second astronaut group to fly in space. His three-orbit mission with Virgil Grissom (*see*) as command pilot was the checkout flight for the Gemini spacecraft. Later in the program, as command pilot on Gemini 10, Young and Pilot Michael Collins (*see*) spent three days in orbit. After the missions, Young was assigned to the backup crew for the first manned Apollo mission.

Young gained additional renown as the man who took part in smuggling the now-infamous corned beef sandwich aboard the Gemini 3, "just in case we got hungry." Fellow astronauts had the sandwich encased in plastic and presented it to Young as a souvenir of the flight.

Young has logged more than 4,000 hours flying time, including more than 3,400 hours in jet aircraft. He is married to the former Barbara V. White of Savannah, Georgia, and they have two children.

J. W. Kroehnke

See also: Apollo, Gemini

Zeppelin, Count Ferdinand von

German airship pioneer
Born: July 8, 1838;
    Konstanz, Germany
Died: March 8, 1917;
    Friedrichshafen, Germany

Count Ferdinand von Zeppelin first became interested in airships (*see*) as weapons of war. Although their use for that purpose was never successful, his 30-year effort in that direction made his name synonymous with the airship.

Von Zeppelin entered military service in 1857, and in 1863 was sent to the U.S. as an observer of the Civil War. While visiting the Union Army field forces in Virginia he saw tethered hydrogen balloons (*see*) being used as observation platforms and began to envision the use of air machines for less passive war roles. On his return to Germany, however, he was unable to interest authorities in his ideas, and immediately set up a floating workshop on Lake Constance to transform his theories into hardware.

For ten years Count von Zeppelin worked on his plans. He theorized that an airship should be large enough to carry engines capable of at least 50 mph and also decided that it should have a rigid metal hull to provide protection for and against the explosive qualities of hydrogen. Since the German government was totally disinterested in his ideas, he invested his own money for the construction of his first airship.

In the summer of 1900 he unveiled his first airship —a 420-foot, cigar-shaped aluminum structure that housed several hydrogen-filled bags and supported an open gondola and two 16-hp boat engines. It flew across the lake at about 15 mph, but had little directional control. Over the next 14 years, however,

Count von Zeppelin built several successful airships, as well as some that came to disastrous ends. His greatest success was the *L.56* which stayed aloft for 97 hours on a flight of 4,180 miles. Although some of his airships later made more spectacular air voyages, Count von Zeppelin did not live to see them.

Robert L. Parrish

See also: Airships, Blimps, Dirigibles, Zeppelins

Zeppelins

The rigid airship, or Zeppelin, was the first commercial means of regular passenger air travel and was widely used militarily in World War I (*see*). These giant dirigibles flew between 1900 and the tragic explosion of the *Hindenburg* at Lakehurst, New Jersey, in 1937.

The rigid airship was given the generic name *Zeppelin* in honor of its first builder, Count von Zeppelin. The LZ-1 made its initial flight from a floating hangar on Lake Constance near Friedrichshafen, Germany, on July 2, 1900. It attained an altitude of 1,300 feet and flew a distance of 3.75 miles in 17 minutes. It consisted of a row of 17 balloons, with a capacity of 399,000 cubic feet confined in a cylindrical shell 416 feet long and 38 feet in diameter. The aluminum frame consisted of 24 longitudinal girders, extending nose to tail, coupled with 16 transverse frames and braced by diagonal wiring. Despite structural weaknesses, the LZ-1 proved the practicability of the Zeppelin design.

The LZ-1 and LZ-2 both were destroyed in accidents, but the LZ-3 was more successful. The LZ-4, built in 1908, was flown all over Germany and was so popular that, when the airship blew away from its mast and burned, money poured in from all over the country to enable more Zeppelins to be built.

DELAG: The First Airline

The first regular commercial air travel was provided by the reorganized Zeppelin Company under the directorship of Dr. Hugo Eckener (*see*). By 1909, the *Deutsche Luftschiffahrts Aktien Gesellschaft*,

Zeppelins

Interior view *(below)* of the passenger compartment of the *Graf Zeppelin*. Intact control cabin *(top right)* of the *L-49* after being shot down behind French lines. Taking off from Albrecht Shed at Ahlhorn *(bottom left),* the *L-39* begins what was its last flight. It was shot down at Compiegne on March 17, 1917. Control car of *L-2* in foreground *(bottom right)* which is being led out for flight.

known as *DELAG*, was in operation between Frankfort, Dresden, Berlin, Hamburg, and other German cities.

The airline's most notable airships were the *Deutschland* which went into operation in 1910 and the *Sachsen* in 1913. By the time the first World War put an end to the company, *DELAG* had logged 170,000 miles and carried 35,000 passengers in about four years of operation, all without a single accident.

Zeppelins in World War I

When the German Army launched its attack on France through Belgium in 1914, all of *DELAG's* airships were requisitioned for military use. The German Army lost interest in Zeppelins after a series of disasters, but the German Navy, under the brilliant Captain Pieter Strasser, found them extremely useful. The Zeppelin Company built 113 of the big ships for the Army and Navy before the war ended in 1918.

In the early days of the war, Zeppelins could outrun and outfight the primitive military aircraft, but

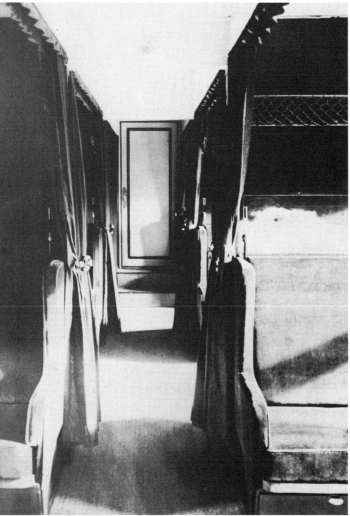

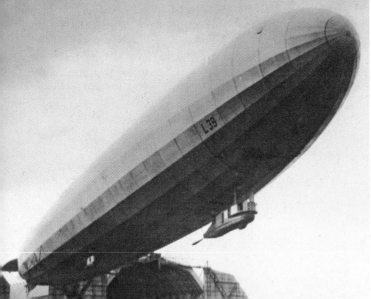

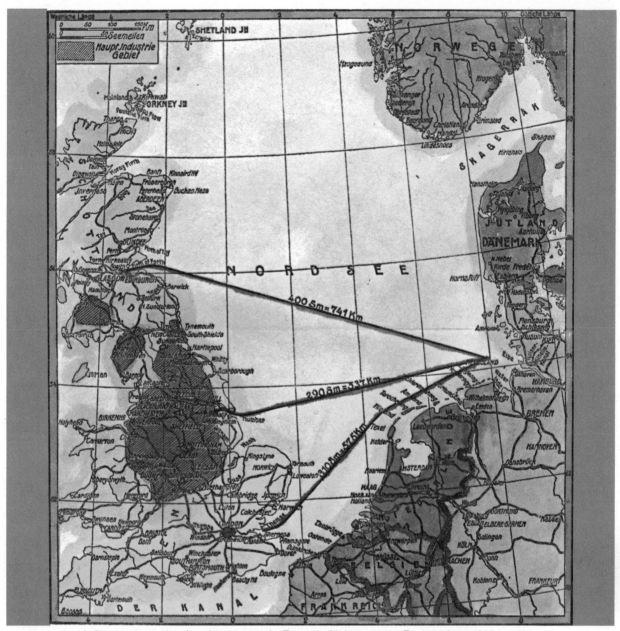

A German map showing the three main Zeppelin flight routes to England from 1914 to 1917.

eventually they began to be vulnerable to airplane attack. As fast as Captain Strasser could turn out better armed, streamlined, and faster Zeppelins, the Royal Flying Corps came up with planes to knock them out of the skies. Synchronized machine guns, incendiary bullets and rockets, and faster climbing aircraft doomed the big ships with their explosive hydrogen lifting gas. The first raids on London began in May, 1915, and by October, 1917, they had ceased.

Zeppelins were used effectively for naval and military reconnaissance. During the Battle of Jutland, a fleet of German airships alerted Admiral Scheer and saved the German fleet from a trap.

One of the outstanding exploits of the war was the 4,180-mile flight of the L-69 into the heart of Africa and back to provide German troops with desperately needed supplies. However, while over Khatroum in the Sudan, the L-69 received a message to return to base in Bulgaria. Upon the L-69's arrival, it was learned that the message was a fake, sent by British intelligence agents.

Postwar Development

When German airshipmen learned that the peace treaty called for them to turn over all airships to the

Allies, they followed the example set by Navy men who had scuttled their fleet at Scapa Flow. Instead of handing over their beloved ships, the airmen destroyed them by allowing the deflated Zeppelins to drop to their hangar floors. One of these was to have gone to the United States.

In order to get back into the Zeppelin building business, Dr. Hugo Eckener, who had taken control of the Zeppelin Company before the war, convinced the U.S. that it would be advantageous to accept a new airship instead of reparations. In October, 1924, the newly built LZ 126 was flown to Lakehurst for delivery to the Navy. She was renamed *Los Angeles* and outlasted all of the Navy's big airships. The *Shenandoah*, the *Akron*, and the *Macon* were all lost to weather and structural failures, but the *Los Angeles* made about 250 passenger flights before she was decommissioned in 1932.

The Zeppelin Company, meanwhile, built the *Graf Zeppelin* and the *Hindenberg* for commercial service between the U.S. and South America. *Graf Zeppelin* turned in an amazing record of service on the South American run. For six years she flew back and forth without a single mishap.

The *Hindenberg* was another story. The last word in comfort and reliability, the *Hindenberg* was a magnificent airship. She was 880 feet long, carried 100 passengers, and could travel at 86 miles an hour. Celebrities flew regularly back and forth between Lakehurst and Frankfurt in luxury.

There was only one matter of great concern to her crew. The *Hindenberg* was filled with inflammable hydrogen. To this day, no one knows what caused her to burst into flame at Lakehurst on May 6, 1937. It took only 34 seconds for the giant ship to crash to the ground with passengers and crew jumping and running through the inferno. A total of 13 passengers and 22 crewmen died, and so did the age of the airship. After this tragedy, the *Graf Zeppelin* was not allowed to fly again.

There is still a small but dedicated minority of rigid airship enthusiasts who maintain that there is a place for the big ships in today's skies. They maintain that the vast improvements in weather forecasting, advanced engineering and building techniques, and the development of new lightweight metal alloys would make it possible to build crash-proof airships which could compete with modern high-speed jets for a share of the air travel business. However, it is likely that airships will remain a part of aviation history. Russ Bufkins

See also: Airships, Blimps, Dirigibles, First World War aircraft, History of aviation

Zero

The number zero represents no value. Basically, it is the starting point of any scale of measurement. Zero degrees Celsius is defined as the freezing point of water under normal conditions. Zero degrees Kelvin, or absolute zero (*see*), is the lowest possible temperature theoretically obtainable.

The term *zero* has several aviation and aerospace applications. To *zero in* means to bring an aircraft exactly into a desired position, as over a target or into a landing position. *Zero ceiling* indicates the ceiling, or cloud cover, is at or near the ground. *Zero visibility* means that visibility on the ground is considered limited to a few feet. *Zero-zero weather* indicates weather conditions in which the ceiling and visibility are nil. *Zero gravity* is weightlessness (zero-g). A *zero-length launcher* is a short mobile launcher designed essentially to hold a space vehicle in position for launching, not to give it guidance. *Zero-length rocket* is a rocket with sufficient thrust to launch a vehicle directly into the air. In World War II, a well-known airplane was the Japanese Mitsubishi Zero Sen (*see*), familiarly called the *Zero*. Charles A. Velaer

Zero defects

In the early 1960's, the increasing complexity of aerospace designs forced the aerospace industry (*see*) to seek new methods for insuring more stringent quality control (*see*). One of the most successful has been the *zero defects* (*ZD*) *system*.

Originating at the Martin Company plant in Orlando, Florida, in 1962 the system simply teaches that defective parts are not a normal part of production and that all output should normally be defect-free. A ZD administrator, with close support of factory managers, is appointed to head the program, aided by a committee representing a cross-section of plant personnel. In all attacks on the problem, the goal is to motivate the worker. The ZD approach has cut production of defective parts by as much as 40 per cent in many plants. Keith Bennett

See also: Materials, Reliability and quality assurance, Systems engineering

Zero-g, *see* Gravity, Weightlessness

Zodiac, *see* Astronomy

Zulu time

Zulu time is the solar time at the Greenwich meridian and is the same as Greenwich Mean Time (*see*). Zulu time is used in aviation radio communications.

CONTRIBUTORS

Abrams, Peter D., Ph.D., Associate Professor of Education, Northern Illinois University; data processing consultant.

Adams, Andrew B., M.S., Supervisor, LTV Space Education Unit, Kennedy Space Center; Lt. Col. USAF (Ret.); Editor and research writer, USAF publications.

Aerospace Industries Association of America.

AeroSpacelines, Inc.

Aerospace Medical Association.

Aircraft Owners and Pilots Association.

Air Force Association.

Air Force Historical Foundation.

Airport Operators Council International.

Air Transport Association.

Air University.

Allen, James G., Ph.D., Chairman, Department of History, University of Colorado; Chairman, History Committee, American Astronautical Society; Honorary member, Arnold Air Society; recipient of American Astronautical Society Recognition Award; consultant to National Aeronautics and Space Administration.

American Association of Airport Executives.

American Aviation Historical Society.

American Helicopter Society.

American Institute of Aeronautics and Astronautics.

American LaFrance.

American Meteorological Society.

Andrews, Walter, B.S., Associate Editor, Military Affairs, *Aerospace Technology.*

Arrasmith, Dan, B.S., Aviation writer, Collins Radio Company publications; Editor, *Contact;* Commercial Pilot and Ground School Instructor.

Atkins, M. C., Ph.D., Director of Technology Application Programs, Space Systems Division, Avco Corporation; formerly, Research and Development Officer, USAF.

Aucremanne, Marcel J., M.S.E.E., Program Manager, Advanced Programs and Technology, National Aeronautics and Space Administration; formerly, Program Manager of ISIS and Explorer programs and sounding rockets.

Bahr, Lauren S., M.S., Staff writer.

Baldwin, B. G., Captain and Manager of Flying, Eastern Airlines; Airline Transport Pilot; Commercial Pilot, Flight Instructor, Advanced Ground School Instructor, Flight Engineer, Airframe and Powerplant license, Aircraft Dispatcher.

Barger, Rev. Robert Newton, M.A., Instructor, Schlarman High School, Danville, Illinois; crewmember on first USAF flight over South Pole; Civil Air Patrol-USAF observer to Operation Deepfreeze II; Pilot.

Bartlett, Hale C., Ph.D., Associate Professor, College of Business Administration, University of Illinois at Chicago Circle; Aviation Committee, Chicago Association of Commerce and Industry; USAF Reserve; Private Pilot.

Bedell, Ralph C., Ph.D., Professor of Education, University of Missouri; formerly, Director of NDEA Counseling and Guidance Institutes Program, U.S. Office of Education; Secretary-General, South Pacific Commission 1955-58; co-author, *Elements of Pre-Flight Aeronautics, General Science for Today;* Chief of Textbook Preparation, Naval Air Training Command.

Bednarski, Gene, Director of Systems and Data Processing, Wells-Gardner Electronics Corporation.

Beech Aircraft Company.

Bekker, Peter O. E., M.A., Lt. Col. USAF; Chief of Radio-TV and Pictorial Division, Office of the Secretary of the Air Force; formerly, USAF Command Pilot.

Bender, Welcome W., M.S., Program Scientist, Planetary Systems; formerly, Voyager Program, Martin Marietta Corporation.

Bendix Corporation.

Bennett, D. William, B.S., Proprietor of Pilotage, the Supply Shop for Pilots, Highland Park, Illinois; formerly, Associate Editor, *One-Design and Offshore Yachtsman.*

Bennett, Keith, B.A., Chicago Regional Editor, *The Iron Age;* free-lance author and journalist.

Bensen, Igor B., M.E., President, Bensen Aircraft Corporation and Popular Rotorcraft Association; Publisher and Editor, *Popular Rotorcraft Flying.*

Bent, Ralph D., Director of Student Personnel Services, Northrop Institute of Technology; recipient of Special Award for Service from California Aerospace Education Association in 1967; author of textbooks on aviation and mechanics; Private Pilot, Ground School Instructor, Airframe and Powerplant license.

Berger, Harold, LL.B., Chairman, Inter-American Bar Association Interplanetary Space Law Committee; National Chairman, Federal Bar Association Committee on Space Law; Fellow, British Interplanetary Society.

Berliner, Don, B.Sc., Free-lance aerospace writer; associated with National Investigations Committee on Aerial Phenomena.

Berry, Robert F., B.S., Director of Training Center, Lear Jet Industries, Inc.; formerly, USAF Test Pilot, Flight Instructor, and Project Engineer; Apollo spacecraft crew station design project engineer.

Blashfield, Jean F., B.A., Editor-in-Chief, *Above and Beyond.*

Blechman, Riva S., B.A., Staff writer.

Blumenthal, Ben, Editor-in-Chief, Minkus Publications, Inc.; professional philatelist.

Boeke, Robert M., M.A.T., Science educator; formerly, physics teacher at Lane Technical High School, Chicago, and Triton College, Northlake, Illinois.

Borsje, Gerard, Supervisor of Stereo Section, Chicago Aerial Survey; International Training Center for Photogrammetry, Delft, Netherlands; graduate of Netherlands Merchant Marine Academy.

Bradbrooke, Joan, M.B.E., A.R.Ae.S., Editor, *Journal of the Royal Aeronautical Society;* Associate, Royal Aeronautical Society; Glider Pilot.

Branigan, Thomas L., B.S.I.E., News Bureau Manager, TRW Systems Group; formerly, Editor, *TRW Space Log;* USAF guided missile controller.

Brannan, Peter, Editor, *Canadian Aviation;* formerly, Royal Air Force; recipient of Aviation Safety Writing Award from Sherman Fairchild Foundation in 1965; regular contributor to *Vertical World.*

Bristow, Frank E., Manager, News Bureau, Office of Public Information, Jet Propulsion Laboratory.

Brown, Frank A., Jr., Ph.D., Morrison Professor of Biology, Northwestern University; formerly, Head of Department of Invertebrate Zoology, Woods Hole Marine Biological Laboratory.

Bueschel, Howard A., M.Ed., Coordinator of Alumni Affairs, Trenton State College; author, *Model Airplanes in the Classroom;* consultant to National Air and Space Museum; Administrative Leader, Academy of Model Aeronautics.

CONTRIBUTORS

Bufkins, Russ, LL.B., Assistant Director of Public Relations, Boy Scouts of America; free-lance author and journalist.

Burnham, Frank A., Aerospace industry editor, *Aerospace Technology;* formerly, USAF Information Officer.

Burton, Frederick V., Free-lance aerospace writer.

Butler, Joseph E., B.A., Director of Computer Services, Northern Illinois University; Management and education consultant.

Butz, Sam, B.S.Ae.E., Technical Editor, *Air Force/Space Digest.*

Camarro, Kenneth D., M.B.A., Operations Research Analyst, Sikorsky Aircraft Division, United Aircraft Corporation; author, *A Description of a VTOL Transportation System.*

Campbell, Dale D., B.S., Technical writer, Abbott Laboratories; free-lance journalist for electronics and pharmaceutical industries and U.S. Army Corps of Engineers.

Caplan, James, M.S., Astromony instructor, Northwestern University.

Caproni Family.

Casey, John W., M.S., Education Specialist, Office of Aviation Medicine, Federal Aviation Administration; technical consultant and lecturer; participated in development of Atlas missile guidance system.

Casey, Louis S., B.S., Curator, Aircraft Division, National Air and Space Museum, Smithsonian Institution; Chairman, Aviation Subcommittee, International Committee of Museums; formerly, Executive Assistant, Board of Civil Aviation, Bermuda; Private Pilot and Senior Ground School Instructor.

Cellini, Beatrice, A.B., Staff writer.

Chapman, G. Courtney, B.S., Director of Research and Development, Sanderson Films, Inc.; formerly, instructor in aviation at universities of Ohio State and Illinois; airline Transport Pilot, Ground and Flight Instructor.

Civil Aviation Medical Association.

Clark, Frank A., Manager of Plant Maintenance and Ground Equipment, United Air Lines.

Clemens, P. L., B.E.E., Assistant Manager, Aerophysics Branch, Von Karman Gas Dynamics Facility, ARO, Inc.

Cobb, Albert W., M.S., Manager of Special Marketing Projects, TRW Systems Group; formerly, member of NACA Subcommittee on Aircraft Noise.

Continental Air Command.

Cornell Aeronautical Laboratory.

Corning Glass Works.

Corso, George J., B.S., Instructor in mathematics and physics; Instructor in Teaching Methods, National Science Foundation Institute for Astronomy, Adler Planetarium.

Coughlin, William J., M.A., Free-lance aerospace writer; formerly, Associate Editor, *Aviation Week;* American Aviation Publications vice-president and editorial director; Editor, *Technology Week;* recipient of National Space Club Press Award in 1967.

Danforth, Paul M., Aeronautical engineer (Great Britain); lecturer and author; aircraft and missile design and research; Landplane, Seaplane, and Glider Pilot.

Davis Aircraft Products, Inc.

Davis, Suzanne W., B.A., Staff writer.

Dembling, Paul G., M.A., J.D., General Counsel, National Aeronautics and Space Administration; formerly, Teaching Fellow, Rutgers University; General Counsel, National Advisory Committee for Aeronautics.

Dettwyler, H. R., B.S., Manager, Advanced System Applications, Marquardt Corporation; 20 years experience in aerospace, supersonic, and hypersonic development.

Dillon, Paul A., B.A., Administrative Assistant, Illinois Wing, Civil Air Patrol; Graduate assistant, College of Education, Northern Illinois University.

Dodson, Tom, Financial Manager, Federal Aviation Administration National Airspace System Program Office; formerly, Air Traffic Control planning officer; author, *Pilot's Radio Handbook.*

Downie, Don, President, Downie and Associates, specialists in aviation magazine writing and photography; Commercial Pilot; Associate member, Society of Experimental Test Pilots; author, *Cockpit Navigation Guide, Airmanship After Solo.*

DuPre, Flint, Chief of Air Force Security Review, Office of the Secretary of the Air Force; author, *USAF Biographical Dictionary, So You Want To Be A Professional Officer, Your Careers in Federal Civil Service.*

Eakle, John A., M.S., Teacher, social studies and aerospace sciences; Major, USAF Reserve.

Edwards Air Force Base.

Edwards, June B., B.A., Proprietor of Agri-Business Information Agency; Project RAND consultant in agriculture and specialized aviation; formerly, operator of fixed-base operation and crop dusting business; Private Fixed-Wing and Helicopter Pilot.

Ehricke, Krafft A., B.A.E., H.L.D., Assistant Director of Astrionics, North American Rockwell Corporation; Annual Space Lecturer, USAF Command and Staff School, Maxwell AFB; formerly, consultant to Department of Defense and USAF; author, *Space Flight;* elected to Aerospace Hall of Fame.

Eiker, Meredith, B.A., Staff writer.

Elgin Air Force Base.

Ellis, Theodore R., M.S., Manager, Systems Engineering, Space Systems Division, Avco Corporation; responsible for research and development in telemetry, instrumentation, electronics, and communications systems.

Engle, Eloise, Free-lance aerospace writer; author, *Escape, Pararescue, Sky Rangers, Medic, Sea of the Bear,* numerous other books and articles.

Ertel, Ivan D., B.B.A., Assistant Historian, NASA Manned Spacecraft Center; author and journalist.

Etter, Edward F., Aviator; Professional photographer, Photographic Mapping Pilot, Corporation Pilot.

Experimental Aircraft Association.

Faget, Maxime A., D.E., Director of Engineering and Development, NASA Manned Spacecraft Center; conceived, designed, and proposed development of Mercury capsule; author, *Manned Space Flight;* co-author, *Engineering Design and Operation of Spacecraft.*

Farwell, Peter, M.S., USAF Public Information Officer.

Feder, Abe H., President of Lighting by Feder, New York; lighting contractor, Kennedy International Airport; member of U.S. Experts' Committee on Lighting Education in Architecture.

Finckle, Earl S., President, Central Weather Service; author, instructor, and consulting meteorologist.

Fisher, Walter C., B.S., Project Manager, Navigation Development Division, Systems Research and Development Service, Federal Aviation Administration; project management of aviation lighting development for 22 years.

Flight Safety Foundation.

CONTRIBUTORS

Flying Physicians Association.

Frantz, David J., M.S., Staff astronomer and lecturer, Adler Planetarium and Astronomical Museum.

Frey, Jordan J., B.A., Sales Manager, Edo Commercial Corporation.

Friedlander, Alan L., M.S.E.E., Research Engineer, IIT Research Institute; formerly, engaged in analytical studies on space vehicle guidance and control at NASA Lewis Research Center; author of numerous technical papers.

Fries, Robert H., M.S., Assistant Director of the Fels Planetarium of The Franklin Institute; research physicist, lecturer in astronomy; Private Pilot.

Frumer, Michael R., B.A., Systems Engineer, International Business Machines Corporation; programmer on information retrieval projects; systems design and installation.

Future Pilots of America.

General Precision Systems.

George, C. L., Publications Analyst, Space Division; North American Rockwell Corporation; journalist.

Gerhart, Howard L., Ph.D., Director of Research and Development, Coatings and Resins Divisions, PPG Industries, Inc.; instructor, author, and lecturer.

Gibbs-Smith, Charles H., Aviation historian (Great Britain); author, *The Invention of the Aeroplane (1799–1909), The Wright Brothers; a brief Account of their Work, 1899–1911, The Birth of European Aviation, 1902–1909,* numerous other books and articles.

Glaettli, Herbert C., B.S., Editor, Crowell Collier Macmillan home study courses; free-lance author; formerly, staff editor *The American Peoples Encyclopedia.*

Glover, Jerry C., M.S., Chief, Satellite Operations Division, National Environmental Satellite Center, Environmental Science Services Administration; Col. USAF (Ret.); 23 years in USAF Air Weather Service.

Goddard, Esther C. (Mrs. Robert H.), Sc.D., Editor, *The Papers of Robert H. Goddard.*

Goddard Space Flight Center.

Goldsmith, Marsha F., A.B., Staff writer.

Gould, Bernard, B.B.A., Marketing Manager, Adhesive Products, PPG Industries, Inc.; lecturer.

Gregg, Gordon, Chief, Research Division, Command Services Unit, Office of Information, Office of the Secretary of the Air Force.

Guell, Carl E., B.S., Chief, Aviation Education and Safety, Division of Aeronautics, Wisconsin Department of Transportation; Lt. Col. USAF Reserve; Commercial Pilot.

Guest, B. Ross, Ph.D., Professor of Earth Sciences, Northern Illinois University; Director of Summer Space Institute at NIU; staff officer, U.S. Department of the Air Force; Pilot.

Haggerty, James J., Free-lance aerospace writer; *Aerospace Yearbook,* Aerospace Industries Association of America; author, *Man's Conquest of Space, The USAF: A Pictorial History in Art.*

Hajek, Thomas J., Captain, Chicago Fire Academy, Bureau of Instruction; author and lecturer.

Hancock, James M., A.B., Deputy Director of the Rockford Housing Authority; formerly, Executive Director, Chicago Planetarium Society; author, *Fundamentals of Aviation and Space Technology;* Pilot.

Hansen, Grant L., B.S.E.E., Vice President, Launch Vehicle Programs, Convair Division of General Dynamics.

Hares, George B., Ph.D., Senior Research Associate, Glass Chemistry Research Department, Corning Glass Works.

Harris, A. W., B.A., Manager, Public Information, Space Systems Division, Avco Corporation; author and aerospace public relations.

Harris, Hugh W., B.A., Public Information Officer, NASA Lewis Research Center; author, journalist, motion picture writer and producer.

Hart, Carl R., B.A., Audio Visual Coordinator, Public Affairs Office, NASA Manned Spacecraft Center; producer of first commercial airborne television program.

Haxton, Morris J., Manager, Still Photographic Services Office, NASA Manned Spacecraft Center; formerly, Editor, Civil Air Patrol publications, *Stars and Stripes.*

Heaton, Norman E., M.S., Executive Director, U.S. Parachute Association; teacher; formerly, U.S. Army Airborne; leader of U.S. Parachute Team in 1966.

Helliwell, Thomas M., Ph.D., Associate Professor of Physics, Harvey Mudd College; consultant to Jet Propulsion Laboratory; author, *Introduction to Special Relativity.*

Heurlin, Victor, Jr., B.S., Consultant for corporate aviation; Corporation Pilot, Morton International; Airline Transport Pilot.

Holmes, Harold J., M.Ed., Director, Driver Education, Aviation Consultant and PERT Analyst, National Safety Council; formerly, director of Aviation Education, South Dakota State University; Pilot; Chief Flight Instructor, Cardinal Aviation; author.

Howard, Jean Ross, B.A., Assistant Director, Vertical Lift Aircraft Council, Aerospace Industries Association of America; founder of Whirly Girls; Helicopter Pilot; member of Federal Aviation Administration Women's Advisory Committee on Aviation.

Howard, John H., A.B., Consultant on aerospace; formerly, with Goddard Space Flight Center.

Hoyt, Kendall K., C.E., Aviation consultant; Senior Editor, *Airport Services Management;* Col. USAF Reserve (Ret.); Pilot.

Hufnagel, Fred A., Jr., Assistant to the Executive Director, National Aeronautic Association.

Hughes Aircraft Company.

International Flying Farmers.

Irvine, T. C., M.S., Manager of Public Relations, Systems Engineering and Integration Division, TRW Systems Group; free-lance writer.

Jacks, Angus, M.S., Manager, Navy Programs, Military Marketing Aircraft Division, McDonnell Douglas Corporation; formerly, engaged in planning and design with Bureau of Aeronautics, Department of the Navy.

Jackson, Ralph B., B.S., Public Affairs Officer, Edwards AFB.

Jaffe, Leonard D., Sc.D., Project Scientist, Surveyor Project, Jet Propulsion Laboratory.

Janey, Mary Jo, B.A., Aviation Education Specialist, Cessna Aircraft Company; teacher and lecturer; formerly, Supervisor of Aviation Education, Montana Department of Public Instruction; Commercial and Glider Pilot.

Jess, L. S., Managing Editor, *Above and Beyond.*

Jet Propulsion Laboratory.

CONTRIBUTORS

Jobe, Inez L., B.S., Staff Manager, Dining Service Practices and Procedures, United Air Lines.

Johnson, Raymond J., M.Ed., Executive Officer, Illinois Wing, Civil Air Patrol; Chairman, Illinois Aerospace Education Committee; Director, Aerospace Education Workshop, National College of Education; Commercial and Glider Pilot.

Jones, Eryl, Director of Public Relations, Flying Tiger Line; formerly, West Coast Editor, *Aviation Daily, American Aviation;* Managing Editor, *Missile-Space Daily.*

Joyce, T. J., B.S., Associate Director, Institute of Gas Technology, IIT Research Institute.

Judge, John F., B.S., Senior Editor, *Aerospace Technology;* aerospace industry technical writer and reporter.

Keith, Ronald A., B.A., Director of Public Relations, Canadian Pacific Airlines; Editor, *Canadian Aviation;* Private Pilot.

Kennedy, Robert Drake, M.A., Staff Engineer, Analytical Research Operations, TRW Systems Group; technical writer.

Kennedy Space Center.

Kimmell Steve, B.S., Director of Industrial Design, Avtech, Inc.; formerly, Staff Industrial Designer, Aero Commander Division of Rockwell Standard Corporation.

King, Clayton T., Administrative assistant, Experimental Aircraft Association; Editor, *Sport Aviation;* Commercial Pilot.

King, H. F., M.B.E., Free-lance writer (Great Britain); Editor, *Flight, Air-Cushion Vehicles;* author, *Aeromarine Engines,* numerous articles.

Kinner, William K., B.A., Coordinator, Product News, Aluminum Company of America.

Kirschner, Edwin J., M.A., Manager, Transportation and Aerospace Management Systems, Litton Industries Applied Science Division; Col. USAF Reserve; author, *The Zeppelin in the Atomic Age, Civil Aviation;* Pilot.

Koch, Alfred A., M.S., Chief, Test Laboratory, Missile Systems Division, Avco Corporation.

Kohn, Leo J., Assistant Editor, *Sport Aviation;* Administrative assistant, Experimental Aircraft Association; aviation historian and journalist.

Kroehnke, J. W., B.S., Consultant, Space Associates, Inc., formerly, Public Information Specialist, White Sands Missile Range; NASA Manned Spacecraft Center.

Kropf, Gene, B.S., Public Affairs Officer—Western Region, Federal Aviation Administration; formerly, Assistant Professor, St. Louis University; recipient of FAA Meritorious Service Award in 1966.

Krysiek, Ronald F., B.S., Manager of Communications, Allis-Chalmers Advanced Electrochemical Products and Research Divisions; free-lance writer and public relations consultant.

Kukowski, James F., Free-lance writer and editor; formerly, Executive Director, National Association of Rocketry.

LaChance, Paul A., Ph.D., Associate Professor, Department of Food Science, College of Agriculture and Environmental Science, Rutgers University; formerly, Flight Food and Nutrition Coordinator, NASA Manned Spacecraft Center; research biologist and consultant in aerospace food and nutrition; author of numerous papers.

Langley Research Center.

Leach, Cara, B.A., Staff, Soaring Society of America.

Lear Jet Industries, Inc.

Lehr, Paul E., Meteorologist, National Environmental Satellite Center, Environmental Science Services Administration; author, *Weather, Storms;* co-author, *Weather Satellites.*

Levy, Gerald S., M.S., Section Manager, Communication Elements Research Section, Jet Propulsion Laboratory.

Loebelson, Robert M., B.A., Editor and Publisher, *Vertical World;* formerly, editor of several aerospace magazines.

Lott, Arnold S., Head, Book Department, U.S. Naval Institute; Lt. Cdr. USN (Ret.); author, *A Long Line of Ships, Most Dangerous Sea, Brave Ship Brave Men.*

LTV Aerospace Corporation.

Ludwig, David W., B.S., Manager, Aircraft Glass, PPG Industries, Inc.; technical liaison to Federal Aviation Administration, Wright Air Development Center.

Luisada, Claude G., Aerospace Education Officer and Squadron Commander, Illinois Wing, Civil Air Patrol.

Magidson, Enid, B.A., Staff writer.

Markey, Howard T., LL.B., M.P.L., Brig. Gen. (ANG); Partner, Parker & Carter Patent Attorneys; Commander, 126th Air Refueling Wing, Illinois Air National Guard; one of the first jet test pilots; formerly National President, Air Force Association.

Marquardt Corporation.

Marshall Space Flight Center.

Marsh, Susan, A.B., Free-lance writer, author.

Martin, Archer N., B.A., Manager of Product Programs, Corning Glass Works; Major USAF Reserve; instructor, 9313th USAF Reserve Squadron.

Marwick, Charles, M.A., M.S., Science correspondent, *Medical World News.*

Mason, Edward M., M.A., Director of Public Affairs, NASA Goddard Space Flight Center; free-lance writer.

May, Dale S., B.S., President, George S. May International Company; Chairman, Soaring Society of America Public Information Board; Editor, *Chicago Glider Council Newsletter;* Commercial Pilot, Ground School and Flight Instructor, Rotorcraft, Hot-Air Balloons.

McCormac, Billy M., Ph.D., Senior physicist, IIT Research Institute; Editor of books on radiation and geophysical phenomena.

McDonnell Douglas Corporation.

Means, J. A., B.A., Staff writer.

Menzel, Donald H., Ph.D., Former director of the Harvard College Observatory, Paine Professor of Practical Astronomy, Harvard University; Research Scientist, Smithsonian Astrophysical Observatory; author.

Mertz, Robert L., Ph.D., Head, Systems Analysis Group, Research and Development Department, AC Electronics Division, General Motors Corporation; formerly, chairman, Wisconsin Aerospace Education Committee.

Michelson, Irving, Ph.D., Professor of Aerospace Engineering, Illinois Institute of Technology; Consultant to USAF, U.S. Navy, RAND Corporation, NATO, Argonne National Laboratory.

Migdal, Nicholas T., B.S.M.E., Aerobee Program Manager, Aerojet-General Corporation.

Military Airlift Command.

Miller, Betty Ann, Motion Picture and Television Department, Convair Division of General Dynamics; writer/director/editor of aerospace documentary films; co-author with K. A. Ehricke, *From Dust To Stars, Exploration of the Solar System and Interstellar Space.*

Miller, Louise R., M.A., Staff writer.

CONTRIBUTORS

Miller, Sister Mary Ivo, M.A., Science Consultant and Co-ordinator, Archdiocese of Chicago Catholic School Board; author of numerous articles for science and education journals; consultant Title III ESEA to U.S. Office of Education; formerly, Chicago area consultant, American Institute of Biological Sciences.

Mitchell, James J., Vice President/Aviation Insurance, Steward & Smith, Inc.

MITRE Corporation.

Mittauer, Richard T., Public Affairs Officer, National Aeronautics and Space Administration.

Moroney, Rita Lloyd, M.A., Writer/editor/researcher, U.S. Post Office Department, Public Information Service; author, *Montgomery Blair, Postmaster General.*

Moyes, Philip J.R., Free-lance aviation writer and historian (Great Britain); formerly, Information Officer, Society of British Aerospace Companies; author, *Bomber Squadrons of the R.A.F. and Their Aircraft;* numerous monographs on aircraft.

Mulquin, James J., B.A., B.A.E., Aircraft-Ship Systems Manager, Advanced Systems Concepts Division, Naval Air Systems Command Headquarters; author of numerous articles on naval aviation and related subjects.

National Aeronautics and Space Administration.

National Aeronautics and Space Council.

National Aerospace Education Council.

National Air Taxi Conference.

National Association of State Aviation Officials.

National Aviation Trades Association.

Naval Aviation Museum.

Nelson, Ed, Traffic Safety Specialist, Public Information Department, National Safety Council; free-lance editor and technical journalist; formerly, Automotive Editor, *Popular Mechanics;* Feature Editor, *Science and Mechanics.*

Nissen, Laura L., Editor, *Defense Contracts Administration Services Region News;* formerly, Chief of Public Affairs, Illinois Civil Defense Agency.

Novosad, Robert S., Ph.D., Chief, Space Systems Operations Analysis, Martin Marietta Corporation.

Novosti Press Agency.

Nyman, John M., M.E., Chief Engineer, Chicago Quadrill Company; Commercial Pilot, Military Test Pilot, Ground, Flight, and Instrument Instructor; Air National Guard, USAF Reserve; Airframe and Powerplant license.

O'Dea, William T., B.Sc., Director-General, Centennial Centre of Science and Technology, Ontario, Canada; formerly, Senior Keeper and Head of the Department of Aeronautics, Sailing Ships, and Agriculture at the Science Museum, London; author, *Aeronautica.*

Oldfield, Daniel G., Ph.D., Assistant Professor, Cytology Laboratory, University of Chicago; formerly, Senior Physicist, Air Force Radiation Laboratory, U. of C.

Oldfield, Ruth L., Diploma in electronics engineering, RCA Institutes; Assistant Director, Trade/Technical Services, Gardner, Jones & Cowell; author, electronics textbooks.

Olian, Helen, A.B., Staff writer.

O'Malley, Grace, M.A., (Sister Mary Frances Therese, B.V.M.), Principal and instructor, schools of the Archdiocese of Chicago.

O'Neil, Robert F., B.A., Special Assistant for Aviation Education, Federal Aviation Administration; formerly, professional Air Traffic Controller; Pilot.

Otis, Thomas, Professional skywriter; Pilot.

Otten, David D., M.S.E.E., Advanced System Manager, Navigation/Control Satellites, TRW Systems Group.

Parker, Patricia K., B.S., Staff writer.

Parrish, Robert L., M.A., West Coast Bureau, *American Aviation;* formerly, Associate Editor, *The AOPA Pilot;* free-lance aviation writer; Pilot.

Pasachoff, Jay M., A.M., Teaching Fellow, Harvard University; Research Assistant, Harvard College Observatory.

Pay, Rex, M.Sc., Proposal Development Manager, Space Vehicles Division, TRW Systems Group; technical journalist and consultant.

Phipps, Robert C., B.A., B.S., Airman Examination Specialist, Federal Aviation Administration Aeronautical Center; 29 years in aviation education and training; Commercial Pilot; Ground, Flight, and Instrument Instructor; Airframe and Powerplant license.

Piccard, Jeannette, Ph.D., Consultant to NASA Manned Spacecraft Center; Balloon Pilot; recipient of Harmon Trophy for 1934 stratosphere balloon flight; educator and science consultant.

Pike, R. D., B.A., Publications Analyst, Space Division, North American Rockwell Corporation; free-lance editor and journalist.

Pohl, Frederik, Editor, *Galaxy;* author and/or editor of over 60 books; lecturer to business, professional, and scientific groups.

Pollack, James B., Ph.D., Staff Scientist, Smithsonian Astrophysical Observatory; Associate, Harvard College Observatory; engaged in research concerning the planets and work in exobiology.

Polmar, Norman, B.A., Public Relations Coordinator, Deep Submergence Systems, Northrop Nortronics; Compiler-Editor United States Section, *Jane's Fighting Ships;* author, *Aircraft Carriers.*

Pool, E. A., Jr., Project Coordinator, Wells-Gardner Electronics Corporation; 25 years in electronics.

PPG Industries, Inc.

Porch, Harriett E., M.B.A., Editor, Economics Department, RAND Corporation; formerly, U.S. Navy Link Trainer instructor; Lecturer in Air Transportation, University of Southern California.

Powers, John O., Ph.D., Aerodynamicist; formerly, Office of Supersonic Transport Development, Federal Aviation Administration; author of numerous technical papers on aircraft and missiles.

Powers, William T., B.S., Electronics Systems Engineer, Lindheimer Astronomical Research Center, Northwestern University; consulting UFO investigator for USAF.

Prewitt, DiAnne, Stewardess instructor, United Air Lines.

Radcliffe, Donald V., Free-lance writer; Editor, Sidebar/Chicago News Service; Chief, Editorial Services, American Institute of Engineering and Technology.

RAND Corporation.

Ripps, Irving, M.A., Information Specialist, Federal Aviation Administration; technical advisor on Air Force operations for motion picture production.

Roberts, Walter Orr, Ph.D., President, University Corporation for Atmospheric Research; Director, National Center for Atmospheric Research.

Rodes, Nick George, B.A., District Science Curriculum Coordinator and Supervisor, Northbrook, Illinois.

Rodinsky, Theodore F., B.A., Free-lance writer.

CONTRIBUTORS

Roscoe, Theodore, Free-lance writer; government consultant; author of numerous short stories, novels, and histories.

Ross, Robert S., Ph.D., Manager, Aero-Mechanical Research and Development, Goodyear Aerospace Corporation; formerly, Technical Director, Daniel Guggenheim Institute, Akron, Ohio; worked on development of Inflatoplane and Ballute; Pilot.

Runge, Fritz C., B.M.E., Program Manager, Advanced Space Stations, Douglas Missile and Space Systems Division, McDonnell Douglas Company; formerly, Test Projects Officer, Matador missile; Launch Operations Engineer, Redstone missile.

Rust, Kenn C., B.A., Editor, *Aero Album;* formerly, Editor, *American Aviation Historical Society Journal;* author, *The 9th Air Force in World War II.*

Saper, Julian, B.S.E.E., Supervisor, Design Liaison, Chicago Aerial Industries.

Sasser, Sanford, Jr., Head staff writer.

Schefter, Jim, Vice President, Space Associates, Inc.; free-lance aerospace writer; aerospace correspondent for *Time* and *Life;* Commercial Pilot.

Schriever, Bernard A., M.M.E., General, USAF (Ret.); formerly, Commander, Air Force Systems Command; President, B. A. Schriever and Associates; President, Air Force Historical Foundation; recipient of American Astronautical Society Recognition Award; Command Pilot.

Schueler, C. J., Chief, Aerodynamics Division, Von Karman Gas Dynamics Facility, ARO, Inc.

Scott Air Force Base.

Serling, Robert J., B.A., Free-lance aviation writer; formerly, aviation editor, UPI; author, *The Probable Cause, The Electra Story, The Left Seat, The President's Plane Is Missing.*

Shell Oil Company.

Sherman, Ronald L., B.S., Captain, USAF, Chief, Community Relations, Midwest Office of Information, USAF.

Sibert, William C., B.S., Colonel, U.S. Army, Chief, Plans and Programs Division, Aviation Directorate, Headquarters, U.S. Army; Senior Army aviator; Master Parachutist.

Siddon, J. David, Free-lance writer; technical brochures for industry; documentary motion pictures.

Siekman, William, Jr., Ph.B., Director, Riverbank Acoustical Laboratories of IIT Research Institute.

Simpson, Len L., Publications Supervisor, Space Division, North American Rockwell Corporation; formerly, journalist, lecturer, public relations consultant.

Sims, Charles, Aviation writer (Great Britain).

Skipper, G. C., B.A., Publicity Representative, United Air Lines; formerly, Head of News and Information Department, NASA Mississippi Test Facility.

Slater, Jan H., B.A., Staff writer.

Slater, Ralph P., B.A., Lt. Col. USAF (Ret.); free-lance aerospace writer and public relations consultant.

Slattery, Edward E., Jr., Director, Office of Public Affairs, National Transportation Safety Board; aviation writer; Pilot.

Smith, F. H., A.R.Ae.S., Librarian, British Transport Staff College (Great Britain); regular contributor to *Engineering.*

Spangler, E. R., M.A., Staff engineer, Advanced Development Operations, Space Vehicles Division, TRW Systems Group; co-author, *Communications Satellites.*

Spence, Charles, Assistant Manager, Utility Airplane Council, Aerospace Industries Association of America; aviation writer; Pilot.

Spengler, Kenneth C., Ph.D., Director, American Meteorological Society.

Sperry Rand Corporation.

Stallings, David W., M.S., Project Engineer, Shock Tunnel Section, Hypervelocity Branch, Von Karman Gas Dynamics Facility, ARO, Inc.

Stamatis, Sam P., B.S., Supervisor of Advanced Development, Wells-Gardner Electronics Corporation.

Stambler, Irwin, M. Aero.E., Associate Editor, *Industrial Research;* formerly, Structures Engineer, Republic Aviation Corporation; Senior Engineer, Chase Aircraft Company; author, *Project Gemini, Project Mariner, Supersonic Transport,* other books on science and space.

Stapp, John P., M.D., Ph.D., Sc.D., Colonel, USAF MC; Chief Medical Scientist, National Highway Safety Bureau; medical scientist specializing in biodynamics.

Stehling, Kurt R., M.A., National Council on Marine Sciences, Executive Office of the President; Past Director, American Rocket Society; formerly, Senior Staff Scientist, NASA; Group Leader, Rocket Research Division, Bell Aircraft Corporation; Fellow, American Institute of Astronautics and Aeronautics; recipient of Galbraith Medal; Balloon Pilot.

Stephens, Hal G., M.A., Staff Geologist in charge of Public Information, Astrogeology Branch, U.S. Geological Survey; produced documentary films of astronaut field trips.

Strickler, Mervin K., Jr., Ed.D., Special Assistant for Aviation Education, Office of General Aviation Affairs, Federal Aviation Administration; 1966–67 Congressional Fellow; Founder and Former Head, USAFI College of Aeronautics; Vice President, National Aerospace Education Council; recipient of Brewer Trophy for Distinguished Services in Aerospace Education; aerospace consultant, lecturer, and author; Associate Editor, *Education;* Pilot.

Strughold, Hubertus, M.D., Ph.D., Chief Scientist, Aerospace Medical Division (AFSC), Brooks AFB; formerly, Chief, Department of Space Medicince, USAF School of Aviation Medicine; author of over 160 technical papers and books.

Sullivan, John S., Air Traffic Control Specialist (Ret.), Federal Aviation Administration; prepared occupational analysis of ATC for FAA; 23 years experience.

Sutfin, Vernon A., M.S., Principal, River Forest Junior High School; member of Illinois Aerospace Education Committee.

Swedlund, Dean L., M.S., Registered representative, Mitchell, Hutchins and Co., Inc., formerly, fixed-base operator; air taxi and charter service operator; Captain, USAF Reserve.

Sweet, Bill, Director, National Air Shows.

Swenson, George W., Jr., Ph.D., Professor of Astronomy and Electrical Engineering, University of Illinois; Director, Vermilion River Observatory; Scientist, National Radio Astronomy Observatory.

Tally, Mary-Louise, M.A., Staff writer.

Temple, Joann T., M.S., Public Information Specialist, Environmental Science Services Administration; formerly, NASA Lewis Research Center Public Information Officer.

Thomason, Leslie L., Ed.D., Director of Plans and Development, Cessna Aircraft Company; aviation consultant to

CONTRIBUTORS

universities; Director, National Aerospace Education Committee; recipient of Alpha Eta Rho Award, International Aero Classics Award for Aerospace Education; USAF Reserve (Ret.); Pilot.

Thomis, Wayne, Aviation Editor, *Chicago Tribune;* pilot.

Thompson, Robert A., B.S.E.E., Director, Wisconsin Regional Space Center; formerly, Director, SOHIO Satellite Tracking Station; Director, Warrensville Heights, Ohio, Planetarium and Space Science Program.

Thompson, Tom, Group Manager, Electronics Engineering, Chicago Aerial Industries.

Tosto, M. A., B.S., Free-lance writer.

Towne, Charles E., M.S.T., Science consultant, School District 107, Highland Park, Illinois; educator.

Uherka, Kenneth L., Ph.D., Associate Scientist, Astro Sciences Center, IIT Research Institute; formerly, research at Jet Propulsion Laboratory.

United States Air Force.

United States Atomic Energy Commission.

Upshaw, James R., III, Public Relations Coordinator, Lockheed Missiles and Space Company.

Van Allen, James A., Ph.D., Professor of Physics and Astronomy, University of Iowa; discoverer of Van Allen radiation belts; Consultant, President's Science Advisory Committee; Consultant to NASA; author of over 130 technical articles and papers.

Vandenberg Air Force Base.

Veal, John B., C.B.E., A.F.C., F.R.Ae.S., Chief Inspector of Accidents, Board of Trade, United Kingdom; formerly, Flying Instructor and Test Pilot, Armstrong Siddeley Development Group.

Velaer, Charles A., Jr., M.S., Chairman, Physics Department, Roosevelt University.

Von Braun, Wernher, Ph.D., Director of the NASA George C. Marshall Space Flight Center; developer of the Saturn rockets; formerly, directed development of Redstone, Jupiter, and Pershing rockets; recipient of the Distinguished Federal Civilian Service Award in 1959.

Wachs, Miller A., M.S., Chief of Engineering Projects, Sikorsky Aircraft Division, United Aircraft Corporation; holder of four patents on helicopter drive mechanisms.

Walgren, Harold N., M.D., Flight Surgeon (Major), Illinois Air National Guard; Assistant Attending Radiologist, Presbyterian-St. Luke's Hospital, Chicago; Pilot.

Watson, L. J., M.A., Instructor, Department of Geography, DePaul University; formerly, Squadron Commander, Illinois Wing, Civil Air Patrol; Pilot.

Weaver, Mark W., B.A., Director of Public Affairs, Federal Aviation Administration Aeronautical Center, Commercial Pilot.

Weintraub, Martha J., B.A., Staff writer.

Wells, George T., B.S., Aviation and model aviation writer.

Welsh, Edward C., Executive Secretary, National Aeronautics and Space Council.

West, Durward, B.A., Manager, School and College Services, United Air Lines; member, National Aerospace Education Council.

White Sands Missile Range.

Whiting, Richard F., B.S., Staff engineer, Ampex Corporation; research and development of digital computers, instrumentation, video recorders, and television cameras.

Wick, Robert L., Jr., M.D., Assistant Director, Aviation Medical Research Laboratory and Assistant Professor of Aerospace Medicine, Ohio State University; formerly, Chief, Aeromedical Standards Branch, Federal Aviation Administration; Airline Transport Pilot; National Director, Flying Physicians Association.

Wicklund, E. J., Honeywell, Inc.

Wilks, Willard E., B.A., West Coast Bureau Chief, American Aviation Publications.

Williams, Aaron, Sergeant, USAF; Midwest Office of Information, USAF.

Williams, Harold R., B.A., President, Space Associates, Inc.; free-lance aerospace reporter.

Wing, Willis G., B.S.M.E., Technical Assistant to the Director of Technical Planning, Sperry Gyroscope Company; holder of 16 patents in navigation and guidance; author of numerous technical articles.

Wittels, Mitchell J., B.S.M.E., Senior Sales Representative, McDonnell Douglas Company—Florida Division.

Wolin, Roger, B.Sc., Director of Public Relations, Chicago Aerial Industries; formerly, technical writer, Lockheed Aircraft Corporation.

Wood, Harold S., M.A., Professor and Chairman, Aeronautical Administration Department, Parks College-St. Louis University.

Wood, Robert D., Captain and Supervisor, Second officers, Eastern Air Lines; formerly, Flight Instructor, Embry-Riddle Aeronautical Institute; Airline Transport Pilot.

Worrell, Edward L., B.F.A., NASA contractor, News producer, AV Corporation, NASA Manned Spacecraft Center; radio and television news production.

Wrobel, Charlene A., Staff writer.

Wylie, K. N., Jr., M.S., Free-lance writer and editor; contributor to various technical publications.

Yerges, Lyle F., B.S., President, Lyle F. Yerges Consulting Engineers; visiting lecturer at universities of Wisconsin and Illinois; Advisory Board of Riverbank Acoustical Laboratories of IIT Research Institute.

Young, Richard S., Ph.D., Sc.D., Chief, Exobiology Program, NASA Office of Space Science and Applications; author of numerous papers on possibility of extraterrestrial life.

Zaharevitz, Walter, M.A., Executive Director, National Aerospace Education Council; member, National Aerospace Education Advisory Committee; Civil Air Patrol; Director, University Aviation Association; Major USAF (Ret); Pilot.

Zoeller, Laurence Woods, B.A., Assistant Managing Editor, *Air Force/Space Digest, Aerospace International.*

Index

The index is alphabetically arranged letter by letter, not word for word; for example, **Aerology** is listed before **Aerol Trophy.** Entries with numbers, however, are entered in alphabetical and numerical order at the beginning of or within a letter section; for example, **C-141 Starlifter** is listed after **C-133 Cargomaster** at the beginning of the C's. **CL-44** is listed at the beginning of all entries beginning with Cl.

Main subject entries and volume numbers appear in **boldface type** and page numbers appear in lightface type. The first letter of the first word of an article title is capitalized. Context entries appear in lower-case letters and are followed by references to article titles. See **Aerodynamics** as an example.

A

A, Attack aircraft, **2** 271
A-1 Skyraider (Douglas)
 Aircraft carriers, **1** 46
 Attack aircraft (chart, picture), **2** 272
 Counter-insurgency aircraft, **4** 577
 United States Naval Aviation (picture),
  13 2383
A-1 Triad (aircraft)
 United States Naval Aviation (picture),
  13 2377
A-3 Skywarrior (Douglas)
 Attack aircraft (chart, picture), **2** 272
A-4 Skyhawk (Douglas)
 Aircraft carriers, **1** 46
 Air forces of the world, **1** 65
 Attack aircraft (picture), **2** 274
 Australia's aviation, **2** 281
 Marine Corps aviation, **8** 1483
 Military aircraft (picture), **9** 1569
 Nationalist China's aviation, **9** 1665
 United States Naval Aviation, **13** 2387
A-5 Vigilante (North American)
 Aircraft carriers (with picture), **1** 46
 Air forces of the world, **1** 65
 Catapult (picture), **3** 424
 Reconnaissance aircraft, **11** 1922
A-6 Intruder (Grumman)
 Air forces of the world, **1** 65
 Attack aircraft (chart, picture), **2** 72
 Marine Corps aviation (picture), **8** 1483
 Military aircraft (picture), **9** 1569

 Nationalist China's aviation, **9** 1665
 Reconnaissance aircraft, **11** 1922
 United States Naval Aviation, **13** 2387
A6M Zeke, see Mitsubishi A6M Zeke
A-7 Corsair II (LTV)
 Aircraft carriers (picture), **1** 49
 Attack aircraft (picture), **2** 272, 274
 Nationalist China's aviation, **9** 1665
 United States Naval Aviation, **13** 2387
A8B oxygen mask
 Oxygen masks, **10** 1752
A-20 and A-24 (Douglas)
 Attack aircraft, **2** 273
A-26, see B-26 Invader
A-37 (Cessna)
 Eglin Air Force Base (picture), **4** 679
AA-2
 Air-to-air missiles, **1** 121
A. A. H. S. Newsletter
 American Aviation Historical Society, **1** 150
AAM, see Air-to-air missiles
A&P mechanics, see Airframe and powerplant
  mechanics
Abacus
 Computers, **3** 556
Abbe (A bee), Cleveland (1838-1916, American
  astronomer and meteorologist), **1** 1
Ablation (ab LA shen), **1** 1
 Heat shields, **6** 1056
 Jupiter rockets, **7** 1261
 PRIME, **10** 1852
 RAND Corporation, **10** 1903
 Re-entry vehicles, **11** 1931, 1935
 Temperature control, **12** 2265
Ablative (a BLA tiv) **heat shield**
 Apollo (picture), **1** 183
 Materials (picture), **8** 1505
Able (monkey)
 Animals in space, **1** 154

Able Star
 Launch vehicles, **7** 1323
ABM, see Antiballistic missile
ABMA, see Army Ballistic Missile Agency
Abort, 1 2
 Launching, **7** 1312
 Terminology of aerospace (table), **12** 2272
Abort Sensing and Implementation System
 Escape systems, **4** 736
Abrahamson, James A. (1933-   , aerospace
  research pilot), **1** 2
 Manned Orbiting Laboratory, **8** 1456
ABRES, see Advanced Ballistic Re-Entry
  Systems
Absolute altimeter
 Electronics, **4** 704
Absolute altitude
 Altitude and altitude records, **1** 146
Absolute magnitude
 Astronomy, **2** 249
 Magnitude, **8** 1420
Absolute scale
 Temperature scales, **12** 2271
Absolute zero, 1 2
 Astronomy, **2** 243
Absorption, 1 2
 Electromagnetism, **4** 691
 Light, **8** 1351
Absorption lines
 Quasars, **10** 1871
Absorption-radiation equilibrium
 Kosmos satellites, **7** 1293
AC-47V, see C-47 Skytrain
Academie des Sciences (a ka day ME day
  see ANS)
 Esnault-Pelterie, Robert, **4** 739
Academy of Model Aeronautics, 1 2
 Aero clubs, **1** 18
 Model aircraft, **9** 1626

Acceleration, 1 2-3
  Carburetion, 3 409
  Environmental simulators, 4 726
  Inertial guidance, 7 1152
  Motion, 9 1640
  Orbits and trajectories, 10 1742
Acceleration error (with diagram)
  Compasses, 3 547-50
Acceleration maneuver
  Orbits and trajectories, 10 1744
Acceleration tests
  Kennedy Space Center, 7 1267
Accelerator
  Radiation, 10 1882
Accelerometer (with diagram), 1 3
  Attitude and attitude control, 2 275
  Inertial guidance, 7 1152
Acceptance test
  Quality control, 10 1868
Access routes
  Instrument flight techniques, 7 1168
Accidental activation
  Instrument panels, 7 1177
Accident Investigation Team
  Crash investigation, 4 581, (team chart) 580
Accident survival
  Aviation medicine (picture), 2 297
Accounts and Statistics, Bureau of
  Civil Aeronautics Board, 3 465
ACE, see Automatic Checkout Equipment
Ace, 1 4
  History of aviation, 6 1107
  Terminology of aerospace (table), 12 2272
  World War I
    Bishop, William A., 2 362
    Fonck, Rene P., 5 869
    Richthofen, Manfred von, 11 1964
    Rickenbacker, Edward V., 11 1964-65
  World War II
    Bader, Douglas Robert, 2 310
    Bong, Richard I., 3 379
Achromatic refracting telescope
  Astronomy, 2 242
  Telescopes and astronomical instruments,
    12 2247
ACME, see Attitude Control and Maneuver
  Electronics System
Acosta, Bert
  Byrd, Richard Evelyn, 3 397
Acoustic homing systems
  Missiles, 9 1614
Acoustics, 1 4-5
  Environmental simulators, 4 726
  jet engines, 1 5
  Radiation, 10 1880
  testing
    Manned Spacecraft Center, 8 1459
Acquisition and tracking radar, 1 6
  Radar, 10 1876
  Terminology of aerospace (table), 12 2272
Acrobatics
  Parachutes, 10 1759
ACS, see Attitude Control Systems
Actinium (ak TIN e um)
  Alpha particle, 1 145
Actinium series
  Elements, 4 705
Actinolite (ak TIN o lite)
  Asbestos, 2 202
Actinuranium
  Piccard family, 10 1790
Action/reaction principle
  Aeolipile, 1 7
Active communication satellite
  Communications satellites, 3 532
Active radar
  Radar, 10 1875
Active repeater satellite, 1 6
Adam, M. J.
  Altitude and altitude records, 1 147
Adams, John Couch (1819-1892, English
    astronomer), 1 6
  Astronomy, 2 242
  Celestial mechanics, 3 428
  Leverrier, Urbain, J. J., 7 1334

  Neptune, 9 1690
Adams, John G.
  Civil Aeronautics Board, 3 463
Adams, Michael J.
  X-15 research program, 14 2533
Adapter housing
  Apollo (picture), 1 175
Adapter panels
  Apollo (picture), 1 180
Adapter section
  Biosatellites, 2 356, (picture) 357
Adaptive control system
  X-15 research program, 14 2530
ADC, see Air Defense Command
Adcock range
  Navigation systems, 9 1674
A.D.D., see Aviatsiya Dalnovo Deistviya
Adding machine
  Computers, 3 556
Adenosine triphosphate
  Sagan, Carl, 11 2002
Ader, Clement
  History of aviation, 6 1097, (table) 1119
ADF, see Automatic direction finder
Adhesive bonding techniques
  Manufacturing, 8 1473
Adhesives
  Plastics, 10 1823
Adiabatic chart
  Aviation weather, 2 299
Adiabatic process (with graph), 1 6-7
  Adiabatic lapse rate, 1 6-7
ADM-20C Quail
  Air-to-surface missiles, 1 124
Administrative
  Careers, 3 417
  Occupations (with table), 10 1730
Adsorption, 1 7
Advanced Aerial Fire Support System
  Army aviation, 2 200
Advanced Ballistic Re-Entry Systems
  Atlas missile and launch vehicle, 2 260
**Advanced Defense Communications Satellite
  Project**
  Defense communications satellites, 4 616
Advanced Orbiting Astronomical Observatories
  Centaur, 3 435
Advanced propellant chemistry
  Advanced Research Project Agency, 1 7
Advanced Research Project Agency, 1 7
  American Rocket Society, 1 151
  Apollo, 1 163-64
  Centaur, 3 433
  Discoverer Project, 4 632
  Explorer satellites, 5 764
  Juno rockets, 7 1260
  Military space program, 9 1591
  NASA, 9 1650
  Nuclear detection satellites, 9 1707
  Reconnaissance satellites, 11 1924
Advanced Technology satellite
  National Environmental Satellite Center,
    9 1664
Advanced Terrier (missile)
  Surface-to-air missiles, 12 2202
Advances in the Astronautical Sciences
  (series of books)
  American Astronautical Society, 1 149
Advancing blade concept
  Helicopters, 6 1069
Advection
  Atmosphere, 2 267
Advent
  Defense communications satellites, 4 615
AEOLE (scientific program)
  GHOST program, 6 979
Aeolipile (e O li pile) (with diagram), 1 7
  gas turbine
    Aircraft propulsion systems, 1 52
  Jet aircraft, 7 1234
Aereon II
  Blimps, 2 366
Aerial application
  Agricultural aviation, 1 39-41
  Crop dusting (diagram), 4 590

Aerial bombs
  Bombs, 3 377-78
Aerial cameras
  Aerial photography, 1 9
  Reconnaissance aircraft, 11 1920
Aerial carriage
  Man-powered flight (picture), 8 1465
Aerial combat
  World War I (picture), 14 2500
  World War II, 14 2511
Aerial Experiment Association, 1 7
  Bell, Alexander Graham, 2 347
  Curtiss, Glenn Hammond, 4 600
Aerial life preserver
  Parachutes, 10 1756
Aerial loop
  Beachey, Lincoln, 2 345
  Oliver, Ruth Law, 10 1736
Aerial Mail Superintendent
  Airmail, 1 71
Aerial mapping
  Economic implications of aerospace, 4 671
Aerial photography, 1 9-14
  Maps and mapping, 8 1476
  Mosaic photography, 9 1639-40
  Photogrammetry, 10 1779-80
  Photography, 10 1785
  World War I, 14 2503
Aerial recovery of capsule
  Discoverer Project, 4 636
Aerial refueling
  Fighter aircraft, 5 810
  Refueling, 11 1937
Aerial Rocket Artillery Battalion
  Army aviation, 2 200
Aerial scouts
  Airships, 1 114
Aerial spotting
  Balloons, 2 323
Aerial Steam Carriage
  Henson, William Samuel, 6 1082
  History of aviation, 6 1095, 1096,
    (picture) 1095
Aerial Steam Transit Company
  Aircraft propulsion systems, 1 57
Aerial surveys
  Infrared detection devices, 7 1161
Aermacchi (ayr MAK kee)
  Italy's aerospace activities, 7 1220, 1221
Aeroballistic range
  Schlieren photography, 11 2015
Aerobatic exhibitions (stunting)
  Sport flying, 12 2151
Aerobatic pilots
  Barnstormers, 2 336
Aerobatics
  Lefebvre, Eugene, 7 1330
  International competitions, 7 1191-92
Aerobee, 1 17-18
  Aerobee 150 (picture, diagram), 1 17
    Aerospace Research Support Programs,
    1 35
  Sounding rockets (with picture), 11 2081
  Animals in space, 1 153
  Explorer satellites, 5 762
  International Geophysical Year (picture),
    7 1194
  Sounding rockets, 11 2082
  X-series aerospace vehicles, 14 2540
Aerobic system
  Man in flight (diagram), 8 1443
Aero Club of America
  Aero clubs, 1 18
  National Aeronautic Association, 9 1647-48
  Women in aerospace, 14 2494
Aero Club of France
  Archdeacon, Ernest, 2 190
  Chanute, Octave, 3 446
  prize won by Bleriot, Louis, 2 363
Aero clubs, 1 18
  France's aerospace activities, 5 888, 889
  Federation Aeronautique Internationale,
    5 804
  General aviation, 6 954
  U.S.S.R. aerospace activities, 13 2328

Aero Commander aircraft
Agricultural aviation, **1** 40
Army aviation, **2** 197
Business aviation (picture), **3** 395
Cockpit (picture), **3** 482
Crop dusting, **4** 585, 586, 591
General aviation aircraft, **6** 961, 966, 967,
(pictures) 959, 962
Instrument panels, **7** 1174
Aerodonetics
Lanchester, Frederick William **7** 1298
Aerodrome (airfield)
Airfield, **1** 61
Charts, **3** 450
Aerodrome (airplane)
Aircraft propulsion systems (picture), **1** 52
History of aviation, **6** 1098, (picture) 1098
Langley, Samuel Pierpont, **7** 1302
Number 5
National Air and Space Museum, **9** 1659
Aerodynamic controls
Launch vehicles, **7** 1316
Aerodynamic disturbance
Schlieren photography, **11** 2016
Aerodynamic heating
Mercury program, **9** 1530
Aerodynamics (with diagrams and pictures),
1 19-25
area rule, Delta Dagger, **4** 621
Dryden, Hugh Latimer, **4** 653
Ilyushin, Sergei Vladimirovich, **7** 1148
Kites, **7** 1279
lift, Aerostatics, **1** 35
noise, Acoustics, **1** 4-5
Preflight training, **10** 1849
principles of
Air, **1** 42
Bird flight, **2** 358
Boomerang, **3** 380
Breguet, Louis Charles, **3** 388
Da Vinci, Leonardo, **4** 611
Penaud, Alphonse, **10** 1774
shock waves (picture), **1** 19
terms (table), **1** 22
wind tunnel (picture), **1** 19
Aerodynamics (book), **7** 1298
Caproni, Count Gianni, **3** 405
Lanchester, Frederick William, **7** 1298
X-15 research program, **14** 2530
Aerodynamic support vehicle
High-speed surface transportation, **6** 1090
Aerodyne, 1 25
Aircraft, **1** 45
Aeroembolism (ar o EM bo lizm)
Aerospace medicine, **1** 33
Bends, **2** 349
Decompression, **4** 613
Aeroemphysema (ar o EM fa see ma)
Decompression, **4** 613
Aeroflot airline
Commercial airlines, **3** 497, 507
Commercial air transports, **3** 527
Mainland China's aerospace activities,
8 1425
Supersonic transports, **12** 2182
U.S.S.R. aerospace activities, **13** 2327,
2330, 2333
Aerojet General Corporation
Aerobee, **1** 17
Antisubmarine missiles, **1** 161
Dunn, Louis G., **4** 655
Manned Orbiting Laboratory, **8** 1452
NERVA, **9** 1691
X-series aerospace vehicles, **14** 2540
Aerojet-General X-8, see X-8
Aerology, 1 25
Aerol Trophy
Trophies and awards (table), **13** 2312
Aeromarine engine
Aircraft propulsion systems, **1** 55
Aeromarine flying boats
Commercial air transports, **3** 517
Aeromedical Acceleration Laboratory
Centrifuge, **3** 437

Aeromedical airlift
Military Airlift Command, **9** 1572
Aeromedical Association
Aviation medicine, **2** 295
Aeromedical Laboratory
Astronauts, **2** 220
Aeromedical Research Laboratory
Animals in space, **1** 153
Aeronautica (book)
Mason, Thomas Monck, **8** 1498
Aeronautical and aerospace engineering
Careers, **3** 416
Aeronautical Annual (book)
History of aviation, **6** 1099
Aeronautical Center, 1 25-26
Federal Aviation Administration **5** 796
Aeronautical Chamber of Commerce
Aerospace industry, **1** 33
Loening, Grover Cleveland, **8** 1369
Aeronautical chart
Charts, **3** 450
Course plotting, **4** 578-79
NOTAM, **9** 1706
Aeronautical Chart and Information Center
Cartography, **3** 423
Aeronautical communications
Communications satellites, **3** 543
Aeronautical engineering, 1 26
Careers (chart), **4** 676
Aeronautical experiments
Paulhan, Louis, **10** 1768
Aeronautical knowledge
Pilot training, **10** 1810
Aeronautical symbols
Charts, **3** 453
Aeronautics, 1 26
Aerospace, **1** 26
Da Vinci, Leonardo, **4** 611
Aeronautics Branch, Department of Commerce
Aviation medicine, **2** 294
Aeronautics, Navy Bureau of
Byrd, Richard Evelyn, **3** 397
Aeronautique Naval (ayr o naw TEEK na VAL)
Air forces of the world (France), **1** 66
Aeronomy
International Year of the Quiet Sun, **7** 1204
Aeronomy Laboratory
Environmental Science Services
Administration, **4** 725
Aerosol
Crop dusting, **4** 588
Aerospace, 1 26-27
Careers, **3** 411, (table) 412
Computers, **3** 558
Educational implications of aerospace,
4 674, (chart) 676
Electronics, **4** 703
Life-support systems, **8** 1337
Oxygen, **10** 1752
Political implications of aerospace, **10** 1837
Production techniques, **10** 1854
Program management, **10** 1858
Aerospace attack
Air Defense Command, **1** 59
Aerospace Audio-Visual Service
Military Airlift Command, **9** 1572
Aerospace Defense Command
United States Air Force, **13** 2370
Aerospace Electronics
Oceanographic research, **10** 1732
Aerospace Historian, The Heritage of Flight
(magazine)
Air Force Historical Foundation, **1** 62
Aerospace Industries Association of America
Aerospace industry, **1** 33
Careers, **3** 411
Pilots and pilot certificates, **10** 1808
Utility Airplane Council, **13** 2394
Aerospace industry, 1 28-33
Careers, **3** 411, 414
Economic implications of aerospace, **4** 671
Information systems, **7** 1158
Japan's aerospace activities, **7** 1231
Lasers, **7** 1304
Lubricants, **8** 1375

Military space program, **9** 1605
Occupations (with tables), **10** 1727-30
Oceanographic, **10** 1731, 1734
Paris Air Shows, **10** 1762
Payloads, **10** 1769
Quality control, **10** 1867
Radiation shield, **10** 1884
Social implications of aerospace, **11** 2066
Aerospace International (journal)
Air Force Association, **1** 62
AeroSpacelines, Inc.
Outsize cargo aircraft, **10** 1749
Aerospace Medical Association, 1 33
Aviation medicine, **2** 295
Civil Aviation Medical Association, **3** 466
Kerwin, Joseph P., **7** 1276
Medical examiner, **8** 1526-27
Aerospace medicine, 1 33-34
Life-support systems, **8** 1338
Man in flight, **8** 1451
Yegorov, Boris, **14** 2548
Aerospace Medicine (journal)
Aerospace Medical Association, **1** 33
Aerospace power, 1 34
Aerospace Rescue and Recovery Service
Military Airlift Command, **9** 1572
Pararescue, **10** 1760
Survival and rescue, **12** 2219
Aerospace research pilot, 1 34
Abrahamson, James A., **1** 2
Bassett, Charles A., II., **2** 337
Bobko, Karol J., **2** 369
Borman, Frank, **3** 382
Crews, Albert H., Jr., **4** 584
Crippen, Robert L., **4** 584
Duke, Charles Moss, Jr., **4** 654
Eisele, Donn F., **4** 681
Engle, Joe Henry, **4** 718
Irwin, James Benson, **7** 1216
Lawrence, Robert H., **7** 1329
Macleay, Lachlan, **8** 1417
Mattingly, Thomas Kenneth, II, **8** 1515
Military space program, **9** 1601
Mitchell, Edgar Dean, **9** 1620
Neubeck, Francis G., **9** 1693
Pogue, William Reid, **10** 1828
Worden, Alfred M., **14** 2497
Yeager, Charles E., **14** 2548
Aerospace Research Pilot School, 1 34
Edwards Air Force Base, **4** 678
Manned Orbiting Laboratory, **8** 1456
Test pilots and test flying, **12** 2277
Aerospace Research Support Program, 1 35
Atlas missile and launch vehicle, **2** 260
Aerospace revolution
International Geophysical Year, **7** 1193
Aerospace Studies Institute
Air University, **1** 141
Aerostat, 1 35
Aircraft, **1** 45
Airships, **1** 105-14
Aerostatics, 1 35
Balloons, **2** 316
Aero thermodynamic duct
Ramjet engines, **10** 1900
Aerothermodynamic/elastic Structural
Systems Environmental Tests
ASSET Program, **2** 206
Lifting-body vehicles, **8** 1349
Aerothermodynamics, 1 36
Aerothermoelastic vehicles
ASSET Program, **2** 206
Aerotrain
High-speed surface transportation
(diagram), **6** 1089
Aerovias Nacionales de Colombia (ar o VE as
na see o NAL es day co LOM be a)
Commercial airlines, **3** 507
Aerozine 50 (rocket fuel)
Titan rockets, **12** 2290, 2292
AEV, see Aerothermoelastic vehicles
AFBMD, see Air Force Ballistic Missile Division
Africa's aviation (with pictures), **1** 36-37
Agricultural aviation, **1** 41

(Continued)

Africa's aviation (Cont.)
Crop dusting (table), 4 587
Launching, 7 1309
Africa, HMS
Aircraft carriers, 1 48
Afrika Corps
World War II, 14 2516
Afterburner (with diagram), 1 38
Aircraft propulsion systems, 1 57
Aft ramps
Jumbo jets, 7 1256
AG-1
Crop dusting, 4 589
Agcat, see Grumman Agcat
Ag-Commander A-9 (Aero Commander)
Crop dusting (pictures), 4 585, 586, 591
Age limitations
Pilot training, 10 1809
Agena D Transtage
Nuclear detection satellites (picture), 9 1708
Agena rockets (with picture), 1 38-39
Discoverer Project, 4 632-39, (diagram) 633, (picture) 635
Gemini, 5 926, 940, 942, 946-50, (pictures) 943, 946, 948
Launch vehicle, 7 1323-24
Military space program (picture), 9 1594
Reconnaissance satellites (with pictures), 11 1925-26
Spacecraft design (with drawing), 11 2101
Vehicle research spacecraft, 13 2406
AGM, see Air-to-surface missiles and Air-to-ground missiles
Agonic (a GON ik) **line** (with diagram)
Compasses, 3 547-50
Agri-Business Information Agency
Women in aerospace, 14 2496
Agricultural aircraft industry
Crop dusting, 4 589
General aviation aircraft, 6 960
Agricultural aviation (with pictures), 1 39-41
Australia's aviation, 2 281
Crop dusting, 4 585
Agricultural Aviation (magazine)
International Agricultural Aviation Centre, 7 1187
Agricultural surveillance
Implications of aerospace, 7 1151
Agriculture, U. S. Department of
Agricultural aviation, 1 39-40
Agusta
Italy's aerospace activities, 7 1220
Agwagon, see Cessna Agwagon
AH-1G HueyCobra (Bell)
Army aviation (picture), 2 199
Helicopters (table), 6 1068, (picture) 6 1074
Marine Corps aviation, 8 1483
AH-56A Cheyenne (Lockheed)
Army aviation (picture), 2 200
Helicopters (table), 6 1068, (chart and picture) 6 1067
Rotary-wing aircraft (with picture), 11 1991
V/STOL aircraft, 13 2444
AHS Annual National Forum
American Helicopter Society, 1 150
AIA, see Aerospace Industries Association
AIAA Astronautics Award
Armstrong, Neil A., 2 193
AIAA Bulletin
American Institute of Aeronautics and Astronautics, 1 150
AIA Aerospace Facts and Figures (1967)
Commercial airlines, 3 498, 500, 511 (tables)
Aiken, Howard
Computers, 3 557
Ailerons (A li rons) (with diagram), 1 41
Aerodynamics, 1 23
Airplane, 1 87
Attitude and attitude control, 2 275
Bank, 2 332
control
Landing techniques, 7 1301
Piloting techniques, 10 1796
Roll, 11 1990

Ailevators (A le vay tors)
Ailerons, 1 41
AIM, see Airman's Information Manual
AIMP, see Anchored Interplanetary Monitoring Platform
AIM-26 and 47
Air-to-air missiles, 1 121
Air, 1 41-42
Atmosphere, 2 261
Atmospheric pressure, 2 268
Airacobra, see P-39 Airacobra
Airacuda
Bell, Lawrence Dale, 2 348
Air Almanac, 1 42
Air Alpes
European aerospace activities, 4 750
Air ambulance service
Airports, 1 100
Helicopters, 6 1072
Air bags
Observatories, 10 1725
Airborne antennas, 1 42-44
Airborne Early Warning
Computers, 3 558
Airborne radar
Airborne antennas, 1 44
Radar, 10 1878
Airborne radio
Radio communications, 10 1894
Airborne troops
Parachutes, 10 1759
World War II (picture), 14 2521
Airborne weather radar
Avionics, 2 307
Air-breathing engine technology
Lewis Research Center, 7 1335
Airbus, 1 44
International project, 7 1200
Jet aircraft (chart), 7 1233
Noise, 9 1699
Air Canada
Canada's aviation, 3 401
Air cargo service
Airports, 1 100
Air carrier, 1 44
Careers, 3 414
Air Cavalry troops
Army aviation, 2 199
Air Charter Airways
Commercial airlines, 3 514
Air Charting and Information Center
Charts, 3 455
Air Command and Staff College
Air University, 1 140
Air Commerce Act, 1 44-45
Aerospace industry, 1 30
Airmail, 1 76
Air traffic control, 1 135
Civil Aeronautics Board, 3 462
Commercial airlines, 3 510
Air Commerce, Bureau of
Air Commerce Act, 1 45
Airports, 1 98
Air-conditioning plants
Aircraft carriers, 1 46
Air-cooled engine
Manly, Charles Matthews, 8 1452
Air-cooling techniques
Jumbo jets, 7 1249
Reciprocating engines, 11 1914
Temperature control, 12 2267
Air Corps Act (1926)
Manufacturing, 8 1468
Air Corps Tactical School
Air University, 1 140
Air corridor
Berlin airlift, 2 351, (diagram) 352
Aircraft, 1 45
accidents, Aviation weather, 2 305
aerospace employment, Careers (table), 3 412
camouflage
World War I, 14 2504
Compasses (with diagram), 3 546
design, Bernoulli's principle, 2 353

Doppler navigation, 4 645
engine, Airplane (picture), 1 85
largest, Airships (picture), 1 105
load, Center of gravity (diagram), 3 435
Paints, 10 1754
patents, Caproni, Count Gianni, 3 405
Reconnaissance, airborne (with picture), 11 1919
Rubber, 11 1997
Aircraft Accident Report
Crash investigation, 4 582
Aircraft carriers (with pictures and table), 1 46-51
Arresting gear, 2 201
Catapult, 3 424
Launching, 7 1311
United States Naval Aviation, 13 2376, 2380-87, 2390
World War II, 14 2521
Aircraft Industries Association
Aerospace industry, 1 33
National Air and Space Museum, 9 1660
Aircraft insignia
Insignia, 7 1163
World War I, 14 2504-05
Aircraft in Warfare (book)
Lanchester, Frederick William, 7 1298
Aircraft Manufacturing Co.
DeHavilland, Sir Geoffrey, 4 620
Aircraft missiles
Air forces of the world, 1 66
Aircraft Owners and Pilots Association, 1 52
Aircraft Production Board
Aerospace industry, 1 29
Aircraft propulsion systems (with diagrams and pictures), 1 52-59
Superchargers, 12 2175
Aircraft race courses
Pylon, 10 1866
Aircraft registrations
Aeronautical Center, 1 26
"Aircraft scandal"
Aerospace industry, 1 29
Aircraft transponder
Plan position indicator, 10 1822
Aircraft Transport and Travel (British)
Commercial airlines, 3 505-06
Aircrew, 1 59
Africa's aviation, 1 37
Aircruiser, see Victa Aircruiser
Air currents
Passenger services, 10 1765
Air-cushion vehicles
Ground-effect machines, 6 1023
Air defense
Semi-Automatic Ground Environment, 11 2039
Military aircraft, 9 1568
Air Defense Command, 1 59
Air National Guard, 1 81
Air-to-air missiles, 1 121
Ballistic Missile Early Warning System, 2 313
Air Defense Identification Zones
Air defense systems, 1 60
Air defense systems, 1 60-61
Air Density Explorers (satellites)
Explorer satellites, 5 767
Air Displays
Cobham, Sir Alan, 3 480
Air distance
Course plotting, 4 578-79
Air evacuation
Flight nurse, 5 846
Airfield, 1 61
Airports, 1 93-102
surface
Jumbo jets, 7 1255
Air fleets
Air forces of the world, 1 63
Airflow
Axial flow, 2 308
Takeoff and climb, 12 2231
Temperature control, 12 2267
Vortex generator, 13 2433

Airfoil (with diagram), **1** 61-62
Aerodynamics (diagrams, picture), **1** 20-21
Airplane, **1** 84, 87
Bernoulli's principle, **2** 353
Bird flights, **2** 360
Boundary layer, **3** 382
Empennage, **4** 709
High-lift devices, **6** 1086
History of aviation, **6** 1097
Hydrofoils, **6** 1140
Penaud, Alphonse, **10** 1774
Propellers, **10** 1862
Reciprocating engines, **11** 1918
shape, Boomerang, **3** 380 (with diagram)
Air Force, see United States Air Force
Air forces of the world, **1** 63-66
Wings, **14** 2489-93
Air Force Academy
Service academies, **11** 2043
Survival and rescue, **12** 2217
United States Air Force, **13** 2358
Air Force Accounting and Finance Center
United States Air Force, **13** 2370
Air Force Armament Laboratory
Eglin Air Force Base, **4** 679
Air Force Association, 1 62
Air Force Astronaut Wings
Astronauts, **2** 215
Borman, Frank, **3** 382
Collins, Michael, **3** 488
Cooper, L. Gordon, Jr., **3** 566
Grissom, Virgil I., **6** 1015
McDivitt, James, A., **8** 1518
Air Force Ballistic Missiles Division
Discoverer Project, **4** 632
Explorer satellites, **5** 765
Air Force Cambridge Research Laboratories
Aerobee, **1** 18
Balloons, **2** 331
Environmental research satellites, **4** 723
Air Force Chaplain School
Air University, **1** 141
Air Force Chief of Staff
Joint Chiefs of Staff, **7** 1242
McConnell, John Paul, **8** 1517
Air Force Command Missileman's Badge
Cooper, L. Gordon, Jr., **3** 566
Air Force Commendation Medal
Medals and decorations (picture), **8** 1525
Air Force Communications Service
United States Air Force, **13** 2370
Air Force Cross
Medals and decorations (picture), **8** 1525
Air Force Eastern Test Range
ASSET Program, **2** 207
Air Force Experimental Test Pilot School
Bassett, Charles A., II, **2** 337
Irwin, James Benson, **7** 1216
Air Force Film Depository
Military Airlift Command, **9** 1572
Air Force Historical Foundation, 1 62
Air Force Institute of Technology
Air University, **1** 140
Cooper, L. Gordon, Jr., **3** 565
Air Force Missile Test Center
Cape Canaveral, **3** 405
Air Force Office of Aerospace Research
Environmental research satellites, **4** 723
Air Force One
Boeing 707, **2** 370
Military air transports, **9** 1574
Air Force Outstanding Unit Citation
Lawrence, Robert H., Jr., **7** 1329
Air Force Reserve
Continental Air Command, **3** 563
United States Air Force, **13** 2370
Air Force ROTC program
Air University, **1** 141
Air forces of the world (with pictures), **1** 63-66
Air Force/Space Digest (journal)
Air Force Association, **1** 62
Air Force Strategic Missile Evaluation Committee
Atlas missile and launch vehicle, **2** 259

Air Force Survival Training School
Astronauts, **2** 226
Air Force Systems Command
Eastern Test Range, **4** 667
Edwards Air Force Base, **4** 678
Eglin Air Force Base, **4** 679
Air Force Technical Laboratory
Eastern Test Range, **4** 667
Air Force Weapons Effectiveness Testing
Eglin Air Force Base, **4** 679
Airframe, 1 66
Airplane, **1** 82
Bird flight, **2** 359
Airframe and powerplant mechanics
Careers, **3** 416
Ground crew, **6** 1021-21
Intercontinental ballistic missiles, **7** 1182
Junkers, Hugo, **7** 1258
Launch vehicles, **7** 1316-17
Mechanics, **8** 1524
Airframe and powerplant ratings
Mechanic ratings, **8** 1523
Air France
Breguet, Louis Charles, **3** 388
Commercial airlines, **3** 505
Farman, Henri and Maurice, **5** 791
France's aerospace activities, **5** 886
Mainland China's aerospace activities, **8** 1425
Air freight
Commercial airlines, **3** 513
Air friction drag
Lamination, **7** 1297
Air intake
Carburetion, **3** 408
Icing, **7** 1145
Air Inter
France's aerospace activities, **5** 886, 887
Air-launched decoy missile
Air-to-surface missiles, **1** 124
Air-launched glide bomb
Air-to-surface missiles, **1** 123
Airless environment
Launch vehicles, **7** 1315
Airlift, 1 66-67
Berlin airlift, **2** 351-52
United States Air Force, **13** 2369, 2372
Vietnam, **13** 2420
Airline, 1 67
Air carrier, **1** 44
contract service, Commercial airlines, **3** 504
equipment, Commercial airlines, **3** 501
meteorologists, Aviation weather, **2** 306
ticket agents, Careers (picture), **3** 415
Airline Medical Examiners Association
Civil Aviation Medical Association, **3** 466
Airliner, 1 67
Airline transportation
Economic implications of aerospace, **4** 670
Airline transport ratings
Aircraft Owners and Pilots Association, **1** 52
Airlock (with diagram), **1** 67
Lunar Receiving Laboratory, **8** 1415
Airmail, 1 68-79
Commercial air transports, **3** 517
first flight, **1** 70, (pictures) 68, 72
Helicopters, **6** 1070
Night Flying Schedule (map), **1** 72
pilots, **1** 74-75
rates, **1** 70, 76
stamps, U.S., Commemorative stamps and medals, **3** 494
Air Mail Acts
Civil Aeronautics Board, **3** 462
Government in aerospace, **6** 1007
Air Mail (Kelly) Act (1925)
Commercial airlines, **3** 509
Airman Education and Commissioning Program
Air University, **1** 141
Airman's Guide
Navigation systems, **9** 1678
Airman's Information Manual, 1 80
Federal Aviation Regulations, **5** 803

NOTAM, **9** 1706
Airman's Medal
Medals and decorations (picture), **8** 1525
Air masses, 1 80-81
Preflight training, **10** 1848
Airmat
Fabrics, **5** 786
Air Medal
Medals and decorations (picture), **8** 1525
Airmen
Federal Aviation Administration, **5** 799, 802
Airmen Advisories
NOTAM, **9** 1706
Airmobile assault carrier
Army aviation, **2** 197
Airmobile Division
Army aviation, **2** 196
Military aviation, **9** 1587
Air molecules
Launch vehicles, **7** 1314, 1316
Quantum theory, **10** 1870
Air movement
Airfoil, **1** 62
Air National Guard, 1 81
Headquarters, **1** 81
United States Air Force, **13** 2370
Air forces of the world, **1** 65
Air navigation facilities
Air Commerce Act, **1** 45
FAA Academy, **5** 785
Air Parcel Post
Airmail, **1** 78
Airplane (with diagram), **1** 82-91
Aerodyne, **1** 25
Aeronautical engineering, **1** 26
Aircraft, **1** 45
Commemorative stamps and medals, **3** 494
comparison, Bird flight, **2** 359
Mechanical energy, **8** 1521-22,
(diagram) 1522
Penaud, Alphonse, **10** 1774
Piloting techniques, **10** 1802
Propellers, **10** 1863
Wings, **14** 2489-93
Airfoil, **1** 61
Airplane Altitude Records 1909-1963
Altitude and altitude records, **1** 147
Airplane Manual
Certification procedures, **3** 443
Airplane engineering department
Materials, **8** 1500
Air pockets
Convection currents, **3** 564
Airport beacon
Lighting facilities, **8** 1354
Airport Commission
Aviation, **2** 290
Airport Directory
Airman's Information Manual, **1** 80
Air port mixture control
Mixture control, **9** 1623
Airport Operators Council International, 1 91
Airports (with diagram and pictures), **1** 93-100
Australia's aviation, **2** 284
Aviation, **2** 291
Cloud seeding, **3** 474
Commercial airlines, **3** 503
complex, **1** 99
Economic implications of aerospace, **4** 670
Emergency landing procedures, **4** 708
Fixed base operation, **5** 826
History of aviation, **6** 1116
Jumbo Jet, **7** 1256
Lighting facilities, **8** 1353-57, (pictures)
1353, 1355, 1356, (diagrams) 1355, 1356
Mainland China's aerospace activities,
8 1426, (map) 1422-23, (pictures) 1425, 1428
Occupations (with table), **10** 1729-30
oldest civil, **1** 98
pressure altitude
Koch chart, **7** 1282
Runways (with picture and diagram),
11 1998

(Continued)

Airports (cont.)
　temperature
　　Koch chart, **7** 1282
Airport surveillance radar
　Airports, **1** 97
　Air traffic control (picture), **1** 130
　Plan position indicator, **10** 1822
Airport tower
　Air traffic control (pictures), **1** 125, 134
Airport traffic controllers
　Radar, **10** 1878
Air power
　Aerospace power, **1** 34
　Military aviation, **9** 1579-87
Air Power—Key to Survival (book)
　De Seversky, Alexander Procofieff, **4** 628
Air pressure
　Atmosphere, **2** 267
　changes, Aviation medicine, **2** 293
　Lana, Francesco de, **7** 1297
　Life-support systems, **8** 1337-38
Air Proving Ground Center
　Eglin Air Force Base, **4** 679
Air Pullman
　Commercial air transports, **3** 518
Air racing, 1 102-04
　Sport flying, **12** 2150
Air raid, 1 104
Air refuelers
　Military aircraft, **9** 1570, (picture) 1566
Air Research and Development Command
　United States Air Force, **13** 2366
Air resistance, 1 104
Air Resources Laboratories
　Environmental Science Services
　　Administration, **4** 725
Air route, 1 104
Air Route Traffic Control
　Control tower, **3** 564
Air Route Traffic Control Center
　Air traffic control, **1** 127, 131-32, 135
　Pilot weather reports, **10** 1812
Air Safety Board
　Civil Aeronautics Board, **3** 462
Air-sea interaction
　Oceanographic research, **10** 1732
Air/sea rescue planes
　Military aircraft, **9** 1570-71
Air Self-Defense Force
　Asia's aviation, **2** 203
　Japan's aerospace activities, **7** 1129
Air Service Medical Research Laboratory
　Aviation medicine, **2** 294
Airships (with diagram and pictures),
　1 105-14
　Aeronautics, **1** 26
　Aerostat, **1** 35
　Aerostatics, **1** 35
　Ballast, **2** 313
　Dirigibles, **4** 631
　Gondolas, **6** 994
　Haenlein, Paul, **6** 1045
　Mason, Thomas Monck, **8** 1498
　United States Naval Aviation, **13** 2379
　Zeppelins, **14** 2549-52
Air shows, 1 115
　Manufacturing, **8** 1468
　Sport flying, **12** 2151
Airsickness, 1 115
Airspace, 1 115-16
　Air Commerce Act, **1** 45
　Airway, **1** 141
　Space law, **12** 2120
Airspeed, 1 116
　Pilot's handbook, **10** 1809
Airspeed indicator (with picture and diagram),
　1 116-17
　Instrument flight techniques, **7** 1167
　Instrument panels, **7** 1176
　Navigation instruments, **9** 1672
　Pitot-static system, **10** 1816
　Pressure gauges, **10** 1849
　Soaring, **11** 2063
　Vertical-scale display instruments, **13** 2410

Airstair doors
　Airplane, **1** 83
Air-superiority fighters
　Air forces of the world, **1** 64
　Interceptor aircraft, **7** 1182
Air Taxi Commercial Operator's Certificate
　Charter flying, **3** 449
　Commuter airlines, **3** 544
Air taxis, 1 117-18
　Charter flying, **3** 447
　Commercial airlines, **3** 499
　Educational implications of aerospace,
　　4 674
　General aviation, **6** 953-54, 956, 958
Air temperature gauge
　Navigation instruments, **9** 1672
Air terminals, 1 118-19
Air test vehicle
　V/STOL aircraft, **13** 2439
Airtight chamber
　Airlock, **1** 67
Air-to-air missiles (with pictures and table),
　1 119-21
　Air Defense Command, **1** 59
　Air defense systems, **1** 61
　Missiles, **9** 1610, (picture) 1613, (diagram)
　　1614, (data table) 1616
Air-to-surface missiles (with pictures and
　table), **1** 122-24
　Air raid, **1** 104
　Missiles, **9** 1610, (picture) 1613, (data
　　table) 1616
Air traffic, 1 124
　corridors, Air traffic control (diagram), **1** 126
　density pattern, Airports (picture), **1** 96
Air traffic control (with diagram, map and
　pictures), **1** 125-39
　abbreviations (glossary), **1** 129
　Airman's Information Manual, **1** 80
　European air traffic control, **4** 752
　FAA Academy, **5** 785
　Federal airways system, **5** 792
　Federal Aviation Administration, **5** 796-98
　Government in aerospace, **6** 1003-04,
　　1006, (picture) 1003
　Ground control approach, **6** 1018
　Holding pattern, **6** 1122
　Inflight emergency procedures, **7** 1155
　Instrument Flight Rules, **7** 1164
　Instrument flight techniques, **7** 1166
　National Airspace System, **9** 1660
　Radar (with picture), **10** 1876
　Radio communications, **10** 1894
　Supersonic transports, **12** 2199
Air transmission
　Radio, **10** 1885
Air Transport Association, 1 139
　Commercial airlines, **3** 504
　National Air and Space Museum, **9** 1660
Air transportation costs
　Aerospace industry, **1** 32
Air Transportation Regulation
　Civil Aeronautics Board, **3** 462
Air Transport Command
　Airlift, **1** 67
　Commercial airlines, **3** 504
Air transports, 1 139
　Commercial air transports, **3** 518
　Military air transports, **9** 1574-78
Air transport system
　Commercial airlines, **3** 504
Air turbulence
　Buffeting, **3** 389
AIR-2A
　Air-to-air missiles, **1** 121
Air University, 1 140-41
Air War College
　Air University, **1** 140
Airway, 1 141
　Air Commerce Act, **1** 45
　Air traffic control, **1** 125
Airway beacons
　Airports, **1** 97
Air Weather Service
　Military Airlift Command, **9** 1572

Airworthiness, 1 141
Airworthiness Certificate
　Airworthiness, **1** 141
　Certification procedures, **3** 441
Airworthiness Directive
　Airworthiness, **1** 141
Akagi (a KA gee)
　Aircraft carriers, **1** 49
Akron
　Airships, **1** 106, 110, 113, (picture) 107
　Dirigibles, **4** 631
Alaska
　Air defense systems, **1** 60
　Airports, **1** 94, 98, 100
　Ballistic Missile Early Warning System,
　　2 313
　Bush flying, **3** 390
　game laws
　　Coast Guard aviation, **3** 479
Alaskan Command (United States)
　Air forces of the world, **1** 65
　United States Air Force, **13** 2370
Albania
　Commemorative stamps and medals, **3** 495
　European aerospace activities, **4** 751
Albatros (airplane)
　First World War aircraft, **5** 816, 824,
　　(pictures) 815-16
　World War I, **14** 2505-06, (picture) 2508
Albatross, see HU-16 Albatross
Albedo
　Atmosphere, **2** 265
Albert I and II (monkeys)
　Animals in space, **1** 153
Albert, Marcel
　World War II (table), **14** 2517
Alcock and Brown, 1 141-42
　Airships, **1** 111
　Commemorative stamps and medals, **3** 495
Alcock, John William (1892-1919, English
　aviator), **1** 141-42
　Royal Air Force, **11** 1995
Alcohol
　Aviation medicine, **2** 297
　Drug effects, **4** 653
　Launch vehicles, **7** 1315
　Liquid-fuel rockets, **8** 1363
Alcor
　Astrophysics, **2** 257
Aldrin, Edwin R., Jr. (1930-　　　), **1** 142
　Astronauts, **2** 216-19, 223, 225, 230 (with
　　pictures)
　Gemini, **5** 949-50, 952, (picture) 949
　Manned spaceflight, **8** 1461, (table) 1462
Alert Station
　Bush flying, **3** 393
Alexander the Great
　Astronomy, **2** 235
Alexandria
　Aristarchus of Samos, **2** 193
　Astronomy, **2** 235
Alfa
　Antisubmarine missiles, **1** 160
Algae, 1 143
　Carbon dioxide, **3** 407
　Closed ecological system, **3** 470
　Life-support systems, **8** 1344
　Photosynthesis, **10** 1790
Aligned composite
　Materials, **8** 1504
Alitalia
　Commercial airlines, **3** 497
Alize aircraft
　Asia's aviation, **2** 204
　Naval aviation, worldwide (India), **9** 1669,
　　1671
Alkali
　Air-to-air missiles, **1** 121
Alkaline-earth metals
　Elements, **4** 705
Al-Kira light jet fighters
　Africa's aviation, **1** 37
All-cargo airlines
　Commercial airlines, **3** 500
　Flying Tigers, **5** 865

Allegheny Airline (regional route map)
  Commercial airlines, 3 512
Allen, H. Julian
  Mercury program, 9 1530
  Re-entry vehicles, 11 1932
Allen, Joseph P., IV (1936-   ), 1 143
  Astronauts, 2 218, 219 (with picture)
Allen, William M.
  Medals and decorations (table), 8 1526
Allied Cockade
  World War I, 14 2504, (picture) 2507
Allison in-line engines
  Aircraft propulsion systems, 1 56
Allison J-35 turbojet engine
  X-series aerospace vehicles, 14 2538
Allowables, see Tolerances
Alloys, 2 143-44
  Beryllium, 2 354
  2219, Aluminum, 1 148
  Magnesium, 8 1419
  Metals and metallurgy, 9 1548
  Nickel, 9 1696
  Titanium, 12 2288-89
All-systems inspection
  Certification procedures, 3 443
All-weather interceptors
  Air forces of the world, 1 64
ALM, see Augmented Lunar Module
Almagest (AL ma jest) (book by Ptolemy)
  Astronomy, 2 236
  Ptolemy, Claudius, 10 1864
Alon (airplane)
  General aviation aircraft, 6 961
Alone (book)
  Byrd, Richard Evelyn, 3 397
Alouette (al oo ET) **helicopter** (Sud-Aviation)
  France's aerospace activities (pictures),
    5 885, 890
  Mainland China's aerospace activities,
    8 1428
  Naval aviation, worldwide (India), 9 1671
Alouette satellites, 1 144-45
  Explorer satellites, 5 772
  International projects, 7 1198
  International Satellite for Ionospheric
    Studies, 7 1201
  NASA, 9 1653
Alpha (ocean data station)
  Oceanographic research (picture), 10 1732
Alpha Centauri (AL fa sen TOR ee) (star)
  Astronomy, 2 249
Alpha Eta Rho (AL fa ATE a RO), 1 145
Alphanumerics
  National Airspace System, 9 1662
  Plan position indicator, 10 1822
Alpha particle, 1 145
  Radiation, 10 1880, 1882
  Surveyor, 12 2212, 2214, 2215, (picture)
    2212
Alpha Proxima (AL fa PROX ee ma) (star)
  Astronomy 2 249
Alps
  Lunar exploration (picture), 8 1407
ALSEP, see Apollo Lunar Surface Experiment
  Package
Altair
  Delta rocket, 4 622
Alternate bands
  Jupiter, 7 1260
Alternating current
  Electricity, 4 685
Alternators, see Generators and alternators
Altimeter, 1 145-46
  Altitude and altitude records, 1 146
  Atmospheric pressure, 2 268
  Barometric pressure, 2 337
  Instrument flight techniques, 7 1167
  Instrument panels, 7 1176-77
  Manufacturing, 8 1469
  Navigation instruments, 9 1672
  Pitot-static system, 10 1816
  Pressure gauges, 10 1849
  Radar, 10 1878
  Radio (with diagram), 10 1888

Altitude
  Airports, 1 95
  Collision avoidance system, 3 489
  Hemisphere rules, 6 1080
  Instrument panels, 7 1176
  Instrument Flight Rules, 7 1165
  Preflight training, 10 1848
  Radar, 10 1878
  requirements, Bailout, 2 310
Altitude and altitude records (with picture and
  table), 1 146-48
  Drop record
    Bailout, 2 311
Altitude chambers
  Kennedy Space Center, 7 1267
Altitude-hold capability
  Automatic pilot, 2 289
Altitude sensor
  Automatic pilot, 2 289
Altocumulus
  Clouds, 3 472-73 (with picture)
Altostratus
  Clouds, 3 473
Aluminosilicate
  Glass, 6 982
Aluminum, 1 148-49
  Alloys, 1 144
  Airships, 1 114
  Boron, 3 382
  forging (picture), 1 149
  Magnesium, 8 1419
  Manufacturing, 8 1467
  Materials, 8 1507-08
Aluminum cocoon
  Escape systems, 4 735
Aluminum honeycomb
  Honeycomb construction, 6 1128
  Materials, 8 1503
Alvarez, L.
  Radiation, 10 1882
Alveoli
  Man in flight, 8 1444
Amber 15
  Air traffic control, 1 135
Amelia Earhart Memorial Award
  Cobb, Geraldyn, 3 480
  Cochran, Jacqueline, 3 481
  Mock, Geraldine C., 9 1624
  Ninety-Nines, 9 1698
America
  Aircraft carriers (data table), 1 51
America (flying boat)
  First World War aircraft, 5 818
America (Fokker trimotor)
  Bennett, Floyd, 2 350
  Byrd, Richard Evelyn, 3 397
American Airlines
  Boeing 707, 2 372
  Charter flying, 3 448
  Commercial airlines, 3 497, 512
  Commuter airlines, 3 544
American Airways
  Commercial airlines, 3 510
American Association of Airport Executives,
  1 149
American Astronautical Society, 1 149
  Achievement Award for 1966
    Conrad, Charles, Jr., 3 561
American Aviation Historical Society, 1 149-50
American bomber and missile forces
  NATO, 9 1704
American Export Airlines
  Commercial airlines, 3 509
American Geophysical Union
  Cunningham, R. Walter, 4 600
American Helicopter Society, 1 150
American Institute of Aeronautics and
  Astronautics, 1 150
  Cunningham, R. Walter, 4 600
American Interplanetary Society
  American Rocket Society, 1 150
American Meteorological Society, 1 150
American Ordnance Association
  Debus, Kurt Heinrich, 4 612

American Overseas Airlines
  Commercial airlines, 3 513
American Radio Relay League
  Communications satellites, 3 534
American Rocket Society, 1 150-51
  American Institute of Aeronautics and
    Astronautics, 1 150
  Durant, Frederick Clark, III, 4 655
  Jet-assisted takeoff, 7 1236
American Society for Testing and Materials
  Manufacturing, 8 1473
American Telephone and Telegraph Co.
  Communications satellites, 3 534
American Volunteer Group
  Flying Tigers, 5 865
  World War II, 14 2520
American Wright Company
  Wright brothers, 14 2526
Ames Aeronautical Laboratory
  Mercury program, 9 1530
Ames Research Center
  NASA, 9 1654
Amex Airlines
  Commercial airlines, 3 513
Amino acids
  Extraterrestrial life, 5 775
Amiot aircraft
  Second World War aircraft, 11 2029
Ammonia
  Balloons, 2 317
  Jupiter, 7 1260
Ammonia quantum generator
  Kosmos satellites, 7 1294
Ammonification
  Nitrogen, 9 1698
Ammunition
  Armament, 2 193
Amoeba
  Biosatellites, 2 356
Amorphous
  Plastics, 10 1823
Ampere
  Electricity, 4 684
Ampere, Andre Marie (am PIER, AN dray)
  Electricity, 4 684
  Electromagnetism, 4 688
Amphibian
  Loening Amphibian, 8 1369 (picture)
Amphibious aircraft, 1 151
Amphibious floats
  Pontoons, 10 1838
Amphibole
  Asbestos, 2 202
Amplification
  Electronics, 4 695
  Intercom, 7 1182
Amplifier
  Compasses, 3 551
Amplifier circuit
  Circuit, 3 461
Amplitude
  Radio, 10 1887
  Modulation, 9 1629-30
  Sound, 11 2077
AMTI
  Radar, 10 1877
Amundsen, Roald (1872-1928, Norwegian
  explorer), 1 151
  Airships, 1 112
  Balchen, Bernt, 2 312
  Dirigibles, 4 631
  Ellsworth, Lincoln, 4 706
  Polar flights, 10 1829, 1834
AMVER, see Automated Merchant Vessel
  Reporting
An-2 (Antonov)
  Crop dusting (picture), 4 593
  Mainland China's aerospace activities,
    8 1426
An-10 (Antonov)
  U.S.S.R. aerospace activities, 13 2332
An-12 (Antonov)
  Military air transports (picture), 9 1575
  U.S.S.R. aerospace activities (table),
    13 2337

An-22 Antheus (Antonov)
Commercial air transports, 3 527, 530
Jumbo jets (pictures), 7 1256
An-24 (Antonov)
Commercial air transports, 3 530
Anaerobic bacteria
Mars, 8 1492
Analog computer
Automatic pilot, 2 289
Computers, 3 553
Analog system
Space communications, 11 2097
Analog-to-digital converter
Data acquisition and processing, 4 605
Analytical engine
Computers, 3 557
Anatomy of birds
Bird flight, 2 358, (diagram) 360
Anatra D (airplane)
First World War aircraft, 5 825
Anaximander
Planetarium, 10 1818
**Anchored Interplanetary Monitoring
Platform** (AIMP)
Explorer satellites, 5 772
Interplanetary Monitoring Platform
satellites, 7 1206
Anders, William A. (1933-   ), 1 152
Astronauts, 2 217-19, 227, 229, 231
(with picture)
Anderson, George
Astronaut wings, 2 232
Andover, Maine
Communications satellites, 3 531
Andree, Salomon August
Polar flights, 10 1828
Android
Robots, 11 1965
Andromeda (an DROM i duh) (constellation)
Astronomy, 2 253
Baade, Walter, 2 309
Galaxies, 5 910, (picture) 911
Andromeda Nebula
Astronomy, 2 242
Hubble, Edwin, 6 1131
Universe, 13 2391
Anechoic chamber
Manned Spacecraft Center, 8 1458,
(picture) 1459
Anemometer (an e MOM e tir), 1 152
Aneroid
Altimeter, 1 145
Aneroid barometer
Barometer, 2 336-37
ANG, see Air National Guard
Angels
Radar, 10 1879
Terminology of aerospace (table), 12 2272
Angle deck
Aircraft carriers, 1 51
Catapult, 3 424
Angle of attack, 1 152
Aerodynamics, 1 22
Airfoil, 1 62
High-lift devices, 6 1088
Maneuvers, 8 1434, (diagram) 1437
Stall, 12 2158
Wings, 14 2491
Angle of glide
Instrument flight techniques, 7 1168
Angle of incidence
Propellers, 10 1862
Wings, 14 2491
Anglo-French Concorde, see Concorde SST
Angular acceleration
Acceleration, 1 2
Angular diameter
Celestial navigation, 3 430
Angular resolution
Radio astronomy, 10 1892
Anhydrous ammonia
X-15 research program, 14 2532
Anhydrous hydrazine
propellant combination
Apollo, 1 173

Aniline-furfuryl (fer fer il) **alcohol**
Aerobee, 1 17
Animals in space (with pictures), 1 153-56
Kosmos satellites, 7 1292
Space biology, 11 2094
Anion
Ion, 7 1215
ANNA (satellite program)
Geodetic satellites, 6 971-72, (table) 973
Annuales de l'Observatoire de Paris
Leverrier, Urbain J. J., 7 1334
Annular eclipse
Eclipse, 4 668
Anode
Electronics, 4 693-94
Anscheuetz-Kaempfe, Hermann
Gyroscope, 6 1044
Ansett-ANA
Australia's aviation, 2 280
Antarctica
Byrd, Richard Evelyn, 3 397
Ellsworth, Lincoln, 4 707
Polar flying, 10 1830
Poles, 10 1830, 1833-34
Ante meridiem
Meridian, 9 1546
Antennas
feeder devices
Kosmos satellites, 7 1292
Instrument landing system, 7 1170
Kennedy Space Center (picture), 7 1273
Orbiting observatories, 10 1741
Plan position indicator, 10 1821
Radar, 10 1874, 1876-77
Space communications (with diagram),
11 2099
test range
Italy's aerospace activities, 7 1223
Antheus, see An-22 Antheus
Antiaircraft weapons, 1 156-58
Radar, 10 1878
Semi-Automatic Ground Environment,
11 2039
Surface-to-air missiles, 12 2199
Vietnam, 13 2423
Antiballistic missile defense, 1 158-59
Antimissile missiles, 1 159
Radar, 10 1879
Antiballistic missiles
Surface-to-air missiles, 12 2199
Anticollision lights
Rotating beacons, 11 1992
Anticyclone, 1 159
Air masses, 1 80
Atmospheric pressure, 2 268
High-pressure area, 6 1089
Antiexposure suits
Personal equipment, 10 1775
Anti-g suits
Personal equipment, 10 1775
Antihistamines
Drug effects, 4 653
Anti-ice fluids
Deicing equipment, 4 620
Antilock system
Brakes, 3 387
Antimissile missiles, 1 159
Antiaircraft weapons, 1 158
Antipersonnel bombs
Bombs, 3 378
Antipodal bomber
Dynamic soaring, 4 656
Antipoison center
Communications satellites, 3 542
Antique Aircraft Association
Air shows, 1 115
Pleasure flying, 10 1826
Antique airplanes
Sport flying, 12 2148-49
Antiradiation missile
Air-to-surface missiles, 1 122-24
Antisatellite missile
Surface-to-air missiles, 12 2199
Antiskid devices
Brakes, 3 387

Antisnag wires
Agricultural aviation, 1 41
Antisubmarine missiles, 1 160
Missiles, 9 1610, (data table) 1616
Antisubmarine rocket
Antisubmarine missiles, 1 160
Antitank systems
Battlefield missile systems, 2 342
Infrared detection devices, 7 1161
Antoinette engine
Aircraft propulsion systems, 1 55-56,
(picture) 53
Antoinette monoplane
Levavasseur, Leon, 7 1333
Antonov An-2, see An-2
Antonov An-10, see An-10
Antonov An-12, see An-12
Antonov An-22, see An-22 Antheus
Antonov An-24, see An-24
AN/USD-501 drone
Drone aircraft, 4 653
Anvil clouds
Aviation weather, 2 301
AO-1 Mohawk, see G-134 Mohawk
AOCI, see Airport Operators Council
International
AOPA, see Aircraft Owners and Pilots
Association
Apache, see Piper Apache
Apache Airlines
Commuter airlines, 3 545
Apennines
Lunar exploration (picture), 8 1407
Aperture
Photography (with diagram), 10 1782-83
APGC, see Air Proving Ground Center
Aphelion, 1 161
Asteroids, 2 207
Comets, 3 490
Pioneer, 10 1813
APN-1
Blimps, 2 365
Apoapsis
Orbits and trajectories, 10 1744
Apocynthion
Rendezvous and docking, 11 1957
Apogee, 1 161
Alouette satellites, 1 144
Ariel satellites, 2 192
engine
Applications Technology Satellites, 2 190
kick rocket
Communications satellites, 3 536
International Satellite for Ionospheric
Studies, 7 1201
Launch vehicles, 7 1317
Orbits and trajectories, 10 1744
PRIME, 10 1853
Apollo, 1 162-84
ablative heat shield
Materials (picture), 8 1505
Aerospace, 1 27
Apollo Applications Program, 2 186
Astrogeology, 2 212
Astronautics, 2 212
Attitude and attitude control, 2 276
Capsule, 3 406
Clean room, 3 468
Closed ecological system, 3 470
Command Module (diagrams), 1 172
Airlock, 1 67
Electrical systems, 4 682-83 (with
diagram)
Heat shields, 6 1058, (pictures) 1057-59
Honeycomb construction, 6 1129
Launch vehicles, 7 1325
Lifting-body vehicles, 8 1346
Manned Spacecraft Center, 8 1458
Manufacturing (picture), 8 1473
Marshall Space Flight Center, 8 1494
Re-entry (with picture), 11 1931
Commemorative stamps and medals, 3 495
Communications satellites, 3 543
Spaceflight simulators, 12 2112
Space propulsion systems, 12 2124

Apollo (Cont.)
  Space stations, **12** 2126
  crews
    Cunningham, R. Walter, **4** 600
    Eisele, Donn F., **4** 681
    Evans, Ronald Ellwin, **4** 757
    Young, John W., **14** 2548
  docking simulator
    Manned Spacecraft Center, **8** 1458
  Earth, **4** 663-66
  Economic implications of aerospace, **4** 672
  Environmental control system, **4** 719-21
    (with diagram and chart)
  Faget, Maxime, **5** 789
  Flight test programs, **5** 856
  Fuel cells, **5** 895
  Gas jet propulsion, **5** 918
  Gemini, **5** 927-50
  Gravity, **6** 1011
  Ground antennas, **6** 1017
  Hatches and doors (picture), **6** 1051
  Ignition systems, **7** 1146
  Inertial guidance, **7** 1155
  Insertion tracking, **7** 1162
  Instrument panels, **7** 1176-78
  Interplanetary travel, **7** 1209-11
  Kennedy Space Center, **7** 1265-67
  Langley Research Center, **7** 1302
  Launching, **7** 1308-09
  Launch vehicle, **7** 1314
  Life-support systems, **8** 1341-43, (pictures) 1342-43
  Lunar bases, **8** 1380-85, 1391, 1393, 1395, (diagrams) 1381, 1382, (tables) 1385, 1386, 1388, 1392, (drawing) 1389, (map) 1390
  Lunar Module (picture), **1** 162, **8** 1408-10, (diagram) 1408
    Launch vehicles, **7** 1325
    Lunar bases, **8** 1391
    Television, **12** 2262
  Lunar Orbiter, **8** 1410
  Manned spaceflight (table), **8** 1461 (diagram) 1462-63
  NASA, **9** 1650, 1653-54, (drawing) 1651, (table) 1652
  Navigation systems, **9** 1681
  Parachutes, **10** 1759
  pressure suit (picture), **1** 176
  Propellants (with picture), **10** 1859, 1861
  Quality control (with picture), **10** 1867
  Radar, **10** 1878
  Reaction control systems, **10** 1912
  Recovery, **11** 1927
  Rescue and Recovery Service, **11** 1960
  Service Module, **1** 173
    Electrical systems, **4** 683
  Space communications, **11** 2098
  Space propusion systems, **12** 2122
  Space stations, **12** 2125
  Spacesuits, **12** 2133, 2135
  Surveyor, **12,** 2209, 2215
  Survival kits, **12** 2222, (picture) 2221
  telescope mount
    Apollo Applications Program, **2** 186
    Marshall Space Flight Center, **8** 1494
  Television, **12** 2263
  Temperature control, **12** 2265
  Testing, **12** 2272, 2273, 2275
  tragedy, **1** 167-68
Apollo Applications Program, 2 185-88
  Apollo, **1** 162
  Astronauts, **2** 232
  Life-support systems, **8** 1344
  Lind, Don Leslie, **8** 1359
  Maneuvering in space, **8** 1430
  Marshall Space Flight Center, **8** 1494
  McCandless, Bruce, II, **8** 1516
  Michel, F. Curtis, **9** 1562
  Musgrave, Franklin Story, **9** 1643
  Rendezvous and docking, **11** 1956, 1958
  NASA (table, Major Launchings), **9** 1652
Apollo lunar surface experiment package
  Lunar exploration, **8** 1404
Apollo mission simulator

Link, Edwin A., 8 1361
Manned Spacecraft Center, 8 1458
  Spaceflight simulators, **12** 2112
  Spaceflight training, **12** 2116
Apollo-Saturn V
  Blockhouse, **2** 367-69
  Kennedy Space Center, **7** 1266-68
  Launching, **7** 1311
  Lunar Module (diagram), **8** 1408
  Major contractors
    NASA (data table), **9** 1655
Apolune
  Explorer satellites, **5** 773
Apparent magnitude
  Astronomy, **2** 249
  Magnitude, **8** 1420
Appleton region
  Atmosphere, **2** 264
Applications Technology Satellites, 2 189-90
  Astronautics, **2** 212
  Atlas missile and launch vehicle, **2** 260
  Centaur, **3** 435
  Communications satellites, **3** 537
  Goddard Space Flight Center, **6** 992
  Launch vehicle, **7** 1324
  Military space program, **9** 1595-96, (picture) 1590
  Television, **12** 2264
  Weather satellites, **13** 2468, 2469
Applied Physics Laboratory
  Aerobee, **1** 17
Appollonius (ap o LON ee us) **of Perga**
  Astronomy, **2** 235, 242
Approach Control
  Air traffic control, **1** 134
  Radio communications, **10** 1895
Approach lights
  Instrument landing system, **7** 1170
  Lighting facilities, **8** 1355-56, (pictures) 1355-56, (diagrams) 1356
  Airports (picture), **1** 95
Approach patterns
  Air traffic control (diagram), **1** 133
Approach procedures
  Instrument Flight Rules, **7** 1165
  Landing techniques, **7** 1300
Aprons
  Ramp, **10** 1903
  Runways, **11** 1998
Apt, Milburn G.
  X-series aerospace vehicles, **14** 2537
Aptitudes
  Educational implications of aerospace, **4** 677
APU exhaust
  Jumbo jets, **7** 1255
Aquarius
  Constellations, **3** 562
ARA Battalion, see Aerial Rocket Artillery Battalion
Arab countries
  Air forces of the world, **1** 64
Arab-Israeli war, 1967
  Counter-insurgency aircraft, **4** 577
  Israeli-Arab conflict—1967, **7** 1216-17
Aratus
  Planetarium, **10** 1818
Arban, Francois (fran SWA)
  Balloons, 317
ARCAS rocket
  International projects (picture), **7** 1198
  Sounding rockets (with picture), **11** 2083
Archdeacon, Ernest (1863-1957, French aviator), **2** 190
Archimedes (ark i MEED ees)
  Fluid mechanics, **5** 857
  Man-powered flight, **8** 1463
Arc-jet engines
  Electric propulsion, **4** 687, with diagram
Arctic
  Aurora, **2** 277
  Balchen, Bernt, **2** 312
  Bush flying, **3** 392
  Byrd, Richard Evelyn, **3** 397
  Polar flights, **10** 1828, 1834

Arctic Circle
  Air defense systems, **1** 60
Arctic ionospheric data
  Alouette satellites, **1** 144
Arcturus
  Sounding rockets (with picture), **11** 2083
Arc welding beams
  Plasma, **10** 1822
Area bombing
  World War II, **14** 2518
Area MTI
  Radar, **10** 1877
Area navigation
  Radio navigation, **10** 1899
Area rule, 2 190-91
  Delta Dagger, **4** 621
  Langley Research Center, **7** 1302
Areas, Law of
  Kepler's laws, **7** 1275
Arend-Roland
  Astronomy, **2** 242
Argentina
  Crop dusting, **4** 587
  International Agricultural Aviation Centre, **7** 1187
  Naval aviation, worldwide, **9** 1672
  South and Central America's aviation, **11** 2089
Argon
  Air, **1** 42
  Gases, **5** 916
  Lasers, **7** 1304
Argonauts
  Astronauts, **2** 229
Argo rockets
  Sounding rockets, **11** 2081
Argosy, see Hawker Siddeley Argosy
Argus, see CP-107 Argus
Argus (carrier)
  Aircraft carriers, **1** 48, (picture) 49
Argus Project, 2 191
  Explorer satellites, **5** 765
Ariel satellites, 2 191-93
  Earth science, **4** 667
  Environmental research satellites, **4** 723
  International projects, **7** 1198
  NASA (table, Major Launchings), **9** 1652
  United Kingdom aerospace activities, **13** 2354, (picture) 2354
Aries
  Constellations, **3** 562
Arigi, Julius
  World War I (table, Top Aces), **14** 2507
Aristarchus (a ris TARK us) **of Samos, 2** 193
  Astronomy, **2** 235, 242
  Copernicus, Nicolaus, **3** 566
  Moon, **9** 1633
  Universe, **13** 2391
Aristotle
  Astronomy, **2** 235
  Atoms, **2** 269
  Celestial mechanics, **3** 426
  Meteorology, **9** 1555
Arithmetic unit
  Computers, **3** 555
Arizona Balloon Buster
  World War I, **14** 2507
Ark Royal (aircraft carrier)
  Naval aviation, worldwide (United Kingdom), **9** 1669, (picture) 1668
ARM, see Antiradiation Missile
Arm
  Launching, **7** 1310
Armament, 2 193
  Pod, **10** 1828
  World War I, **14** 2503-04
Armed Forces
  Electronics, **4** 704
Armed Forces Reserve Act (1952)
  Air National Guard, **1** 81
Armed Forces Reserve Medal
  Medals and decorations (picture), **8** 1525
Armed Forces Unification Act (1947)
  Air National Guard, **1** 81

Armed strike helicopters
Air forces of the world, **1** 64
Armee de l'Air (ar MAY de lair), (France)
Air forces of the world, **1** 65-66
Armstrong, Neil A. (1930-   ), **2** 193
Astronauts, **2** 216-17, 219, 229-30 (with
picture)
Gemini, **5** 942-43
Manned spaceflight (table), **8** 1461
Recovery, **11** 1928
Rendezvous and docking, **11** 1957-58
X-15 research program, **14** 2533
Army Air Corps
Aerospace industry, **1** 29
Arnold, Henry Harley, **2** 201
Attack aircraft, **2** 271
Army Air Forces
United States Air Force, **13** 2363
Army Air Service
Aerospace industry, **1** 30
Airports, **1** 97
Army Aviation, 2 194-200
Army Ballistic Missile Agency
Explorer satellites, **5** 762
Jupiter rockets, **7** 1261
Army Chief of Staff
Joint Chiefs of Staff, **7** 1242
Army Industrial College
Arnold, Henry Harley, **2** 201
Army Missile Command
Battlefield missile systems, **2** 342
Army of Occupation Medal
Medals and decorations (picture), **8** 1525
Army Ordnance
Bumper Project, **3** 390
Army Reorganization Act, 1920
Airports, **1** 97
Army Signal Corps Aviation Service
Airmail, **1** 70
Army Weapons Command
Battlefield missile systems, **2** 341
Arnold, Henry Harley (1886-1950, American
general), **2** 201
Air University, **1** 140
Barnstormers (picture), **2** 333
Cochran, Jacqueline, **3** 481
Crop dusting, **4** 586
National Air and Space Museum, **9** 1659
Program management, **10** 1857
United States Air Force, **13** 2359, 2363
World War II, **14** 2523
Arnold, Kenneth
Unidentified flying objects, **13** 2321
Arnstein, Karl
Airships, **1** 112
ARPA, see Advanced Research Project Agency
Arrachart (AR uh shar), **Ludovic**
Distance records (table), **4** 640
Arrachart, Paul
Distance records (table), **4** 640
Arresting gear, 2 201-02
Aircraft carriers, **1** 47-48
Arrhenius, S.
Mars, **8** 1491
Arromanches (aircraft carrier)
Naval aviation, worldwide (France), **9** 1669
Arrow, 2 202
Arrow, see CF-105 Arrow
ARS, see American Rocket Society
ARSP, see Aerospace Research Support
Program
ARTCC, see Air Route Traffic Control Center
Artificial earth satellite
Radio astronomy, **10** 1890
Artificial gravity, 2 202
Launch vehicles, **7** 1318
Artificial horizon
Instrument panels, **7** 1176
Manufacturing, **8** 1469
Artificial precipitation
Icing, **7** 1145
Artificial pressure
Pressurization, **10** 1851
Artificial radiation belt
Environmental research satellites, **4** 722

AS.20
Missiles (table), **9** 1616
Asbestos, 2 202
ASCS, see Attitude Stabilization and Control
System
A-scope
Radar, **10** 1875
Ash
Air-to-air missiles, **1** 121
Asia
Boron, **3** 382
Asia's aviation (with pictures), **2** 203-05
Crop dusting, **4** 587
Asimov, Isaac
Robots, **11** 1965
Science fiction, **11** 2020
ASIS, see Abort Sensing and Implementation
System
Aspirin
Drug effects, **4** 653
ASR, see Airport Surveillance Radar
ASROC, see Antisubmarine rocket
Assault, 2 206
Assault helicopter company
Army aviation, **2** 199
Assault vehicle
Battlefield missile systems, **2** 342
Assembly-in-orbit
Military space program, **9** 1604
Assembly line production
Bell, Lawrence Dale, **2** 348
Asset Program, 2 206-7
Military space program, **9** 1599-1600
START, **12** 2163
Vehicle research spacecraft, **13** 2406
Association of Commuter Airlines
Commuter airlines, **3** 499-544
Association of Third Level Airlines
Commercial airlines, **3** 499
Asteroids, 2 207-9
Astronomy, **2** 244
Interplanetary travel, **7** 1212
Meteors, meteorites, and meteroids,
9 1560-61
Astor Mark 45
Antisubmarine missiles, **1** 160
Astrobee 200
Aerospace Research Support Program, **1** 35
Astrobiology, 2 210
Mars, **8** 1490
Astrocompass
Compasses, **3** 551
Astrodynamics, 2 210
Herrick, Samuel, **6** 1083
Astrogation, 2 210
Astrogeology, 2 210-12
Astrolabe
Telescopes and astronomical instruments,
12 2258, (picture) 2256
Astrology
Astronomy, **2** 234
Constellations, **3** 562
Astronaut draft
Astronauts, **2** 217
Astronautics, 2 212
Aerospace, **1** 26
Doppler effect, **4** 645
Mars, **8** 1490
Orbits and trajectories, **10** 1742
Terminology of aerospace (table), **12** 2272
Astronautics and Aeronautics (magazine)
American Institute of Aeronautics and
Astronautics, **1** 150
Astronaut maneuvering unit, 2 213
Apollo Applications Program, **2** 187
Maneuvering in space, **8** 1430,
(picture)
Spacesuits, **12** 2132
Astronauts (with pictures and table), **2** 214-32
Bends, **2** 349
Decontamination, radiological, **4** 615
Food and nutrition, **5** 873-79
Human fatigue, **6** 1135
Kennedy Space Center, **7** 1266

Launching, **7** 1308, 1312
Launch vehicles, **7** 1318
Life-support systems, **8** 1339-1340
Pilot and crew wings, **10** 1795
Recovery, **11** 1927
Spacecraft design, **11** 2103
Spaceflight safety, **12** 2111
Spaceflight training, **12** 2114-18
Temperature control, **12** 2265
Testing, **12** 2276
noise levels
Acoustics, **1** 5
Astronauts, rescue of
International aviation and space
agreements, **7** 1190
Astronaut wings, 2 232
Astronauts, **2** 216
Astronavigation
Astrogation, **2** 210
Astronomia Nova (book)
Kepler's laws, **7** 1275
Astronomical boundary
Nebula, **9** 1688-89 (with pictures)
Poles, **10** 1834
Astronomical telescope
Coronagraph, **3** 567
Astronomical unit, 2 232
Comets, **3** 493
Earth, **4** 661
Astronomy, 2 233-254
Apollo Applications Program, **2** 185
Azimuth, **2** 308
Cosmogony, **3** 568
Cosmology, **3** 568
Doppler effect, **4** 645
Herschel family, **6** 1083
Important Events Table, **2** 242
Luminosity, **8** 1377
Orbiting observatories, **10** 1738
Planetarium, **10** 1818, 1820
Quantum theory, **10** 1870
Radiation, **10** 1882
Astrophysics, 2 255-258
Apollo Applications Program, **2** 185
ASV, see Aerothermodynamic structural
vehicles
AT-5A, see Curtiss AT-5A
AT-6 Texan (North American)
Counter-insurgency aircraft, **4** 577
Military aircraft, **9** 1567
Skywriting (picture), **11** 2057
T-6, North American, **13** 2314
Trainer aircraft, **13** 2306
AT-11 (Beech)
Military aircraft, **9** 1567
AT-17 (Cessna)
Military aircraft, **9** 1567
ATA, see Air Transport Association
Atanassova, Maria
Women in aerospace, **14** 2495
Atar-9 engines
Australia's aviation, **2** 280
ATC, see Air traffic control
ATC, see Air Transport Command
Atchley, Barbara
Cernan, Eugene Andrew, **3** 440
ATCO, see Air Taxi and Commercial Operator's
Certificate
ATDA, see Augmented target docking adapter
Atgier, Charles
Medals and decorations (table), **8** 1526
Athodyd engines
Pulsejet engine, **10** 1865
Ramjet engines, **10** 1900
Atlantic Missile Range
Jupiter rockets, **7** 1261
Kennedy Space Center, **7** 1266
Atlantic Ocean
Air defense systems, **1** 60
Cape Canaveral, **3** 405
NATO, **9** 1704
Atlantic Oceanographic Laboratories
Environmental Science Services
Administration, **4** 725

Atlantic Research Series
Sounding rockets, **11** 2084
Atlantic sweepstakes
Alcock and Brown, **1** 142
Atlantic test range
Ballistics, **2** 314
Atlas-Able
Pioneer, **10** 1813
Atlas-Agena
Applications Technology Satellites, **2** 189
Atlas missile and launch vehicle, **2** 260
Launch vehicles (tables), **7** 1319-20, 1328
Lunar Orbiter, **8** 1411
Mariner probes, **8** 1485
NASA, **9** 1653, (table) 1653
Orbiting observatories, **10** 1741
Atlas Centaur
Applications Technology Satellites, **2** 189
Atlas missile and launch vehicle, **2** 260
Centaur (with picture and diagram), **3** 433
Launch vehicles (tables), **7** 1319-20
Surveyor, **12** 2209, 2213
Atlas-Mercury
Atlas missile and launch vehicle (diagram), **2** 260
Atlas missile and launch vehicle, 2 259-60
(with picture)
Aerospace Research Support Program, **1** 35
Agena rockets, **1** 38-39
Dunn, Louis G., **4** 655
Edwards Air Force Base, **4** 679
Ehricke, Krafft Arnold, **4** 680
Environmental research satellites, **4** 723
Escape systems, **4** 736
Intercontinental ballistic missiles, **7** 1182-83
Launch vehicles, **7** 1319-24
Mercury program, **9** 1533-35, 1537
Metals and metallurgy, **9** 1550
Military space program, **9** 1601-02
Missiles, **9** 1612, (data table) 1616
Photography (picture), **10** 1788
Reconnaissance satellites, **11** 1926
United States Air Force, **13** 2369, (picture) 2367
Atmosphere, 2 261-67
Atmospheric pressure, **2** 268
Carbon dioxide, **3** 407
Earth science, **4** 666
Extraterrestrial life, **5** 776-77
Helium, **6** 1079
International Geophysical Year, **7** 1196
Interplanetary travel, **7** 1212
Mars, **8** 1491-92
Matter, **8** 1513
Meteorology **9**, 1555-59
Piccard family, **10** 1790
Precipitation, **10** 1844
Radiosonde units, **10** 1899
Re-entry, **11** 1930
Rocket propulsion systems, **11** 1967
Stratosphere, **12** 2170
Troposphere, **13** 2313
Venus, **13** 2407-08
Weather maps and charts, **13** 2445
Weather satellites, **13** 2459
Wind, **13** 2485
Atmosphere Explorer (satellite)
Explorer satellites, **5** 768
Atmospheric composition
Kites, **7** 1279
Atmospheric dust
Atmosphere, **2** 263
Atmospheric gases
Jupiter, **7** 1260
**Atmospheric Physics and Chemistry
· Laboratory**
Environmental Science Services
Administration, **4** 725
Atmospheric pressure, 2 268
Atmosphere, **2** 267
Aviation weather, **2** 299
Bends, **2** 349
Pioneer, **10** 1813
Pressure suits, **10** 1851

Pulsejet engine, **10** 1865
Supercharger, **12** 2175
Weather, **13** 2449
Wind, **13** 2485
Atmospheric radiation
Atmosphere, **2** 265
Atmospheric research
Aerobee, **1** 17
Atmospheric resistance
Launch vehicles, **7** 1316
Atmospherics, 2 268
Atmospheric zones
Atmosphere, **2** 264
Atoll
Missiles (table), **9** 1616
Atomic bomb, 2 269
Bombs, **3** 378
Fermi, Enrico, **5** 806
History of aviation, **6** 1114
Kiwi, **7** 1281
Manhattan Project, **8** 1442
United States Air Force, **13** 2364, (picture) 2364
World War II, **14** 2523
Atomic carbon
Carbon, **3** 406
Atomic energy
Energy, **4** 712
Atomic Energy Commission, see also United
States Atomic Energy Commission
National Aeronautics and Space Council, **9** 1657
NERVA, **9** 1691
Nuclear energy, **9** 1711
Program management, **10** 1857
Radiation, **10** 1883
Service academies, **11** 2045
Atomic ions
Radiation, **10** 1882
Atomic mass
Atoms, **2** 271
Atomic number
Atoms, **2** 271
Atomic oxygen
Aurora, **2** 277
Atomic radiation
Paints, **10** 1754
Atomic-sized particles
Quantum theory, **10** 1868
Atomic structure
Atoms, **2** 269
Atomic weight
Atoms, **2** 271
Atoms, 2 269-71
Fission, **5** 826
Ion, **7** 1215
Kiwi, **7** 1281
Lasers, **7** 1303
Matter, **8** 1513
Nuclear energy, **9** 1709-11
Nuclear physics, **9** 1715-16
Quantum theory, **10** 1868
Radioisotope, **10** 1899
ATR pilots
Aviation medicine, **2** 296
ATS satellites
Applications Technology Satellites, **2** 190, (picture) 189
Communications satellites, **3** 537
NASA (table, Major Launchings), **9** 1652
Attack aircraft, 2 271-75
helicopter, **2** 275
Military aircraft, **9** 1569 (with pictures)
United States Air Force, **13** 2372
Attack capability
Reconnaissance aircraft, **11** 1922
Attack missiles
Air-to-surface missiles, **1** 122-24
Attack support systems
Air-to-surface missiles, **1** 122-24
Attainment of Celestial Bodies, The (book)
Hohmann orbits, **6** 1122
Attitude and attitude control, 2 275-76
Aerobee, **1** 18
Inertial guidance, **7** 1155

Instrument panels, **7** 1173, 1176-77
Kennedy Space Center, **7** 1267
Reaction control systems, **10** 1912
Terminology of aerospace (table), **12** 2272
Attitude control booms
Orbiting observatories, **10** 1741
Attitude indicator, 2 276-77
Attitude instrument flying
Instrument flight techniques, **7** 1166
Attitude-Vertical Velocity Indicator
Vertical-scale display instruments, **13** 2411, (picture) 2411
Audio-frequency waves
Radiation, **10** 1880
Augmented Lunar Module
Lunar exploration, **8** 1407
Augmented target docking adapter
Gemini, **5** 944-95, (picture) 944
Auriol, Jacqueline
Medals and decorations (table), **8** 1526
Women in aerospace, **14** 2495
Aurora, 2 277
Argus project, **2** 191
Ionosphere, **7** 1215
International Geophysical Year, **7** 1197
Solar winds, **11** 2071
Sun, **12** 2172
Aurora australis
Atmosphere, **2** 265
Aurora, **2** 277
Poles, **10** 1834
Aurora borealis
Aurora, **2** 265, (picture) 277
Plasma, **10** 1822
Poles, **10** 1834
U.S. Atomic Energy Commission, **13** 2375
Aurora 7 (spacecraft)
Carpenter, Malcolm Scott, **3** 422
Manned spaceflight, (table) **8** 1461
Mercury program, **9** 1540-42, (picture) 1541, (table) 1544
NASA (table, Major Launchings), **9** 1652
Recovery, **11** 1928
Austenitic steels
Steels, **12** 2165
Austin, Fred
Polar flights, **10** 1831
Australian aborigines
Boomerang, **3** 380-81
Australia's aviation, 2 278-84
Air forces of the world, **1** 64
Australian air force, **2** 280
Commercial airlines, **3** 509
Commemorative stamps and medals, **3** 495
Communications satellites, **3** 538
Crop dusting, **4** 587, 593
European Launcher Development
Organization, **4** 754
Flying doctor services, **5** 861
International projects, **7** 1199
P-40, Curtiss, **10** 1776
Woomera rocket range, **14** 2496
WRESAT, **14** 2524
Austria
Crop dusting, **4** 587
European aerospace activities, **4** 743
Austrian Airlines
European aerospace activities, **4** 743
Austrian Air Rescue Guard
European aerospace activities, **4** 743
Austrian Air Transport
European aerospace activities, **4** 743
Autoclave
Lunar Receiving Laboratory, **8** 1415
Autocoupled autopilots
Automatic landing, **2** 287
Autoflare
Electronics, **4** 703
Autogiros, 2 285-86
Aircraft, **1** 45
Cierva, Juan de la, **3** 460
Earhart, Amelia, **4** 658
History of aviation, **6** 1109, (picture) 1110
Rotary-wing aircraft (with picture), **11** 1991

Autograph
Photogrammetry, **10** 1779
Autokinetic illusion
Illusions, **7** 1147
Automated Merchant Vessel Reporting
Coast Guard aviation, **3** 479
Automated power loading system
Jumbo jets, **7** 1252
Automated spacecraft
Legal implications of aerospace, **7** 1331
Automatic attitude control
Maneuvering in space, **8** 1430
Automatic Checkout Equipment
Blockhouse, **2** 368
Automatic controls
Power management, **10** 1840
Automatic direction finder, 2 286-87
Airborne antennas, **1** 43-44
Radio navigation, **10** 1899
Automatic exposure systems
Photography, **10** 1788
Automatic fire control system
Air-to-air missiles, **1** 119
Automatic flight control system
Radio altimeter, **10** 1888
Automatic guidance equipment
Beam-rider guidance, **2** 346
Automatic landing, 2 287-88
Automatic leveling devices
Kennedy Space Center, **7** 1272
Automatic measuring device
Kosmos satellites, **7** 1292
Automatic Picture Transmission
Meteorology (picture), **9**
Weather satellites, **13** 2462, 2464, 2465,
2470, (pictures) 2462, 2463, 2464, 2466
Automatic pilot (with diagrams), 2 288-89
Air-to-surface missiles, **1** 124
Automatic landing, **2** 287
Guidance and control systems, **6** 1035
Invader, Douglas A-26, B-26, **7** 1214
Jumbo jets, **7** 1252
Manufacturing, **8** 1469
Oceanographic research, **10** 1734
Onboard computers, **10** 1737
Phantom II, McDonnell-Douglas F-4A,
10 1777
Robot, **11** 1965
Spacecraft design, **11** 2102
Automatic terminal information
Instrument flight techniques, **7** 1167
Automation
Cybernetics, **4** 602
National Airspace System, **9** 1661-62
Automobile
History of aviation, **6** 1097
Autopilot, see Automatic pilot
Auto-rotation, 2 290
Autumnal equinox
Equinox, **4** 729
Auxiliary, 2 290
Auxiliary illumination
Photography, **10** 1789
Auxiliary power unit
Jumbo jets, **7** 1255
Radiation shield, **10** 1884
Auxiliary rockets
Launch vehicles, **7** 1316-17
Avco Corporation
NASA (table, Apollo/Saturn V Major
Contractors), **9** 1655
Avenger, see Grumman TBF Avenger
AVIANCA, see Aerovias Nacionales de
Colombia
Aviation, 2 290-92
electronics, Avionics, **2** 307
Patents, **10** 1766
research
Bellanca, Giuseppe, **2** 348
safety

Bean, Alan LaVern, **2** 346
Byrd, Richard Evelyn, **3** 397
Aviation Corporation
Commercial airlines, **3** 510
Aviation Electronics Centre
Italy's aerospace activities (picture),
7 1224
Aviation gasoline
Airports, **1** 100
Aviation insurance, see Insurance, aviation
Aviation Medical Examiners
Aviation medicine, **2** 294
Aviation medical research
Aeronautical Center, **1** 25-26
Aviation Medical Research Board
Aviation medicine, **2** 294
Aviation medicine, 2 292-96
Aerospace medicine, **1** 33
Life-support systems, **8** 1338
Man in flight, **8** 1450
Medical examiner, **8** 1526
Aviation Medicine (book)
Aviation medicine, **2** 294
Aviation of the Air Defense of the Country
(Russia)
Air forces of the world, **1** 65
Aviation radios
Radio communications, **10** 1898
Aviation Research
RAND Corporation, **10** 1903
Aviation Safety, Bureau of
Crash investigation, **4** 579
Aviation weather, 2 298-306
Aviatsiya Dalnovo Deistviya (Russia)
Air forces of the world, **1** 65
World War II, **14** 2515-16
Aviolinee Siciliane
Italy's aerospace activities, **7** 1221
Avionics, 2 307-8
Battery, **2** 338
Ceramics, **3** 440
Jumbo jets, **7** 1256
Phantom II, **10** 1777
Avions Marcel Dassault (Co.)
Mirage IV, **9** 1609
Avro 504-K trainer
Roe, Alliott Verdon, **11** 1989
Avro (aircraft)
World War I, **14** 2501-02
Avro Aircraft of Toronto
Canada's aviation, **3** 403-4
Avro Arrow, see CF-105 Arrow
Avro Blue Steel
Air-to-surface missiles, **1** 123
Avro CF-100, see CF-100
Avro Lancaster, see Lancaster bomber
Awl
Air-to-air missiles, **1** 121
Axel-weight-limit laws
Outsize cargo aircraft, **10** 1748
Axes of rotation (with diagram), 2 308
Aerodynamics, **1** 23
Centrifugal and centripetal forces, **3** 436
Axial flow, 2 308
Aircraft propulsion systems, **1** 58
Gas turbine engines, **5** 919
Axis
Parabola, **10** 1755
Azimuth, 2 308
Plan position indicator (with illustration),
10 1821
Radar, **10** 1874, 1876
Azimuth angles
Kennedy Space Center, **7** 1267
Azimuth errors
Launching, **7** 1309
Azon
Air-to-surface missiles, **1** 123
Azores
Commercial airlines, **3** 509
Aztec C, see Piper Aztec

B

B-1 Flying Boat, see Boeing B-1
B.(1)MK.8, see Canberra, B.Mk.
B-10 (Martin)
Bomber aircraft, **2** 374
B-15 (Boeing)
Bomber aircraft, **2** 374
Military aviation, **9** 1582
B-17 Flying Fortress (Boeing)
Boeing 707, **2** 370
Bomber aircraft, **2** 373, 374, (picture) 375
Commercial air transports, **3** 523
Flying Fortress (table, pictures), **5** 863
History of aviation (picture), **6** 1113
Second World War aircraft (with picture),
11 2036
World War II, **14** 2518
B-19 (Douglas)
Military aviation, **9** 1582
B-24 Liberator (Consolidated)
Bomber aircraft, **2** 373, 374
History of aviation, **6** 1112
Liberator, **7** 1335-36
World War II (picture), **14** 2519
B-25 Mitchell (North American)
Attack aircraft, **2** 273
Bomber aircraft, **2** 373
Mitchell, North American B-25 (picture),
9 1621
Second war world aircraft, **11** 2036
B-26 Invader (Douglas)
Asia's aviation, **2** 204
Attack aircraft, **2** 273
Bomber aircraft (picture), **2** 375
Counter-insurgency aircraft, **4** 577
Invader, Douglas A-26, B-26 (table,
pictures), **7** 1214
Korean war, **7** 1286
B-26 Martin Marauder (Martin)
Second World War aircraft (with picture),
11 2036
World War II (picture), **14** 2518
B-29 Superfortress (Boeing)
Boeing 707, **2** 370
Bomber aircraft **2** 373, 374, (picture) 375
History of aviation (picture), **6** 1113
Second World War aircraft (picture),
11 2026, 2037
World War II, **14** 2523
B-36 (Convair)
Bomber aircraft, **2** 375
Military aviation, **9** 1586
X-series aerospace vehicles, **14** 2540
B-47 Stratojet (Boeing)
Bicycle gear, **2** 354
Bomber aircraft, **2** 373, 375
Flight simulators, **5** 854
Military aviation, **9** 1587
Reconnaissance aircraft, **11** 1922
B-50 (Boeing)
Bomber aircraft **2** 374
Refueling, **11** 1938
B-52 Stratofortress (Boeing)
Air forces of the world, **1** 54
Air raid (picture), **1** 104
Air-to-surface missiles, **1** 124
Bicycle gear, **2** 354
Bomber aircraft, **2** 373, (picture) 375
Cross-wind landing, **4** 595
History of aviation, **6** 1117
Military aviation, **9** 1583, 1587
X-15 research program (picture), **14** 2529
B-57 Canberra (Martin)
Asia's aviation, **2** 204
Bomber aircraft (table, picture), **3** 373
Martin B-57 (table, picture), **8** 1495

B-58 Hustler (Boeing)
Air forces of the world, **1** 65
Bomber aircraft, **2** 373, 375 (picture) 376
Flight simulators, **5** 854
History of aviation, **6** 1120
Hustler B-58 (chart, picture), **6** 1137-38
Inertial guidance, **7** 1152
B-70, see XB-70
Baade, Walter (1893-1960, German-American astronomer), **2** 309
Baby Ace (airplane)
Homebuilt aircraft, **6** 1125, (picture) 1125
Babbage, Charles
Computers, **3** 554, 557
Babylonians
Astronomy, **2** 242
BAC One-eleven
Africa's aviation, **1** 36
Commercial air transports, **3** 527, (picture) 529
BAC-Sud Aviation Concorde, see Concorde SST
Bach, James
Lafayette Escadrille, **7** 1295
Bachem Ba 394A
Rockets and rocketry, **11** 1981
Bacillus thuringiesis
Crop dusting, **4** 593
Backbone
Bird flight, **2** 360
Back course
Instrument landing system, **7** 1170
Background radio noise
Radio astronomy, **10** 1889
Backing plate
Brakes, **3** 385
Backout, 2 309
Backscatter over-the-horizon-radars
Ballistic Missile Early Warning System, **2** 314
Back-suction mixture control
Mixture control, **9** 1623
Backup, 2 310
Astronauts, **2** 226
Spaceflight safety, **12** 2111
Terminology of aerospace (table), **12** 2272
Backup confirmation
Instrument flight techniques, **7** 1166
Back-Up Interceptor Control
NORAD, **9** 1703
Semi-Automatic Ground Environment, **11** 2040
Backward thrust
Reaction engines, **10** 1912
Bacon, Francis T.
Fuel cells, **5** 896
Bacon, Roger
Man-powered flight, **8** 1463
Bacqueville, Marquis
Man-powered flight, **8** 1464
Bacteria
Air, **1** 42
Mars, **8** 1492
Bader, Douglas Robert Stuart (1910-British aviator), **2** 310
Badger bomber, see Tu-16 Badger
Baekeland, Leo H.
Plastics, **10** 1823
Baggage
Air terminals, **1** 118
Commercial airlines, **3** 503
Flight, **5** 831-38
Bailey, Lady Mary
Women in aerospace, **14** 2494
Bailout, 2 310-11
Partial pressure suit, **10** 1763
Personal equipment, **10** 1775
Nuclear energy, **9** 1713
Baka bomb
Air-to-surface missiles, **1** 123
Kamikaze, **7** 1263
Baker (monkey)
Animals in space, **1** 154
Baker, Newton D.
Airmail, **1** 70

Baker-Nunn camera
Telescopes and astronomical instruments, **12** 2253
Tracking systems and networks, **13** 2300, (picture) 2299
Woomera rocket range, **14** 2497
Balair
European aerospace activities, **4** 750
Balbo, Italo (1896-1940, Italian aviator), **2** 311-12
Flying boats, **5** 858
Medals and decorations (table), **8** 1526
Balchen, Bernt (1899- , Norwegian-American aviator), **2** 312
Byrd, Richard Evelyn, **3** 397
Coast Guard aviation, **3** 479
Polar flights, **10** 1830
Baldwin, Frederick W. ("Casey")
Aerial Experiment Association (with picture), **1** 7-8
Baldwin Airship
Dirigibles (picture), **4** 630
Ballast, 2 313
Balloons, **2** 318
Ballistic missile, 2 313
Advanced Research Project Agency, **1** 7
Air defense systems, **1** 60
Battlefield missile systems, **2** 340
Bombs, **3** 377
Ballistic Missile Early Warning System, **2** 313-14
Air defense systems, **1** 60
station locations (map), **2** 313
NORAD, **9** 1702
Radar, **10** 1877
Ballistic missiles
Missiles, **9** 1611
Surface-to-surface missiles, **12** 2204
Ballistics, 2 314
Woomera rocket range, **14** 2496
Ballistic trajectory, 2 314
Antiballistic missile defense, **1** 158
Orbits and trajectories, **10** 1746
Polaris missiles, **10** 1832
Ballonets
Airships, **1** 106
Blimps, **2** 364
Dirigibles, **4** 629
Balloonist
Astronauts, **2** 229
Blanchard, Jean Pierre Francois, **2** 363
Balloons, 2 315-31
Aerial photography, **1** 9
Aerostat, **1** 35
Aerostatics, **1** 35
Aircraft (with picture), **1** 45
Airmail, **1** 69
Air transports, **1** 139
Blanchard, Jean Pierre Francois, **2** 363
Charles, Jacques Alexandre Cesar, **3** 447
chronological table of events, **2** 321
Commemorative stamps and medals, **3** 493
diagram, **2** 319
Fabrics, **5** 786
First World War aircraft, **5** 817
GHOST program, **6** 979
Giffard, Henri, **6** 980
Gondolas, **6** 994
Gusmao, Bartholemeu de, **2** 321, **6** 1043
History of aviation, **6** 1094, (pictures) 1094-95
Hot-air balloons, **6** 1130
Hydrogen
Pilatre de Rozier, Jean Francois, **10** 1792
International competitions, **7** 1191
Lowe, Thaddeus S. C., **8** 1373
Mechanical energy, **8** 1522, (diagram) 1522
Meteorology, **9** 1557, (pictures) 1556
Montgolfier brothers, **9** 1632
Photogrammetry, **10** 1779
Piccard family, **10** 1791
Pilatre de Rozier, Jean Francois, **10** 1792
Polar flights, **10** 1828, 1830
Radiation, **10** 1882
Radiosonde units, **10** 1899

Ross, Malcolm D., **11** 1990
Santos-Dumont, Alberto, **11** 2005
Sopwith, Thomas, **11** 2075
Wise, John, **14** 2493
Balloon-type parachutes
Parachutes, **10** 1757
Ballute
Escape systems, **4** 737
Fabrics, **5** 786-87
Baltic Fleet (Russia)
Air forces of the world, **1** 65
Balzar, S. M.
Aircraft propulsion systems, **1** 54
Bambi
Military space program, **9** 1604
Bamboo dragonfly
Mainland China's aerospace activities, **8** 1421
Banana River
Cape Canaveral, **3** 405
Band, radio, 2 332
Bank, 2 332
Ailerons, **1** 41
Instrument flight techniques, **7** 1166
Instrument panels, **7** 1173
Maneuvers, **8** 1433
Bantam
Missiles (table), **9** 1616
Barbiturates
Drug effects, **4** 653
Baracca, Francesco
World War I, **14** 2508, (table) 2507
Bardeen, John
Electronics, **4** 693
Barkhorn, Gerhard
World War II (table), **14** 2517
Barnaby, Ralph S.
Medals and decorations (table), **8** 1526
Barnett, William
Aircraft propulsion systems, **1** 53
Barnstormers, 2 332-36
Aerospace industry, **1** 30
Canada's aviation, **3** 400
Barometer, 2 336-37
Barometric pressure, **2** 337
Meteorology, **9** 1556
Sensors, **11** 2042
Barometric altimeter
Instrument panels, **7** 1173
Radio altimeter, **10** 1888
Barometric pressure, 2 337
Air traffic control, **1** 134
Barometer, **2** 337
Isobar, **7** 1216
Lana, Francesco de, **7** 1297
Mars, **8** 1491-92
Baron, see T-42 Baron
Barracchini, Flavio
World War I (table, Top Aces), **14** 2507
Barrage balloon
Balloons (picture), **2** 324
Barred pattern
Radar, **10** 1879
Barrel roll
Maneuvers, **8** 1440, (diagram) 1441
Barrett, Joan C.
Roosa, Stuart Allen, **11** 1990
Bartol Research Foundation
Balloons, **2** 327
Basaltic rock
Astronomy, **2** 242, 244
Base axis
Instrument panels, **7** 1177
Base leg
Airports, **1** 97
Base operations modules
Lunar bases, **8** 1389
Base precursor phase
Lunar bases, **8** 1389, 1391, 1395
Basic Flight Manual
Airman's Information Manual, **1** 80
Basic life processes
Biosatellites, **2** 357
Basic piloting techniques
Pilot's training, **10** 1811

Bassett, Charles A., II (1931-1966), **2** 337
  Astronauts, **2** 216, 218-19 (with picture)
  Cernan, Eugene Andrew, **3** 440
Basutair, Ltd.
  Africa's aviation, **1** 36
Bates, Allan (with picture)
  Astronauts, **2** 215
Bathymeters
  Oceanographic research, **10** 1731
Bathyscaph
  Balloons, **2** 321, 325
  Piccard family, **10** 1790-91
Batten, Jean
  Medals and decorations (table), **8** 1526
Battens
  Airships, **1** 106
Battery, 2 338-39
  Electrical systems, **4** 683
  Electricity, **4** 685
  Wet cell battery, **13** 2480
Battlefield missile systems, 2 339-43
Battle of Britain, 2 343-44
  Bader, Douglas Robert Stuart, **2** 310
  Luftwaffe, **8** 1375-76
  Military aviation, **9** 1584
  World War II, **14** 2514-15
Battle of Leyte Gulf
  Aircraft carriers, **1** 50
  World War II, **14** 2523
Battle of Midway
  Aircraft carriers, **1** 49
  Military aviation, **9** 1584
  World War II, **14** 2522
Battle zone, localized
  Reconnaissance aircraft, **11** 1920
Batwing glider
  Lilienthal, Otto, **8** 1358
Bauer, Louis H.
  Aerospace Medical Association, **1** 33
  Aviation medicine, **2** 294
  Civil Aviation Medical Association, **3** 466
Bauersfeld, Walther
  Planetarium, **10** 1818
B&W Trainer
  Boeing, William Edward, **2** 369
Bavarian Aero-Club
  Commemorative stamps and medals, **3** 495
Bayerische Flugzeugwerke
  Messerschmitt, Willy, **9** 1546
Bayerische Motoren Werke (BMW)
  Aircraft propulsion systems, **1** 55
Bayless, Lowell
  Air racing, **1** 103
Bazooka
  Goddard, Robert Hutchings, **6** 991
Bazooka-launched antitank system
  Battlefield missile systems, **2** 340
B.E. 2 (airplane)
  First World War aircraft, **5** 820
Beachey, Lincoln (1887-1915, American
    aviator), **2** 344-45
  Altitude and altitude records, **1** 146-47
  Barnstormers (picture), **2** 333
Beacon Explorer (satellite)
  Explorer satellites, **5** 770
  Geodetic satellites, **6** 974, (table) 973
  NASA (table, Major Launchings), **9** 1652
Beacon Project
  General aviation, **6** 958
Beacon, radio, 2 345
Beacons
  Airmail, **1** 74
  Airports, **1** 96
  Lighting facilities, **8** 1354
Beagle bomber, see Il-28 Beagle
Beagle Pup 100
  General aviation aircraft (picture), **6** 964
  United Kingdom aerospace activities,
    13 2349, 2352, (picture) 2349
  Manufacturing, **8** 1469
Beam power tubes
  Electronics, **4** 697
Beam, radio, 2 345
Beam-rider guidance, 2 346
  Missiles, **9** 1613

Bean, Alan La Vern (1932-), **2** 346
  Astronauts, **2** 217-19, (picture) 320
Bear bomber, see TU-20 Bear
Bearing, 2 346
  Plotter, **10** 1827
Bearing selector
  Navigation techniques, **9** 1683-85
Beau fighter, see Bristol Beau fighter
Beaufort scale (with table), **2** 346
Beaver, see DHC-2 Mark I
Beaver Mark IV submarine
  Oceanographic research (picture), **10** 1733
Becquerel, A. H.
  Radiation, **10** 1881
Beech Aircraft Company
  Beech, Walter H., **2** 347
  Women in aerospace, **14** 2496
Beech AT-11, see AT-11
Beech Bonanza (table, diagram, picture),
  3 379
  Empennage, **4** 710
  General aviation (picture), **6** 953
Beechcraft
  Air forces of the world (Sudan), **1** 64
  Commuter airlines, **3** 545
  General aviation aircraft, **6** 961, 964-66
Beech B-18
  Air taxis, **1** 117
Beech Musketeer 19
  Trainer aircraft, **13** 2307
Beech, Olive
  Beech, Walter H., **2** 347
  Medals and decorations (table), **8** 1526
  Women in aerospace, **14** 2496
Beech Queen Air
  Business aviation, **3** 396
Beech Seminole
  Army aviation, **2** 197
Beech 17 Staggerwing
  Australia's aviation, **2** 283
  Staggerwing Beech 17, **12** 2157
Beech T-42, see T-42 Baron
Beech U-21, see U-21
Beech, Walter H. (1891-1950, American
    airplane manufacturer), **2** 347
  Cessna, Clyde V., **3** 445
Belfast
  Military air transports, **9** 1575
Belgian Congo
  Airlift, **1** 67
  Commemorative stamps and medals, **3** 493
  Crop dusting, **4** 587
  European aerospace activities, **4** 743-44
  European air traffic control, **4** 752
  European Launcher Development
    Organization, **4** 754
  European Space Research Organization,
    4 755
  International Agricultural Aviation
    Centre, **7** 1187
  Italy's aerospace activities, **7** 1222
  Launch vehicles, **7** 1327
  NATO, **9** 1703-04
  World War II, **14** 2512
Belka (dog)
  Animals in space, **1** 155
Bell 47-G helicopter, see OH-13 Sioux
Bell Aerosystems Company
  Dornberger, Walter Robert, **4** 646
  Ground-effect machines (picture), **6** 1023
  Ornithopter, **10** 1748
  X-series aerospace vehicles, **14** 2534-36
Bell Aircraft Corporation
  Aircraft propulsion systems, **1** 58
  Bell, Lawrence Dale, **2** 348
  Jet engine, first U.S.
Bell, Alexander Graham (1847-1922, English-
    American inventor), **2** 347
  Aerial Experiment Association, **1** 7-8,
    (with picture)
  Curtiss, Glenn Hammond, **4** 600
Bell helicopters
  Crop dusting, **4** 588
  Helicopters, **6** 1069-70, 1074, 1076,

  (pictures) 1071-72, 1074, 1076,
  (table) 1068
Bell HueyCobra, see AH-1G HueyCobra
Bell JetRanger helicopter
  Reconnaissance aircraft, **11** 1923
Bell, Lawrence Dale (1894-1956, American
    aircraft manufacturer), **2** 348
Bell P-39, see P-39
Bell P-59, see XP-59
Bell Rascal
  Air-to-surface missiles, **1** 123
Bell Telephone Laboratories
  Antiballistic missile defense, **1** 159
  Astronomy, **2** 254
Bell UH-1, see UH-1 Iroquois
Bell X-1, see X-1
Bell X-2, see X-2
Bell X-5, see X-5
Bell X-9, see X-9
Bell X-14, see X-14
Bell X-16, see X-16
Bell X-22, see X-22
Bell XS-1
  Manufacturing, **8** 1472
Bellanca (airplane)
  General aviation aircraft, **6** 961
Bellanca, Giuseppe (1886-1960, Italian-
    American airplane designer), **2** 348-49
Bellanca Airplane School
  Bellanca, Giuseppe, **2** 348
Bellanca CF monoplane
  Bellanca, Giuseppe, **2** 348
Bellanca Pacemaker
  Bush flying (picture), **3** 392
Bellcomm, Inc.
  NASA (table, Apollo/Saturn V Major
    Contractors), **9** 1655
Bellonte, Maurice
  Distance and distance records, **4** 640
Bellows
  Pressure gauges, **10** 1850
  Miniaturization, **9** 1608
Belly gun
  World War I, **14** 2510
Belyayev (bi LYA' iv), **Pavel** (1925-
    Russian cosmonaut), **2** 349
  Cosmonauts, **4** 572, (pictures) 570-71, 575,
    (table) 574
  Manned spaceflight (table), **8** 1461
  U.S.S.R. aerospace activities, **13** 2344
  Voskhod, **13** 2433
Bench marks
  Charts, **3** 455
Bendix Corporation
  NASA (table, Apollo/Saturn V Major
    Contractors), **9** 1655
Bendix Field Engineering Corporation
  NASA (table, Apollo/Saturn V Major
    Contractors), **9** 1655
Bendix Transcontinental Race
  Air racing, **1** 103
  Cochran, Jacqueline, **3** 481
Bendix Trophy
  Air racing, **1** 103
  Beech, Walter H., **2** 347
  Doolittle, James Harold, **4** 643
  Trophies and awards (table), **13** 2312
Bends (with diagram), **2** 349
  Balloons, **2** 324
  Decompression, **4** 613
  Man in flight, **8** 1449
Bennett Coupe Internationale
  Air racing, **1** 102
Bennett, Floyd (1890-1928, American
    aviator), **2** 350
  Byrd, Richard Evelyn, **3** 397
  Polar flights, **10** 1829
Bennett, James Gordon
  Balloons, **2** 322, 332
Benoist flying boat
  Commercial air transports, **3** 517
Bentley (English engine)
  World War I, **14** 2502
Benz, Karl
  Aircraft propulsion systems, **1** 54, 55

History of aviation, 6 1097, (table) 1119
Berblinger, Joseph
　Man-powered flight, 8 1464
Berel (airplane)
　First World War aircraft, 5 823
Beriev M-12
　Flying boats (picture), 5 860
　U.S.S.R. aerospace activities (table),
　　13 2337
Berkner, Lloyd Viel (1905-1967, American
　　space scientist), 2 350-51
　International Geophysical Year, 7 1195
Berlin Airlift, 2 351-352
　Aircraft carriers, 1 51
　Airlift, 1 67
　Air traffic control, 1 130
　Cargo aircraft, 3 418
　Douglas C-54, 4 648
　Liberator, Consolidated B-24, 7 1336
　Powers, John A., 10 1843
　Royal Air Force, 11 1996
　United States Air Force, 13 2365
Berliner
　Balloons, 2 322
Bermuda High
　Air masses, 1 80-81
Bernoulli, Daniel, (1700-1782)
　Aerodynamics, 1 21
　Bernoulli's principle, 2 353
　Carburetion, 3 408
Bernoulli's principle (with diagram), 2 353
　Aerodynamics, 1 21
　Airfoil, 1 62
Berry, Dr. Charles
　Astronauts, 2 230, (picture) 221
　Gemini, 5 939
　Space medicine, 12 2120
Berry, Suzanne M.
　Weitz, Paul J., 13 2474
Bert, Paul
　Aviation medicine, 2 293
Beryllium (bi RIL e um), 2 354
　Alloys, 1 144
　Kiwi, 7 1281
Beryllium brakes
　Jumbo jets, 7 1254
Besnier
　Man-powered flight (drawing), 8 1464
Bessel, Friedrich Wilhelm (1784-1846, German
　　astronomer and mathematician), 2 354
　Universe, 13 2391
Best economy
　Mixture control, 9 1623
　Power management, 10 1840
Beta fiber
　Apollo (picture), 1 176
Beta particle, 2 354
Bethe, Hans A.
　Nuclear energy, 9 1711
　Radiation, 10 1881
Betty bomber
　Bomber aircraft, 2 373
　Kamikaze, 7 1264
Beurling, G. F.
　World War II (table), 14 2517
Bias cloth
　Fabrics, 5 786
Bicycle gear, 2 354
　Landing gear, 7 1298
Biffle, Ira O.
　Airmail, 1 75
Bifrost
　Aurora, 2 277
Big Bang theory
　Astronomy, 2 242
　Space, 11 2093
　Universe, 13 2391
Big Dipper
　Astrophysics, 2 257
"Big E"
　Aircraft carriers, 1 46
"Big Four"
　Commercial airlines, 3 498

Big Joe
　Mercury program, 9 1535
　NASA (table, Major Launchings), 9 1652
Bikle, Paul F.
　Medals and decorations (table), 8 1526
Binary mode
　Computers, 3 553
Binary numbers, 2 355
Binary stars, 2 355
　Astrophysics, 2 257
Binary system
　Space communications, 11 2097
Bingham-Parker-Merritt bill
　Commercial airlines, 3 510
Bioastronautics, 2 355-56
　Mars, 8 1493
　X-15 research program, 14 2530
Bioinstrumentation
　Man in flight, 8 1451
Biological activity
　Oceanographic research, 10 1732
Biological clock
　Circadian rhythm, 3 460
　Space biology, 11 2095
Biological experiments
　Spacecraft sterilization, 11 2104
Biological space
　Aerospace, 1 27
Biological specimens
　Lasers, 7 1306
Biologistics
　Closed ecological systems, 3 470
Biology
　Aerospace medicine, 1 33
　Bionics, 2 356
　Man in flight, 8 1443-51
　Space biology, 11 2094-95
　Technological projections, 12 2237
Biomedicine
　Apollo Applications Program, 2 185
Bionics, 2 356
Bioregenerating system
　Food and nutrition, 5 877-79, (diagram)
　　879
Biosatellites (with diagrams), 2 356-58
　Animals in space, 1 156
　Delta rocket, 4 622
　NASA, 9 1652-53; (table, Major Launchings),
　　1652
Bioscience experiments
　Animals in space, 1 153
Bioscience laboratory
　Apollo Applications Program, 2 185
Biot, Jean Baptiste
　Balloons, 2 324
Biplane, 2 358
　Airplane, 1 86
　History of aviation, 6 1106
　World War I, 14 2506
Bipropellant
　Oxidizers, 10 1751
Bird
　Terminology of aerospace (table), 12 2272
Bird Dog, see O-1 Bird Dog
　Reconnaissance aircraft (with picture),
　　11 1924
Bird flight, 2 358-62
　airplanes compared, 2 359
　bird wing (diagram), 2 360
　Lilienthal, Otto, 8 1358
Bird migration patterns
　Radar, 10 1879
Birmingham
　Aircraft carriers, 1 48
Bishop, William Avery (1894-1956, American
　　aviator), 2 362
　World War I, 14 2506, (table) 2507, 2508,
　　2510
Bison (Myasishchen)
　Bomber aircraft, 2 373
　U.S.S.R. aerospace activities, (table) 13 2337
Bisquit landing gear
　Airplane, 1 89
Bistatic system
　Radar, 10 1874

Bjerknes, J.
　Meteorology, 9 1557
Black Arrow (rocket)
　United Kingdom aerospace activities,
　　13 2354, (picture) 2354
Black body, 2 362
　Planck's Law, 10 1817
　Quantum theory, 10 1868
Black box, 2 362
　Terminology of aerospace (table), 12 2272
Black Brant
　Aerospace Research Support Program
　　(picture), 1 35
Black, Joseph
　Cavallo, Tiberius, 3 425
Black Maria (Raymond Collinshaw)
　World War I, 14 2508
Blackout, 2 362
　Acceleration, 1 2
　Centrifuge, 3 437
　G-suit, 6 1033
　Partial pressure suit, 10 1763
　Terminology of aerospace (table), 12 2272
Black Sea Fleet (Russia)
　Air forces of the world, 1 65
Black, S. W.
　Balloons, 2 318
Blaha, Charlotte Ann
　Holmquest, Donald Lee, 6 1122
Blanchard, Jean Pierre (1753-1809, French
　　balloonist), 2 363
　Airmail, 1 69
　Aviation medicine, 2 293
　Balloons, 2 317-18
　Parachutes, 10 1756
Blanchard, Sophie
　Balloons, 2 320
　Blanchard, Jean Pierre, 2 363
Bland, William
　Australia's aviation, 2 278
BLB oxygen mask
　Oxygen masks, 10 1752
Blenheim
　Second World War aircraft (with picture),
　　11 2030
Bleriot (airplane)
　World War I, 14 2502
Bleriot (BLAY ri oh), **Louis** (1872-1936, French
　　aviator and manufacturer), 2 363-64
　Barnstormers, 2 332
　Commemorative stamps and medals, 3 494
　History of aviation, 6 1103, (table) 1119
　Instrument panels, 7 1173
　Latham, Hubert, 7 1306
　Manufacturing, 8 1466
　Rheims Air Meet, 11 1963
　Spad, 12 2138
　World War I, 14 2500
Blimps, 2 364-66
　Aircraft (with picture), 1 45
　Airships (with drawing), 1 105-6, 112
　data table, 2 365
　Dirigibles, 4 631
Blinder bomber, see Tu-22 Blinder
Blip
　Terminology of aerospace (table), 12 2272
Blitzkrieg, 2 366
　Luftwaffe, 8 1375
　World War II, 14 2512
Blitz of London
　World War II, 14 2514
Bloch M. D. 200 and 210
　Second World War aircraft, 11 2029
Blockade
　Berlin airlift, 2 351
Blockhouse, 2 366-69
　Launch facilities, 7 1307
Bloody April
　World War I, 14 2508
Blue alert, 2 369
Blue Angels
　Demonstration teams (with picture),
　　4 623-26
　Formation flying and techniques, 5 883

Blue Mouse
Gliders, 6 985
Blue Scout
Edwards Air Force Base, 4 679
Blue shift
Astronomy, 2 250
Blue stellar objects
Astronomy, 2 254
Blue Streak
EUROPA 1, 4 741
European Launcher Development
Organization, 4 754
Launch vehicles, 7 1327
United Kingdom aerospace activities,
13 2354
Bluie West One
Balchen, Bernt, 2 312
Blunt-body principle
Mercury program, 9 1530
Blur circle
Photography, 10 1785
BMk 2 Victor, see Handley Page Victor
BMk 2 Vulcan (Hawker Siddeley)
Air forces of the world, 1 66
Bomber aircraft, 2 373
Royal Air Force (picture), 11 1995
BMW, see Bayerische Motoren Werke
BOAC, (see British Overseas Airways
Corporation)
Boardman, Russell N.
Distance and distance records, 4 640
Bobcat
Commuter airlines, 3 545
Bobko, Karol J. (1938-   , American
aerospace research pilot), 2 369
Manned Orbiting Laboratories, 8 1456
Bode's law
Asteroids, 2 208
Boeing 40 A
Commercial air transports (picture),
3 517, 526
Boeing 80
Commercial air transports (picture), 3 518
Boeing 247
Commercial air transports, 3 519, 520,
(picture) 518
History of aviation, 6 1109
Manufacturing, 8 1469
Boeing 307 Stratoliner
Commercial air transports, 3 523,
(picture) 520
Manufacturing, 8 1469
Boeing 314 Clipper
Commercial air lines 3 509, (picture) 508
Flying boats 5 860, (picture) 859
Boeing 377 Stratocruiser
Commercial air transports, 3 523
History of aviation, 6 1115, (picture) 1115
Outsize cargo aircraft, 10 1750
Boeing 707 (picture, cutaway diagram),
2 370-72
Aerospace industry, 1 31
Africa's aviation (picture), 1 37
Brakes, 3 385
Cargo aircraft (picture), 3 418
Commercial airlines, 3 497
Commercial air transports (picture),
3 525, 527
Government in aerospace, 6 1003
History of aviation, 6 1116
Jet aircraft, 7 1235
Jumbo jets (table, 747 compared), 7 1252
Military air transports, 9 1574
Polar flights, 10 1831
Boeing 720
Commercial airlines, 3 501, 502
Commercial air transports, 3 527
Boeing 727
Aerospace industry (picture), 1 28
Australia's aviation, 2 280
Cargo aircraft, 3 419, (picture) 420
Certification procedures, 3 441, (picture) 444
Commercial airlines (picture), 3 501
Commercial air transports, 3 525-26,
(picture) 529

Flight, 5 835, 837
History of aviation (pictures), 6 1093, 1116
Radio communications (picture), 10 1895
Wings (picture), 14 2489
Yaw damper (picture), 14 2547
Boeing 737
Aerospace industry (picture), 1 32
Commercial air transports, 3 525-26, 527,
(picture) 529
Empennage (diagram), 4 710
Boeing 747
Aerospace industry (picture), 1 28
Canada's aviation, 3 401
Commercial airlines, 3 502, 515
Commercial air transports, 3 526, 527
Flight recorder, 5 849
Jumbo jets (pictures), 7 1243-58
Materials, 8 1506, 1508
Navigation systems (diagram), 9 1676
Boeing 2707, see Boeing SST
Boeing Air Transport
Commercial airlines, 3 498, 509-10
Boeing B-1 Flying Boat
Boeing, William Edward, 2 369
Boeing B-15, see B-15
Boeing B-17, see B-17 Flying Fortress
Boeing B-29, see B-29 Superfortress
Boeing B-47, see B-47 Stratojet
Boeing B-50, see B-50
Boeing B-52, see B-52 Stratofortress
Boeing B-58, see B-58 Hustler
Boeing C-135, see C-135
Boeing C-700 biplane
Commercial air transports, 3 517
Boeing Clipper
China Clipper, 3 458
Commercial air transports, 3 526
Flying boats (picture), 5 860
Boeing Company
Apollo, 1 165
Chinook CH-47, 3 458
Commercial air transports, 3 518
Electric propulsion, 4 685
Federal Aviation Administration, 5 801
Jumbo jets, 7 1246
Lunar Orbiter, 8 1411
Military air transports, 9 1578
NASA (table, Apollo/Saturn V Major
Contractors), 9 1655
Titanium, 12 2288
Boeing F3B-1, see F3B-1 bomber
Boeing FB-3, see FB-3
Boeing KC-135 Stratotanker, see KC-135
Stratotanker
Boeing P-26, see P-26 Peashooter
Boeing SM-80
Intercontinental ballistic missiles (picture),
7 1182
Boeing Stratocruiser, see Boeing 377
Boeing Stratoliner, see Boeing 307
Boeing SST
Commercial airlines, 3 514
Commercial air transports, 3 526, 530
Supersonic transport, 12 2179, 2184, 2188
2190, 2192, 2193, 2195-99, (pictures)
2194
Boeing Transport
Airmail, 1 76 (picture)
Boeing Trimotor
Airmail, 1 77
Boeing-Vertol CH-21, see CH-21 Shawnee
Boeing-Vertol CH-46, see CH-46 Sea Knight
Boeing-Vertol CH-47 helicopter, see CH-47
Chinook
Boeing X-20 Dyna-Soar, see X-20 Dyna-Soar
Boeing, William Edward (1881-1956,
American aircraft manufacturer), 2 369-70
Commercial airlines, 3 510
International airmail (picture), 7 1188
Radio communications, 10 1895
Boelke, Oswald
World War I, 14 2506
Bogan, Brenda
Balloons, 2 320

Bohr, Niels
Atoms, 2 269
Quantum theory, 10 1868
Bohr's Atom
Atoms (diagram), 2 270
Boilerplate
Apollo, 1 165-67
Flight test programs, 5 856
Terminology of aerospace (table), 12 2272
Testing, 12 2273
Bolivia
South and Central America's aviation,
11 2089
Bolometric magnitude
Magnitude, 8 1420
Bomarc (missile)
Guidance and control systems, 6 1041
Missiles, 9 1612
Surface-to-air missiles, 12 2201, (picture)
2201, (table) 2204
X-series aerospace vehicles, 14 2540
Bomarc B
Air Defense Command, 1 59
Air defense systems (picture), 1 61
Bombardier, 2 372
Observer, 10 1726
Bomb craters
World War II (picture), 14 2514
Bomber aircraft, 2 372-76
Air defense systems, 1 60
Air forces of the world, 1 64
Air raid, 1 104
Battle of Britain, 2 344
Fighter aircraft, 5 808-11
Flying Fortress, Boeing B-17, 5 863
Gotha bombers, 6 996
Handley Page, Sir Frederick, 6 1048
History of aviation, 6 1112, 1117
Hustler B-58, 6 1137
Military aircraft, 9 1569 (with picture)
table, historical and current, 2 373
Reconnaissance, airborne, 11 1920
Refueling, 11 1941
United States Air Force, 13 2373
World War I, 14 2508-10
World War II, 14 2511-23
Bombing training flights
Oil burner routes, 10 1735
Bombload
Bombardier, 2 372
Bombs, 3 377-78
Air raid, 1 104
Armament, 2 193
Bomber aircraft, 2 372
Weaponry, 13 2448
Bombs and Bombing (book)
Ley, Willy, 7 1335
Bombsight
Bombardier, 2 372
De Seversky, Alexander Procofieff, 4 627
Bonanza, see Beech Bonanza
Bonanza Airlines
Charter flying, 3 448
Commercial airlines, 3 513
Bonaventure (aircraft carrier)
Naval aviation, worldwide (Canada), 9 1671
Bong, Richard Ira (1921-1945), 3 379-80
Ace, 1 4
World War II (table), 14 2517
Bonnet, Adj. A.
Speed and speed records (table), 12 2141
Boomerang (with picture and diagram), 3 380
Boom operator
Refueling (with diagram), 11 1939-40
Boom system
Refueling, 11 1938
Tanker aircraft, 12 2232
Bo-105 (helicopter)
West Germany's aerospace activities,
13 2478
Booster, 3 381
Aerobee, 1 17
Launch vehicles, 7 1313, 1318-19, 1328
Booster rockets
Jet-assisted takeoff, 7 1236

Booster spacecraft
Launch facilities, 7 1307
Boost-glide vehicles, 3 381
Dynamic soaring, 4 656
Bootes (BO ot ees)
Astronomy, 2 253
Boothman, J. M.
Air racing, 1 102
Boots
Personal equipment, 10 1775
Borates
Boron, 3 382
Borax
Boron, 3 382
Bore
Reciprocating engines, 11 1916
Borelli, Giovanni
Man-powered flight, 8 1464
Ornithopter, 10 1748
Boriding
Boron, 3 382
Borman, Frank (1928-), 3 381-82
Astronauts, 2 216, 219, 224, 230, 231, (pictures) 217, 222, 228
Distance and distance records, 4 641
Gemini, 5 940-42, (picture) 941
Manned spaceflight, 8 1461 (table)
Boron, 3 382
Kiwi, 7 1281
Materials, 8 1506
Metals and metallurgy (picture and diagram), 9 1549
Radiation shield, 10 1884
Borosilicates
Glass, 6 982
Boselli, Elizabeth
Women in aerospace, 14 2495
Boseman, Nina
Medals and decorations (table), 8 1526
Bossoutrot (bo su TRO), **Lucien**
Distance and distance records, 4 640-41
Boston, Massachusetts
Airports, 1 95
Careers (table), 3 414
Boston
Attack aircraft (picture), 2 271
Bosun (aircraft) (Tupolev)
U.S.S.R. aerospace activities (table), 13 2337
Bottlesuit, 3 382-83
Spacesuits, 12 2129-35
Bottoms, Benjamin A.
Coast Guard aviation, 3 479
Boulders
Rangers, 10 1911
Boundary layer (with diagram), 3 383
Aerodynamics, 1 22
Wings, 14 2492-93
X-series aerospace vehicles, 14 2544
Boundary markers
Airmail, 1 74
High-lift devices, 6 1088
Boundary of outer space
Life-support systems, 8 1338
Bourdon tube
Engine instruments, 4 715-16
Pressure gauges, 10 1850
Box kite
Australia's aviation, 2 278, (picture) 279
Delagrange, Leon, 4 621
Kites (picture), 7 1280
Boyd, Alan S.
Commercial airlines, 3 501, 503
Boyeau, Maurice
World War I (table, Top Aces), 14 2507
Boyington, Gregory
World War II (table), 14 2517
Boyle, George
Airmail, 1 68
Boyle, Robert (1627-1691)
Atoms, 2 269
Boyle's Law, 3 384
Boyle's Law (with diagram), 3 383-84
Meteorology, 9 1556

BQM-34A
Drone aircraft, 4 653
Br-1150 Atlantic
Naval aviation, worldwide (France), 9 1670
Brabazon of Tara, (Lord), (1864-1964, British aviator), 3 384
Brack-Papa, Francesco
Speed and speed records (table), 12 2141
Brahe Tycho (BRAH he, TY ko) (1546-1601, Danish astronomer), 3 385
Astronomy, 2 236, 237, 242
Celestial mechanics, 3 427
Kepler, Johannes, 7 1274
Brake horsepower
Measurement of power, 8 1519
Brake linings
Brakes, 3 387
Brakes, 3 385-87
Piloting techniques, 10 1801
Branca, Giovanni
Aircraft propulsion systems, 1 52
Brancker, Sir Sefton
Cobham, Sir Alan, 3 480
Brand, Vance DeVoe (1931-), 3 388
Astronauts, 2 216, 219, (picture) 218
Braniff International
Commercial airlines, 3 498, 512
Branly coherer
Radio, 10 1887
Brantley rotorcraft
Crop dusting, 4 590
Brattain, Walter
Electronics, 4 693
Braun, Wernher von, see Von Braun, Wernher
Brazil
Naval aviation, world wide, 9 1672
South and Central America's aviation, 11 2090
Breakdown potential
Lightning (picture), 8 1387
Break-off phenomenon
Sensory deprivation, 11 2043
Terminology of aerospace (table), 12 2272
Breccia
Meteors, meteorites, and meteoroids, 9 1561
Breemsstrahlung
Radiation, 10 1882
Breese, J. L., Jr.
Coast Guard aviation, 3 476
Breguet (BRA guay), **Louis Charles** (1880-1955, French airplane manufacturer and executive), 3 388
Helicopters, 6 1062
Breguet (airplane)
First World War aircraft, 5 823
Breguet bomber
Military aviation (picture), 9 1583
Breit
Astronomy, 2 242
Bremen (airship)
Bennett, Floyd, 2 350
Brewer (aircraft) (Yakovlev)
U.S.S.R. aerospace activities (table), 13 2337
Brewer, Louise
Shepard, Alan B., 11 2046
Brewer trophy
National Aeronautic Association, 9 1648
Bridgeman, Bill
X-series aerospace vehicles, 14 2538
Bridle
Catapult, 3 423
Briefing, 3 388
Bright-line spectrum
Astronomy, 2 250
Brillance control
Plan position indicator, 10 1821
Brintnell, Leigh
Bush flying, 3 392
Bristol Beaufighter
Second World War aircraft (with picture), 11 2030
World War II (picture), 14 2523
Bristol Britannia
Cargo aircraft, 3 418
Commercial air transports, 3 526

United Kingdom aerospace activities, 13 2347
Bristol Fighter
First World War aircraft, 5 816, 818
History of aviation (picture), 6 1105
Britain, see United Kingdom aerospace activities
Britannia, see Bristol Britannia
British Aircraft Corporation
Africa's aviation, 1 36
Supersonic transports, 12 2182
United Kingdom aerospace activities, 13 2351
British Air Transport Auxiliary
Cochran, Jacqueline, 3 481
British Airways
Commercial airlines, 3 506
British bomber and missile forces
NATO, 9 1704
British Eighth Army
World War II, 14 2516
British European Airways
Commercial airlines, 3 497, 506, (route map) 507
British Experimental (airplane)
World War I, 14 2502
British/French Concorde
Aerospace industry (picture), 1 32
Aluminum, 1 148
British Hunter subsonic jets
Asia's aviation, 2 204
British Hovercraft Company
Ground-effect machines, 6 1025
British Overseas Airways Corporation
Africa's aviation, 1 36
Canada's aviation, 3 401
Commercial airlines, 3 497, 506
United Kingdom aerospace activities, 13 2347
British thermal unit
Measurement of power, 8 1520
Broadcast band
Band, radio, 2 332
Broadwick, Charles
Parachutes, 10 1756
Brocq Corrector
Antiaircraft weapons, 1 157
Bronco, see OV-10A Bronco
Brooks, Allison C.
Rescue and Recovery Service, 11 1958
Brookhaven National Laboratory
Berkner, Lloyd Viel, 2 351
Brookins, Walter R.
Altitude and altitude records, 1 147
Brow, Lieutenant Harold J.
Speed and speed records, 12 2141
Brown, Arthur Whitten (1886-1948, English aviator), 1 141-42
Brown, Walter Folger
Airmail, 1 77
Commercial airlines, 3 508
Brownian motion
Einstein, Albert, 4 680
Brumowsky, Godwin
World War I, 14 2508, (table) 2507
Bryan, Leslie A.
Medals and decorations (table), 8 1526
B-seat
Escape systems, 4 735
BT-13 (Vultee)
Military aircraft, 9 1567
Buccaneer, see Hawker Siddeley Buccaneer
Bucker Bestmann monoplane
Africa's aviation, 1 37
Bucket seat
Kamikaze, 7 1264
Buffalo, see DHC-5 Buffalo
Buffer area
Decontamination, radiological, 4 614
Buffeting, 3 389
Supersonic flight, 12 2177
Bugbee, Susan
Borman, Frank, 3 382
Building blocks
Propellants, 10 1860

Built-in-clocks
Circadian rhythm, 3 460
Bulgaria
Crop dusting, 4 587
European aerospace activities, 4 744
Bull (aircraft)
U.S.S.R. aerospace activities (table), 13 2337
Bull, John Sumter (1934-), 3 389
Astronauts, 2 217-19 (with picture)
Bullpup (missile)
Guidance and control systems, 6 1041
International projects, 7 1201
Marine Corps Aviation (picture), 8 1483
Bullpup A
Air-to-surface missiles (picture), 1 124
Bullpup B
Missiles (table), 9 1616
Bumper Project, 3 389-90
Blockhouse, 2 367
Bundesluftwaffe (West Germany)
Air forces of the world, 1 66
Italy's aerospace activities, 7 1220
NATO, 9 1704
Bungee landing gear
Airplane, 1 89
Buoyancy, 3 390
Aircraft, 1 45
Bird flight, 2 360
Pontoons, 10 1838
Buoys
Oceanographic research, 10 1731
Burble
Angle of attack, 1 152
Maneuvers, 8 1436
Wings, 14 2492
Bureau of Standards
Chronometer, 3 459
Dryden, Hugh Latimer, 4 654
Burke, B.
Astronomy, 2 242
Burleson, Albert S.
Airmail, 1 68
Burma
Asia's aviation, 2 205
Burma Road
Airlift, 1 67
Hump airlift, 6 1136
Burn
Terminology of aerospace (table), 12 2272
Burner
Combustion chamber, 3 489
Burner mounting
Balloons (picture), 2 322
Burnett, B. K.
Distance and distance records, 4 640
Burning chamber
Ignition systems, 7 1147
Burnout, 3 390
Burns, Ann
Medals and decorations (table), 8 1526
Burzinski, Zbigniew
Medals and decorations (table), 8 1526
Bush flying, 3 390-93
Economic implications of aerospace, 4 670
Bush, Vannevar
Computers, 3 558
Program management, 10 1857
Business aviation (with table), 3 394-96
Plastics, 10 1825
Business flying
Business aviation, 3 394-96
Safety statistics, 11 2002
Bussy, A.
Magnesium, 8 1418
Butterfly
Empennage, 4 710
Butt rib
Airplane, 1 86
Wings, 14 2491
Butyl
Airships, 1 108
Buzz, 3 396
Buzz bombs (see also V-2 rocket missile)
Pulsejet engines, 10 1866

Bykovsky, Valeri (1934- , Russian
cosmonaut), 3 397
Cosmonauts, 4 574, (pictures) 570, 572,
(table) 574
Manned spaceflight (table), 8 1461
U.S.S.R. aerospace activities, 13 2344
Vostok, 13 2435
Byrd, Richard Evelyn, (1888-1957, American
aviator and explorer), 3 397
Amundsen, Roald, 1 151
Balchen, Bernt, 2 312
Bennett, Floyd, 2 350
Berkner, Lloyd Viel, 2 350
Bush flying, 3 392
Polar flights, 10 1829
Byrd Station
Aurora, 2 277
By Rocket to Interplanetary Space (book)
Oberth, Hermann, 10 1721
Peenemuende, 10 1770

C

C-I-A- Trader (Grumman)
Aircraft carriers, 1 47
C-2A Greyhound (Grumman)
Military air transports (table), 9 1578
C-4A, see Grumman Gulfstream I
C-5A Galaxy (Lockheed)
Aluminum, 1 148
Cargo aircraft, 3 418
Government contracts, 6 999
Jumbo jets (picture), 7 1243,
(performance chart) 1245-46, 1249,
1253-54
Landing gear (picture), 7 1299
Materials, 8 1508
Military air transports (table), 9 1578
Military aviation, 9 1583
C-11 Jet Instrument Trainer
Flight simulators, 5 853
C-47 Skytrain (see also Douglas DC-3)
Air forces of the world (Sudan), 1 64
Asia's aviation, 2 204-05
Attack aircraft, 2 273
Berlin airlift, 2 351
Cargo aircraft, 3 418
Douglas DC-3, 4 648-49
History of aviation (picture), 6 1110
Military air transports, 9 1574, (table)
1578
Second World War aircraft (with picture),
11 2037
United States Air Force (with picture), 13
2365
World War II (picture), 14 2521
C-54 Skymaster (Douglas) (picture), 4 647-48
Canada's aviation, 3 401
Cargo aircraft, 3 418
Commercial air transports (picture), 3 521
Douglas C-54, 4 647
Douglas, Donald Wills, 4 649
History of aviation, 6 1114-15
Military air transports (picture), 9 1576,
(table) 1578
C-97 Stratofreighter (Boeing)
Continental Air Command, 3 563
Military air transports (picture), 9 1574,
(table) 1578
Refueling, 11 1938

C-118 Liftmaster (Douglas)
Military air transports (table), 9 1578
C-119 Flying Boxcar (Fairchild)
Continental Air Command, 3 563
Fairchild C-119 Flying Boxcar (chart,
pictures), 5 789
History of aviation (picture), 6 1115
Korean war, 7 1285
Military air transports (table), 9 1578
C-123 Provider (Fairchild)
Military air transports (table), 9 1578
Parachutes, 10 1757
C-124 Globemaster (Douglas)
Continental Air Command, 3 563
Military air transports (picture), 9 1576,
(table) 1578, 1583
C-130 Hercules (Lockheed)
Canada's aviation, 3 404
Cargo aircraft, 3 418-419
Marine Corps Aviation, 8 1483
Military air transports (table), 9 1578
PRIME, 10 1853
Vietnam, 13 2420
C-131 (Convair)
Military air transports (picture), 9 1576,
(table) 1578
C-133 Cargomaster (Douglas)
Military air transports (picture), 9 1577,
(table) 1578
C-135 (Boeing)
Boeing 707, 2 372
Military air transports (pictures), 9 1574,
(picture and cutaway) 1576, (table) 1578
C-141 Starlifter (Lockheed)
Canada's aviation, 3 404
Cargo aircraft, 3 418-419
Jumbo jets, 7 1254
Military Airlift Command (picture), 9 1573
Military air transports (table), 9 1578
Parachutes, 10 1758
C-700, see Boeing C-700
CAA, see Civil Aeronautics Administration
CAAC, see Civil Aviation Administration of
China
CAAG, see Civil Aviation Assistance Groups
CAB, see Civil Aeronautics Board
Cab (aircraft)
U.S.S.R. aerospace activities (table),
13 2337
Cabin equipment
Interiors of aircraft, 7 1184
Cabin floors
Interiors of aircraft, 7 1184
Cabin pressure
Airplane, 1 84
Cabin systems
Certification procedures, 3 442
Cabin-temperature control
Environmental control system, 4 721
Cable load
Airships, 1 106
Cable system
Parawing, 10 1761
Cab, tower
Air traffic control, 1 128
Cadmium
Radiation shield, 10 1884
Caisson disease
Balloons, 2 324
Calcium metabolism
Man in flight, 8 1451
Calculus
Newton, Sir Isaac, 9 1693
Calcutta, see Short Calcutta
Calderas
Moon, 9 1638
Caldwell, Turner
X-series aerospace vehicles, 14 2537
Calibrated airspeed
Airspeed, 1 116
California Institute of Technology
Explorer satellites, 5 763
Caliper
Brakes, 3 386

Callaire
Crop dusting, **4** 589
Callisto
Astronomy, **2** 245, 246
Jupiter, **7** 1261
Interplanetary travel (drawing), **7** 1207
Call signs, 3 398
Call-up
Air traffic control, **1** 129
Calorie
Heat energy, **6** 1054
Measurement of power, **8** 1519
Cam, see Contract Air Mail
CAMA, see Civil Aviation Medical Association
Camber, airfoil
Airplane, **1** 85
Wings, **14** 2490
Cambered airfoils
Phillips, Horatio F., **10** 1777
Cambodia
Asia's aviation, **2** 203, 205
Camel (aircraft), see Sopwith Camel
Camel (Soviet aircraft)
U.S.S.R. aerospace activities (table),
13 2337
Cameras
Aerial photography, **1** 9-10
Television, **12** 2258, 2262-63
Camera-telescope
Tracking systems and networks, **13** 2300
Camm, Sir Sydney (1893-1966, British
aircraft designer), **3** 398
Hawker Hurricane, **6** 1052
Camouflage, 3 398
Camouflage detection
Infrared detection devices, **7** 1161
Infrared radiation, **7** 1162
Campbell, Douglas
Ace, **1** 4
World War I (table, Top Aces), **14** 2507
Canada
Air forces of the world, **1** 64
Alouette satellites, **1** 144
Bush flying, **3** 390
Communications satellites, **3** 538
Crop dusting, **4** 587
International Agricultural Aviation Centre,
7 1187
International Flying Farmers, **7** 1193
International projects, **7** 1198-99
International Satellite for Ionospheric
Studies, **7** 1201
NATO, **9** 1703-04
Canadair CF-5, see CF-5
Canadair CL-41 G
Reconnaissance aircraft (with picture),
11 1924
Canadair CL-44
Canada's aviation (picture), **3** 403
Cargo aircraft, **3** 418, (picture) 419
Canadair CL-84 Dynavert
Canada's aviation **3** 404, (picture) 402
Rescue and Recovery Service
(with picture), **11** 1959
Canadair CL-215
Canada's aviation (picture), **3** 403
Canadair CP-107, see CP-107 Argus
Canadair Ltd.
Canada's aviation, **3** 404
Canadair Sabre
Canada's aviation, **3** 404
Canada's aviation (with map), **3** 399-404
**Canadian Armed Forces Air Defense
Command**
Air defense systems, **1** 60
NORAD, **9** 1701
Canadian CF-104
NATO, **9** 1704
Canadian commemorative stamps
Canada's aviation, **3** 404
Canadian Fighter Squadron
Bader, Douglas Robert Stuart, **2** 310
Canadian Pacific Airlines
Canada's aviation, **3** 401
Canali
Astronomy, **2** 244

Canard configuration
Empennage, **4** 709
Canberra (Martin), see B-57 Canberra
Canberra, B.Mk. (English Electric)
Air forces of the world, **1** 66
Attack aircraft (table, picture), **2** 272
Australia's aviation, **2** 280
Bomber aircraft (table, pictures),
2 373, 375
NATO, **9** 1704
United Kingdom aerospace activities,
13 2347
Cancer
Constellations, **3** 562
Nuclear energy, **9** 1715
Cannegieter, H. G.
Medals and decorations (table), **8** 1526
Canopus
Mariner probes, **8** 1485
Surveyor, **12** 2211, 2213
Canopy, airplane, 3 405
Airplane, **1** 83
Cant
Maneuvers, **8** 1433
Cantilever
Landing gear, **7** 1299
Cantilever wing
Airplane, **1** 86
Junkers, Hugo, **7** 1258
Junkers J-4, **7** 1258
Wings, **14** 2491-92, (pictures)
2489, 2491-92
Cant Z-501 (flying boat)
Flying boats, **5** 859
Capacitance
Electricity, **4** 685
Capacitor
Electricity, **4** 685
CapCom
Terminology of aerospace (table),
12 2272
Cape Canaveral, 3 405, see also Kennedy
Space Center
Astronauts, **2** 224
Blockhouse, **2** 367
Mercury program, **9** 1534, 1536-38,
(map) 1534, (picture) 1536
Cape Kennedy, see Cape Canaveral and
Kennedy Space Center
Cape Kennedy launch pad
Mercury program (picture), **9** 1529
Capital Airport
Airports (picture), **1** 97
Capricornus
Constellations, **3** 562
Caproni aircraft
Caproni, Count Gianni, **3** 405
World War I, **14** 2509-10
Caproni Ca (airplane)
First World War aircraft (picture), **5** 822
Caproni-Campini
Jet engines, **7** 1238
Caproni Company
jet flight, first
Aircraft propulsion systems, **1** 57
Caproni, Count Gianni (1886-1957, Italian
airplane designer and manufacturer)
3 405-06
CAP, see Civil Air Patrol
Capsule, 3 406
Console, **3** 561
Discoverer Project, **4** 637
Captured air bubble craft
Ground-effect machines, **6** 1023
Caquot balloon
Balloons, **2** 324
Caravelle (Sud-Aviation)
Africa's aviation, **1** 36-37
Asia's aviation, **2** 203-04
Commercial air transports (picture), **3** 529
France's aerospace activities, **5** 886,
(picture) 887
Military air transports, **9** 1575
Caravelle, Super, see Super Caravelle
Carbide and Carbon Chemicals Corp.
Plastics, **10** 1824

Carbon-12
Atoms, **2** 271
Carbon, 3 406-07
Extraterrestrial life, **5** 776
Carbonaceous chondrites
Lunar bases, **8** 1387
Carbon-arc solar simulator
Environmental simulators, **4** 729
Carbon button microphone
Microphone, **9** 1563
Carbon cycle
Carbon, **3** 406
Carbon dioxide, 3 407-08
Air, **1** 42
Atmosphere, **2** 261
Balloons, **2** 326
Carbon, **3** 406
Extraterrestrial life, **5** 776
Photosynthesis, **10** 1789
Venus, **13** 2408
Carbon dioxide molecules
Quantum theory, **10** 1870
Carbon monoxide
Aviation medicine, **2** 297
Carbon dioxide-oxygen cycle
Atmosphere, **2** 263
Carbon plate
Battery, **2** 338
Carbon residue
Lubricants, **8** 1375
Carbon steel
Steels, **12** 2164
Carburetion, 3 408-09
Power management, **10** 1840
Venturi tubes, **13** 2406
Carburetor air temperature gauge, see
Temperature gauges
Carburetor icing
Aviation weather, **2** 303
Carburetion, **3** 409
Cardiac pacemakers
Nuclear energy, **9** 1715
Careers (with tables), **3** 411-17
Educational implications of aerospace
(chart), **4** 676
largest labor market areas
Careers (table), **3** 414
Photogrammetry, **10** 1780
Cargo aircraft, 3 417-21
Flying Tigers, **5** 865
General aviation, **6** 954
Interiors of aircraft, **7** 1186
Jumbo jets, **7** 1252, 1256
Cargo airport
Airports, **1** 93
Cargo nose door
Jumbo jets, **7** 1252
Cargo pod
Pod, **10** 1828
Cargo protection
Outsize cargo aircraft, **10** 1749
Caribou, DHC-4A (deHavilland of Canada)
Army aviation, **2** 197
Canada's aviation, **3** 404
Carl, Ann Baumgartner
Women in aerospace, **14** 2495
Carl, Major Marion
Speed and speed records (table), **12** 2141
X-series aerospace vehicles, **14** 2537
Carpenter, Malcolm Scott (1925-   ), **3** 422
Astronauts, **2** 215, 216, 217, 219, 224, 229,
230, (picture) 222
Manned spaceflight (table), **8** 1461
Mercury program, **9** 1531, 1540-42,
(picture) 1541, (table) 1544
Naval Aviation Museum, **9** 1672
Recovery, **11** 1928
Telemetry (picture), **12** 2243
Carr, Gerald Paul (1932-   ), **3** 422-23
Astronauts, **2** 217, 219, (picture) 218
Carrier warfare
Aircraft carriers, **1** 49
Carrier wave, 3 423
Radio, **10** 1887
Transmitters, **13** 2308

(Continued)

Carstedt Starliner
DeHavilland Dove, **4** 619
Cartography, 3 423
Cartoon print
Objects of art, **10** 1722
CAS, see Calibrated airspeed
CAS, see Collision Avoidance System
CAS, see Crewman alignment sight
Casale, Jean
Altitude and altitude records, **1** 147
Speed and speed records (table), **12** 2141
Cassegrainian telescope
Telescopes and astronomical instruments,
12 2249, 2251, 2253, (pictures) 2249,
2253
Cassiopeia (kas i o PE a)
Astronomy, **2** 251
Brahe, Tycho, **3** 385
Constellations, **3** 562
Cassutt (airplane)
Homebuilt aircraft(picture), **6** 1127
Castle of the Sky (Brahe's observatory)
Astronomy (picture), **2** 239
Castor, Anna Margaret
Glenn, John Herschel, Jr., **6** 984
Castor landing gear
Airplane, **1** 89
Jumbo jets, **7** 1254
Landing gear, **7** 1298
CAT, see Clear air turbulence
Catalina flying boat, see Consolidated PBY
Catalyst
Carbon, **3** 407
Catalytic-Dow
NASA (table, Apollo/Saturn V Major
Contractors), **9** 1655
Catapult, 3 423-24
Aircraft carriers, **1** 47-51
Coast Guard aviation, **3** 476
Catcher
Electronics, **4** 700
Category I, II, and III landing systems
Automatic landing, **2** 288
Instrument landing categories, **7**
1169, 1171
Instrument landing system, **7** 1170-71
Lighting facilities, **8** (diagrams I, II) 1356
Caterpillar Club
Bailout, **2** 311
Cathode ray oscilloscope
Radar, **10** 1875
Cathode ray tube
Avionics, **2** 307
Electronics, **4** 693, 98-99, (diagram) 699
Cation
Ion, **7** 1215
Catwalks
Airships, **1** 106
Cat whisker
Miniaturization, **9** 1608
Caudron (airplane)
First World War aircraft, (picture) **5** 823
Caudron-G-4
World War I, **14** 2510
Caution and warning system
Electrical systems, **4** 681
Caution lights
Instrument panels, **7** 1177
Cavallo, Tiberius (1749-1809, Italian-English
physicist and inventor), **3** 424
Balloons, **2** 316
Cavendish, Henry
Balloons, **2** 316, 321
Cavallo, Tiberius, **3** 424
Charles, Jacques Alexandre Cesar, **3** 447
Cayley, Sir George (1773-1857, English
inventor) **3** 425
Aircraft propulsion systems, **1** 53
Airfoil, **1** 62
Dirigibles, **4** 629
Gliders, **6** 985
Helicopters, **6** 1062
History of aviation, **6** 1094, (table) 1119
Man-powered flight, **8** 1465
Ornithopter, **10** 1748
Rheims Air Meet, **11** 1963

Sailplanes, **11** 2002
Cayley glider (with diagrams), **3** 426
Cayuse helicopter, see OH-6A Cayuse
CDA, see Command and data acquisition
Cebus monkeys
Algae, **1** 143
Cecconi, Fausto
Distance records, **4** 640
Cecil, W.
Aircraft propulsion systems, **1** 53
Ceiling, 3 426
Weather, **13** 2451
Ceilometers
Ceiling, **3** 426
Celestial bodies
Kepler's laws, **7** 1275
Kosmos satellites, **7** 1290
Legal implications of aerospace, **7** 1331
Moon, **9** 1633-35
Orbits and trajectories, **10** 1742, 1746
Retrograde motion, **11** 1961
Celestial equator
Astronomy, **2** 236
Celestial Equator System of Coordinates
Celestial sphere (with diagram), **3** 431
Celestial globes
Planetarium, **10** 1818
Celestial mechanics (with diagrams),
3 426-28
Astrodynamics, **2** 210
Orbital velocity, **10** 1737
Orbits and trajectories, **10** 1742
Celestial meridian
Astronomy, **2** 240
Celestial sphere, **3** 431, 433
Celestial navigation (with diagrams),
3 428-31
Air traffic control, **1** 135
Astronomy, **2** 240
Chronometer, **3** 459
Guidance and control systems, **6** 1037
Planetarium, **10** 1820
Spaceflight training, **12** 2118
Celestial sensor
Celestial navigation, **3** 430
Celestial sphere, 3 431-33
Astronomy, **2** 240
Ecliptic, **4** 669
Equator, **4** 729
Parallax, **10** 1760
Planetarium, **10** 1818
Precession, **10** 1843
Celsius, Anders
Temperature control, **12** 2271
Celsius scale, see Temperature scales
Centaur, 3 433-35
Atlas missile and launch vehicle, **2** 260
Ehricke, Krafft Arnold, **4** 680
Launch vehicles, **7** 1324
Lewis Research Center, **7** 1334
NASA, **9** 1653, (table, Major Launchings)
1652
Centaure (rocket)
France's aerospace activities (picture),
5 885
Centaurus XR-2
X-ray stars, **14** 2533
Center Controller
Air traffic control (picture), **1** 134
Centerline lights
Lighting facilities, **8** 1357, (diagrams)
1355,1356
Centerline thrust
Airplane, **1** 90
Center of gravity, 3 435-36
Attitude and attitude control, **2** 275
Axes of rotation, **2** 308
Cayley glider, **3** 426
Da Vinci, Leonardo, **4** 611
Re-entry vehicles, **11** 1933
Wings, **14** 2490
Yaw, **14** 2547
Center of lift
Center of gravity, **3** 435

Center of pressure
Aerodynamics, **1** 24
Center of rotation
Axes of rotation, **2** 308
Center of the universe
Astronomy, **2** 235
Centigrade scale
Temperature scales, **12** 2271
Central America
Crop dusting, **4** 587
South and Central America's aviation,
12 2087
Central Bay
Surveyor, **12** 2215
Central computing facility
Data acquisition and processing, **4** 609
Central equatorial band
Jupiter, **7** 1260
Central force field
Orbits and trajectories, **10** 1742-43
Central Intelligence Agency, see CIA
Central reservation-control computer
Commercial airlines (picture), **3** 504
Central signal processor
Data acquisition and processing, **4** 607
Centrifugal and centripetal forces
(with diagram), **3** 436
Artificial gravity, **2** 202
Launch vehicles, **7** 1314
Orbits and trajectories, **10** 1744
Centrifugal-flow engine
Aircraft propulsion systems, **1** 58
Gas turbine engines, **5** 919
Centrifuge, 3 437-38
Cosmonauts, **4** 570
Manned Spacecraft Center (picture), **8**
1458
Space biology, **11** 2094
Centrifuge training
Manned spaceflight, **8** 1460
Centripetal force
Centrifugal and centripetal forces, **3** 436
Centurion, see Cessna 210 Centurion
Cepheid (SEE fee id) **variable**
Astronomy, **2** 251
Stars, **12** 2160
Ceramics, 3 438-40
Materials, **8** 1507, 1508
Ceres
Asteroids, **2** 208
Astronomy, **2** 244
Cernan, Eugene Andrew (1934-), **3** 440
Astronauts, **2** 217, (picture) 218, 219,
(picture) 223, 230
Gemini, **5** 944-45
Manned spaceflight, **8** 1461, (table) 1462
Certification of pilots
Man in flight, **8** 1449
Certification procedures, 3 440-45
**Certificate of Public Convenience and
Necessity**
Charter flying, **3** 448
Cessna 150
Africa's aviation, **1** 36
Seaplanes (picture), **11** 2025
Trainer aircraft, **13** 2307
Cessna 172 Skyhawk (T-41)
Africa's aviation, **1** 36
Army aviation, **2** 197
Pleasure flying, **10** 1826
Cessna 180
Africa's aviation, **1** 36
Agricultural aviation (picture), **1** 40
Bush flying, **3** 393
Canada's aviation, **3** 402
Cessna 182 Skylane
Africa's aviation, **1** 36
Cessna 188, see Cessna Agwagon
Cessna 206
Canada's aviation, **3** 403
Cessna 210 Centurion
Landing gear (with picture), **7** 1300
Cessna 310 Executive Skyknight
Airplane, **1** 90
Icing, **7** 1145

(Continued)

Cessna 310 Executive Skyknight (Cont.)
Pleasure flying (picture), **10** 1826
Power management, **10** 1841
Cessna 411
Icing (picture), **7** 1145
Cessna A-37, see A-37
Cessna Agwagon (188)
Agricultural aviation (picture), **1** 39, 40
Airplane, **1** 83, 89
Crop dusting, **4** 589, 590
Cessna aircraft
Australia's aviation, **2** 283
Commuter airlines, **3** 545
General aviation (pictures), **6** 954, 956
General aviation aircraft, **6** 961, 962,
965-67, (pictures) 960, 963, 965
Cessna Aircraft Company, see Cessna,
Clyde V.
Cessna AT-17, see AT-17
Cessna AW
Wings (picture), **14** 2491
Cessna, Clyde V. (1880-1954, American
aircraft manufacturer), **3** 445
Trainer aircraft, **13** 2306
Cessna O-1, see O-1 Bird Dog
Cessna Skymaster
Pursuit airplane (with picture), **10** 1866
Ceti
Ozma project, **10** 1753
Citus the Whale
Astrophysics, **2** 258
Ceylon
Asia's aviation, **2** 205
CF-5 (Canadair)
Canada's aviation (picture), **3** 402
CF-100 (Avro)
Canada's aviation, **3** 404
CF-105 Arrow (Avro Canada)
Canada's aviation, **3** 404
CH-21 Shawnee helicopter (Boeing-Vertol)
Army aviation (picture), **2** 196
CH-34 Choctaw helicopter (Sikorsky)
Army aviation, **2** 197
CH-37 Mojave helicopter (Sikorsky)
Army aviation, **2** 198
CH-46 Sea Knight helicopter (Boeing-Vertol)
Marine Corps Aviation, **8** 1483
CH-47 Chinook helicopter (Boeing-Vertol)
Army aviation (pictures), **2** 195, 198
Chinook CH-47 (chart, pictures), **3** 458
Helicopters, **6** 1066, 1074, (picture) 1066,
(table) 1068
Vietnam, **13** 2416
CH-53 Sea Stallion helicopter (Sikorsky)
Marine Corps Aviation, **8** 1483
United States Naval Aviation, **13** 2390
CH-54 (S-64) Skycrane helicopter (Sikorsky)
Army aviation, **2** 199
General aviation (picture), **6** 953
Helicopters (picture), **6** 1072
United States Naval Aviation, **13** 2390
Chaff
Antiaircraft weapons, **1** 157
Chaffee, Roger B. (1935-1967), **3** 445
Apollo, **1** 168 (with picture)
Astronauts, **2** 216, (picture) 218, 219, 228
Challe, Leone
Distance records, **4** 640
Challenge of the Space Ship (book)
Clarke, Arthur Charles, **3** 467
Chamanal
Astronomy, **2** 242
Chamberlin, Clarence D.
Bellanca, Giuseppe, **2** 349
Distance records, **4** 640
Chambers, Washington Irving
Aircraft carriers, **1** 48
Champion, C.C.
Altitude and altitude records, **1** 147
Champion aircraft
Crop dusting, **4** 588-89
General aviation aircraft, **6** 961
Trainer aircraft, **13** 2307
Chance-Vought aircraft, see LTV
Chandelle
Maneuvers, **8** 1436, (diagram) 1438

Chandler, Charles D.
Barnstormers (picture), **2** 333
Change course
Omni navigation, **10** 1737
Changing of the seasons
Aristarchus (ARisTARcus) of Samos, **2** 193
Channel Command
NATO, **9** 1704
Chanute, Octave (1832-1910, French-American
civil engineer, inventor), **3** 446
Ferber, Ferdinand, **5** 805
Gliders, **6** 985
History of aviation, **6** 1099, 1100, (table)
1119
Manufacturing, **8** 1466
Wright brothers, **14** 2524
Chaparral
Battlefield missile systems, **2** 343,
(picture) 342
Surface-to-air missiles, **12** 2201,
(picture) 2202, (table) 2204
Chapman, Philip K. (1935-   , Australian-
American astronaut), **3** 446
Astronauts, **2** 216, (picture) 218, 219
Chapman, Victor
Lafayette Escadrille, **7** 1295
Chapperal race car
Charter flying (picture), **3** 448
Charger
Counter-insurgency aircraft, **4** 576
Charles, Jacques Alexandre Cesar (1746-
1823, French builder of first hydrogen
balloon), **3** 447
Aviation medicine, **2** 292
Balloons, **2** 316, 321
Blanchard, Jean Pierre, **2** 363
Lunardi, Vincent, **8** 1401
Montgolfier brothers, **9** 1632
Pilatre de Rozier, Jean Francois, **10** 1792
Charles' Law
Charles, Jacques A. C., **3** 447
Charliere
Balloons, **2** 316, 318
Charles, Jacques A. C., **3** 447
Montgolfier brothers, **9** 1632
Charney, Jule
Meteorology, **9** 1558
Charter Air Taxi
Charter flying, **3** 449
Charter flying, 3 447
Charts, 3 450-55
Gnomonic projection, **6** 991
Maps and mapping, **8** 1476-80
Pilotage, **10** 1794
Chatham Aviation
Commuter airlines, **3** 544
Chavez, Georges
Altitude and altitude records, **1** 147
Checklist, 3 455-56
Cockpit, **3** 486
Checkout, 3 456
Kennedy Space Center, **7** 1267, 1269
Launch facilities, **7** 1307
Chemical elements
Elements, **4** 704-05
Stars, **12** 2160, 2162
Chemical energy, 3 456-57
Battery, **2** 338
Mechanical energy, **8** 1521
Photosynthesis, **10** 1789
Chemical rocket
Ion propulsion, **7** 1215
Chemicals
Agricultural aviation, **1** 39-41
Chemical substances
Oceanographic research, **10** 1732
Chemistry
Educational implications of aerospace
(chart), **4** 676
Chemosphere
Atmosphere, **2** 264
Chennault, Claire Lee (1890-1958,
American aviator), **3** 457
Flying Tigers, **5** 865
P-40, Curtiss, **10** 1777
World War II, **14** 2520

Chernuska (sher NEWS ka) (dog)
Animals in space, **1** 155
Cherokee, see Piper Cherokee Six
Chest belt
Rocket sled, **11** 1986
Chester, Art
Air racing, **1** 103
Cheyenne helicopter, see AH-56A Cheyenne
Chicago Aerial Industries
Aerial photography, **1** 10
Chicago ARTCC
Air traffic control, **1** 131
Chicago Fire Department helicopter
Police and fire services (picture), **10** 1835
Chicago Helicopter Airways, Inc.
Helicopters, **6** 1070
Chicago Pile
Nuclear energy, **9** 1710 (with picture)
Chicago route map
Commuter airlines, **3** 545
Chickasaw helicopter, see UH-19 Chickasaw
Chief of Naval Operations
Joint Chiefs of Staff, **7** 1242
Chile
South and Central America's
aviation, **11** 2090
China
Air forces of the world, **1** 63
Asia's aviation, **2** 203
Astronomy, **2** 235
Chennault, Claire Lee, **3** 457
Crop dusting, **4** 587, 593
Kites, **7** 1277-79
Mainland China's aerospace activities,
8 1421-29
Nationalist China's aviation, **9** 1664-66
Naval aviation, worldwide, **9** 1671
P-40, Curtiss, **10** 1777
Propellants, **10** 1859
China Air Lines
Nationalist China's aviation, **9** 1666
China Civil Aviation Corporation
Mainland China's aerospace activities,
8 1424
China Clipper, see Martin M-130
China National Aviation Corporation
Commerical airlines, **3** 509
Chinese kite
Kites (picture), **7** 1278
Chinese Nationalist Air Force
Nationalist China's aviation, **9** 1664-66
Chinese origin
Rockets and rocketry, **11** 1972
Chinese People's Aviation Corporation
Mainland China's aerospace activities,
8 1424
Chinook see CH-47 Chinook
Chlorella
Algae, **1** 143
Carbon dioxide, **3** 407
Closed ecological (EK o log ic al) system,
3 470
Life-support systems, **8** 1344
Chlorophyll
Algae, **1** 143
Atmosphere, **2** 265
Photosynthesis, **10** 1789
Chloroplasts
Photosynthesis, **10** 1789
Choctaw helicopter, see CH-34 Choctaw
Choisnet-Gohard, Marcelle
Medals and decorations (table), **8** 1526
Chokes, 3 459
Chondrites
Meteors, meteorites, and meteoroids,
9 1561
Chondrules
Meteors, meteorites, and meteoroids,
9 1561
Chord, airfoil
Airplane, **1** 85
Wings, **14** 2490
Chromal R (picture)
Apollo, **1** 176

Chromatic aberration
Telescopes and astronomical instruments, **12** 2247
Chromium atoms
Lasers, **7** 1305
Chromosphere
Astronomy, **2** 241
Sun, **12** 2173
Chromospheric flares
Kosmos satellites, **7** 1293
Chronographs
Chronometer, **3** 459
Chronometer (with picture), **3** 459
Chrysotile
Asbestos, **2** 202
Church, Ellen
Stewards and stewardesses, **12** 2165
Women in aerospace, **14** 2495
CIA
Intelligence, military, **7** 1180-81
U-2, **13** 2396
Cierva (see AIR va), **Juan de la** (1895-1936, Spanish engineer), **3** 459-60
Autogiros, **2** 185
Helicopters, **6** 1062-63
History of aviation, **6** 1109
Medals and decorations (table), **8** 1526
Cierva Autogiro Co., Ltd.
Autogiros, **2** 285
Cigognes Escadrille
World War I, **14** 2506
Circadian (Sir KAY dee an) **rhythm**, **3** 460-61
Aviation medicine, **2** 297
Man in flight, **8** 1449
Psychological factors of flight, **10** 1864
Circle
Astronomy, **2** 235
Photography, **10** 1782
Circuit, **3** 461
Circular arc supersonic airfoil (diagram)
Airfoil, **1** 61
Circular motion
Orbits and trajectories, **10** 1743
Circular orbit
Launch vehicles, **7** 1317
Orbital velocity, **10** 1738
Orbiting observatories, **10** 1739
Orbits and trajectories, **10** 1744
Circular velocity
Orbits and trajectories, **10** 1744
Circumference
Circumnavigation, **3** 462
Circumnavigation, **3** 462
Circumpolar constellations
Constellations, **3** 562
Cirrocumulus clouds
Clouds, **3** 472
Cirrus clouds
Clouds (picture), **3** 472
Cislunar space, **3** 462
Interplanetary Monitoring Platform satellites, **7** 1205
Citizen's band (radio frequency)
Transceivers, **13** 2308
Citizens League Against the Sonic Boom
Supersonic transports, **12** 2195
City of New York (airplane)
Lowe, Thaddeus S. C., **8** 1373
City of San Francisco (airplane)
Loening Amphibian, **8** 1369
Civil Aeromedical Institute
Aeronautical Center, **1** 25-26
Aviation medicine, **2** 295
Federal Aviation Administration, **5** 802
Civil Aeronautics Act of 1938
Aerospace industry, **1** 30
Air carrier, **1** 44
Airmail, **1** 77
Airports, **1** 98
Civil Aeronautics Board, **3** 462
Commercial airlines, **3** 512
Civil Aeronautics Administration
Commercial air transports, **3** 522
Federal Aviation Administration, **5** 794
Government in aerospace, **6** 1009

Civil Aeronautics Authority
Airports, **1** 98
Civil Aeronautics Board, **3** 462
Civil Aeronautics Board (with picture and organization chart), **3** 462-65
Air carrier, **1** 44
Air Commerce Act, **1** 45
Airlift, **1** 67
Airmail, **1** 77
Air route, **1** 104
Air taxis, **1** 117
Careers, **3** 413, 417
Charter flying, **3** 447
Commuter airlines, **3** 545
Crash investigation, **4** 579-81
Federal Aviation Administration, **5** 794
Government in aerospace, **6** 1008-09
Light aircraft, **8** 1352
National Air Taxi Conference, **9** 1662
National Aviation Trades Association, **9** 1663
Regional airlines, **11** 1944
Safety statistics, **11** 2001
Civil Air Patrol, **3** 466
National emergency airlift plans, **9** 1663
Radio communications, **10** 1895
Search and rescue, **11** 2025
United States Air Force, **13** 2370
Civil Air Transport
Nationalist China's aviation, **9** 1666
Civil and structural engineering
Careers (table), **3** 416
Civil aviation, **3** 466
Careers, **3** 411
General aviation, **6** 953
Civil Aviation Administration of China
Mainland China's aerospace activities, **8** 1424-26, 1428, (map) 1422-23
Civil Aviation Assistance Groups (CAAG)
Federal Aviation Administration, **5** 801
Civil Aviation Bureau
Mainland China's aerospace activities, **8** 1424
Civil Aviation Emergency Airlift Plans
National emergency airlift plans, **9** 1663
Civil Aviation Medical Association, **3** 466
Civil defense, **3** 467
Civilian air traffic
European air traffic control, **4** 752
Civil investigations
Crash investigation, **4** 579-82
Civil Reserve Air Fleet (see also National Emergency Defense Airlift)
Airlift, **1** 67
National emergency airlift plans, **9** 1663
Civil War (U.S.)
Aerial photography, **1** 10
Army aviation, **2** 194
Balloons, **2** 323
Photogrammetry, **10** 1779
Civil Works Administration
Airports, **1** 98
CL-44, see Canadair CL-44
CL-84, see Canadair CL-84
CL-215, see Canadair CL-215
CL-475 (Lockheed)
V/STOL aircraft, **13** 2444
Claiborne, Dorothy Meade
Duke, Charles Moss, Jr., **4** 654
Clark 1000
Crop dusting, **4** 589
Clarke, Arthur Charles (1917   , British science fiction author), **3** 467
Communications satellites, **3** 532
Science fiction, **11** 2017-20
Clark "Y" Airfoil (diagram)
Airfoil, **1** 61
Class I and II physicals
Medical examiner, **8** 1526-27
Classified information, **3** 467
Classified payloads
Military space program, **9** 1594-95
Class III Medical Certificate
Pilot's training, **10** 1811
Clayton, Richard
Airmail, **1** 69

Clean room, **3** 467-68
Kennedy Space Center, **7** 1267
Clear air turbulence, **3** 468-69
Aviation weather, **2** 303
Mountain, desert, and jungle flying, **9** 1642
U-2, **13** 2397
Weather maps and charts, **13** 2458
Wind, **13** 2485
Clear, Alaska
Ballistic Missile Early Warning System, **2** 313
Clearance
Control tower, **3** 564
Instrument Flight Rules, **7** 1165
Instrument flight techniques, **7** 1167
Clear ice
Aviation weather (picture), **2** 301
Icing, **7** 1145
Cleat (aircraft)
U.S.S.R. aerospace activities (table), **13** 2337
Cleland, Cook
Air racing, **1** 103
Clemenceau (aircraft carrier)
Naval aviation, worldwide (picture), **9** 1669
Cleveland Air Show of 1949 (picture)
Air shows, **1** 115
Cleveland National Air Races
Air racing, **1** 102
Climatic Laboratory
Elgin Air Force Base, **4** 679
Climb
Instrument panels, **7** 1176
Maneuvers, **8** 1434-37, (diagram) 1436
Propellers, **10** 1863
Climb-out, **3** 469
Clock, see Circadian rhythm
Clipper
China Clipper, **3** 457
Instrument panels, **7** 1177-78
Piper, William T., **10** 1815
Close air support
United States Air Force, **13** 2372
Vietnam, **13** 2419
Closed circuit television
Blockhouse, **2** 369
Communications satellites, **3** 542
Closed ecological system, **3** 469-71
Carbon dioxide, **3** 407
Life-support systems, **8** 1344
Closed environmental system
Algae, **1** 143
Closed-in space taxis
Maneuvering in space, **8** 1431
Closed-loop control
Guidance and control systems, **6** 1034
Closing rate
Collision avoidance system, **3** 489
Clostermann, Pierre
World War II (table), **14** 2517
Cloud Car (aircraft)
World War I, **14** 2509
Cloud patterns
Air masses (map), **1** 81
Kosmos satellites, **7** 1290
Clouds (with pictograph), **3** 471-74
Composition analysis
Kites, **7** 1279
Evaporation and condensation, **4** 758
Precipitation, **10** 1844
Rain, **10** 1900
Venus, **13** 2407
Cloud seeding (with picture), **3** 474
Cloudster (airplane)
Douglas, Donald Wills, **4** 649
Cloverleaf
Maneuvers (diagram), **8** 1441
Cluster
Apollo Applications Program, **2** 185
Terminology of aerospace (table), **12** 2272
Clustering
Juno rockets, **7** 1260
Launch vehicles, **7** 1315

Clutter
Radar, **10** 1879
CM, see Apollo Command Module
C. Mk 1, see Hawker Siddeley Argosy
Coach (aircraft)
U.S.S.R. aerospace activities (table),
13 2337
Coalescence
Precipitation (with chart), **10** 1844
Rain, **10** 1900
Coal Sack
Astronomy, **2** 252
Coastal (airship)
First World War aircraft, **5** 821
Coast and Geodetic Survey
Environmental Science Services
Administration, **4** 724
National Aviation Trades Association,
9 1663
Coast Guard Academy
Service academies, **11** 2044
Coast Guard aviation, 3 475-80
Coast Guard Institute
Aeronautical Center, **1** 25-26
Coaxial cable
Television, **12** 2260
Cobalt
Materials, **8** 1508
Cobb, Geraldyn (1931-   , American
aviatrix), **3** 480
Women in aerospace (picture), **14** 2495
Cobham, Sir Alan (1894   , British
aviator), **3** 480
Medals and decorations (table), **8** 1526
Cobra helicopter, see AH-1G HueyCobra
Cochran, Jacqueline (1910-   , American
aviatrix), **3** 481
Air racing, **1** 103
Medals and decorations (tables), **8** 1526
Women in aerospace, **14** 2495
Cockburn Lange photograph
World War I, **14** 2500
Cockerell, Sir Christopher
Ground-effect machines, **6** 1025
United Kingdom aerospace activities,
13 2355
Cockpit, 3 481-87
Airplane, **1** 83
Certification procedures, **3** 443
Console, **3** 561
Instrument flight techniques, **7** 1166
Instrument panels, **7** 1177
Cocoons
Cargo aircraft, **3** 421
Coded radar beacon transponder
Positive control areas, **10** 1839
Coded reference signal
Beam-rider guidance, **2** 346
Codos, Paul
Distance and distance records, **4** 640
Cody, Samuel Franklin (1861-1913,
American British aviator), **3** 487
Coefficient of expansion
Glass, **6** 981
Coffey, Harry K.
Medals and decorations (table), **8** 1526
Coffin, E. A.
Coast Guard aviation, **3** 476
Coherent light
Lasers, **7** 1303
Coherent translation
Transponders, **13** 2309
Coherer
Radio, **10** 1887
COIN, see Counter-insurgency aircraft
"Coke bottle" fuselage (picture)
Aerodynamics, **1** 23
Cold front
Aviation weather, **2** 303
Preflight training, **10** 1848
Cold-soaking
Polar flights, **10** 1828
Cold war
Aerospace industry, **1** 31
Aircraft carriers, **1** 51

Cold welding
Metals and metallurgy, **9** 1550
College Park, Maryland
Airports (picture), **1** 98
Colleges
Educational implications of aerospace,
4 675
Collier Trophy
Airmail, **1** 73
Autogiros, **2** 286
Douglas, Donald Wills, **4** 649
National Aeronautic Association, **9** 1648
Collins, Michael (1930-   ), **3** 487-88
Astronauts, **2** 217-19, 229, (with picture)
Gemini, **5** 946-47
Instrument panels, **7** 1177
Maneuvering in space, **8** 1430
Manned spaceflight (table), **8** 1461
Spaceflight training (picture), **12** 2115
Collinshaw, Raymond
World War I, **14** 2506, (table) 2507, 2508
Collision avoidance system (with diagrams),
3 488-89
Air traffic control, **1** 137
Colombia
Crop dusting, **4** 593
South and Central America's aviation,
11 2090
Colonial Air Transport
Commercial airlines, **3** 509
Colonization
Implications of aerospace, **7** 1150
Lunar bases, **8** 1395
Color code
Lighting facilities, **8** 1353, (diagram) 1355
Color index
Astronomy, **2** 249
Colt (aircraft)
U.S.S.R. aerospace activities (table),
13 2337
Columbia (Wright-Bellanca monoplane)
Bellanca, Giuseppe, **2** 349
Columbium
Materials, **8** 1507
Column of thrust
Launch vehicles, **7** 1328
Coma
Comets, **3** 490
Combat air patrol and cover fighters
Air forces of the world, **1** 64
Combat cargo hospital aircraft
Korean war (picture), **7** 1289
Combat Control Center
Ballistic Missile Early Warning System,
2 313
Combat Operations Center
Air defense systems, **1** 60
NORAD, **9** 1700-01 (with picture)
Combat Readiness Medal
Medals and decorations (picture), **8** 1525
Combe, A. N.
Distance and distance records, **4** 640
Combustible fuels
Matter, **8** 1513
Combustion, 3 489
Combustion chamber, 3 489-90
Launch vehicles, **7** 1325
Oxidizers, **10** 1751
Combustion engines
Junkers, Hugo, **7** 1258
Combustion gases
Nozzles, **9** 1707
Comet (airplane), see DeHavilland Comet
Comets (with diagram and pictures), **3** 490-93
Astronomy, **2** 235
Halley, Edmund, **6** 1047
Interplanetary travel, **7** 1212
Kepler, Johannes, **7** 1274
Orbits and trajectories, **10** 1745
Command
Space communications, **11** 2098
Terminology of aerospace (table), **12** 2272
Command and data acquisition, 3 493
Weather satellites, **13** 2461, 2463, 2465,
2466

Command and General Staff School
Arnold, Henry Harley, **2** 201
Command guidance system
Aircraft carriers, **1** 48
Missiles, **9** 1613
Command Module, see also Apollo
Aluminum, **1** 148
Apollo (with pictures and diagrams),
1, 164-77
Apollo Applications Program, **2** 185
Instrument panels, **7** 1178
Lunar exploration, **8** 1401
Module, **9** 1630
Commander (airplane)
General aviation (picture), **6** 953
Commando activities
Intelligence, military, **7** 1180
Command of the Air (book)
Douhet, Giulio, **4** 650
Military aviation, **9** 1582
Commemorative stamps and medals, 3 493-95
Balloons, **2** 331
Objects of art, **10** 1721-23
Commentariolus (book)
Copernicus, Nicolaus, **3** 566
Commerce, Department of
Airmail, **1** 76
Airports, **1** 98
Aviation medicine, **2** 294
Charts, **3** 455
Commercial aircraft
Call signs, **3** 398
Interiors of aircraft (pictures), **7** 1184-85
Japan's aerospace activities, **7** 1128
Commercial airlines, 3 496-515
Airmail (picture), **1** 79
Food and nutrition, **5** 871, 872
South and Central America's aviation,
11 2087
Commercial airport
Airports, **1** 93
Commercial air transports, 3 516-43
U.S. Airlines (chart and table), **3** 526
Commercial aviation, 3 530
Airmail, **1** 75
Cargo aircraft, **3** 417-24
History of aviation, **6** 1107, 1115, 1116
Italy's aerospace activities, **7** 1222
Knight, James H., **7** 1281
Commercial flying
Safety statistics, **11** 2001
Commercial models
Model aircraft, **9** 1625
Commercial pilot certificates
Aircraft Owners and Pilots Association, **1** 52
Commercial procedures
Radio communications, **10** 1898
Commercial radio
Radio, **10** 1887
Committee on Peaceful Uses of Outer Space
United Nations, **13** 2357
Committee on Space Flight
American Rocket Society, **1** 151
Committee on Space Research of the
International Council of Scientific Unions
Alouette satellites, **1** 144
Ariel satellites, **2** 191
International Council of Scientific
Unions, **7** 1193
Spacecraft, **11** 2100
Common bulkhead
Manufacturing, **8** 1474-75, (picture) 1475
Commonwealth Department of Civil Aviation
Australia's aviation, **2** 279
Communication range
Radio, **10** 1885
Communications
Aerospace, **1** 27
Aircraft carriers, **1** 50-51
Air traffic control, **1** 129
Applications Technology Satellites, **2** 189
Cybernetics, **4** 602
Occupations (with tables), **10** 1729-30
Spacecraft design, **11** 2101

Communications and Control Center
Aircraft carriers, 1 47
Communications, Command, and Telemetry System
Mission Control Center, 9 1617, 1618
Communications relays
Air defense systems, 1 60
Communications Satellite Corporation, 3 538
Goddard Space Flight Center, 6 992
International Telecommunications Satellite Consortium, 7 1202-03
NASA, 9 1653, (table, Major launchings) 1652
Communications Satellite Project Office
Defense communications satellites, 4 615
Communications satellites, 3 531-43
Act of 1962, 3 538
Aerospace industry, 1 33
Aircraft carriers, 1 51
Apollo, 1 184
Clarke, Arthur Charles, 3 467
Ground antennas, 6 1016
Implications of aerospace, 7 1151
Legal implications of aerospace, 7 1331
Manufacturing, 8 1475
Military implications of space, 9 1589
Military space program, 9 1591, 1596-97, (pictures) 1590, 1596, (data table) 1605
NASA, 9 1653, (table, Major Launchings) 1652
National Aeronautics and Space Council, 9 1658
Satellites, 11 2007
Television, 12 2263
Transponder, 13 2310
U.S.S.R. aerospace activities, 13 2340
Communications Support Element
United States Strike Command, 13 2390
Communications terminals
Radar (picture), 10 1876
Communist Chinese Airlines
Mainland China's aerospace activities, 8 1422, 1424
Commutator
Space communications, 11 2097
Commuter airlines, 3 544-46
Commercial airlines, 4 499
Commuter-Air Taxi Service
Commercial airlines, 3 499
Compagnie des Messageries Arienne
(come pa NE day may SA jer ees ar ee EN)
Breguet, Louis Charles, 3 388
Compania Mexicana de Aviacion
Commercial airlines, 3 508
Company-owned airplanes
Business aviation, 3 394
Comparative polarimetric studies
Mars, 8 1491
Compass, 3 546-51
Instrument panels, 7 1176
Navigation instruments, 9 1672
Precision measurements, 10 1845
Compass card
Compasses, 3 547
Compass correction card (with diagram)
Compasses, 3 548
Compass courses
Course plotting, 4 578
Compass locator
Instrument landing system, 7 1170
Compass rose
Compasses, 3 547
Compatible land-use planning
Noise, 9 1700
Competitive models
Model aircraft, 9 1626
Complexes 19, 34 and 37
Blockhouse, 2 367, 368 (with picture)
Component testing
Kennedy Space Center, 7 1267
Composite material
Materials, 8 1504, 1506-07
Composite rocket/air breathing engine, 3 551

Compositors
Plastics, 10 1825
Compound aircraft
Helicopters, 6 1068, (pictures) 1069
Compressibility of air
Aerodynamics, 1 24
Compression, 3 551
Sound, 11 2077
Compression ribs
Airplane, 1 85
Wings, 14 2491
Compression stroke
Aircraft propulsion systems, 1 53
Compressor
Gas turbine engines, 5 918-25, (diagrams) 920, 921
Supercharger, 12 2175
Compressor assembly
Pulsejet engine, 10 1865
Computer Assisted Instruction
Computers, 3 559
Computer center
Service academies, 11 2045
Computer correspondence
Communications satellites, 3 543
Computer display channel
National Airspace System, 9 1661
Computer-driven inputs
Launching, 7 1309
Computerized automatic pilots
Avionics, 2 307
Computerized flight director instruments
Automatic landing, 2 287
Computers, 3 552-60
Air Defense Command, 1 59
Aviation weather, 2 300
Blockhouse, 2 368
Electronics, 4 693, 703, 704
Flight simulators, 5 851, 852, 853, 854
Government contracts, 6 999
Guidance and control systems, 6 1038, 1039
Launching, 7 1310
Launch vehicles, 7 1316
Materials, 8 1512
Meteorology, 9 1558
Morse code, 9 1639
National Airspace System, 9 1660
Solid-state physics, 11 2073
Spaceflight simulators, 12 2142
Spinoff, 12 2142
Systems engineering, 12 2226
Tracking systems and networks, 13 2297
Weather maps and charts, 13 2454, 2455, 2458
Computer update equipment
National Airspace System, 9 1660
COMSAT, see Communications Satellite Corp.
Concorde SST (supersonic transport)
Canada's aviation, 3 401
Commercial air transports (pictures), 3 529, 530
France's aerospace activities, 5 886, 887, 888, (picture) 885
Fuel systems, 5 905
International projects, 7 1200
Life-support systems (diagram), 8 1339
Manufacturing (table and diagram), 8 1471
Supersonic transports, 12 2182, 2184-89, 2193, 2197, 2199, (pictures) 2179, 2184-86
Condensation
Atmosphere, 2 263
Fog, 5 866
Condensation nuclei
Evaporation and condensation, 4 758
Precipitation, 10 1844
Condenser lenses
Planetarium, 10 1818
Condenser microphones
Microphone, 9 1563
Condor
Air-to-surface missiles, 1 122, 124
Condor (airplane), see Curtiss Condor

Conduction
Atmosphere, 2 266
Heat energy, 6 1055
Conductors
Electricity, 4 683
Electronics, 4 694
Cone
Lambert projection, 7 1296
Cone-of-position
Celestial navigation, 3 429
Cone of silence
Navigation techniques, 9 1684
Conference on High Altitude Meteorology and Space Weather
American Meteorological Society, 1 150
Configuration, 3 560
Attack aircraft, 2 273
Commercial airlines, 3 502
Spacecraft design, 11 2100
Congressional Aviation Policy Board
Careers, 3 413
Congressional Gold medal
Ellsworth, Lincoln, 4 707
Congressional Medal of Honor
Bong, Richard Ira, 3 380
Doolittle, James Harold, 4 644
Lindbergh, Charles Augustus, 8 1359
Rickenbacker, Edward Vernon, 11 1965
Congreve
Missiles (table), 9 1616
Conical radar
Radar, 10 1877
Conjunction, 3 560
Connecting rods
Reciprocating engines, 11 1916
Connie, see Lockheed Constellation
Conrad, Charles, Jr. (1930-   ), **3** 560
Astronauts, 2 216, 217, 219, 226, 231, (with picture)
Gemini, 5 937-39, 947-49
Manned spaceflight (table), 8 1461
Rendezvous and docking (with picture), 11 1956, 1960
Spaceflight training (picture), 12 2118
Conrad, Max
Medals and decorations (table), 8 1526
Consciousness, loss of
Blackout, 2 362
Conservation
Energy, 4 715
Console, 3 561
Control tower, 3 564
Planetarium, 10 1819
Consolidated Aircraft Corporation
Bell, Lawrence Dale, 2 348
Consolidated B-24, see B-24 Liberator
Consolidated P2Y flying boat
Flying boats, 5 859
Consolidated PBY
Coast Guard aviation (picture), 3 477, 479
Flying boats, 5 859, 860
History of aviation, 6 1114
Consolidated Vultee aircraft
Commercial air transports, 3 524
Constant-airspeed cruise
Cruising flight, 4 595
Constantinesco gear
World War I, 14 2505
Constantinesco, George
World War I, 14 2505-06
Constant-level
Balloons, 2 331
Constant-pitch
Propellers, 10 1862
Constant-speed propeller
Power management, 10 1841
Constant-wear garment
Terminology of aerospace (table), 12 2272
Constellation, see Lockheed Constellation
Constellations (with diagrams), **3** 561-63
Interplanetary travel, 7 1209
Planetarium, 10 1818
Constraints
Launch window, 7 1329

Construction and Repair, Bureau of
Coast Guard aviation, **3** 477
Consumer Price Index
Aerospace industry, **1** 31-32
Contact flying, 3 563
Contact ion microthrustor
Electric propulsion (diagram), **4** 687
Containment vessel
Airlock, **1** 67
Contamination
Legal implications of aerospace, **7** 1331
Conte Rosso
Aircraft carriers, **1** 48
Continental Air Command, 3 563
Tactical Air Command, **12** 2228
United States Air Force, **13** 2370
United States Strike Command, **13** 2390
Continental Airlines
Commercial airlines, **3** 498
Continental land mass
Poles, **10** 1833
Continental model 0-200-A (picture)
Airplane, **1** 85
Contingency recovery areas
Launching, **7** 1311
Recovery, **11** 1927
Continual wave signals
Astronomy, **2** 242
Continuous composite
Materials, **8** 1504
Continuous filament
Materials, **8** 1506
Continuous strip camera
Aerial photography, **1** 10
Continuous-wave
Radar, **10** 1872-75
Contos, Jim
Balloons, **2** 322
Contour
Photogrammetry, **10** 1780
Contoured deck
Pontoons (with diagram), **10** 1838
Contour feathers
Bird flight, **2** 361
Contour interval
Maps and mapping, **8** 1477
Contour lines
Maps and mapping (picture), **8** 1476
Contour map
Maps and mapping, **8** 1477, (picture) 1476
Contract Air Mail
Airmail, **1** 75
Contrail, 3 563
Battle of Britain (picture), **2** 343
Control (see also Guidance and control)
Mercury program, **9** 1530
Space communications, **11** 2098
Spacecraft design, **11** 2100
Control car
Airships, **1** 106-08
Control circuitry
Kosmos satellites, **7** 1292
Control circuits
Electrical systems, **4** 681
Control consoles
Air traffic control, **1** 131
Control equipment
Reconnaissance aircraft, **11** 1924
Control grid
Electronics, **4** 695, 698
Controllable-pitch propeller
Power management, **10** 1841
Controlled airspace
Instrument Flight Rules, **7** 1165
Control-line models
Model aircraft, **9** 1624
Control loop
Automatic pilot, **2** 289
Controls
Lunar Module, **8** 1408-10
Reciprocating engines, **11** 1919
Control stick
Contrail, **3** 563
Control surfaces
Airplane, **1** 86-87
Hydraulic systems, **6** 1139

Control system
Launch vehicles, **7** 1316
Control tower, 3 563-64
Air terminals, **1** 118
Air traffic control, **1** 133
Radio communications, **10** 1897
Control valves
Airlock, **1** 67
Control zone
Instrument Flight Rules, **7** 1165
Convair 340 (picture)
Commercial air transports, **3** 524
Convair 880
Environmental control system (diagram),
4 719
Nationalist China's aviation, **9** 1666
(picture), 1665
Convair 990 (picture)
Commercial air transports, **3** 529
Convair (Division of General Dynamics
Corporation)
Business aviation, **3** 396
Cargo aircraft, **3** 418
Centaur, **3** 433
Commercial air transports, **3** 524
Ehricke, Krafft Arnold, **4** 680
Convair B-36, see B-36
Convair C-131, see C-131
Convair F-102, see F-102 Delta Dagger
Convair F-106, see F-106 Delta Dart
Convair R3Y-1 Tradewinds flying boat
Flying boats, **5** 861
Convair X-11, see X-11
Convair X-12, see X-12
Convection
Atmosphere, **2** 266
Clouds, **3** 471
Heat energy, **6** 1055
Kosmos satellites, **7** 1293
Convection currents (with diagram), **3** 564-65
Atmosphere, **2** 264
Convective thunderstorms
Aviation weather, **2** 301
Convertiplane, 3 565
Rotary-wing aircraft, **11** 1991
Conway jet engine
United Kingdom aerospace activities,
13 2350
Cook, James
Poles, **10** 1834
Cooling fins
Reciprocating engines, **11** 1916
Cooling properties
Oxidizers, **10** 1752
Cooling system
Radiators, **10** 1884
Cooperative target
Radar, **10** 1875
Cooper, L. Gordon, Jr. (1927-   ), **3** 565-66
Astronauts, **2** 215, 216, 217, 219, 225,
226, 229, 230, 231, 232 (with pictures)
Atlas missile and launch vehicle, **2** 260
Gemini, **5** 937-39, (picture) 939
Manned spaceflight, **8** 1460, (table) 1461
Mercury program, **9** 1531, 1539, 1543,
1545, (pictures) 1544, 1545, (data
table) 1544
Reciprocating engines, **11** 1917
Rendezvous and docking (with picture),
11 1956, 1960
Spaceflight training (picture), **12** 2118
Coordination
Piloting techniques, **10** 1796
Coordination of launchings
Legal implications of aerospace, **7** 1331
Coot (aircraft)
U.S.S.R. aerospace activities (table),
13 2337
Copernicus (crater)
Astrogeology (picture), **2** 210
Craters, **4** 584
Lunar exploration, **8** 1402
Copernicus, Nicolaus (1473-1543, Polish
astronomer and mathematician), **3** 566

Apollo, **1** 163
Aristarchus of Samos, **2** 193
Astronomy, **2** 236, 237, 242
Brahe, Tycho, **3** 385
Celestial mechanics, **3** 427
Earth science, **4** 665
Galileo Galilei, **5** 912
Kepler, Johannes, **7** 1274
Ptolemy, Claudius, **10** 1864
Copilot
Aircrew, **1** 59
Coppens, Willy
World War I (table), **14** 2507, 2508
Copper mass
Intercontinental ballistic missiles, **7** 1183
Coralie
Launch vehicles, **7** 1327
Coral Sea
Aircraft carriers, **1** 50, 51
Coral Sea, Battle of the
Aircraft carriers, **1** 49
Core
Earth, **4** 660
Coriolis force
Wind, **13** 2485
Cornell Aeronautical Laboratory, 3 566
Cornu, Paul
Helicopters, **6** 1062
Corona
Astronomy, **2** 241
Astrophysics, **2** 256
Eclipse, **4** 669
Sun, **12** 2174
Corona, solar, 3 567
Coronado (flying boat)
Flying boats (picture), **5** 860
History of aviation, **6** 1114
Coronagraph, 3 567
Astronomy, **2** 240
Astrophysics, **2** 256
Eclipse, **4** 669
Sun, **12** 2172
Corpuscular flows
Kosmos satellites, **7** 1290
Corpuscular radiation
Radiation, **10** 1880
Corpuscular theory of matter
Atoms, 269
Corrected altitude
Altitude and altitude records, **1** 146
Corrigan, Douglas (1907-   , American
aviator), **3** 567
Corrosion
Lubricants, **8** 1375
Corrosion-resistant primers
Paints, **10** 1754
Corrugated metal skin covering
Junkers J-4, **7** 1259
Corsair, see F4U Corsair
Corsair II, see A-7 Corsair II
Cosmic dust, 3 568
Astrogeology, **2** 212
Data acquisition and processing, **4** 607
Mariner probes, **8** 1488
Cosmic radiation
Aerobee, **1** 18
Aerospace Research Support Program, **1** 35
Radiation, **10** 1882
Cosmic radio noise
Astronomy, **2** 242
Cosmic ray flux
International Geophysical Year, **7** 1197
Cosmic rays, 3 568
Astronomy, **2** 249
Balloons, **2** 321, 325, (picture) 329
Geomagnetic field, **6** 977
Interplanetary Monitoring Platform
satellites, **7** 1205
Milky Way, **9** 1605
Orbiting observatories, **10** 1741
Piccard family, **10** 1790-91
Pioneer, **10** 1813
Polar flights, **10** 1831
Radiation, **10** 1880

Cosmic ray telescope
Mariner probes, **8** 1488
Cosmic space
Legal implications of aerospace, **7** 1331
Cosmobiology
Mars, **8** 1490
Cosmogony, 3 568
Cosmological research
Radio astronomy, **10** 1892
Cosmology, 3 568
Radio astronomy, **10** 1891
Universe, **13** 2391
Cosmonauts, 4 569-75 (with pictures and table)
Astronauts, **2** 217
Food and nutrition, **5** 876
Life-support systems, **8** 1339-40
Sputniks, **12** 2153, 2154
Cosmos, 3 568
Cosmos satellites, see Kosmos satellites
COSPAR, see Committee on Space Research
Costa Rica
Commemorative stamps and medals, **3** 495
Crop dusting, **4** 587
Costes, Dieudonne
Distance records, **4** 640
Medals and decorations (table), **8** 1526
Cost of training
Astronauts, **2** 229
Cost-plus-incentive-fee contracts
Titan III, **12** 2291
Cost-sharing basis
Launch vehicles, **7** 1327
Coude-experimental laboratory
Observatories, **10** 1725
Coude focus
Observatories, **10** 1725
Coude spectrograph
Observatories, **10** 1725
Cougar (airplane)
Homebuilt aircraft, **6** 1125
Coulomb, Charles Augustin
Electricity, **4** 684
Countdown, 4 576
Apollo (picture), **1** 179
Backout, **2** 309
Go-no-go decision, **6** 996
Launching, **7** 1308-09
Terminology of aerospace (table), **12** 2272
Counter drum pointer altimeter
Altimeter, **1** 146
Counter-espionage
Intelligence, military, **7** 1180
Counterflow beams
Kosmos satellites, **7** 1294
Counter-insurgency aircraft, 4 576-77, (with table, Principal U.S. Aircraft)
Attack aircraft, **2** 273
Eglin Air Force Base, **4** 679
History of aviation, **6** 1118
Counter-Invader
Counter-insurgency aircraft, **4** 576
Counter pointer altimeter
Altimeter, **1** 146
Country surveys
Intelligence, military, **7** 1181
Courier
Communications satellites, **3** 533, 543
Defense communications satellites, **4** 615
Military space program, **9** 1594
Course
Instrument Flight Rules, **7** 1165
Course fluctuations
Launch vehicles, **7** 1316
Course plotting, 4 578-79 (with picture)
Course records
World records and round-the-world flights, **14** 2498-99
Court of inquiry
Pearl Harbor, **10** 1770
Coutelle, Jean Marie Joseph (1748-1835)
Balloons, **2** 323
Coverall harness
Recovery, **11** 1929

Coveralls, flying
Rocket sled, **11** 1986
Covert propaganda
Intelligence, military, **7** 1180
Cowdin, Elliott C.
Lafayette Escadrille, **7** 1295
Cowl, 4 579
Cowl flaps
Airplane, **1** 90
Reciprocating engines, **11** 1918-19
Cowling
Reciprocating engines, **11** 1918
Coxwell, Henry Tracy
Balloons, **2** 317
CP-107 Argus (Canadair)
Canada's aviation, **3** 404
Naval aviation, worldwide (Canada), **9** 1672
CPA, see Canadian Pacific Airlines
Crab angle
Automatic landing, **2** 287
Crabbing approach
Cross-wind landing, **4** 594
Piloting techniques, **10** 1080
Crab Nebula
Astronomy, **2** 251, (picture) 252
Nova, **9** 1707
Radiation, **10** 1882
X-ray stars, **14** 2533
Crack root
Material fatigue, **8** 1498
CRAF, see Civil Reserve Air Fleet
Crane, Joe
Medals and decorations (table), **8** 1526
Crankshaft
Reciprocating engines, **11** 1914, 1916
Crash investigation, 4 579-83 (with pictures)
Flight recorder, **5** 848
Crash trucks, 4 583-84 (with picture)
Emergency landing procedures, **4** 708
Helicopters, **6** 1071
Crater of Archimedes
Lunar probes, **8** 1378
Crater of Copernicus
Lunar exploration (chart), **8** 1402
Crater of Theophilus
Lunar charts (picture), **8** 1400
Craters, 4 584
Astronomy, **2** 243
Mariner probes, **8** 1488
Mercury, **8** 1528
Orbits and trajectories, **10** 1744
Ranger (with pictures), **10** 1909
Crawford, Frederick C.
Medals and decorations (table), **8** 1526
Crawler transporter
Launch facilities, **7** 1307
Crawlerway
Kennedy Space Center, **7** 1272
Creek (aircraft)
U.S.S.R. aerospace activities (table), **13** 2337
Crepe Ring
Astronomy, 246
Crescent moon
Moon, **9** 1634, (with picture)
Cress, Barbara H.
Lawrence, Robert H., Jr., **7** 1329
Crew equipment
Lunar Module, **8** 1410
Crew reception area
Lunar Receiving Laboratory, **8** 1415
Crews, Albert H., Jr. (1929-   , American aerospace research pilot), **4** 584
Manned Orbiting Laboratory, **8** 1456
Crew systems equipment
Life-support systems, **8** 1341-43, (pictures) 1342-43
Crime detection
Police and fire services, **10** 1834
Crippen, Robert L.
Manned Orbiting Laboratory, **8** 1456
Crissy, Myron
Bombs, **3** 377
Croce-Spinelli, J. E.
Aviation medicine, **2** 293
Balloons, **2** 324

Crocidolite
Asbestos, **2** 202
Crookes, William
Electronics, **4** 693
Vacuum tubes, **13** 2398
Crop dusting (with diagrams, pictures and table), **4** 585-94
Economic implications of aerospace, **4** 671
Utility aviation, **13** 2394
Crosby, Harry
X-series aerospace vehicles, **14** 2535
Crossbars
Instrument flight techniques, **7** 1168
Lighting facilities, **8** 1355
Cross, Carl S.
Test pilots and test flying, **12** 2280
Cross-country flying
Pilot's training, **10** 1811
Crossfield, Albert Scott, Jr. (1921-   , American aeronautical engineer), **4** 594
Test pilots and test flying, **12** 2279
X-15 research program, **14** 2530, 2533
Cross pointer indicator
Instrument landing system, **7** 1171
Cross range
PRIME, **10** 1853
Crosswind
Piloting techniques, diagrams, **10** 1800-01
Cross-wind landing (with diagram), **4** 594
Landing techniques, **7** 1301
Cruciform array
Reaction control systems, **10** 1912
Cruise performance
Power management (data chart), **10** 1841
Cruising altitude
Instrument Flight Rules, **7** 1165
Penetration, **10** 1774
Cruising flight, 4 595
Crusader, see F-8 Crusader
Crust
Earth, **4** 660
Crux
Constellations, **3** 562
Cryogenic oxidizer
Oxidizers, **10** 1752
Cryogenics (with diagram and pictures), **4** 596-99
Aluminum, **1** 148
Computers, **3** 560
Electrical systems **4** 683 (with diagram)
Kennedy Space Center, **7** 1267
Launch vehicles, **7** 1315-16
propellants, **4** 595
Cruising flight, **4** 595-96
Launch vehicles, **7** 1315
storage system, **4** 597
surgery, **4** 597
Cryopumping
Cryogenics, **4** 597
Cryotron
Cryogenics, **4** 597
Crystal
Materials, **8** 1506
Crystal detector
Radio, **10** 1887
Crystalline lattice
Solid-state physics (diagram), **11** 2072
Crystallography, 4 598-99
Crystal microphones
Microphone, **9** 1563
Crystal system
Crystallography, **4** 598
C. Star (airship)
First World War aircraft, **5** 821
Cub (airplane), see Piper Cub
Cub (Russian airplane)
U.S.S.R. aerospace activities (table), **13** 2337
Cuba
Airmail, **1** 78
Commemorative stamps and medals, **3** 495
missile crisis
Aerial photography (picture), **1** 12
Aircraft carriers, 51
South and Central America's aviation, **11** 2090

Cuban eight
Maneuvers, **8** 1441
CUE, see Computer update equipment
Cultural Symbols
Charts, **3** 454
Culver, H. P.
Airmail, **1** 70
Cumuliform
Clouds, **3** 471
Cumulonimbus clouds
Aviation weather, **2** 301
Cumulus clouds
Clouds, **3** 472, 473
Cunningham, Alfred A.
Marine Corps Aviation, **8** 1481
Cunningham, John
Altitude and altitude records, **1** 147
Cunningham, R. Walter (1932-   ),
4 599-600
Apollo (picture) **1** 171
Astronauts, **2** 217, 218, 219, 226, 228,
230 (with picture)
Curtin, Richard D.
Reconnaissance satellites, **11** 1926
Curtis, Frazier
Lafayette Escadrille, **7** 1295
Curtiss (airplane)
First World War aircraft, **5** 818
Curtiss Aeroplane and Motor Company
Curtiss, Glenn Hammond, **4** 600
Curtiss AT-5A
Manufacturing, **8** 1469
Curtiss Carrier Pigeon
Commercial air transports, (picture) **3** 517
Curtiss Condor
Commercial air transports (with picture),
3 518
Second World War aircraft, **11** 2033
Curtiss, Glenn Hammond (1878-1930,
American air pioneer and inventor), **4** 600
Aerial Experiment Association
(with picture), **1** 7-8
Aerospace industry, **1** 29
Aircraft propulsion systems, **1** 52
Air racing, **1** 102, 103
Air shows, **1** 115
Armament, **2** 193
Barnstormers, **2** 332
Bell, Alexander Graham, **2** 347
Fabre, Henri, **5** 785
Flying boats, **5** 858
History of aviation, **6** 1105, (table) 1119
Manufacturing, **8** 1467
United States Air Force, **13** 2359
United States Naval Aviation, **13** 2377
Curtiss H-10 Flying Boat
Coast Guard aviation (picture), **3** 476
Curtiss HA
Airmail, **1** 71
Curtiss Hawk 75A
Second World War aircraft, **11** 2029
Curtiss JN-4 Jenny (drawings, table),
7 1231-32
Aerospace industry, **1** 30
Aircraft propulsion systems, **1** 56
Airmail, **1** 68, 71
Canada's aviation, **3** 400
Curtiss, Glenn Hammond, **4** 600
History of aviation (picture), **6** 1103
Curtiss Manufacturing Company
Curtiss, Glenn Hammond, **4** 600
Curtiss Model D Hydro (with diagram),
4 600-01
Curtiss, Navy see Navy Curtiss
Curtiss Navy flying boats
Commercial air transports, **3** 517
Curtiss Oriole
Bennett, Floyd, **2** 350
Commercial air transports, **3** 517
Curtiss OX-5 engine
Aircraft propulsion systems, **1** 56
Curtiss P-36
History of aviation (picture), **6** 1110
Curtiss P-40, see P-40
Curtiss R2C racers (with diagram and data
chart), **4** 601

Aerospace industry (picture), **1** 30
Curtiss R-4-L
Airmail, **1** 71
Curtiss-Wright Airplane Company
Beech, Walter H., **2** 347
Curtiss-Wright rocket engine
X-series aerospace vehicles, **14** 2537
Curtiss-Wright X-19, see X-19
Curvature of the lens
Photography, **10** 1782
Custance, Fred
Australia's aviation, **2** 279
Cutoff, 4 602
CV-2 Caribou, see Caribou, DHC-4A
CVA(N)65
Aircraft carriers, **1** 46
CX-4
Jumbo jets, **7** 1246
Cybernetics, 4 602-03
Robots, **11** 1965
Cycle
Kilocycle, **7** 1276
Cycle engines
Aircraft propulsion systems, **1** 53
Cycle of the phases
Planetarium, **10** 1819
Cyclone, 4 603
Atmospheric pressure, **2** 268
Clouds, **3** 471
Low-pressure area, **8** 1374
Cyclotron
Radiation, **10** 1882
Cygnet, see Hawker Cygnet
Cygnet I and II
Aerial Experiment Association, **1** 7-8
Cygni (star)
Bessel, Friedrich Wilhelm, **2** 354
Cygnus X-2
X-ray stars, **14** 2533
Cylinder
Reciprocating engines, **11** 1913-16
Cylinder assemblies
Reciprocating engines (with illustrations),
11 1915
Cylinder baffles
Reciprocating engines, **11** 1918
Cylinder wall
Reciprocating engines, **11** 1916
Cylindrical body
Kosmos satellites, **7** 1293
Cyprus
European aerospace activities, **4** 751
Czechoslovakia
Crop dusting, **4** 587
European aerospace activities, **4** 744
International competitions, **7** 1192
Czechoslovakian State Airline
European aerospace activities, **4** 744

D

D-18 Beech, see Beech D-18
Dacron
Airships, **1** 108
Balloons (picture), **2** 330
Fabrics, **5** 786
Daedalus and Icarus (DED a lus—IK uh rus)
4 604
Aviation, **2** 290
Commemorative stamps and medals, **3** 493
Man-powered flight, **8** 1463, 1465
Ornithopter, **10** 1748

Daedalus Project (1968)
Man-powered flight, **8** 1465
Dagasso, Roberto
Distance records, **4** 641
Daily Mail prize
Brabazon of Tara, Lord, **3** 384
Daily window
Launch window, **7** 1329
Daimler, Gottlieb
Aircraft propulsion systems, **1** 54
Dakota, see C-47 Skytrain, Douglas DC-3
Dalton, John
Atoms, **2** 269
Damage caused by space vehicles
Legal implications of aerospace, **7** 1331
**Daniel and Florence Guggenheim Aviation
Safety Center**
Guggenheim Fund for the Promotion of
Aeronautics, **6** 1033
**Daniel and Florence Guggenheim Center
for Aerospace Health and Safety**
Guggenheim Fund for the Promotion of
Aeronautics, **6** 1033
Daniel Guggenheim Medal
Camm, Sir Sydney, **3** 398
DeHavilland, Sir Geoffrey, **4** 620
Dryden, Hugh Latimer, **4** 654
Eckener, Hugo, **4** 668
Trophies and awards (table), **13** 2312
Danilin, Sergei
Distance records, **4** 640
Daredevil
Jenny, Curtiss, JN-4D, **7** 1232
D'Arguell, P.
World War I (table, Top Aces), **14** 2507
Dark-line spectrum
Astronomy, **2** 250
Dark nebulae
Astronomy, **2** 252
Astrophysics, **2** 258
Nebula, **9** 1689
Dark rooms
Observatories, **10** 1725
d'Arlandes, Marquis (mar KEE dar LAHND)
Balloons, **2** 316, 321
Dart Herald, see Handley Page
Dart Herald
Dash 80, see also Boeing 707
Commercial air transports **3** 525
Dassault Falcon, see Falcon
Dassault fighters
Air forces of the world (France), **1** 64
Dassault Super Mystere, see Super
Mystere
Data, 4 604
Adapter
Computers, **3** 558
Data acquisition and processing (with
diagram and pictures), **4** 604-10
Cybernetics, **4** 602
Flight recorder, **5** 848
Kennedy Space Center, **7** 1267
Tracking systems and networks, **13** 2297
Data automation system
Mariner probes, **8** 1488
Data link
Data acquisition and processing, **4** 610
Onboard computers, **10** 1737
Data-link radio system
Aerial photography, **1** 9, 13-14
Air Defense Command, **1** 59
Data processing
Oceanographic research, **10** 1732
Data reduction
Kennedy Space Center, **7** 1273
Terminology of aerospace (table),
12 2272
Datums
Earth, **4** 663
Daugherty, Dr. Dora
Women in aerospace, **14** 2495
David C. Schilling Flight Trophy
Borman, Frank, **3** 382
Davidson, James J.
Aircraft carriers, **1** 51

Davies-Jones, Valerie Mya
Llewellyn, John Anthony, **8** 1365
Davies, T. D.
Distance records, **4** 640
Da Vinci, Leonardo (1452-1519, Italian
engineer and inventor), **4** 610-11
Aircraft propulsion systems, **1** 53
Bellanca, Giuseppe, **2** 348
Bird flight, **2** 358
Cierva, Juan de la, **3** 460
Commemorative stamps and medals,
3 493
Helicopters, **6** 1061-1062
History of aviation, **6** 1094, (table) 1119
Italy's aerospace activities, **7** 1219
Man-powered flight, **8** 1463
Model aircraft, **9** 1624
Mythology, **9** 1646
Ornithopter, **10** 1748
Parachutes, **10** 1756
Skydiving, **11** 2054
Davis, Arlene
Medals and decorations (table), **8** 1526
Davis, Doug
Air racing, **1** 102
Davis quadrant
Telescopes and astronomical instruments
(picture), **12** 2257
Davy Crockett
Battlefield missile systems, **2** 341
Surface-to-surface missiles, **12** 2205
DC-1—10, see Douglas
DC-3: The Story of a Fabulous Airplane
(book)
Douglas DC-3, **4** 648
DC-325 (compound)
Ablation, **1** 1
DCA, see Commonwealth Department of
Civil Aviation
DCA, see Defense Communications Agency
DCX-2
Nuclear energy, **9** 1712, (picture) 1711
D-Day
United States Air Force, **13** 2364
DDT dusts
Crop dusting, **4** 588
Dead reckoning (with diagram), **4** 611-12
Air traffic control, **1** 135
Compasses, **3** 551
Magnetic course, **8** 1419
Mountain, desert, and jungle flying,
9 1642
Navigation techniques, **9** 1685-87
(with map and diagrams)
Phantom II, **10** 1777
Dead Sea
Mars, **8** 1491
De Analisi (book)
Newton, Sir Isaac, **9** 1693
Death-defying dive
Barnstormers, **2** 333
De Bernardi, Mario
Macchi M.39 racer, **8** 1416
Debriefing, 4 612
Testing, **12** 2276
DeBroglie, Louis
Quantum theory, **10** 1869
Debus, Kurt Heinrich (1908- , German-
American rocket scientist), **4** 612
Kennedy Space Center, **7** 1266
NASA, **9** 1650
Decameter wavelengths
Jupiter, **7** 1261
Deceleration, 4 612-13
Acceleration, **1** 2
Orbits and trajectories, **10** 1742
Rocket sled, **11** 1988
Deceleration error (with diagram)
Compasses, **3** 547
Deception
Electronic countermeasures, **4** 691
Decimeter wavelengths
Jupiter, **7** 1260
Decision height
Instrument landing categories, **7** 1169
Radio altimeter, **10** 1888

Decker, Martin M.
Medals and decorations (table), **8** 1526
Declination (with diagram)
Astronomy, **2** 240
Poles, **10** 1834
Decompression (with picture), **4** 613-14
Decompression chambers
Cosmonauts **4** 570
Decontamination, radiological, 4 614-15
Decoy missile
Missiles, **9** 1616
De-crab computer
Automatic landing, **2** 287
Decrease pitch attitude
Maneuver, **8** 1433
Dedalo (helicopter-carrier)
Naval aviation, worldwide (Spain), **9** 1671
Deep Freeze I
Byrd, Richard Evelyn, **3** 397
Deep sea divers
Capsule, **3** 406
Deep sea exploration
Oceanographic reseach, **10** 1731-34
Piccard family, **10** 1791
Deep Sea Instrumentation Facility
Data acquisition and processing, **4** 606
Deep Space Network, **4** 615
International Geophysical Year, **7** 1197
NASA, **9** 1653
Tracking systems and networks, **13** 2304
Deep space, 4 615
Deep Space Network, 4 615
Jet Propulsion Laboratory, **7** 1240
Pioneer, **10** 1814
Tracking systems and networks, **13** 2303
Deep space probe
Tracking systems and netowks, **13** 2303
U.S.S.R. aerospace activities, **13** 2343
Deep-space trajectory
Orbits and trajectories, **10** 1747
Defense, Department of, 4 626-27
Advanced Research Project Agency **1** 7
Aerospace industry, **1** 32
Aerospace Research Support Program
1 35
Civil defense, **3** 467
Defense communications satellites, **4** 615
Explorer satellites, **5** 762
Government contracts, **6** 997
Government in aerospace, **6** 1006
Jupiter rockets, **7** 1261
Mercury program, **9** 1529-30, 1533
Military implications of space, **9** 1588-89
Military space program, **9** 1591-1605
National Aeronautics and Space Council,
9 1657
Reconnaissance satellites, **11** 1924, 1926
United States Air Force, **13** 2358
Defense Act of 1950
Civil defense, **3** 467
Defense Communications Agency
Defense communications satellites, **4** 615
Defense communications satellites (with
picture), **4** 615-17
Defense Research Telecommunications
Establishment
Alouette satellites, **1** 144
Deferent circle
Astronomy, **2** 235
Celestial mechanics, **3** 427
DeForest, Lee
Electronics, **4** 693
Transmitters, **13** 2308
DeForest triode
Radio, **10** 1887
Vacuum tubes, **13** 2398
Deformed metal
Metals and metallurgy, **9** 1548
Defries, Colin
Australia's aviation, **2** 279
Degree of drag
Laminar flow, **7** 1296
DeHavilland Aircraft Company, Ltd.
Aerospace industry, **1** 30
Airmail, **1** 71

Australia's aviation, **2** 283
DeHavilland, Sir Geoffrey, **4** 620
DeHavilland Comet (with diagram and
picture), **4** 617-618
Canada's aviation, **3** 401
Commercial air transports (picture), **3** 524
History of aviation, **6** 1116
Jet aircraft, **7** 1235
Supersonic transports, **12** 2198
United Kingdom aerospace activities,
13 2347
DeHavilland CV-2, see Caribou
DeHavilland DH-4, see DH-4
DeHavilland DH-108, see DH-108
DeHavilland DHC-2 Mark I, see DHC-2
Mark I
DeHavilland DHC-2 Mark III, see DHC-2
Mark III
DeHavilland DHC-3, see DHC-3 Otter
DeHavilland DHC-5, see DHC-5 Buffalo
DdHavilland DHC-6, see DHC-6 Twin Otter
DeHavilland Dove (with chart and picture),
4 619
Air forces of the World (Sudan) **1** 64
Air taxis, **1** 117
Asia's aviation, **2** 205
DeHavilland Dove, **4** 619
DeHavilland Mosquito, see DH-98 Mosquito
DeHavilland of Canada Company
Canada's aviation, **3** 400, 403
DeHavilland, Sir Geoffrey (1882-1965,
British aviation pioneer), **4** 620
Medals and decorations (table), **8** 1526
DeHavilland Trophy
Trophies and awards (table), **13** 2312
DeHenricourt deGrunne, R.
World War II (table), **14** 2517
Deicing equipment, 4 620
Cockpit, **3** 483
Precipitation, **10** 1845
Utility aviation, **13** 2396
Deimos
Astronomy, **2** 244
De la Vaulx, Henri (de la VOH, ahn REE)
Balloons, **2** 318
DELAG
Airships, **1** 111
Zeppelins, **14** 2549-50
Delagrange, Leon (?-1910, French aviator),
4 621
Distance records, **4** 640
De la Roche, Baroness
Women in aerospace, **14** 2494
De Laval, Carl Gustaf
Nozzles, **9** 1707
Delfin L-29
European aerospace activities, **4** 744
Delmotte, Raymond
Speed and speed records (table), **12** 2141
DeLome, Dupuy (de LUM, dew PWEE)
Dirigibles, **4** 631
Del Prete, C. P.
Distance and distance records, **4** 640
Delta
Launch vehicle, **7** 1319-20, 1323
NASA, **9** 1653, (table), Major Launchings,
1653
Delta Air Lines
Commercial airlines, **3** 498, 512
Delta Air Service
Crop dusting, **4** 588
Delta Dagger, see F-102 Delta Dagger
Delta Dart, see F-106 Delta Dart
Delta Orionis (star)
Astrophysics, **2** 258
Delta rocket (with picture), **4** 622
Delta wing
Aerodynamics, **1** 23, (picture) 22
Delta Dagger, **4** 621
Wings, **14** 2489-93
Delta-wing aircraft
Supersonic transports, **12** 2185
DeMairan, M.
Circadian rhythm, **3** 460

Democritus (dem MOK rit us) (460-370 BC)
Atoms, **2** 269
Demoiselle (dem wa ZEL) (with data chart
and picture), **4** 623
Demolition bombs
Bombs, **3** 377-378
Demonstration-Participation Units
Regional space centers, **11** 1945
Demonstration teams (with diagrams and
pictures) **4** 623-26
Formation flying and techniques, **5** 883
Maneuvers, **8** 1433-41
De Motu Animalium (book)
Man-powered flight, **8** 1464
Newton, Sir Isaac, **9** 1693
DeMozay, Jean
World War II (table), **14** 2517
Demuyter, Ernest
Balloons, **2** 322
Denahy, Marilyn J.
See, Elliot M., Jr., **11** 2038
Denitrification
Nitrogen, **9** 1698
Deniuytek, Ernest
Medals and decorations (table), **8** 1526
Denmark
Crop dusting, **4** 587
European aerospace activities, **4** 745
European Space Research Organization,
4 755
International Agricultural Aviation
Centre, **7** 1187
International projects, **7** 1199
NATO, **9** 1703-04
World War II, **14** 2512
Density, 4 626
Air, **1** 41-42
Jupiter, **7** 1260
Density altitude, 4 626
Aviation weather, **2** 305
Mountain, desert, and jungle flying, **9** 1641
De-orbit sequence
Biosatellites, **2** 357
Departure control
Air traffic control, **1** 134
Instrument flight techniques, **7** 1167
Radio communications, **10** 1895
Departure point
Pilotage, **10** 1794
Deperdussin (de pair du SAN)
Air racing, **1** 102
Australia's aviation (picture), **2** 280
First World War aircraft, **5** 823
Depew, Dick
Aerospace industry, **1** 30
Depletion area
Electronics, **4** 701
Depressurization
Supersonic transports, **12** 2198
De Revolutionibus Orbium Coelestium
Astronomy, **2** 236
Copernicus, Nicolaus, **3** 566
De Rochas, Beau
Reciprocating engines, **11** 1914
De Rue (pseudonym of Ferdinand Ferber),
5 805
Descending turns
Maneuvers, **8** 1434
Descent
Instrument panels, **7** 1176
Desert flying
Mountain, desert, and jungle flying, **9** 1642
De Seversky, Alexander Procofieff (1894-
, Russian-American aviator,
aeronautical engineer), **4** 627-28
Design
Materials, **8** 1502
Quality control, **10** 1867
Rotating combustion engine (with
diagram), **11** 1992
Sailplanes, **11** 2003
Design changes
Spacecraft design, **11** 2102
Design integration
Spacecraft design, **11** 2102
Design Notes

Flight Safety Foundation, **5** 849
Design phase
Reliability and quality assurance, **11** 1954
Dessau aircraft works
Jumbo jets, **7** 1258
Destination point
Pilotage, **10** 1794
Destroyer
Recovery, **11** 1928
Destroyer escorts
Launching, **7** 1311
Destruct
Launching, **7** 1310
Terminology of aerospace (table), **12** 2272
Destruction
NORAD, **9** 1702
Destructive testing
Materials, **8** 1512
Detectable oxygen
Spacecraft sterilization, **11** 2104
Detection
NORAD, **9** 1702
Detection range
Radar, **10** 1873
Detection system
Reconnaissance satellites, **11** 1925
Detection/tracking/warning
Air defense systems, **1** 60-61
Detergent oils
Lubricants, **8** 1375
Determination of intent
NORAD, **9** 1702
Detre, Georges
Altitude and altitude records, **1** 147
Deuterium
Radiation, **10** 1881
Urey, Harold Clayton, **13** 2393
Detroit Trophy
Cessna, Clyde, V., **3** 445
Deutsche Arbeitsgemeinschaft Airbus
International projects, **7** 1200
Deutscher (DOICH er), **Aero Lloyd**
Commercial airlines, **3** 505
Deutsche Lufthansa
Commercial airlines, **3** 497, 504-505
Deutsche Luft Reederei
Commercial airlines **3**, 505
Jumbo jets, **7** 1258
West Germany's aerospace activities,
13 2475-80
Deutschland
Zeppelins, **14** 2550
Deutsche Luftschiffahrts Aktien Gesellschaft
Zepplins, **14** 2549-50
Developing areas
Economic implications of aerospace, **4** 670
Development
Sailplanes, **11** 2004
Spacecraft design, **11** 2100
Deviation
Compasses, **3** 547
Deviation indicator
Naviagation techniques (pictures),
9 1683-85
Devon
DeHavilland Dove, **4** 619
Dewar, James
Cryogenic propellants, **4** 596
Cryogenics, **4** 596
Dewar flask
Cryogenic propellants, **4** 596
Cryogenics, **4** 596
DeWitt, J. H.
Astronomy, **2** 242
DEW Line, 4 628
Air defense systems, **1** 60
Geodesics, **6** 970
Poles, **10** 1834
Radar, **10** 1877
Radome, **10** 1900
Dewoitine aircraft
Second World War aircraft, **11** 2029
Dew point, 4 628
Clouds, **3** 471
Evaporation and condensation, **4** 757
Humidity, **6** 1136

DH-4 (DeHavilland)
Airmail (pictures), **1** 71
Commercial air transports, **3** 517,
(with picture)
DeHavilland DH-4 (with data chart),
4 618-19
First World War aircraft, **5** 816, 818, 820,
821, (pictures), 815, 821
Refueling, **11** 1937
Royal Air Force, **11** 1995
World War I, **14** 2507, 2510
DH-98 Mosquito (DeHavilland)
History of aviation, **6** 1112
Second World War aircraft (with picture),
11 2030
DH-108 Swallow (DeHavilland)
DeHavilland, Sir Geoffrey, **4** 620
DH-125, see Hawker Siddeley DH-125
DHC-2 Mark I Beaver (DeHavilland of Canada)
Army aviation, **2** 197
DHC-2 Mark III Turbo-Beaver (DeHavilland
of Canada)
Canada's aviation (picture), **3** 403
DHC-3 Otter (DeHavilland of Canada)
Army aviation, **2** 197, (picture) 199
Canada's aviation **3** 403
DHC-4A, see Caribou
DHC-5 Buffalo (DeHavilland of Canada)
Canada's aviation (picture), **3** 399, 404
DHC-6 Twin Otter (DeHavilland of Canada)
Australia's aviation (picture), **2** 281
Canada's aviation, **3** 403
Commuter airlines (picture), **3** 544
V/STOL aircraft (table), **13** 2443
Diagnostic communications center
Communications satellites, **3** 542
Cayley glider, **3** 426
Diamant
Launch vehicles, **7** 1326
Diamond
Carbon, **3** 407
Diana Project
Communications satellites, **3** 532
Diaphragm
Altimeter, **1** 145
Pressure gauges, **10** 1850
Shock tubes and tunnels, **11** 2047
Diatomic atoms
Plasma, **10** 1822
Dickins, C. H. "Punch"
Bush flying, **3** 392
Diel
Circadian rhythm, **3** 460
Diesel aircraft engines
Reciprocating engines, **11** 1918
Diesel, Rudolf
Reciprocating engines, **11** 1918
Diffraction
Light, **8** 1352
Diffuse light
Light, **8** 1352
Diffuse nebulae
Nebula, **9** 1688-89 (with picture)
Diffusion bonding
Production techniques, **10** 1856
Digital computer
Binary numbers, **2** 355
Computers, **3** 553
Cybernetics, **4** 602-3
Jumbo jets, **7** 1255
Digital system
Space communications, **11** 2097
Telemetry, **12** 2243-44
Digitizer
National Airspace System, **9** 1661
Sailplanes, **11** 2004
Dihedral, 4 628
Du Temple, Jean-Marie Felix de la Croix,
4 656
Cayley glider, **3** 426
Diode
Computers, **3** 557
Electronics, **4** 693, 695, (diagram) 696
Miniaturization, **9** 1608
Diogene 2
Launch vehicles, **7** 1327

Dipoles
Communications satellites, 3 535
Dirac, Paul
Quantum theory, 10 1869
Direct ascent
Apollo, 1 164
Launch vehicles, 7 1317
Direct current
Electricity, 4 685
Direct dialing
Communications satellites, 3 542
Direction
Instrument flight techniques, 7 1167
Oceanographic research, 10 1732
Directional antenna
Airborne antennas (picture), 1 43
Ground antennas, 6 1015
Directional axis
Airplane, 1 87
Directional control
Maneuvers, 8 1433
Directional gyro (with picture), 4 628-29
Automatic pilot, 2 289
Instrument panels, 7 1176
Jumbo jets, 7 1255
Directly heated cathode
Electronics, 4 695
Direct Measurement Explorer
Alouette satellites, 1 144
Explorer satellites, 5 772
Direction of motion
Inertial guidance, 7 1153
Direction signals
Instrument landing system, 7 1170
Directrix
Parabola, 10 1755
Dirigibles (with diagram, picture and table),
4 629-32
Aeronautics, 1 26
Aircraft, 1 45
Airships, 1 105
Air transports, 1 139
Forlanini, Enrico, 5 881
Gondolas, 6 994
Lebaudy, Paul, 7 1330
Manufacturing, 8 1468
Reciprocating engines, 11 1918
Renard, Charles, 11 1955
Santos-Dumont, Alberto, 11 2005
United States Naval Aviation, 13 2380
Zeppelins
Dirigible, bimotor
Polar flying, 10 1829
Disc brakes
Brakes, 3 385
Discharges
Crash trucks, 4 583
Discontinuous composite
Materials, 8 1504
Discontinuous fibers
Materials, 8 1506
Discoverer Project (with diagrams, pictures
and table), 4 632-39
Earth science, 4 666
Environmental research satellites, 4 722
Launch vehicle, 7 1323
Military space program, 9 1593
Reconnaissance satellites, 11 1924-25
Thor rockets, 12 2286
Vehicle research spacecraft, 13 2406
Discovery (book)
Byrd, Richard Evelyn, 3 397
Diseased crops
Infrared detection devices, 7 1161
Infrared radiation, 7 1162
Diskey
Teminology of aerospace (table), 12 2272
Dispersal equipment
Crop dusting, 4 591-92
Dispersion strengthening
Metals and metallurgy, 9 1553-54
Display
Terminology of aerospace (table),
12 2272
Display models
Model aircraft, 9 1625

Distance and distance records, 4 639-41
Distance in a straight line without landing
Distance and distance records, 4 639
Distance Measuring Equipment (with
diagrams), 4 641-42
Air traffic control, 1 128
Cockpit, 3 485
Instrument landing system, 7 1170
Navigation instruments, 9 1672-73, 1675,
1678-80
Omni navigation, 10 1736
Distance record
Balloons, 2 321
Distance and distance records (table),
4 640-41
Distant Early Warning Line, see DEW Line
Distilling plants
Aircraft carriers, 1 46
Distress signals (data table)
Panel codes, 10 1755
Distribution
Economic implications of aerospace, 4 670
Disturbed motion
Celestial mechanics, 3 428
Ditching, 4 642-43
Distinguished Service Medal
Life raft, 7 1336 (with pictures)
Medals and decorations (picture), 8 1525
Distinguished Flying Cross
Medals and decorations (picture), 8 1525
Dittmar, Helen J.
Pogue, William Reid, 10 1828
Diurnal
Circadian rhythm, 3 460
Dive, 4 643
Dive bombers
Military aircraft, 9 1569
Dive bombing
Bomber aircraft, 2 376
Bombs, 3 378
Dive, 4 643
Diving moment
Aerodynamics, 1 25
D layer
Atmosphere, 2 264
DME, see Distance Measuring Equipment
DN-1, Blimps, 2 364
DNA
Extraterrestrial life, 5 775
Docking
Apollo, 1 176
Lunar Module (with pictures), 1 180, 182
Armstrong, Neil A., 2 193
Kosmos satellites, 7 1292
Manned spaceflight, 8 1462
Spaceflight training, 12 2117
Docking adapter
Apollo Applications Program, 2 185, 186
Dogfight
Battle of Britain, 2 343
Bishop, William Avery, 2 362
Dive, 4 643
Nationalist China's aviation, 9 1666
Roll, 11 1990
World War I, 14 2506
Do-it-yourself aircraft
Experimental Aircraft Association, 4 760
Dolder, Fred
Medals and decorations (table), 8 1526
Dolfus, Charles
Medals and decorations (table), 8 1526
Dolland, John
Astronomy, 2 242
Telescopes and astronomical instruments,
12 2247
Dollar ceiling level
Program management, 10 1859
Dollfus, A.
Mars, 8 1491
Saturn, 11 2009
Dome diameter
Planetarium, 10 1820
Domestic Air Parcel Post
Airmail, 1 78
Domestic trunk airlines
Commercial airlines, 3 498

Dominican Republic
South and Central America's aviation,
11 2090
Dominion Explorers
Bush flying, 3 392
Donahue, R.
Coast Guard aviation, 3 476
Donati, Renato
Altitude and altitude records, 1 147
Doolittle, James Harold (1896-
American aviator), 4 643-44
Air racing (picture), 1 103
Barnstormers, 2 336
Curtiss R2C racers, 4 601
Fuels, 5 898
History of aviation (table), 6 1119
Instrument panels, 7 1173, 1176
Medals and decorations (table), 8 1526
Mitchell, North American B-25, 9 1621
Parachutes, 10 1758
Speed and speed records (table), 12 2141
United States Air Force, 13 2362, 2363,
(picture) 2364
World War II, 14 2522
Doors, see Hatches and doors
Dope, 4 644
Airplane, 1 82
Fabrics, 5 786
Doping
Electronics, 4 701
Materials, 8 1511
Semiconductors, 11 2041
Doppler, Christian
Astrophysics, 2 257
Doppler navigation, 4 645
Doppler effect (with diagrams), 4 644-45
Astronomy, 2 242, 250
Astrophysics, 2 257
Quasar, 10 1871
Radar, 10 1872, 1876
Radio astronomy, 10 1891
Tracking systems and networks, 13 2302
Doppler frequency
Doppler navigation, 4 645
Radar, 10 1875
Doppler navigation (with diagram), 4 645-46
Avionics, 2 307
Dead reckoning, 4 612
Jumbo jets, 7 1255
Radar, 10 1875
Radio navigation, 10 1899
Doppler radar
Airborne antennas, 1 44
Air traffic control, 1 135
Boeing 707, 2 370
Doppler effect, 4 645
Electronics, 4 703
Radar, 10 1872, 1878
Sextant, 11 2045
Doppler shift
Airborne antennas, 1 44
Doppler navigation, 4 645
Quasar, 10 1871
Radar, 10 1872, 1878
d'Orcy, Ladislas
Quiet Birdmen, 10 1871
Dordilly, Francis
Distance and distance records, 4 640
Doret, Marcel
Distance records, 4 641
Dornberger, Walter Robert (1895-   ,
German American rocket scientist), 4 646
Peenemuende, 10 1770
Rockets and rocketry, 11 1979
Dornier, Claude (1884-   , German
Aircraft designer and manufacturer),
4 647
Flying boats, 5 858, 859
Dornier (bomber)
History of aviation, 6 1112
Dornier Do-17
Second World War aircraft (with picture),
11 2028
World War II (picture), 14 2513
Dornier Do-24
Commercial airlines (picture), 3 505

Dornier Do-27
Africa's aviation, **1** 36
Dornier Do-31
V/STOL aircraft, **13** 2442, (table) 2443
Dornier flying boats
Amundsen, Roald, **1** 151
Dornier Metallbauten Gesellschaft
Dornier, Claude, **4** 647
Dornier Skyservant
V/STOL aircraft (table), **13** 2443
West Germany's aerospace activities,
13 2478, (picture) 2477
Dornier Werke GmbH
Dornier, Claude, **4** 647
Dorsal fin
Empennage, **4** 710
Double delta
Supersonic transports, **12** 2190
Double wedge supersonic airfoil
Airfoil (diagram) **1** 61
Dougherty, Earl
Barnstormers, **2** 335
Douglas A-1 Skyraider, see A-1 Skyraider
Douglas A-3 Skywarrior, see A-3
Skywarrior
Douglas A-4 Skyhawk, see A-4 Skyhawk
Douglas A-20 and A-24, see A-20 and A-24
Douglas Aircraft Company
Aerospace industry, **1** 31
Air-to-air missiles (Genie), **1** 121
Antiballistic missile defense, **1** 159
Bumper Project, **3** 390
Douglas Aircraft Company
X-series aerospace vehicles, **14** 2536
Douglas B-19, see B-19
Douglas B-26, see B-26 Marauder
Douglas C-47, see C-47 Skytrain
(see also Douglas DC-3)
Douglas C-54, see C-54 Skymaster
Douglas C-118, see C-118
Douglas C-124, see C-124 Globemaster
Douglas C-133, see C-133
Douglas D-558-I Skystreak
Crossfield, Albert Scott, Jr., **4** 594
X-series aerospace vehicles, **14** 2537
Douglas D-558-2 Skyrocket
X-series aerospace vehicles, **14** 2537
Douglas DC-1
Commercial air transports, **3** 519
Douglas DC-2
Commercial air transports (picture),
3 520, 521
Douglas DC-3 (see also C-47 Skytrain)
(table, pictures), **4** 648-49
Commercial airlines, **3** 512
Commercial air transports, **3** 520,
(picture) 521, 526
Douglas DC-3 (book), **4** 648
Flight recorder, **5** 849
Government in aerospace, **6** 1001
History of aviation, **6** 1109, (picture) 1110
Douglas DC-5
Commercial air transports, **3** 521
Douglas DC-6
Cargo aircraft, **3** 418
Commercial air transports, **3** 522, (with
picture) 526
Nationalist China's aviation, **9** 1666
Douglas DC-7
Cargo aircraft, **3** 418
Commercial air transports, **3** 522,
(picture) 523
Douglas DC-8
Air traffic control (picture), **1** 138
Asia's aviation, **2** 204
Canada's aviation, **3** 401, (picture) 402
Certification procedures, **3** 441
Commercial airlines, **3** 497
Commercial air transports (picture),
3 522, 526
flight simulator
Commercial airlines, **3** 502
Flight simulators, **5** 855
History of aviation (picture), **6** 1116

Douglas DC-9
Asia's aviation (picture), **2** 205
Australia's aviation, **2** 280
Canada's aviation, **3** 401
Certification procedures, **3** 441
Commercial air transports (picture),
3 522, 526
Flying Tigers, **5** 866
Landing gear (with picture), **7** 1299
Douglas, Donald Wills (1892-   ,
American airplane designer and
manufacturer), **4** 649
Medals and decorations (table), **8** 1526
Douglas M-4 mail planes
Airmail, **1** 71, 76
Douglas Thor booster
Douglas, Donald Wills, **4** 649
Douglas World Cruiser (with data chart and
picture), **4** 649-50
Douglas X-3, see X-3
Douhet, Giulio (Du AY, JU lee o) (1869-
1930, Italian military officer), **4** 650
Air raid, **1** 104
Bomber aircraft, **2** 374
Dove, see DeHavilland Dove
Military aviation, **9** 1582
World War II, **14** 2512
Downrange
Terminology of aerospace (table), **12** 2272
Downrange guidance stations
Launch vehicles, **7** 1327
Down the slot
Terminology of aerospace (table), **12** 2272
Downtowner (airplane)
Helicopters, **6** 1068
Downward Ejection Seat
Escape systems, **4** 734
Downwash
Aerodynamics, **1** 21
Downwind leg
Airports, **1** 97
DO-X (flying boat)
Dornier, Claude, **4** 647
Flying boats, **5** 858
Doyle, Bernice
McCandless, Bruce, II, **8** 1516
Drag, 4 651
Aerodynamics (with diagram), **1** 20, 22, 24
Airplane, **1** 85
Air resistance, **1** 104
Bird flight, **2** 358
Expansion waves, **4** 760
Piloting techniques, **10** 1797
Propellers, **10** 1862
Reciprocating engines, **11** 1918
Spaceflight principles, **12** 2105, 2106
Wings, **14** 2490
Dragon (missile)
Surface-to-surface missiles, **12** 2208,
(table) 2208
Dragonfly DH90
Australia's aviation, **2** 283
Drag parachute
Drift **4** 652
Drag rope
Balloons, **2** 317
Drake, Frank
Extraterrestrial life, **5** 784
Draken (aircraft)
Fighter aircraft (picture), **5** 809
Sweden's aviation, **12** 2224, (picture) 2223
Draper, Charles Stark (1901-   ,
American aerospace teacher and
researcher), **4** 651
Inertial guidance, **7** 1152
Drexel, Anthony
Altitude and altitude records, **1** 147
Drieberg, Friedrich von (1845)
Man-powered flight, **8** 1464
Drift (with diagram), **4** 651
Cross-wind landing, **4** 594
Life raft, **7** 1336
Magnetic course, **8** 1419
Drift meter
Dead reckoning, **4** 612

Drift, **4** 652
Navigation instruments, **9** 1673
Driver, K. W.
World War II (table), **14** 2517
Drive systems
Airships, **1** 106
Drizzle
Precipitation, **10** 1844
Drogue parachute
Drift, **4** 652
Parachutes, **10** 1759
Re-entry vehicles, **11** 1933
Drone aircraft (with picture), **4** 652
Aircraft, **1** 45
Eglin Air Force Base, **4** 679
Reconnaissance airborne, **11** 1920, 1923
Dropsondes
Aviation weather, **2** 299
Drop tanks
World War II, **14** 2519
Drouhin, Maurice (drew ANN, moh REES)
Distance and distance records, **4** 640
Drug effects, 4 653
Aviation medicine, **2** 297
Drum brake
Brakes, **3** 385, (diagram) 386
Dry air
Adiabatic process, **1** 6-7
Air, **1** 42
Dryden, Hugh Latimer (1898-1965,
American aeronautical research scientist),
4 653-54
Mercury program, **9** 1530
Dry ice
Carbon dioxide, **3** 408
Cloud seeding, **3** 474
Dry run, 4 654
Dual-wave particle
Quantum theory, **10** 1869
DuBois, Coert (du BWAH, KURT)
Crop dusting, **4** 586
DuBose, Jane
Conrad, Charles, Jr., **3** 561
Ductile
Aluminum **1** 148
DuFay, Charles
Electricity, **4** 683
Dufek, George
Polar flights, **10** 1830
Duke, Charles Moss, Jr. (1935-   ), **4** 654
Astronauts, **2** 217, 218, 219 (with picture)
Dulles International Airport
Airports, **1** 98
Air traffic control (picture), **1** 134
Dumbbell Nebula
Astonomy (picture), **2** 248
Du Monceau de Bergandal, I.
World War II (table), **14** 2517
Dumont, A. Santos, see Santos-Dumont, A.
Dump
Terminology of aerospace (table), **12** 2272
Dunn, Louis G. (1908-   , South African-
American aerodynamicist), **4** 655
Dunwoody, General
Radio, **10** 1887
Duplicate flight and navigation instruments
Jumbo jets, **7** 1256
Durant, Frederick Clark III (1916-   ,
American aviator), **4** 655
Duration record
Balloons, **2** 321, 322
Dust
Extraterrestrial life, **5** 779
Milky Way, **9** 1605
Dust clouds
Orbiting observatories, **10** 1740
Dust-devils
Mountain, desert, and jungle flying, **9** 1642
Dutch roll
Yaw damper, **14** 2547
Du Temple, Jean-Marie Felix de la Croix,
(Du TAWMP) (1823-1890, French
aviation pioneer), **4** 555
History of aviation, **6** 1095, (table) 1119
Dye markers
Recovery, **11** 1928

Dyke Delta (airplane)
Homebuilt aircraft (picture), **6** 1125
Dynamic crew procedures simulator
Manned Spacecraft Center, **8** 1458
Dynamic fixtures
Kennedy Space Center, **7** 1267
Dynamic lift
Airships, **1** 114
Balloons, **2** 330
Dynamic loads
Aluminum, **1** 148
Dynamic microphones
Microphone, **9** 1563
Dynamics, 4 656
Dynamic soaring, 4 656, 657
Soaring, **11** 2062
Dyna-Soar program (with pictures), **4** 657
(see also X-20 Dyna-Soar)
Crews, Albert H., Jr., **4** 584
Dornberger, Walter Robert, **4** 646
Dynamic soaring, **4** 656
Dysbarisms
Aviation medicine, **2** 297
Man in flight, **8** 1448-49

E

E-1-B Tracer (Grumman)
Aircraft carriers, **1** 47
Eaker, Ira
United States Air Force, **13** 2362
Eagle (aircraft carrier)
Naval aviation, worldwide, **9** 1669, (picture) 1668
Earhart, Amelia (1898-1937, American aviatrix), **4** 658
Autogiros, **2** 286
Commemorative stamps and medals, **3** 495
Ninety-Nines, **9** 1697
Women in aerospace, **14** 2494, 2495
Early Bird
Commemorative stamps and medals, **3** 495
Communications satellites, **3** 537-21, 543 (with diagram and pictures)
Defense communication satellites, **4** 616
Internal systems
International Telecommunications Satellite Consortium (picture), **7** 1202
Military space program (picture), **9** 1590
NASA, **9** 1653
Television, **12** 2263
Early-warning aircraft
Air defense systems, **1** 60
Early-warning satellites
Military implications of space, **9** 1588-89
Ears
Aerospace medicine, **1** 34
Earth (with diagrams, picture, and table), **4** 659-64
Aerial photography (picture), **1** 9
Age of
Baade, Walter, **2** 309
Air, **1** 41-42
Quantum theory, **10** 1870
Astronomy, **2** 242, 243
Atmosphere, **2** 265
Aerospace, **1** 26
Reaction control systems, **10** 1911
Carbon, **3** 406
Celestial mechanics, **3** 427
Circumference
Eratosthenes, **4** 729
Cloud cover

Infrared radiation, **7** 1162
crust
Reconnaissance airborne, **11** 1920
Earth science, **4** 667
Equator
Inclination, **7** 1151
Galaxy
Intergalactic space, **7** 1184
Geodetic satellites, **6** 971
Gravity, **6** 1011
Hoyle, Fred, **6** 1130
Inner radiation belt
Pegasus, **10** 1773
International Geophysical Year, **7** 1195
Interplanetary travel, **7** 1210-11
Kepler's laws, **7** 1275
Latitude and longitude, **7** 1306
Launching, **7** 1309
Launch vehicles, **7** 1314
Magnetic field
Compasses (diagram), **3** 546
Moon (picture), **9** 1633
Orbital velocity, **10** 1737
Orbiting observatories, **10** 1738, 1741
Orbit rendezvous, Apollo, **1** 164-65
Rendezvous and docking, **11** 1956 (with illustration)
Orbits and trajectories, **10** 1744-45
Apollo Applications Program, **2** 186, 187
Propellants, **10** 1860
Parallax, **10** 1760
Photography, **10** 1788
Pioneer, **10** 1814
Planck's Law, **10** 1817
Planetariums, **10** 1819
Planets, **10** 1820
Poles, **10** 1834
Precession, **10** 1843
Ptolemy, Claudius, **10** 1864
Radar, **10** 1874
Radiation, **10** 1882-83
Recovery, **11** 1927
Rotation, **11** 1993
Solar system
Ozma project, **10** 1753
Retrograde motion, **11** 1961
Space, **11** 2092
Surface
Quantum theory (with diagram), **10** 1870
Surface temperature, Carbon dioxide, **3** 407
Surplus population
Implications of aerospace, **7** 1150
Earth escape velocity
Rockets and rocketry, **11** 1977
Earth indicator compass
Manufacturing, **8** 1469
Earth landing system
Escape systems, **4** 737
Earth microorganisms
Spacecraft sterilization, **11** 2103
Earth-Moon transportation
Lunar bases, **8** 1393, 1395
Earthquakes
International Geophysical Year, **7** 1195
Earth radiation belt emissions
Kosmos satellites, **7** 1293
Earth satellite
Jet Propulsion Laboratory, **7** 1240
Radio, **10** 1888
RAND Corporation, **10** 1903
Satellites, **11** 2006
Earth satellite vehicle
Vanguard, **13** 2403
Earth science, 4 665-67
Earth Sciences Laboratory
Environmental Science Services Administration, **4** 725
EAS, see Equivalent airspeed
East accelerometer
Inertial guidance, **7** 1153
East African Airways
Africa's aviation, **1** 36
Eastern Airlines
Aerospace industry, **1** 30
Charter flying, **3** 448

Commercial airlines, **3** 497, 512
Eastern Test Range, 4 667
Kennedy Space Center, **7** 1266
Military space program, **9** 1602
Missile test ranges, **9** 1617
East Germany (map)
Berlin airlift, **2** 352
East longitude
Latitude and longitude, **7** 1307
Eating in space
Food and nutrition, **5** 873-79
Man in flight, **8** 1451
Eaton, P. P.
Coast Guard aviation, **3** 476
Eccentric circle
Astronomy, **2** 235
Eccentric orbits
Orbiting observatories, **10** 1738, 1741
Echo I and II
Communications satellites, **3** 533, 543
Defense communications satellites, **4** 615
Delta rocket, **4** 622
Electromagnetism, **4** 691
NASA, **9** 1653, (table, Major Launchings) 1652
Zeppelins, **14** 2549-50
Eckener, Hugo (1868-1954, German airship designer), **4** 668
Airships, **1** 112
Commemorative stamps and medals, **3** 494
Medals and decorations (table), **8** 1526
Echoes
Radar, **10** 1874
Eckert, Alfred
Medals and decorations (table), **8** 1526
Eckert, J. P.
Computers, **3** 557
Electronics, **4** 693
Eclipse (with diagram), **4** 668-69
Moon, **9** 1634
Sun, **12** 2172
Ecliptic, 4 669
Aristarchus of Samos, **2** 193
Astronomy, **2** 236
ECM, see Electronic countermeasures
Ecology, 4 669
Economic future
Lunar bases, **8** 1393
Economic implications of aerospace (with graph), **4** 670-72
Economics, Bureau of
Civil Aeronautics Board, **3** 465
Economy seats
Jumbo jets (charts), **7** 1251
ECS, see Environmental control system
Ecuador
Commemorative stamps and medals, **3** 495
South and Central America's aviation, **11** 2090
Eddington, Arthur S. (1882-1944, English astronomer), **4** 673
Eddy current testing
Materials, **8** 1512
Edge slats
Cockpit, **3** 482
Edison effect
Electronics, **4** 693, (diagram) 694-95
Edison, Thomas A.
Electronics, **4** 693, 695
Vacuum tubes, **13** 2398
Educational implications of aerospace (with charts and pictures), **4** 673-78
EDVAC, see Electronic Discrete Variable Automatic Computer
Edwards Air Force Base, 4 678
Aerospace research pilot, **1** 34
Test pilots and test flying, **12** 2277-80
X-15 research program, **14** 2529
Edwards, Glen W.
Test pilots and test flying, **12** 2278
Edwards, June B.
Women in aerospace, **14** 2496
Edzard, Cornelius
Distance and distance records, **4** 640
Effective diameter
Photography, **10** 1785

Eglin Air Force Base, 4 679
Egypt
Aeolipile, **1** 7
Africa's aviation, **1** 37
Air forces of the world, **1** 64
Astronomy **2** 234, (with picture) 242
Boomerang, **3** 380
Egyptian Air Force
Israeli-Arab Conflict, **7** 1217
Ehricke, Krafft Arnold (ERR i kee),
(1917-   , German American
aeronautical engineer), **4** 680
Eielson, Carl Ben
Polar flights, **10** 1829
Eight ball
Instrument panels, **7** 1177
18-A Autogiro
Autogiros (picture), **2** 286
Eights
Maneuvers, **8** 1439
Eight stage preparation
Kennedy Space Center, **7** 1269
Eindecker Scout (airplane)
First World War aircraft, **5** 824
Einstein, Albert (1879-1955, German-
American physicist), **4** 680-81
Gravity, **6** 1012
Leverrier, Urbain, J. J., **7** 1334
Quantum theory, **10** 1868
Relativity theory, **11** 1948-53
Eisele, Donn F. (IZE lee) (1930-   ),
4 681
Apollo (picture), **1** 171
Astronauts, **2** 217, 218, 219, 226, 229
(with picture)
Eisenhower, Dwight D.
American Rocket Society, **1** 151
Astronauts, **2** 220
Explorer satellites, **5** 762
United States Air Force (picture), **13** 2365
Ejection seats
Aviation medicine, **2** 296
Escape systems, **4** 731
Elastic medium
Sound, **11** 2078
Elastomers
Materials, **8** 1508, 1510
Plastics, **10** 1823
Elayer
Atmosphere, **2** 264
ELDO, see European Launcher Development
Organization
Electra, see Lockheed Electra
Electrical connectors
Oceanographic research, **10** 1734
Electrical energy
Battery, **2** 338
Energy, **4** 712
Mechanical energy, **8** 1521
Semiconductors, **11** 2041
Electrical engineering
Careers (table), **3** 416
Electrical experiments
Relativity theory, **11** 1949, 1951
Electrical generators
Power units, auxiliary, **10** 1843
Electrical igniters
Ignition systems, **7** 1147
Electrical power
Lunar bases, **8** 1391, (table) 1392
Electrical pulse
Sonar, **11** 2073
Electrical systems, 4 681-83
Apollo, **1** 177
Cockpit, **3** 482
Jumbo jets, **7** 1252
Kennedy Space Center, **7** 1271
Preflight inspection, **10** 1846
Reciprocating engines, **11** 1919
Electric current
Battery, **2** 338
Electromagnetism, **4** 689
Electric gas tube signs
Plasma, **10** 1822
Electricity (with diagram), **4** 683-85
Fuel cells, **5** 894

Magneto, 8 1420
Electric power
Spacecraft design, **11** 2101
Electric propulsion, 4 685-88
Electric sign
Airships (picture), **1** 108
Electric spaceships
Electric propulsion, **4** 687
Electric waves
Marconi, Guglielmo, **8** 1480
Electro-acoustic system
Sonar, **11** 2073
Electrocardiogram
Man in flight, **8** 1451
Electrochemical devices
Lewis Research Center, **7** 1335
Electrodes
Battery, **2** 338
Electronics, **4** 693
Electrodynamics
Electricity, **4** 684
Electroencephologram
Man in flight, **8** 1451
Electroluminescent numbers
Instrument panels, **7** 1178
Electrolyte
Battery, **2** 338
Electromagnetic accelerometer
Miniaturization (picture), **9** 1607
Electromagnetic energy
Quantum theory, **10** 1868
Electromagnetic equations
Radar, **10** 1872
Electromagnetic-pulse detector
Nuclear detection satellites, **9** 1709
Electromagnetic radiation
Celestial navigation, **3** 430
Infrared detection devices, **7** 1159
International Years of the Quiet Sun, **7** 1204
Quantum theory, **10** 1868
Radiation, **10** 1880
Radio, **10** 1885
Tracking systems and networks, **13** 2298
Ultraviolet radiation, **13** 2317
X-rays, **14** 2533
Electromagnetic spectrum
Band, radio, **2** 332
Celestial navigation, **3** 430
Electromagnetism, **4** 690-91 (with graphs)
Radio astronomy, **10** 1890
Electromagnetic systems
Plasma propulsion, **10** 1823
Electromagnetic wave
Electromagnetism, **4** 689
Television, **12** 2258
Electromagnetism, 4 688-91
Relativity theory, **11** 1949
Electromagnets
Electromagnetism, **4** 689
Electromechanical equipment
Oceanographic research, **10** 1734
Electromotive force
Electromagnetism, **4** 689
Electron
Atoms, **2** 269
Battery, **2** 338
Electronics, **4** 692, 693
Interplanetary Monitoring Platform
satellites, **7** 1205
Ion, **7** 1215
Jupiter, **7** 1260
Matter, **8** 1513
Nuclear energy, **9** 1710
Photosynthesis, **10** 1790
Plasma, **10** 1822-23
Quantum theory, **10** 1868-70
Radiation, **10** 1880, 1882
Electron beam
Radar, **10** 1875
Electron cloud
Atoms, **2** 270
Electron gun
Electronics, **4** 698
Electronic automatic checkout equipment
Launch facilities, **7** 1307

Electronic bombing systems
Phantom II, McDonnell-Douglas F-4A,
10 1777
Electronic brain
Launch vehicles, **7** 1316
Electronic clocks
Radio astronomy, **10** 1893
Electronic computers
Planetarium, **10** 1820
Electronic console
Console, **3** 561
Electronic converters
Infrared radiation, **7** 1162
Electronic countermeasures, 4 691
Electronic data processing system
Computers, **3** 556
**Electronic Discrete Variable Automatic
Computer**
Computers, **3** 557
Electronic equipment
Oceanographic research, **10** 1734
Electronic eye
Radar, **10** 1872
Electronic flash systems
Photography, **10** 1789
Electronic flight control
Avionics, **2** 307
Electronic gear
Oceanographic research, **10** 1732
Reconnaissance aircraft, **11** 1922
Electronic impulse
Radio altimeter, **10** 1888
Electronic intelligence
Electronic countermeasures, **4** 691
Electronic launch control equipment
Launch facilities, **7** 1307
Electronic mapmaking
Maps and mapping, **8** 1480
Electronic materials
Materials, **8** 1511
**Electronic Numerical Integrator and
Calculator**
Computers, **3** 547
Electronics, **4** 693
Electronic observation
Reconnaissance, airborne, **11** 1919
Electronic photoflash equipment
Reconnaissance, airborne, **11** 1920
Electronics, 4 692-704
Battery, **2** 338
Bionics, **2** 356
Cutoff, **4** 602
Masers, **8** 1496
Silicon, **11** 2052
Vacuum tubes, **13** 2398
Electronic servosystem
Photography, **10** 1785
Electronics reconnaissance
Reconnaissance, airborne, **11** 1920
Electronics Research Center
NASA, **9** 1650, 1655
Electronic warfare
Electronic countermeasures, **4** 691
Electron lens system
Electronics, **4** 698
Electron microscope
Electronics, **4** 704
Electron radiation
Pegasus, **10** 1773
Electron tubes
Electronics, **4** 695
Electro-optically guided antitank weapon
Battlefield missile systems, **2** 343
Electrostatics
Electricity, **4** 684
Plasma propulsion, **10** 1823
Electrothermal engines
Electric propulsion, **4** 687
Electrothermal systems
Plasma propulsion, **10** 1823
Elektron
U.S.S.R. aerospace activities, **13** 2340,
(pictures) 2338
Elements, 4 704-705

(Continued)

Elements (Cont.)
Atoms, **2** 269
Matter, **8** 1513
Elevation, 4 706
Elevation control
Orbiting observatories, **10** 1738
Elevator action
Aerodynamics, **1** 23
Elevator control loop
Automatic pilot, **2** 289
Elevator controls
Landing techniques, **7** 1301
Piloting techniques, **10** 1796
Elevators, 4 706
Aircraft carriers, **1** 47-48
Airplane, **1** 86, 87-88
Attitude and attitude control, **2** 275
Empennage, **4** 709, 710
Elevator trim tab
Airplane, **1** 88
Elevons
Ailerons, **1** 41
Eliminate Range Zero System
Collision avoidance system, **3** 488
Ellehammer, Jacob Christian (1871-1946,
Danish inventor and aviation pioneer),
4 706
Ellesmere Island
Bush flying, **3** 393
Ellipse
Ballistic trajectory, **2** 314
Celestial mechanics, **3** 427
Kepler's laws, **7** 1275
Orbital velocity, **10** 1738
Orbits and trajectories (with diagram),
10 1742-46
Elliptic orbit
Interplanetary travel, **7** 1212
Kepler's laws, **7** 1275
Elliptical galaxies
Astronomy, **2** 253
Ellsworth Antarctic Expeditions
Balchen, Bernt, **2** 312
Ellsworth, Lincoln (1880-1951, American
aviator, Polar explorer), **4** 706-07
Amundsen, Roald, **1** 151
Polar flights, **10** 1829
Ellyson, T. G.
United States Naval Aviation, **13** 2377-78
ELM, see Extended Lunar Module
Elmer A. Sperry Award
DeHavilland, Sir Geoffrey, **4** 620
ELS, see Earth landing system
El Salvador
Crop dusting, **4** 587
South and Central America's aviation,
11 2091
Ely, Eugene
Aircraft carriers, **1** 48 (with picture)
United States Naval Aviation, **13** 2377
Embrittlement
Metals and metallurgy, **9** 1549
Embryo Space Station
Apollo Applications Program, **2** 185
EMC van
Kennedy Space Center (picture), **7** 1273
Emeraude
Launch vehicles, **7** 1327
Emergency channel
Radio communications, **10** 1895
Emergency egress room
Kennedy Space Center, **7** 1273
Emergency facilities
Inflight emergency procedures, **7** 1156
(with diagram)
Emergency landing fields
Airmail, **1** 74
Emergency landing procedures, 4 707-08
Emergency Rescue Squadron
Survival and rescue, **12** 2219
Emergency signals, 4 708-09
Emergency systems
Apollo, **1** 166, 174-5
Cockpit, **3** 485

Emission nebulae
Astrophysics, **2** 258
Nebula, **9** 1689, (picture) 1688
Emission spectra
Quasar, **10** 1871
Empennage (Ahm pen AHJ), **4** 709-11
Airplane, **1** 86
Jumbo jets (picture), **7** 1249
Empire Air Training Scheme
Canada's aviation, **3** 402
Enamels
Paints, **10** 1754
Encapsulated escape
Escape systems, **4** 735
Encapsulated primer
Paints, **10** 1754
Encounter sequence plan
Data acquisition and processing, **4** 608
Endogenous hypothesis
Circadian rhythm, **3** 460
Endothermic reactions
Chemical energy, **3** 456
Endurance and endurance records (with
table), **4** 711-12
Piloting techniques, **10** 1802
Enemy defense line
Penetration, **10** 1774
Energetic geometry
Geodesics, **6** 970
Energetic Particle Explorer (satellite)
Explorer satellites, **5** 767
Energy (with diagrams and tables), **4** 712-15
Bernoulli's principle, **2** 353
Chemical energy, **3** 456
Extraterrestrial life, **5** 775
Heat energy, **6** 1054
Jupiter, **7** 1260
Kosmos satellites, **7** 1292
Launch vehicles, **7** 1315
Orbital velocity, **10** 1737
Planck's Law, **10** 1817
Radiation, **10** 1880-81
Relativity theory, **11** 1950
Spaceflight principles, **12** 2105, 2110
Space power systems, **12** 2120
Thermodynamics, **12** 2283
Weather satellites, **13** 2460
X-rays, **14** 2533
Energy level
Orbits and trajectories, **10** 1744
Quantum theory, **10** 1869
Energy quanta
Quantum theory, **10** 1870
Radiation, **10** 1880
Enforcement, Bureau of
Civil Aeronautics Board, **3** 465
Engine cycles
Reciprocating engines, **11** 1915
Engineer Gerin's Hyperboloid (book)
Blimp, **2** 366
Engineering techniques
Orbiting observatories, **10** 1738
Engine instruments (with picture), **4** 715-17
Cockpit, **3** 485
Instrument panels, **7** 1176
Jumbo jets, **7** 1256
Engineers
Aerospace medicine, **1** 33
Careers, **3** 413, (tables) 412, 416
Engine failure
Piloting techniques (with diagram), **10** 1802
Engine knock
Fuels, **5** 898
Engine mounts, 4 717
Engine pod
Jumbo jets, **7** 1255
Engine power
Landing techniques, **7** 1301
Engine-pressure ratio indicator
Engine instruments, **4** 716
Power management, **10** 1842
Engine restart capability
Launch vehicles, **7** 1324
Engines, 4 717
Airships, **1** 106, 109
Controls, Cockpit, **3** 482

Cowling, Airplane, **1** 90
Launch vehicles, **7** 1317
England, see also Great Britain; United
Kingdom
Airmail, **1** 75
Airports, **1** 95
Air shows, **1** 115
Bomber aircraft, **2** 374
Military aviation, **9** 1580-85
Women in aerospace, **14** 2494
England, Dr. Anthony W. (1942-   ),
4 717
Astronauts, **2** 218-219, 223 (with picture)
Engle, Joe Henry (1932-   ), **4** 718
Astronauts, **2** 216-219, 222 (with picture)
X-15 research program (picture),
14 2531, 2533
English Electric Canberra, see Canberra,
B.Mk. (English Electric)
English Electric P-11 Lightning, see P-11
Lightning
English Channel
Airmail, **1** 69
Balloons, **2** 317, 321
Enhancement technique
Photography, **10** 1785
ENIAC, see Electronic Numerical Integrator
and Calculator
Enos (chimpanzee)
Atlas missile and launch vehicle, **2** 260
Mercury program, **9** 1537
Enroute automation installations
National Airspace System, **9** 1662
Enroute center
National Airspace System, **9** 1662
Enroute High Altitude Charts
Charts, **3** 450
Enroute Low Altitude Charts
Charts, **3** 450
ENTAC
Battlefield missile systems, **2** 342
Ent Air Force Base
Air Defense Command, **1** 59
Enterprise (ship)
Aircraft carriers, **1** 46-51, (picture) 50
Catapult (picture), **3** 424
Nuclear energy, **9** 1713 (with picture)
United States Naval Aviation, **13** 2380,
2382-2383, (pictures) 2385, 2387, 2389
Envelope
Airships, **1** 106
Terminology of aerospace (table), **12** 2272
Environmental control systems, 4 718-21
Apollo, **1** 177
Closed ecological system, **3** 470
Kennedy Space Center, **7** 1267
Life-support systems, **8** 1344
Manned Orbiting Laboratory, **8** 1452
Spacecraft design, **11** 2101
Spacesuits, **12** 2130
Temperature control, **12** 2265
Environmental Data Service
Environmental Science Services
Administration, **4** 724
Environmental equipment centers
Jumbo jets, **7** 1257
Environmental research satellites (with
diagram and picture), **4** 722-24
**Environmental Science Services
Administration, 4** 724-29
ESSA spacecraft, **4** 739
GHOST program, **6** 979
NASA, **9** 1653
National Environmental Satellite Center,
9 1664
Weather, **13** 2454
Environmental simulators (with pictures),
4 726
NASA (picture), **9** 1656
Environmental stress
Quality control, **10** 1868
Environmental Survey Satellites
ESSA spacecraft, **4** 739
Weather satellites, **13** 2463, (pictures)
2466-67, (table) 2470

Enzian (missile)
  Surface-to-air missiles, **12** 2200
Enzymes
  Mars, **8** 1492
  Photosynthesis, **10** 1789, 1790
Epicycle
  Astronomy, **2** 235
  Celestial mechanics, **3** 427
EPS, see Electrical power system
Epsilon Eridani
  Ozma project, **10** 1753
Equator, **4** 729
Equatorial bulge
  Precession, **10** 1843
Equatorial gnomonic projection
  Maps and mapping (table), **8** 1478
Equatorial orbit
  Communications satellites, **3** 536
Equilibrium
  Astrophysics, **2** 257
  Ballast, **2** 313
Equinox, **4** 729
  Ecliptic, **4** 669
Equivalence, Principle of
  Relativity theory, **11** 1951
Equivalent airspeed
  Airspeed, **1** 116
Eratosthenes (Era TOS then ees) (276 B.C.-
  195 B.C., Egyptian astronomer,
  geographer and mathematician), **4** 729
Ercoupe
  Rockets and rocketry, **11** 1982 (with
  picture)
Erection mechanism
  Compasses, **3** 550
Erg
  Energy, **4** 712
  Mechanical energy, **8** 1521
  Quantum theory, **10** 1869
Ergonomics, see Human engineering
ESCAPAC seats
  Attack aircraft, **2** 274
Escape balloon
  Balloons (picture), **2** 322
Escape energy
  Mechanical energy, **8** 1522
Escape systems (with diagrams and
  pictures), **4** 730-38
Escape tower
  Escape systems, **4** (picture) 736-737
Escape trajectory
  Launch vehicle **7** 1314, (diagram) 1318
Escape velocity, **4** 738
  Earth, **4** 662
  Launch vehicles, **7** 1314
  Mechanical energy, **8** 1522
  Moon, **9** 1637-38
Escort duty
  Airships, **1** 114
Escort fighter
  Military aircraft, **9** 1568-69
ESDAC
  European Space Research Organization,
  4 756
ESLAB
  European Space Research Organization,
  4 756
E-66A jet monoplane
  Altitude and altitude records, **1** 148
Esnault-Pelterie (Ez NOH-Pelt air EE)
  Robert (1881-1957, French
  aeronautical engineer), **4** 738-39
  History of aviation (table), **6** 1119
Espionage
  Intelligence, military, **7** 1180
Espionage Act of 1916
  Coast Guard aviation, **3** 477
ESRANGE
  European Space Research Organization,
  4 756
ESRIN
  European Space Research Organization,
  4 756
ESRO, see European Space Research
  Organization

ESSA, see Environmental Sciences and
  Services Administration
ESSA spacecraft (with charts and pictures),
  4 739-41
  National Environmental Satellite Center,
  9 1664
Essex (ship)
  Aircraft carriers (picture), **1** 49
  United States Naval Aviation, **13** 2382-83,
  (picture) 2382
ESTEC
  European Space Research Organization,
  4 755
ESTRACK
  European Space Research Organization,
  4 756
ETA, **4** 741
ETD, **4** 741
ETE, **4** 741
Etendard strike-fighter
  Naval aviation, worldwide (France), **9** 1669
  (with picture)
Ether
  Astronomy, **2** 235
  Relativity theory, **11** 1949
Ethiopia
  International Agricultural Aviation Centre,
  7 1188
Ethiopian Airways
  Africa's aviation, **1** 36, (picture) 37
Etienne, Jacques
  Balloons, **2** 321
Etrich, Igo
  World War I, **14** 2500-01
Etude sur l'Aerostation (book)
  Man-powered flight, **8** 1464
Euclidean plane geometry
  Relativity theory, **11** 1952
Eudoxus of Cnidus (U DOX us of NI dus)
  Astronomy, **2** 235
  Planetarium, **10** 1818
Euler, Leonhard (1707-1783)
  Astronomy, **2** 238
Eurocontrol
  European air traffic control, **4** 752
Europa
  Astronomy, **2** 245
  Jupiter, **7** 1261
EUROPA 1, **4** 741
  European Launcher Development
  Organization, **4** 754, 755
  Launch vehicles, **7** 1327
European aerospace activities, **4** 743-51
European air traffic control, **4** 752-53
European Conference for Satellite
  Communications, **4** 753-54
  International projects, **7** 1198
  Italy's aerospace activities, **7** 1222
European Launcher Development
  Organization, **4** 754-55
  EUROPA 1, **4** 741
  International projects, **7** 1197-98
  Italy's aerospace activities, **7** 1222
  Lamination, **7** 1297
  Launch vehicles, **7** 1327
  West Germany's aerospace activities, **13**
  2479
European Southern Observatory
  Telescopes and astronomical instruments,
  12 2253
European Space Research Organization,
  4 755-56
  International projects, **7** 1197
  West Germany's aerospace activities,
  13 2479
EUROSPACE, **4** 756-57
  International projects, **7** 1198
EVA, see Extravehicular activity
Evans, Ronald Ellwin (1933-   ), **4** 757
  Astronauts, 218, 219, 226 (with picture)
Evaporation and condensation (with
  diagram), **4** 757-58
  Rain, **10** 1900
Evening stars
  Astronomy, **2** 242

Everest, Frank Kendall, Jr. (1920-   ,
  American Air Force officer, test pilot),
  4 758
  Medals and decorations (table), **8** 1526
  Speed and speed records (table), **12** 2141
  Test pilots and test flying, **12** 2280
Everest, Pete
  X-series aerospace vehicles, **14** 2537
Everly, Clyde
  Distance and distance records, **4** 641,
  (table) 640
Ewen, Harold Irving (1922-   , American
  radio astronomer), **4** 759
  Radio astronomy, **10** 1890
EWR VJ 101C, X-1, X-2 (aircraft)
  V/STOL aircraft (table), **13** 2443
Examiners
  Patents, **10** 1766
Exceptional Civil Service Award
  Debus, Kurt Heinrich, **4** 612
Exciters
  Environmental simulators, **4** 727
Executive Skyknight, see Cessna 310
Exhaust gases
  Reaction engines, **10** 1912
Exhaust gas analyzer, **4** 759
Exhaust gas temperature gauge
  Engine instruments, **4** 716
Exhaust generator
  Crop dusting, **4** 588
Exhaust nozzle
  Launch vehicles, **7** 1316
Exhaust opening
  Jet engines, **7** 1239
Exhaust pipes
  Exhaust system, **4** 759
Exhaust stacks
  Exhaust system, **4** 759
Exhaust stroke
  Aircraft propulsion systems, **1** 53
Exhaust system, **4** 759
Exhaust velocity
  Cryogenic propellants, **4** 596
  Plasma propulsion, **10** 1823
Exit heating
  Launch vehicles, **7** 1316
Exit nozzle
  Pulsejet engine, **10** 1865
Exobiology
  Mars, **8** 1490
  Space biology, **11** 2094
Exogenous hypothesis
  Circadian rhythm, **3** 460
Exosphere, **4** 759-60
  Atmosphere, **2** 264
Exothermic reactions
  Chemical energy, **3** 456
Expander shoe and tube brakes
  Airplane, **1** 90
Expansion waves, **4** 760
Experiment Array A
  Lunar exploration (diagram), **8** 1405
Experimental aircraft, **4** 760
Experimental Aircraft Association, **4** 760
  Air shows, **1** 115
  Homebuilt aircraft, **6** 1126, 1125
  Pleasure flying, **10** 1826
Experimental Airworthiness Certificate
  Certification procedures, **3** 443
Experimental Astronomy Laboratory
  Chapman, Philip K., **3** 447
Experimental gas engines
  Junkers, Hugo, **7** 1258
Exploration
  Space, **11** 2092
Exploration of Space (book)
  Clarke, Arthur Charles, **3** 467
Exploration of Space by Rocket Devices
  (book)
  Rockets and Rocketry, **11** 1975
Exploration of the universe
  Implications of aerospace, **7** 1149
Explorer satellites (with diagrams, map and
  table), **5** 761-73

(Continued)

Explorer satellites (Cont.)
Alouette satellites, **1** 144
Argus project, **2** 191
Blockhouse, **2** 367
Commemorative stamps and medals, **3** 495
Communications satellites, **3** 532
Earth science, **4** 666
Geodetic satellites (table), **6** 973
Goddard Space Flight Center, **6** 992
Jet Propulsion Laboratory, **7** 1240
Juno rockets, **7** 1259
Langley Research Center, **7** 1302
Launch vehicles, **7** 1322, 1325
Military implications of space, **9** 1588
Military space program, **9** 1593
NASA (table, Major Launchings), **9** 1652
Surveyor, **12** 2209
Thor rockets, **12** 2286
Tracking systems and networks, **13** 2300
Van Allen radiation belts, **13** 2400
Weather satellites, **13** 2459-60, (table) 2470

Explosive decompression
Decompression, **4** 613
Explosive flares
Photography, **10** 1789
Explosive forming
Production techniques, **10** 1856-57
Explosive stars
Astrophysics, **2** 258
Exposure
Photography, **10** 1782
Extended Lunar Module
Lunar exploration **8** 1407
Extended lunar surface stay
Lunar bases, **8** 1381-83
External combustion engine
Reciprocating engines, **11** 1913
Externally braced wing
Airplane, **1** 86
Wings, **14** 2491-92
Extraterrestrial flight
Launch vehicles, **7** 1314
Extraterrestrial life (with pictures), **5** 774-84
Mars, **8** 1490
Space biology, **11** 2094
Extraterrestrial relays
Clarke, Arthur Charles, **3** 467
Extravehicular activity
Aldrin, Edwin E., Jr., **1** 142
Apollo Applications Program, **2** 187
Cosmonauts, **4** 572
Gemini, **5** 935-37, 944-45, 947-50, (diagram) 935, (picture) 936
Lunar Module, **8** 1410
Manned spaceflight, **8** 1461
Spacesuits, **12** 2131
Walk in space, **13** 2447
Extrusion
Production techniques, **10** 1854
Eyeballs in and out
Aerospace medicine, **1** 34
Terminology of aerospace (table), **12** 2272
Eyes
Aerospace medicine, **1** 34

F3B-1 bomber
Boeing, William Edward, **2** 270
F3D Operational Flight Trainer
Flight simulators, **5** 852

F-4 Phantom (McDonnell)
Aerospace industry (picture), **1** 30
Aircraft carriers (picture) 47, 51
Air forces of the world, (picture) **1** 63, 65, 66
Air-to-air missiles, (picture) **1** 119, 121
Arresting gear, (picture) **2** 202
Bull, John Sumter, **3** 389
Configuration, **3** 560
Fighter aircraft (pictures), **5** 808, 809
International projects, **7** 1201
Marine Corps Aviation, **8** 1482, (pictures) 1483
Military aircraft (picture), **9** 1566
Nationalist China's aviation, **9** 1665
NATO, **9** 1704
Phantom II, McDonnell-Douglas F-4A, **10** 1777
Reconnaissance aircraft, **11** 1921, (with picture) 1922
United States Naval Aviation, **13** 2387
F4U Corsair (Vought)
Aircraft carriers (picture), **1** 49
Fighter aircraft, **5** 811
Korean war, **7** 1287
Marine Corps Aviation (picture), **8** 1481, 1483
Mitsubishi Zero-Sen, **9** 1622
F-5 Freedom Fighter (Northrop)
Air-to-surface missiles (picture), **1** 124
Asia's aviation, **2** 204-05
Canada's aviation, **3** 404
Nationalist China's aviation, **9** 1665 (with picture)
Northrop F-5 Freedom Fighter (table, diagrams, and picture), **9** 1705
Reconnaissance aircraft, **11** 1922
F-6 Hellcat (Grumman)
Aircraft (picture), **1** 45
Hellcat (chart, pictures), **6** 1080
History of aviation (picture), **6** 1113
Second World War aircraft (with picture), **11** 2035
F-8 Crusader (LTV)
Aircraft carriers, **1** 46
Air forces of the world, **1** 65, 66
Escape systems, **4** (picture) 732, 733
Nationalist China's aviation, **9** 1665
Naval aviation, worldwide, **9** 1669, (picture) 1670
Reconnaissance aircraft (table), **10** 1923
United States Naval Aviation, **13** 2387
F-11 Tiger (Grumman)
Demonstrations teams (picture), **4** 624, 626
F-12A, see YF-12A fighter
F-27 transport, see Fairchild-Hiller F-27
F-80 Shooting Star (Lockheed), **8** 1366-67 (with pictures, chart)
Bong, Richard Ira, **3** 380
Counter-insurgency aircraft, **4** 577
Johnson, Clarence Leonard, **7** 1242
Korean war, **7** 1287-88
ramjet engine
Aircraft propulsion systems, **1** 59
Rocket sled, **11** 1986
United States Air Force (picture), **13** 2365
F-84 Thunderstreak (Republic)
Air forces of the world, **1** 64-66
Cockpit, **3** 483
History of aviation (picture), **6** 1117
F-86 Sabre (North American)
Air forces of the world, **1** 64
Asia's aviation, **2** 203-05
Fighter aircraft, **5** 811
Korean war, **7** 1284, 1287-88
Sabre, **11** 2000
Women in aerospace, **14** 2495
F-94 Starfire (Lockheed)
Lockheed F-80/T-33, **8** 1367
F-100 Super Sabre (North American)
Air forces of the world, **1** 65
Bomber aircraft (picture), **2** 376
Demonstrations teams, **4** (picture) 624, 625, 626

History of aviation, **6** 1118
Nationalist China's aviation, **9** 1665
NATO, **9** 1704
F-101 Voodoo (McDonnell)
Air Defense Command, **1** 59
Air defense systems, **1** 60-61
Air forces of the world, **1** 65
Air-to-air missiles (picture), **1** 121
Nationalist China's aviation, **9** 1665
NATO, **9** 1704
F-102 Delta Dagger (Convair), **4** 621-22 (with chart, pictures)
Air Defense Command, **1** 59
Air defense systems, **1** 60-61
Air forces of the world, **1** 65
Air-to-air missiles (picture), **1** 119
Area rule (picture), **2** 191
Flight simulators, **5** 854
History of aviation, **6** 1118
NATO, **9** 1704
F-104 Starfighter (Lockheed)
Aerodynamics (picture), **1** 23
Air Defense Command, **1** 59
Air defense systems, **1** 60-61
Air forces of the world, **1** (pictures) 63, 64-66
Altitude and altitude records, **1** 148
Asia's aviation, **2** 204
Canada's aviation, **3** 404
Fighter aircraft, **5** 811
Flight simulators, **5** 855
History of aviation, **6** 1120
Johnson, Clarence Leonard, **7** 1242
NASA (picture), **9** 1656
Nationalist China's aviation (with picture), **9** 1665
NATO, **9** 1704
Naval aviation, worldwide (Germany), **9** 1670
Pursuit airplane, **10** 1866
F-105 Thunderchief (Republic)
Ace (picture), **1** 4
Military aircraft, **9** 1568
NATO, **9** 1704
F-106 Delta Dart (Convair)
Air Defense Command (picture), **1** 60-61
Air forces of the world, **1** 65
History of aviation, **6** 1118
F-111 variable-wing fighter (Grumman), (chart, pictures), **5** 870
Air forces of the world, **1** 65, 66
Australia's aviation, **2** 280
Computers, **3** 555
Fighter aircraft, **5** 810, (picture) 810
Flight simulators, **5** 855
Hydraulic systems, **6** 1139
Metals and metallury (picture), **9** 1549
Reconnaissance aircraft, **11** 1922
Rocket sled (with picture), **11** 1988
Windows and windshields, **13** 2486
X-15 research program, **14** 2530
FAA, see Federal Aviation Administration
FAA Academy, 5 785
FAA Aeromedical Center
Sensors (with picture), **11** 2042
FAA-approved school
Pilot training, **10** 1809
FAA P16 (airplane)
European aerospace activities (picture), **4** 751
Fabre, Henri (1882- , French engineer), **5** 785
Fabrication
Manufacturing (diagram), **8** 1471
Fabricius, D.
Astrophysics, **2** 258
Fabrics, 5 786-88
Face
Propellers, **10** 1862
Facsimile transmission
Communications satellites, **3** 534
Faget, Maxime A. (1921- , American aerospace scientist), **5** 788
Mercury program, **9** 1530

F

Re-entry vehicles, 11 1932
Fagot (aircraft)
U.S.S.R. aerospace activities (table),
13 2337
Fahrenheit, Gabriel Daniel
Temperature scales, 12 2271
Fahrenheit scale
Meteorology, 9 1556
Temperature scales, 12 2271
FAI, see Federation Aeronautique
Internationale
FAI Gold Air Medal
Medals and decorations, 8 1524,
(table) 1526
FAI Gold Space Medal
Medals and decorations, 8 1524 (with table)
Fail-safe design
Redundancy, 10 1930
Reliability and quality assurance, 11 1954
Fairchild C-119, see C-119 Flying Boxcar
Fairchild C-123, see C-123
Fairchild-Hiller Corp.
Commercial air transports, 3 526
International projects, 7 1201
Fairchild-Hiller Bikini
Reconnaissance aircraft, 11 1924
Fairchild-Hiller F-27
Commercial air transports, 3 526
Fairchild-Hiller FH-1100 (helicopter)
Helicopters (diagrams), 6 1063, 1064
Fairchild monoplane
Military aircraft, 9 1567
Fairchild, Muir S.
Air University, 1 140
Fairchild Petrel
Air-to-surface missiles, 1 123
Fairey, Sir Charles Richard (1887-1956,
British airplane designer), 5 790
Fairey Swordfish
Fairey, Sir Charles, 5 790
Fairing, 5 790 (with picture)
Launch vehicles, 7 1316
Nacelle, 9 1647
Nose cone, 9 1705
Pioneer (with diagram), 10 1812
Propellers, 10 1862
Faith 7 (spacecraft)
Astronauts, 2 215
Cooper, L. Gordon, Jr., 3 565
Manned spaceflight (table), 8 1461
Mercury program, 9 1543, 1545, (pictures)
1543, 1544, 1545, (table) 1544
NASA (table, Major Launchings), 9 1652
Falcon (Dássault)
Business aviation (picture), 3 395
Falcon missile
Air defense systems (picture), 1 61
Air-to-air missiles, 1 119-21, (pictures)
119, 121
Missiles (diagram), 9 1614
Fall breaker (Da Vinci)
Mythology, 9 1646
Falling body
Orbits and trajectories (with diagram),
10 1743
"Fallout"
Aerospace industry, 1 33
Apollo, 1 184
False echoes
Radar, 10 1879
Fan-Ejector Ramjet
Hypersonic flight, 6 1144
Fanjet, see Turbofan engine
Fan marker beacons
Instrument landing system, 7 1170
Navigation systems, 9 1675
Fan patch
Airships, 1 106
FAR, see Federal Aviation Regulations
Faraday dark space
Electronics, 4 693
Faraday, Michael
Electromagnetism, 4 689
Electronics, 4 693

Faraday rotation
Astronomy, 2 242
Farcot, Leon
Robots, 11 1965
Fares
International Air Transport Association,
7 1189
Farman F. 222
Second World War aircraft, 11 2029
Farman Goliath
Commercial airlines (picture), 3 505
World War I, 14 2500
Farman, Henri and Maurice (Henri, 1874-
1958, Maurice, 1877-1964, French
aviation pioneers), 5 790-91
Distance records (Henri), 4 640
History of aviation (Henri), 6 1101, 1103,
(table) 1119
Levavasseur, Leon (Henri), 7 1333
Rheims Air Meet, 11 1963
Farmer, see MiG 19
Far Side
Military space program, 9 1592
Fascination, 5 791
Fast transfers
Interplanetary travel, 7 1207
Fatigue
cracks
Lumination, 7 1297
Human fatigue, 6 1135
Material fatigue, 8 1498
Materials, 8 1508
Metals and metallurgy, 9 1549
Psychological factors of flight, 10 1864
test
Certification procedures (picture), 3 442
FB-3 fighter (Boeing)
Marine Corps Aviation (picture), 8 1481
FBM submarine (picture)
Polaris missiles, 10 1832
F-corona, see Fraunhofer coroner
FD-1 Phantom
Aircraft carriers, 1 51
Fear
Psychological factors of flight, 10 1864
Feathers
Bird flight, 2 360
Reciprocating engines, 10 1918
Fedden, Sir Roy (1885-   , British airplane
engine designer), 5 791-92
Federal Aid to Airports Program
Airports, 1 98
Careers, 3 413
Federal Air Regulations, see Federal
Aviation Regulations
Federal Airways System, 5 792-93 (with
diagram)
Visual Flight Rules, 13 2426
Federal Aviation Act
Air Commerce Act, 1 45
Air traffic control, 1 136
Charter flying, 3 447
Civil Aeronautics Board, 3 464
Federal Aviation Administration, 5 794-802
(with diagrams, map, pictures, table)
Aeronautical Center, 1 25-26
Aeronautics, 1 26
Air Commerce Act, 1 45
Aircraft, 1 45
Airports, 1 98, 100
Airman's Information Manual, 1 80
Air taxis, 1 117
Air traffic control, 1 125
Air traffic, 1 124
Airworthiness, 1 141
Automatic landing, 2 288
Balloons, 2 319
Careers, 3 413, 416-17
Certification procedures, 3 440
Commuter airlines, 3 545
Crash investigation, 4 579
Economic implications of aerospace, 4 670
Emergency signals, 4 708
FAA Academy, 5 785

Flight service station
Aviation weather, 2 298
General aviation, 6 954
Government in aerospace, 6 1006, 1008
Ground service and maintenance, 6 1027
Hemisphere rules, 6 1080
Homebuilt aircraft, 6 1126
Instrument landing categories, 7 1168
Jumbo jets, 7 1258
Kites, 7 1280
Lighting facilities, 8 1353-54
Mechanic ratings, 8 1523
Medical examiner, 8 1526
National Airspace System, 9 1660
National Aviation Trades Association,
9 1663
Navigation systems, 9 1678
Outsize cargo aircraft, 10 1750
Pilots and pilot certificates, 10 1802, 1808
Pilot training, 10 1809-10
Pilot weather reports, 10 1812
Positive control areas, 10 1839
Preflight training, 10 1846-49
Program management, 10 1857
Radio communications, 10 1894
Registration of aircraft, 11 1948
Runways, 11 1998
Safety belts, 11 2000
Safety statistics, 11 2001
Sensors, 11 2042
Supersonic transports, 12 2195, 2196,
2199
Survival kits, 12 2221
Women in aerospace, 14 2496
Federal Aviation Agency
Air Commerce Act, 1 45
Air traffic control, 1 136
Aviation weather, 2 298
Civil Aeronautics Board, 3 464
Federal Aviation Administration, 5 795
Maneuvers, 8 1438
Man in flight, 8 1449
Federal Aviation Agency Gold Medal
Mock, Geraldine C., 9 1624
Federal Aviation Regulations 5 802-04
Air traffic, 1 124
Ceiling, 3 426
Charter flying, 3 448
Commuter airlines, 3 544
Crash investigation, 4 579
Ground service and maintenance, 6 1027
Homebuilt aircraft, 6 1123
Instrument Flight Rules, 7 1165
Man in flight, 8 1450
Visual Flight Rules, 13 2425
Federal Bureau of Investigation
Crash investigation, 4 581
Federal Communications Commission
Communications satellites, 3 540
Radio, 10 1885
Federal Electric Corporation
NASA (table, Apollo/Saturn V Major
Contractors), 9 1655
Federal excise tax
Airports, 1 100
Federal Maritime Commission
Civil Aeronautics Board, 3 465
Federal Republic of Germany, see Germany
Federation Aeronautique Internationale
(FAI), 5 804
Academy of Model Aeronautics, 1 2
Aero clubs, 1 18
Altitude and altitude records, 1 146
Australia's aviation, 2 282
Balloons, 2 319
Cobb, Geraldyn, 3 480
Cochran, Jacqueline, 3 481
DeHavilland, Sir Geoffrey, 4 620
Distance and distance records, 4 639
Endurance and endurance records, 4 711
International competitions, 7 1191
Latham, Hubert, 7 1306
Medals and decorations, 8 1524, 1526

(Continued)

Federation Aeronautique Internationale (Cont.)
Model aircraft, 9 1626
Model rocketry, 9 1628
National Aeronautic Association, 9 1647-48
National Pilots Association, 9 1666
Nikolayeva-Tereshkova, Valentina, 9 1697
Speed and speed records, 12 2140
World records and round-the-world flights, 14 2497-99
Feedback, 5 805
Cybernetics, 4 602
Feedback control, see Closed-loop control
Felix, Julien
Altitude and altitude records, 1 147
Felixstowe F.2 (flying boat)
First World War aircraft, 5 820
Feoktistov, Konstantin (1926-   ), 5 805
Cosmonauts (pictures), 4 570-72, (table) 574
Manned spaceflight (table), 8 1461
Medals and decorations (table), 8 1524
U.S.S.R. aerospace activities, 13 2344
Voskhod, 13 2433
Ferber, Ferdinand (1862-1909, French military officer, aviation pioneer), 5 805-06
History of aviation, 6 1099-1000, (table) 1119
Ferguson, James
Manned Orbiting Laboratory, 8 1452
Fermi, Enrico (1901-1954, Italian-American physicist), 5 806
Manhattan Project, 8 1442
Nuclear energy, 9 1710
Ferrarin, Arturo
Distance records, 4 640
Ferry vehicle
Military space program, 9 1604
Fertilizer
Agricultural aviation, 1 39-41
Australia's aviation, 2 282
FH-227 (Fairchild-Hiller)
Commercial air transports, 3 526
FH-1100 helicopter, see Fairchild-Hiller FH-1100
Fiala, Benno
World War I (table, Top Aces), 14 2507
Fiat
Air forces of the world, 1 64, 66
Italy's aerospace activities, 7 1220-25
Fiat CR 42
Second World War aircraft, 11 2028
Spanish Civil War, 12 2139
Fiber glass, 5 806-07 (with pictures)
Fibers
Metals and metallurgy, 9 1554
Fickel, J. E.
Armament, 2 193
Fiddler, see Tupolev Fiddler
Field, Barbara
Gordon, Richard F. Jr., 6 996
Field effect transistors
Electronics, 4 703
Field elevation
Elevation, 4 706
Field emission
Electronics, 4 694-95
Field operations
Crash investigation, 4 581-82
Field pattern
Instrument landing system, 7 1170
Fieseler Fi 156
Second World War aircraft, 11 2033
Fighter aircraft, 5 807-11 (with diagram, pictures, table)
Aircraft carriers, 1 51
Air defense systems (picture), 1 61
Hellcat, Grumman F6F, 6 1080
History of aviation, 6 1111, (pictures) 1105
Interceptor aircraft, 7 1182
Military aircraft, 9 1568-69 (with pictures)
Pursuit airplane, 10 1866
Refueling, 11 1941

Spad, 12 2138
Super Sabre, North American F-100, 12 2176
United States Air Force, 13 2373
Fillet space
Jumbo Jets, 7 1257
Film
Photography, 10 1781
Film emulsion
Photography, 10 1785
Film-fabric
Fabrics, 5 786
Filtering
Radar, 10 1877
Fin, 5 812
Airplane, 1 86
Arrow, 2 202
Finagle's First Law of Physics, 5 812
Final approach
Landing techniques, 7 1301
Finch, Harrison
Polar flights, 10 1831
Fineg, Jerry
Animals in space, 1 155
Finegan, Patricia E.
White, Edward H., II, 13 2482
Finger patch
Airships, 1 106
Finland
Crop dusting, 4 587
European aerospace activities, 4 746
Second World War aircraft, 11 2031
Finley, John L. (1935-   , aerospace research pilot), 5 812
Manned Orbiting Laboratory, 8 1456
Finnair
European aerospace activities, 4 746
Finnegan, Patricia
Collins, Michael, 3 488
Finucane, Brendan
World War II (table), 14 2517
Fire
NASA (table, Major Launchings), 9 1652
Firebar, see YAK-28
Firebee
Drone aircraft, 4 652
Fire bomb
Balloons, 2 324
Bombs, 3 378
Fire extinguishers, 5 812-13 (with diagram)
Fire fighters
Smokejumpers, 11 2059
Fireflies
Mercury program, 9 1539, 1541
Fire injection motors (with diagram)
Launch vehicles, 7 1319
Firepower, 5 813
Avionics, 2 307
Fire-repressant chemicals
Police and fire services, 10 1835
Firewalls, 5 813-14
Fireworks, 5 814
Firing room
Launch complex, 7 1307
Launching, 7 1310
1st Air Force
Air Defense Command, 1 59
First burn
Launch vehicles, 7 1318
First Officer
Aircrew, 1 59
First quarter
Moon, 9 1634 (with picture)
First Strategic Aerospace Division
Vandenberg Air Force Base, 13 2402
First World War aircraft, 5 815-25 (with pictures)
Fishbed, see MiG 21
Fishpot, see Su-9
Fission, 5 826
Kiwi, 7 1281
Nuclear energy, 9 1709-10
Fissionable atoms
Nuclear fuel, 9 1715
Fitter, see SU-7B

FitzPatrick, James L.
Ornithopter, 10 1748
Five Freedoms, 5 826
Five O'Clock Taube
World War I, 14 2501
Five Year Program Acts
Aerospace industry, 1 30
Fixed base operation, 5 826-27 (with picture)
Airports, 1 99
General aviation, 6 957-58
Ground crew, 6 1020
National Aviation Trades Association, 9 1663
Fixed blockhouses
Blockhouse, 2 367
Fixed landing gears
Airplane, 1 89
Landing gear, 7 1300
Fixed-launch concept
Kennedy Space Center, 7 1267
Fixed-pitch
Propellers, 10 1862
Fixed stars
Celestial mechanics, 3 427
Fixed-wing aircraft
Aircraft, 1 45
Flak
Antiaircraft weapons, 1 157
Flak suits
World War II (picture), 14 2519
Flaming Coffin, The
DeHavilland DH-4, 4 618
Flammability of materials
Apollo Applications Program, 2 186
Flamsteed, John (1646-1719, English astronomer), 5 827-28
Astronomy, 2 242
Flapping cycle
Bird flight, 2 360
Flaps, 5 828-29 (with diagram and picture)
Aerodynamics, 1 22, (diagram) 21
Airplane, 1 88
Cockpit, 3 482
High-lift devices, 6 1088
Manufacturing, 8 1469
Flareout, 5 829
Agricultural aviation, 1 40
Flares, 5 829
Panel code, 10 1755
Flashlight, see YAK-25
Flash point
Lubricants, 8 1375
Flat hatting
Buzz, 3 396
Fleet Air Arm (Great Britain)
Air forces of the world, 1 66
Fleet Canuck
Canada's aviation, 3 403
Fleming, John A.
Electronics, 4 693, 695
Fleming valve
Electronics, 4 693
Vacuum tubes, 13 2398
Fletcher FU-24
Crop dusting, 4 589
Flexible skirt craft
Ground-effect machines, 6 1023
Flex wing
Parawing, 10 1760, (picture) 1761
Flichettes (Fli SHAY)
World War I, 14 2502
Flickinger, Donald Davis (1907-   , aerospace medical pioneer), 5 829
Pararescue, 10 1760
Rescue and Recovery Service, 11 1959
Flight, 5 830-38 (with pictures)
Flight acceleration facility
Manned Spacecraft Center, 8 1458
Flight check
High altitude flight training, 6 1086
Flight computers, 5 838 (with picture)
Acquisition and tracking radar, 1 6
Density altitude, 4 626
Navigation instruments, 9 1672

Flight computers (Cont.)
  Preflight training, **10** 1848
Flight control
  Airframe, **1** 66
  Attitude and attitude control, **2** 275
  Bird flight, **2** 359
  Cockpit, **3** 481
  Cybernetics, **4** 602
  Insertion tracking, **7** 1162
  Instrument landing categories, **7** 1169
  Jumbo jets, **7** 1252
  Surveyor, **12** 2211
Flightcraft
  Lunar bases, **8** 1391, 1393, (drawings) 1394
Flight crew
  Aircrew, **1** 59
  Careers, **3** 414
  Occupations (with tables), **10** 1729-30
Flight data on line
  National Airspace System, **9** 1661
Flight deck
  Cockpit, **3** 481
Flight deck launch crew
  Aircraft carriers (picture), **1** 47
Flight director, 5 839-40 (with diagram)
  Aircraft carriers, **1** 47-48
  Attitude indicator, **2** 276
  Instruments, Avionics, **2** 307
  Instrument panels, **7** 1177
  Jumbo jets, **7** 1252
  Spaceflight simulators, **12** 2112
Flight engineer, 5 841
  Aircrew, **1** 59
  Cockpit (picture), **3** 486
  Preflight inspection, **10** 1846
Flight envelope, 5 841
Flight hours
  Safety statistics (with graph), **11** 2001
Flight information
  Air Commerce Act, **1** 45
Flight instruction, 5 841-42 (with pictures)
  General aviation, **6** 956
Flight instructor, 5 842-43
  Careers, **3** 417, (picture) 415
  General aviation, **6** 958
Flight instruments, 5 843 (with picture)
  Cockpit, **3** 485
  Instrument panels, **7** 1176
  Manufacturing, **8** 1469
Flight level
  Air traffic control, **1** 127
  Instrument flight techniques, **7** 1168
Flight line, 5 843
  Aerial photography, **1** 9
Flight management, 5 843-46 (with pictures)
Flight maneuvers
  Maneuvers (pictures), **8** 1432
Flight manual
  Cockpit, **3** 486
Flight mobility
  Lunar bases, **8** 1391, 1393
Flight nurse, 5 846
Flight path, 5 846
  Instrument flight techniques, **7** 1167
  Lunar bases (diagram), **8** 1381
  Navigation systems, **9** 1678
  Orbits and trajectories (with illustration),
    10 1742-45, 1747
Flight physical, 5 846-47
Flight plan, 5 847
  Air traffic control (picture), **1** 130
  Aviation weather, **2** 301
  Instrument flight rules, **7** 1165
  Instrument flight techniques, **7** 1167
  Navigation techniques, **9** 1681-83
Flight planning, 5 847-48 (with diagrams)
Flight progress strips
  Air traffic control, **1** 130-32
Flight recorder, 5 848-49 (with picture)
Flight Research Center
  NASA, **9** 1655
Flight safety
  Airmen's Information Manual, **1** 80

Flying safety, **5** 864-65
Flight Safety Foundation, 5 849
Flight service stations, 5 849-51 (with pictures)
  Airports, **1** 100
  Air traffic control, **1** 134-35, (pictures) 130,
    135
  Federal Aviation Administration, **5** 798
  Oil burner routes, **10** 1735
Flight simulation training
  Mercury program, **9** 1532
Flight simulators, 5 851-55 (with pictures)
  Commercial airlines, **3** 503
Flight stability
  Aerodynamics, **1** 23-24
Flight Steps Leading to the Moon (diagram)
  Apollo, **1** 163
Flight suits
  Personal equipment, **10** 1775
Flight surgeon, 5 855
Flight systems, 5 855-56
Flight test programs, 5 856-57 (with pictures)
  Applications Technology Satellites, **2** 189
  Eastern Test Range, **4** 667
  Italy's aerospace activities (picture),
    7 1220
Flight training
  Flight Instruction, **5** 841-42
  High altitude flight training, **6** 1086
  Pilot training, **10** 1809-10
Flint, I. E.
  Altitude and altitude records, **1** 147
Floating aileron
  Airplane, **1** 87
Floating fortresses
  Aircraft carriers, **1** 46
Floatplanes
  History of aviation, **6** 1113
Floats
  Airplane (picture), **1** 90
  Pontoons, **10** 1838
Float type carburetor (picture and diagram)
  Carburetion, **3** 408-09
Floor length, extension
  Jumbo jets, **7** 1253
Flotation bags
  Aircraft carriers, **1** 48
Flotation collar
  Recovery (with picture), **11** 1928
Flowage fee
  Airports, **1** 100
Fludd, Robert
  Atoms, **2** 269
Fluid
  Viscosity, **13** 2424
Fluidic circuits
  Circuit, **3** 461
Fluid mechanics, 5 857-58 (with diagram)
Fluids
  Materials, **8** 1510
Fluid statics
  Fluid mechanics, **5** 857
Fluorescence
  Comets, **3** 492
  Light, **8** 1351
Fluorescent lights
  Plasma, **10** 1822
Flux
  Magnetic field, **8** 1419
Fly Baby (airplane)
  Homebuilt aircraft (picture), **6** 1127
Flyby, 5 858
Flyby orbit
  Orbits and trajectories, **10** 1746-47
Flyer, see Wright Flyer
Flying ambulance
  Utility aviation, **13** 2395
Flying bird
  Da Vinci, Leonardo, **4** 611
Flying boats, 5 858-60 (with pictures)
  Aerospace industry, **1** 29
  Airplane, **1** 90
  Commercial air transports, **3** 524
  Curtiss Model D Hydro, **4** 601

Flying bombs
  Bombs, **3** 377
Flying Boxcar, see C-119 Flying Boxcar
Flying Circus, 5 861
  Military aviation, **9** 1580
  World War I (picture), **14** 2505-06
Flying Crane helicopters
  Commercial airlines, **3** 503
  Helicopters, **6** 1074
Flyingdales Moor
  Ballistic Missile Early Warning System,
    2 313-14
Flying doctor services, 5 861-62 (with
    pictures)
  Australia's aviation (picture), **2** 284
Flying Dude, The
  Barnstormers, **2** 335
Flying Dutchman, The
  Fokker, Anthony Herman Gerard, **5** 867
Flying Fortress, see B-17 Flying Fortress
Flying guppy configuration
  X-series aerospace vehicles, **14** 2538
Flying lifeboat
  Coast Guard aviation, **3** 478
Flying lounges
  Commercial airlines, **3** 503
Flying machine
  Phillips, Horatio F., **10** 1778
Flying Physicians Association, 5 863-64
  Medical examiner, **8** 1527
Flying platform
  Maneuvering in space, **8** 1431
Flying Razor Blade (airplane)
  Fokker D-8, **5** 867
Flying safety, 5 864-65 (with diagram)
Flying speed
  Jet engines, **7** 1239
Flying Squad (book)
  Bishop, William Avery, **2** 362
Flying stovepipe
  Missiles, **9** 1612
Flying tail (see also Rotating stabilizer)
  Elevators, **4** 706
Flying Tank, see Lockheed AH-56A Cheyenne
Flying technique
  Seaplanes, **11** 2024
Flying the beam
  Beam, radio, **2** 345
Flying the Hump
  Airlift, **1** 67
Fly the needle
  Navigation systems, **9** 1675
Flying Tiger Lines
  Cargo aircraft, **3** 418
  Charter flying, **3** 448
  Commercial airlines, **3** 500, 514
Flying Tigers, 5 865-66 (with picture)
  Chennault, Claire Lee, **3** 457
  P-40, Curtiss, **10** 1777
  World War II, **14** 2520
Flying vehicles
  Lunar exploration (drawings), **8** 1402-03
Flying washboard
  Commercial air transports, **3** 518
Flywheel
  Brakes, **3** 387
FM radio stations
  Radio communications, **10** 1894
FM transmission
  Receivers, **10** 1912
Foam
  airframe insulator
    Launch vehicles, **7** 1317
  Emergency landing procedures, **4** 708
Foch (aircraft carrier)
  Naval aviation, worldwide (France), **9** 1669
Focke-Achgelis FA-61 (helicopter)
  Helicopters, **6** 1062
Focke-Wulf Condor
  Bomber aircraft, **2** 375
Focke-Wulf FW 190 fighter
  History of aviation (picture), **6** 1111

(Continued)

Focke-Wulf FW 190 fighter (Cont.)
Luftwaffe, **8** 1377
Rockets and rocketry, **11** 1980
Second World War aircraft (picture),
11 2026-27
Focke-Wulf FW 200
Second World War aircraft, **11** 2033
Focke-Wulf Kurrier aircraft
World War II, **14** 2515
Focus
Parabola, **10** 1755
Fog, **5** 866 (with picture)
Bush flying, **3** 392
Clouds, **3** 471
Evaporation and condensation, **4** 758
Weather, **13** 2450-51
Fogging
Decontamination, radiological, **4** 614
Fokker (aircraft)
World War I, **14** 2506
Fokker Aircraft Corporation
Balchen, Bernt, **2** 312
Fokker, (FOKE er) **Anthony Herman Gerard**
(1890-1939, Dutch-American aircraft
designer), **5** 867
Commercial air transports, **3** 518
First World War aircraft, **5** 816, 818,
823-24
History of aviation, **6** 1107, (table) 1119
Manufacturing, **8** 1468
World War I, **14** 2505
Fokker, DR-1 triplane, **5** 868-69 (with chart
and diagram)
First World War aircraft (picture), **5** 825
History of aviation (picture), **6** 1105
Fokker D-VII (fighter)
History of aviation (picture), **6** 1105, 1108
Fokker, D-VIII, **5** 867-68 (with chart, diagram)
World War I, **14** 2505
Fokker Eindecker
World War I (picture), **14** 2501
Fokker F. 28 Fellowship
European aerospace activities (picture),
4 747
Fokker Super Universal
Bush flying (picture), **3** 393
Commercial air transports (picture), **3** 518
Fokker T-2
Macready, Lt. John, and Lt. Oakley
Kelly, **8** 1417
Fokker Tripe
World War I, **14** 2506
Fokker Triplane
World War I (picture), **14** 2507
Folding fin rockets
Air defense systems, **1** 61
Folding gear
Jumbo jets, **7** 1253
Fonck, Rene (FONK, Ray NEAY), (1894-1953,
French aviator), **5** 869
Ace, **1** 4
World War I, **14** 2506, (table) 2507, 2510
F-1 engine
Rocket propulsion systems (with diagram),
11 1968
Food and nutrition, **5** 871-79 (with pictures,
diagrams)
Space stations, **12** 2127
Foot-pound
Energy, **4** 712
Mechanical energy, **8** 1521
Footprint
Recovery, **11** 1927
Force, **5** 879
Energy, **4** 712
Gravity, **6** 1011
Forced convection
Clouds, **3** 471
Force de Frappe
Air forces of the world, **1** 65-66
France's aerospace activities, **5** 891
Force of acceleration
Kepler's laws, **7** 1275

Forces Aeriennes Strategiques (FORS Air
i ENS Strat ai JEEK) (France)
Air forces of the world, **1** 65
Ford, Henry
Commercial air transports, **3** 518
Ford Trimotor
Aerospace industry, **1** 29
Aircraft propulsion systems (picture), **1** 57
Comercial air transports, **3** 518 (with
picture), 526 (table)
History of aviation (pictures), **6** 1093, 1108
Tin Goose, Ford Trimotor 4-AT, **12** 2288
Ford Trophy
Trophies and awards (table), **13** 2312
Forecast chart
Aviation weather, **2** 300
Foreign Aircraft Certification
Certification procedures, **3** 441
Foreign countries
Airmail, **1** 78
Foreign nonmilitary aircraft
Air Commerce Act, **1** 45
Foreign wings
Pilot and crew wings, **10** 1795
Forer, Fred
Medals and decorations (table), **8** 1526
Forest fire control, **5** 879-81 (with pictures)
Economic implications of aerospace, **4** 671
Police and fire services, **10** 1834
Forest penetrator
Rescue and Recovery Service (with
picture), **11** 1959
Forestry
Utility aviation, **13** 2395
Forging
Production techniques, **10** 1854
Forgotten Eagle
Beachey, Lincoln, **2** 344
Forlanini, Enrico (1848-1930, Italian
engineer), **5** 881
Formation flying and techniques, **5** 883
(with diagram, picture)
Precision flying, **10** 1845
Form drag
Aerodynamics, **1** 22-23
Former ribs
Airplane, **1** 85
Wings, **14** 2490
Forming machines
Production techniques, **10** 1854
Formosa
Airlift, **1** 67
Forrestal (ship)
Aircraft carriers (data table), **1** 51
Fort Sumter National Monument
Aerial photography (picture), **1** 10
Forward Air Controllers
Vietnam, **13** 2420
Forward biased
Electronics, **4** 701
Forward ramps
Jumbo jets, **7** 1256
Forward slip
Maneuvers, **8** 1436
Forward speed
Reaction engines, **10** 1912
Foss, Joseph
World War II (table), **14** 2517
Foster, John
Manned Orbiting Laboratory, **8** 1456
Foucault, Leon
Telescopes and astronomical instruments,
12 2250
Foucault pendulum, **5** 884
Foudre
Aircraft carriers, **1** 48
Foulois, Benjamin Delehauf (1879-1967,
American aviation pioneer), **5** 884
United States Air Forces, **13** 2359, 2361
Four-course radio range
Navigation systems, **9** 1674
Fourny, Georges
Distance records, **4** 640

Four-stroke cycle engines (with diagram)
Aircraft propulsion systems, **1** 53
4th Air Force
Air Defense Command **1** 59
14th Air Force
Air Defense Command, **1** 59
NATO, **9** 1704
Fowler, Elizabeth Jennifer
Thornton, William E., **12** 2283
Fowler wing flap
Airplane, **1** 88
Fox (bomber)
Fairey, Sir Charles, **5** 790
Fox, Sidney W. (1912- , American
educator and chemist), **5** 884
Fractional Orbit Bombardment System
Military implications of space, **9** 1588
Surface-to-surface missiles, **12** 2205
Fractostratus clouds
Clouds, **3** 473
France
NATO, **9** 1703-04
Naval aviation, worldwide, **9** 1669-70 (with
pictures)
Second World War aircraft, **11** 2029
World War II, **14** 2512, 2517
France's aerospace activities, **5** 885-91
(with pictures)
Air forces of the world, **1** 63-66
Air-to-air missiles, **1** 120
Air-to-surface missiles, **1** 123
Commemorative stamps and medals, **3** 493
Commercial air transports, **3** 530
Crop dusting, **4** 587, 593
European air traffic control, **4** 752
European Launcher Development
Organization, **4** 754
European Space Research Organization,
4 755
International Agricultural Aviation
Centre, **7** 1187
International projects, **7** 1199
Launch vehicles, **7** 1326, 1327
Franco-Prussian War
Balloons, **2** 323
Frank A. Scott Gold Medal Award
Debus, Kurt Heinrich, **4** 612
Frank, Ernst
Medals and decorations (table), **8** 1526
Franklin, Benjamin
Airmail, **1** 69
Balloons, **2** 317, 323
Electricity, **4** 684
Kites, **7** 1279
Parachutes, **10** 1759
Franklin Institute Gold Medal
Clarke, Arthur Charles, **3** 467
Franklin, K.
Astronomy **2** 242
Fraser, Josephine
Schirra, Walter M., Jr., **11** 2015
Fraunhofer corona (F-corona)
Sun, **12** 2174
Fraunhofer, Joseph von (1787-1826, German
optician and physicist), **5** 892
Astrophysics, **2** 255
Infrared radiation, **7** 1162
Fraunhofer lines
Sun, **12** 2172
Telescopes and astronomical instruments,
12 2255
Frecci Tricolori
Demonstration teams, **4** 626
Frederick L. Feinberg Award
Trophies and awards (table), **13** 2312
Free convection
Clouds, **3** 471
Freedom Fighter see F-5 Freedom Fighter
Freedom 7 (spacecraft)
Manned spaceflight (table), **8** 1461
Mercury program, **9** 1536, (picture) 1536,
(table) 1544
NASA (table, Major Launchings), **9** 1652

Free fall
Bailout, **2** 311
Weightlessness, **13** 2473
Free falling body
Orbits and trajectories, **10** 1743
Free-flight models
Model aircraft, **9** 1624, (picture) 1625
Freeman, Theodore C. (1930-1964), **5** 892
Astronauts, **2** 218, 219 (with picture)
Freeze-thaw cycle
Mars, **8** 1492
Freezing rain
Precipitation, **10** 1844
Freitag, Robert Frederick (1920-   ,
aerospace engineer), **5** 892
French Academie des Sciences
Airships, **1** 111
Charles, Jacques Alexandre Cesar, **3** 447
French Aerospace Industries Association
Paris Air Shows, **10** 1762
French Air Forces
Air forces of the world, **1** 65-66
French Armee de l'air
International projects, **7** 1201
French Astronomical Society
Lowell, Percival, **8** 1374
French Spad (see also Spad)
Biplane, **2** 358
Frequency, 5 893
Hertz, **6** 1084
Kilocycle, **7** 1276
Megacycle, **8** 1527
Megahertz, **8** 1527
Radar (with sketch), **10** 1875
Radio, **10** 1885
Sound, **11** 2077
Frequency assignments
Radio communications, **10** 1895
Frequency-division multiplexing
Telemetry, **12** 2242
Frequency modulation
Modulation, **9** 1629-30
Fresco, see MiG-17
Fresnel, Augustin Jean
Quantum theory, **10** 1868
Friction, 5 893
Heat shields, **6** 1056
Temperature control, **12** 2265
Friction drag
X-series aerospace vehicles, **14** 2543
Friction wheels
Jumbo jets, **7** 1253
Friedman, Herbert (1916-   , American
astrophysicist), **5** 893-94
Friedrichshafen (German bomber)
World War I, **14** 2509
Friendship 7 (spacecraft)
Commemorative stamps and medals, **3** 495
Glenn, John Herschel, Jr., **6** 983
Manned spaceflight (table), **8** 1461
Mercury program, **9** 1538-38, (table) 1544
NASA (table, Major Launchings), **9** 1652
Frise aileron
Airplane, **1** 87
Fritsch, Friherr Werner von
Aerial photography, **1** 10
Frog
Missiles (table), **9** 1616
Frogman
Recovery (with picture), **11** 1928
FR-1A
NASA, **9** 1653
Front, 5 894
Irwin, James Benson, **7** 1216
Frontal Aviation (Russia)
Aerospace activities, **13** 2336
Air forces of the world, **1** 65
Frontal Weather Systems
Aviation weather, **2** 303
Frontal zones
Air masses, **1** 80
Front course
Instrument landing system, **7** 1170

Frontier Airlines
Charter flying, **3** 448
Commercial airlines, **3** 513
Frost, 5 894
Frostflies
Mercury program, **9** 1541
Frostfree windshield
Piccard family, **10** 1791
Frost, May
Lenoir, William B., **7** 1332
FSS, see Flight Service Stations
Fuel/air mixture
Mixture control, **9** 1622-23
Rotating combustion engine, **11** 1993
Fuel cell modules
Electrical systems, **4** 682
Fuel cells, 5 894-96 (with diagram, pictures)
Electricity, **4** 685
Lewis Research Center, **7** 1335
Manned spaceflight, **8** 1461
Oxygen, **10** 1752
Rendezvous and docking, **11** 1956
Fuel core
Nuclear energy, **9** 1713
Fuel economy
Reciprocating engines, **11** 1918
Fuel elements
Nuclear fuel, **9** 1715
Fuel flow meter
Engine instruments, **4** 717
Fuel gauges
Engine instruments, **4** 715
Instrument panels, **7** 1176-78
Fuel injection, 5 896-97
Reciprocating engines, **11** 1917
Fuel pressure gauge
Pressure gauges (with diagram), **10** 1849
Fuel regulation
Carburetion, **3** 408
Fuel requirements
Instrument Flight Rules, **7** 1165
Fuels, 5 897-903 (with diagrams, pictures)
Chemical energy, **3** 456
Ground support equipment, **6** 1029
Jumbo jets, **7** 1255
Launch vehicles, **7** 1315
Propellants, **10** 1859
Rocket propulsion systems, **11** 1967
Temperature control, **12** 2268
Titan rockets, **12** 2290
Fuel supply
Instrument flight techniques, **7** 1168
Fuel supply units
Patents, **10** 1767
Fuel systems, 5 903-06 (with diagrams)
Cockpit, **3** 482
Fuel injection, **5** 896
Gravity, **6** 1011
Hybrid systems, **6** 1138
Fuji Cessna L-19E
Japan's aerospace activities (picture),
7 1230
Fuji T-1A
Japan's aerospace activities (picture),
7 1128
Fujita, Yuzo
Distance and distance records, **4** 641
Full cantilever wing
Airplane (picture), **1** 86
Full-disc brakes
Brakes, **3** 386
Fuller, Frank
Air racing, **1** 103
Fuller, Richard Buckminster (1895-   ,
American designer), **5** 906
Geodesics, **6** 970-71
Radome, **10** 1900
Fullerton, Charles G. (1936-   , aerospace
research pilot), **5** 906-07
Manned Orbiting Laboratory, **8** 1456
Full-feathering
Propellers, **10** 1862-63
Full moon
Moon, **9** 1634 (with picture)

Full-stall landing
Landing techniques, **7** 1301
Fulton Skyhook
Survival and rescue, **12** 2220
Fumes, 5 907
Funk (airplane)
Crop dusting, **4** 589
Furious (aircraft carrier)
World War I, **14** 2503
Fury
Camm, Sir Sydney, **3** 398
Fuseau-morteur
Nacelle, **9** 1647
Fuselage, 5 907-08 (with diagrams)
Area rule, **2** 191
Airframe, **1** 66
Airplane, **1** 82-83
Bicycle gear, **2** 354
Interiors of aircraft, **7** 1184
Pusher propeller, **10** 1866
Fusion, 5 908
Nuclear energy, **9** 1709-12
Radiation, **10** 1880-81
Fusion processes
Plasma, **10** 1822

Future Pilots of America, 5 908

G

G, see G force, Gravity
G91-Y
Jet aircraft (picture), **7** 1236
G-134 Mohawk (Grumman)
Army aviation (picture), **2** 195
Gabreski, Francis Stanley (1919-
American ace), **5** 909
World War II (table), **14** 2517
Gagarin (gah GAR ihn), **Yuri Alekseyevich**
(1934-1968), **5** 909-10
Astronauts, **2** 217
Aviation, **2** 290
Bykovsky, Valeri, **3** 397
Cosmonauts, **4** 569, (picture) 570,
(table) 574
Korolev, Sergei, **7** 1290
Manned spaceflight (table), **8** 1461
Medals and decorations (table), **8** 1526
Popovich, Pavel, **10** 1838
U.S.S.R. aerospace activities, **13** 2343
Vostok, **13** 2434
Gain control
Plan position indicator, **10** 1821
Gaine, M. L.
Distance and distance records, **4** 640
Galactic astronomy
Milky Way, **9** 1607
Shapley, Harlow, **11** 2046
Space, **11** 2093
Galactic radio noise
Ariel satellites, **2** 192
Galaxies, 5 910-12 (with pictures)
Astronomy, **2** 251
Extraterrestrial life, **5** 774
Hoyle, Fred, **6** 1130
Milky Way, **9** 1605-07
Nebula (pictures), **9** 1688-89
Orbiting observatories, **10** 1740
Planetarium, **10** 1820
Quasars, **10** 1871

(Continued)

Galaxies (Cont.)
  Radio astronomy, mapping of, 10 1890-91
    structure of, 10 1891
  Stars, 12 2162
  Universe, 13 2391
Galaxy (aircraft), see C-5A Galaxy
Galileo Galilei (1564-1642, Florentine
    physicist), 5 912
  Apollo, 1 163
  Astrogeology, 2 211
  Astronomy, 2 237, 242, 245, 251
  Barometer, 2 336
  Gravity, 6 1012
  Jupiter, 7 1261
  Kepler, Johannes, 7 1274
  Meteorology, 9 1556
  Moon, 9 1633; (drawing by), 1634
  Radio astronomy, 10 1890
  Telescopes and astronomical instruments,
    12 2245
  Temperature gauges, 12 2269
Gallaudet (GAL oh day) **biplane**
  Coast Guard aviation, 3 475
Galle, Johann G. (1812-1910)
  Celestial mechanics, 3 428
  Leverrier, Urbain, J. J., 7 1334
Galley, 5 912-13
  Interior of aircraft, 7 1186
Gallium arsenide semiconductor lasers
  Lasers, 7 1304
G.A.M. Dassault Falcon (aircraft)
  France's aerospace activities (picture),
    5 888
GAM-63 Rascal air-to-ground missile
  X-series aerospace vehicles, 14 2540
Gamma ray detector
  Nuclear detection satellites, 9 1709
Gamma ray emissions
  Orbiting observatories, 10 1738
Gamma ray experiment
  Orbiting observatories, 10 1738
Gamma rays, 5 913
  Carbons, 3 406
  Observatories, 10 1726
  Radiation, 10 1880, 1882
    shield, 10 1884
  X-rays, 14 2533
Gamma ray telescopes
  Explorer satellites, 5 767
G&N, see Guidance and navigation system
Gandia, Norm
  Demonstration teams, 4 623
Gannet (airplane)
  Air forces of the world (Great Britain),
    1 66
  Asia's aviation, 2 205
  Australia's aviation, 2 281
Ganswindt (GAN svint), **Hermann**
  Fireworks, 5 814
Gantry, 5 913
  Launch facilities, 7 1307
Ganymede
  Astronomy, 2 245-46
  Jupiter, 7 1261
Gardener, Edward
  Airmail (picture), 1 70
Garden Grove, California
  Careers (table), 3 414
Gargoyle
  Air-to-surface missiles, 1 123
Garino, Joe
  Astronauts, 2 222
Garnerin, Andre-Jacques (1769-1823,
    French inventor), 5 913-14
  Parachutes, 10 1756
  Skydiving, 11 2054
Garnerin, Elisa
  Balloons, 2 320
Garriott, Owen K. (1930-   ), 5 914
  Astronauts, 2 217-18-19,
    222 (with picture)
Garros, Roland (1888-1918, French aviator),
    5 914-15

Altitude and altitude records, 1 147
  World War I, 14 2505
Garuda Airlines of Indonesia
  Asia's aviation, 2 204
  Mainland China's aerospace activities,
    8 1425
Gas burner
  Balloons (picture), 2 322
Gas cell
  Airships, 1 106, 108
Gas chromatograph
  Extraterrestrial life, 5 781
Gas engines
  Model aircraft, 9 1626
Gases, 5 915-16 (with picture)
  Air, 1 41-42
  Electronics, 4 692
  Extraterrestrial life, 5 775
  Heat energy, 6 1054
  Heat exchangers, 6 1055
  Helium, 6 1079
  Hydrogen, 6 1141
  Matter, 8 1513-14
  Milky Way, 9 1605
  Stars, 12 2159, 2160
  Sun, 12 2172
Gas expansion
  Aviation medicine, 2 297
Gas-filled tubes
  Electronics, 4 700
Gas jet propulsion, 5 917-18 (with diagram,
    picture)
Gas laser
  Lasers, 7 1303
Gas maser
  Masers, 8 1497
Gas molecules
  Quantum theory, 10 1870
Gas tanks
  Airplane, 1 91
Gas turbine engines, 5 918-25 (with diagrams,
    pictures)
  Aircraft propulsion systems, 1 57
  Fuels, 5 901
  Griffith, Alan Arnold, 6 1014
  Jet aircraft, 7 1232
  Jet engines, 7 1237
  Power management, 10 1840
  Pulsejet engine, 10 1865
  Reciprocating engines, 11 1917
  Rotating combustion engine, 11 1992
Gas turbine powerplants
  Power management, 10 1842
Gates Flying Circus
  Air shows, 1 115
Gatling-type weapons
  Air forces of the world, 1 66
  Post, Wiley, 10 1839
  Winnie Mae, 14 2493
Gatty, Harold
  World records and round-the-world flights,
    14 2497
Gaty, John P.
  Medals and decorations (table), 8 1526
Gauss, K. F.
  Orbits and trajectories, 10 1742
Gawron PZL 101
  Crop dusting (picture), 4 587
GA-X armored attack plane
  Boeing, William Edward, 2 369
Gayford, O. R.
  Distance and distance records, 4 640
Gay-Lussac, Joseph Louis
  Balloons, 2 324
Gay-Lussac's Law
  Charles, Jacques Alexandre Cesar, 3 447
GCA, see Ground control approach
Gear pod
  Jumbo jets, 7 1255
GeeBee Racer R-1 (airplane)
  Air races (picture), 1 103

Gehriger, A.
  Medals and decorations (table), 8 1526
Geiger-Mueller tube
  Explorer satellites, 5 764
Gelaxias kyklos
  Astronomy, 2 251
Gemini
  Constellations, 3 562
Gemini, 5 926-52 (with diagrams, map,
    pictures, table)
  Agena rockets, 1 38
  Apollo, 1 162, 164
  Astronautics, 2 212
    Attitude and attitude control, 2 275
  Astronauts
    Aerial photography, 1 9
  Augmented Target Docking Adapter,
    11 1957
  Blockhouse, 2 367
  Capsule, 3 406
    Ablation, 1 1
    Agena rockets, 1 38
    Clean room, 3 468
  Commemorative stamps and medals, 3 495
  Cornell Aeronautical Laboratory, 3 567
  Environmental control systems, 4 718
  Escape systems, 4 736-37
  Faget, Maxime, 5 789
  Fuel cells, 5 895
  Gemini 2
    Aldrin, Edwin E., Jr., 1 142
    Anders, William A., 1 152
    Blockhouse, 2 368
  Gemini 4
    McDivitt, James A., 8 1517-18
  Gemini 5
    Conrad, Charles, Jr., 3 560
    Cooper, L. Gordon, Jr., 3 565
    Reusable launch vehicles, 11 1962
  Gemini 6
    Schirra, Walter M., 11 2014
    Stafford, Thomas P., 12 2157
  Gemini 7
    Aerospace medicine (picture), 1 34
    Borman, Frank, 3 381
    Distance and distance records, 4 641
    Launching (picture), 7 1311
    Lovell, James A., Jr., 8 1373
  Gemini 8
    Armstrong, Neil A., 2 193
  Gemini 9
    Cernan, Eugene Andrew, 3 440
    Bassett, Charles A., II, 2 337
  Gemini 10
    Bean, Alan LaVerne, 2 346
    Collins, Michael, 3 487
    Recovery, 11 1929
  Gemini 11
    Conrad, Charles, Jr., 3 560
  Gemini 12
    Cernan, Eugene Andrew, 3 440
    Lovell, James A., Jr., 8 1373
    Recovery (pictures), 11 1928
  Government in aerospace (picture),
    6 1005
  Hatches and doors (picture), 6 1052
  Heat shields, 6 1057, (pictures) 1057-58
  Honeycomb construction, 6 1129
  Instrument panels, 7 1175-77
  Kennedy Space Center, 7 1267
  Langley Research Center, 7 1302
  Life raft, 7 1336
  Life-support systems, 8 1339, 1340-41,
    (diagrams) 1338, 1342, (pictures) 1342
  Manned Orbiting Laboratory, 8 1454
  Manned spaceflight, 8 1460-62, (table)
    1461, (diagram) 1462
  Military space program, 9 1600-01
  NASA, 9 1650, (pictures) 1649, 1651,
    (table, Major Launchings) 1652
  Oceanographic research, 10 1732
  Outsize cargo aircraft, 10 1749
  Reaction control systems, 10 1912
  Recovery (with picture), 11 1926-27
  Rendezvous missions

Launch vehicle, 7 1324
  Rendezvous and docking (pictures),
    11 1956-57
Simulator
  Rendezvous and docking (with picture),
    11 1956
Spacecraft
  Agena rockets, 1 38
  Airlock, 1 67
  Beryllium, 2 354
  Space garbage, 12 2119
  Spacesuits, 12 2130
  Survival kits, 12 2222
  Target vehicles
    Atlas missile and launch vehicle, 2 260
  Temperature control, 12 2265
  Transponder, 13 2309
  Young, John W., 14 2548
Gemini-Titan II
  Launch vehicles (table), 7 1319-20
  Titan rockets, 12 2289, 2291
**General aviation, 6 953-59 (with pictures,
    table)**
  Aircraft Owners and Pilots Association,
    1 52
  Airports, 1 93, (picture) 94
  Careers, 3 411-12, (table) 414
  Economic implications of aerospace, 4 671
  History of aviation, 6 1116
  Japan's aerospace activities, 7 1128
  Pilot training, 10 1809
  Pleasure flying, 10 1825
  U.S.S.R. aerospace activities, 13 2328
**General aviation aircraft, 6 960-69
    (with pictures)**
General Bureau of Civil Aviation
  Mainland China's aerospace activities,
    8 1424-25
General Dynamics Corp.
  Atlas missile and launch vehicle, 2 259
  Battlefield missile systems, 2 343
  Centaur, 3 433
  Swing-wing aircraft
    Air forces of the world, 1 65
General Electric Company
  Biosatellites, 2 356
  Bumper Project, 3 390
  Federal Aviation Administration, 5 801
  Manned Orbiting Laboratory, 8 1452
  NASA (table, Apollo/Saturn V Major
    Contractors), 9 1655
  Whittle engine
    Aircraft propulsion systems, 1 58
General Motors Corporation
  Manned Orbiting Laboratory, 8 1452
General Precision Systems, Inc.
  Link, Edwin A., 8 1361
**General Sheridan air-transportable
    reconnaissance**
  Battlefield missile systems, 2 342
General theory of relativity
  Relativity theory, 11 1948
Generation, 6 969
  Astronauts, 2 215
  Terminology of aerospace (table), 12 2272
**Generators and alternators, 6 969-70 (with
    diagram and picture)**
  Ground support equipment, 6 1029
Genetic changes
  Radiation sickness, 10 1884
Geneva Disarmament Conference
  Nuclear detection satellites, 9 1707
Genie
  Air Defense Command, 1 59
  Air defense systems, 1 61
  Air-to-air missiles (picture), 1 121
Gentry, Jerauld
  PILOT, 10 1793
Gentry, Viola
  Women in aerospace, 14 2494
Geocentric, 6 970
  Astronomy, 2 236, 242
  Parallax, 10 1760
  Presentation planetarium, 10 1818

Geodesic dome
  Hangers, 6 1049
Geodesics, 6 970-71 (with pictures)
  Fuller, Richard Buckminster, 5 906
Geodesy
  Earth, 4 663
Geodetic, 6 971
**Geodetic satellites, 6 971-76 (with diagram,
    pictures, table)**
  Explorer satellites, 5 771
  Military space program (data table), 9 1604
Geographical barriers
  South and Central America's aviation,
    11 2087
Geographic pole
  Poles, 10 1833
Geography (book)
  Ptolemy, Claudius, 10 1864
Geological survey
  Charts, 3 455
  Economic implications of aerospace, 4 671
  Reconnaissance airborne, 11 1920
Geologic moon maps
  Lunar charts, 8 1400
Geology
  Photogrammetry, 10 1780
Geomagnetic cavity
  Geomagnetic field, 6 977
Geomagnetic field, 6 977 (with diagram)
  Orbiting observatories, 10 1741
Geomagnetism
  International Geophysical Year, 7 1195
Geometry
  Ramjet engine, 10 1902
Geophysical Fluid Dynamics Laboratory
  Environmental Science Services
    Administration, 4 725
Geophysical surveys
  Utility aviation, 13 2395
Geophysics, 6 978
**George C. Marshall Space Flight Center
    8 1494**
  Bottlesuit, 3 382
  NASA, 9 1650, 1654, 1657
Geos (satellite)
  Geodetic satellites, 6 975, (table) 973
  NASA (table, Major Launchings), 9 1652
Geospace
  Technological projections, 12 2235
Geosynchronous orbit
  Orbits and trajectories, 10 1746
Gerlach, Marilyn
  Lovell, James A., Jr., 8 1373
German Army development facility (picture)
  Peenemuende, 10 1771
German Industrial Standards
  Measurement of power, 8 1519
Germanium wafer
  Solid-state physics (with diagram), 11 2072
German Rescue Service
  Survival and rescue, 12 2218
German rocketry
  Rockets and rocketry, 11 1980
German Rocket Society
  Jet-assisted takeoff, 7 1236
**Germany (see also West Germany's
    aerospace activities)**
  Ace, 1 4
  Aerial photography, 1 10
  Aircraft propulsion systems, 1 54, 57
  Airmail, 1 75
  Blitzkrieg, 2 366
  Bomber aircraft, 2 374
  Commemorative stamps and medals, 3 494
  Commercial airlines, 3 505
  Crop dusting, 4 587
  European air traffic control, 4 752
  International Agricultural Aviation Centre,
    7 1187
  Launch vehicles, 7 1327
  Military aviation, 9 1580-86
  Naval aviation, worldwide, 9 1670
  World War II, 14 2512, 2517-20

Gething, R. T.
  Distance and distance records, 4 640
GE YT-58-8D turboshaft engines
  X-series aerospace vehicles, 14 2544
G-force
  Acceleration, 1 3
  Accelerometer, 1 3
  Aerospace medicine, 1 34
  Deceleration, 4 612
  Negative-g, 9 1689
  Re-entry corridor, 11 1930
  Terminology of aerospace (table), 12 2272
Ghana
  Commemorative stamps and medals, 3 495
Ghana Airways
  Africa's aviation, 1 36
**GHOST program, 6 978-79 (with diagrams,
    pictures)**
  Balloons, 2 318, 321, 331
Giacconi (juh KO nee), Riccardo
  Aerobee, 1 18
  Radiation, 10 1882
Giant planets
  Astronomy, 2 241
  Earth, 4 663
Gibbs-Smith, Charles H.
  Cayley, Sir George, 3 425
Gibb, Walter F.
  Altitude and altitude records, 1 147
Gibraltar
  European aerospace activities, 4 751
Gibson, Edward G. (1936-   ), 6 980
  Astronauts 2 217-19, 222, 226 (with picture)
Gieser, Arthur
  International Agricultural Aviation Centre,
    7 1187
**Giffard, Henri (1825-1882, French engineer),
    6 980**
  Airships, 1 111
  Dirigibles, 4 629
Giffard's steam-driven airship
  Airship (picture), 1 111
Gilbert, Beverly
  Macleay, Lachian, 8 1417
Gilbert, G. K.
  Astrogeology, 2 211
Gilbert, William
  Electricity, 4 683
Gilbreth, Frank B. and Lillian M.
  Human engineering, 6 1133
Gilliland, Whitney
  Civil Aeronautics Board, 3 463
**Gilruth, Robert Rowe (1913-   , American
    aeronautical engineer), 6 980-81**
  Astronauts, 2 220
  Gemini, 5 926, 952
  Mercury program, 9 1530
Gimbal rig
  Bioastronautics, 2 355
Gimbal rings
  Inertial guidance, 7 1153-54
Girard, Peter F.
  X-series aerospace vehicles, 14 2541
Girier (ZHIR ee ay), Andre
  Distance and distance records, 4 640
Givens, Edward Galen, Jr. (1930-1967), 6 981
  Astronauts, 2 216, 218-19, 222 (with picture)
Glacier movements
  Aerial photography, 1 11
Glaciology
  International Geophysical Year, 7 1195
Glass, 6 981-83 (with pictures)
  Materials, 8 1506
  Windows and windshields, 13 2486
Glass-ceramics
  Ceramics, 3 439 (with picture)
Glass filaments
  Production techniques, 10 1856
Glass wool
  Fiber glass, 5 807
Glenn H. Curtiss Silver Medal for Achievement
  Mock, Geraldine C., 9 1624
**Glenn, John Herschel, Jr. 1921-   ),
    6 983-84**   (Continued)

Glenn, John Herschel (Cont.)
Astronauts, **2** 215-17, 219, 224-25, 229-30 (with picture)
Atlas missile and launch vehicle, **2** 260
Commemorative stamps and medals, **3** 495
Instrument panels, **7** 1177
Manned spaceflight (table), **8** 1461
Mercury program, **9** 1533, 1537-38, 1539-40, 1542, 1545; (pictures), 1538, 1539; (data table) 1544
Re-entry vehicle **11** 1933
Glennan, Dr. Keith
Explorer satellites, **5** 765
Mercury program, **9**, 1530
Glenn L. Martin Company
Martin, Glenn L., **8** 1496
Glennon, Nan
Women in aerospace, **14** 2496
Glide, 6 984
Maneuvers, **8** 1435
Glide angle
Sailplanes, **11** 2002
Glibe bomb
Air-to-surface missiles, **1** 123-24
Glide path
Airports, **1** 96
Landing techniques, **7** 1301
Glide ratio
Gliders, **6** 984
Gliders, 6 984-85 (with pictures)
Aerodyne, **1** 25
Aeronautics, **1** 26
Aircraft, **1** 45
Beech, Walter H., **2** 347
Cayley, Sir George, **3** 425
Chanute, Octave, **3** 446
Cody, Samuel Franklin, **3** 487
Da Vinci, Leonardo, **4** 611
France's aerospace activities, **5** 891
History of aviation, **6** 1097, 1108, 1114, (pictures) 1095, 1097-99
International competitions, **7** 1192
Lilienthal, Otto, **8** 1358
Ornithopter, **10** 1748
Pilcher, Percy Sinclair, **10** 1792-93
Soaring, **11** 2062
Wright brothers, **14** 2524-25
Glide slope
Airborne antennas, **1** 44
Automatic landing, **2** 287-88
Instrument flight techniques, **7** 1168
Instrument landing system, **7** 1170
Lighting facilities, **8** 1356
Glideway, see T-rail
Gliding, 6 985-91 (with diagram, pictures)
Bird flight, **2** 361
History of aviation, **6** 1099
International competitions, **7** 1191-92
Parawing, **10** 1761
Re-entry vehicles, **11** 1935
Sport flying, **12** 2150
West Germany's aerospace activities, **13** 2477
Gliding Federation
Australia's aviation, **2** 282
G-line
Model aircraft, **9** 1624
Glitch
Terminology of aerospace (table), **12** 2272
Global Horizontal Sounding Technique, see GHOST program
Global lunar expeditions
Lunar bases, **8** 1391
Global Navigation Charts
Charts, **3** 455
Globemaster, see C-125 Globemaster
Globes
Lambert projection, **7** 1296
Globular clusters
Milky Way, **9** 1607, (picture and diagram), 1606
Glomb
Air-to-surface missiles, **1** 123

Gloster Aircraft Company
Aircraft propulsion systems, **1** 58
Jet
Manufacturing, **8** 1472
Gloster Gladiator
Second World War aircraft (with picture), **11** 2027
Gloster Meteor
United Kingdom aerosapce activities, **13** 2347
Gloves
Personal equipment, **10** 1775
G-meter
Accelerometer, **1** 3
Gnat
Air forces of the world (picture), **1** 63
Asia's aviation, **2** 204
European aerospace activities (picture), **4** 748
Gnome-Monosoupape (NOM mah no soo PAP) engine
Aircraft propulsion systems, **1** 55
Gnome rotary engine
History of aviation, **6** 1103
World War I, **14** 2502
Gnomonic projection, 6 991
Maps and mapping, **8** 1478-79, (table) 1478
Gobe, Andre
Distance records, **4** 640
Goddard Day
National Aerospace Educational Council, **9** 1658
Goddard, Esther
Rockets and rocketry, **11** 1977
Goddard, Robert Hutchings (1882-1945, American physicist), **6** 991-92
Commemorative stamps and medals, **3** 495
Cyrogenics, **4** 597
Electric propulsion, **4** 685
Fireworks, **5** 814
History of aviation, **6** 1109, (table) 1119
Jet-assisted takeoff, **7** 1236
Launch vehicles, **7** 1315
Missiles, **9** 1611
Patents, **10** 1766
Propellants, **10** 1859
Rockets and rocketry (picture), **11** 1975-76
Goddard Space Flight Center, 6 992-93 (with map, picture)
Alouette satellites, **1** 145
Ariel satellites, **2** 192
Data acquisition and processing, **4** 606, 609
Environmental simulators, **4** 728
Lasers, **7** 1304-05
Launching, **7** 1309-10, 1312
Lind, Don Leslie, **8** 1359
NASA, **9** 1650, 1654, 1655
Goddess of the Dawn
Aurora, **2** 277
Goebbels, Joseph
Peenemuende, **10** 1770
Goering, Hermann
Fokker DR-1 triplane, **5** 869
World War I, **14** 2508
World War II, **14** 2518
Goett, Harry Joseph (1910-   , American aeronautical engineer), **6** 994
Golden Arrow
Curtiss, Glenn Hammond, **4** 600
Golden Flyer
Air racing, **1** 102
Barnstormers, **2** 332
Golden Triangle
National Airspace System, **9** 1662
Golden Wings
Cobb, Geraldyn, **3** 480
Gold Medal of the Royal Aeronautical Society
DeHavilland, Sir Geoffrey, **4** 620
Eckener, Hugo, **4** 668
Goldstein, Eugen
Electronics, **4** 693
Goliath (aircraft)
Farman, Henri and Maurice, **5** 791

Golovin, Dr. Nicholas E.
Titan III, **12** 2291
Gomez, Don Luis Vicente Juez
Medals and decorations (table), **8** 1526
Gondolas, 6 994-95 (with pictures)
Balloons (picture), **2** 322
Hot-air balloons, **6** 1130
Go-no-go decision, 6 996
Launch complex, **7** 1307
Good Conduct Medal
Medals and decorations (picture), **8** 1525
Goodlin, Chalmers
X-series aerospace vehicles, **14** 2535
Good, Shirley Ann
Kerwin, Joseph P., **7** 1276
Good, Walter A.
Medals and decorations (table), **8** 1526
Goodyear blimp
Airships (picture), **1** 108
Goodyear Tire & Rubber Company
Airships, **1** 109, 112
Blimps, **2** 366
Goodyear Zeppelin Corporation
Airships (picture), **1** 107, 112
Gooney Bird
Douglas DC-3, **4** 648
Gora, Tadeusz
Medals and decorations (table), **8** 1526
Gordon Bennett race
Air races (picture), **1** 103
Gordon Bennett International
Balloons, **2** 321
Trophies and awards (table), **13** 2312
Gordon, Louis
Earhart, Amelia, **4** 658
Gordon, Richard F., Jr. (1929-   ), **6** 996
Astronauts, **2** 218-19 (with picture)
Gemini, **5** 947-49
Manned spaceflight (table), **8** 1461
Gores
Manufacturing, **8** 1474
Gorrie, John
Cryogenics, **4** 596
Gotha bombers, 6 996-97 (with chart, picture)
Bomber aircraft, **2** 373, 374
First World War aircraft, **5** 824
World War I (picture), **14** 2502, 259
Gotha Go-242
Military aircraft (picture), **9** 1567
Government Aircraft Manufacturing Center
Asia's aviation, **2** 203
Government contracts, 6 997-99 (with diagram)
Patents, **10** 1766
Government in aerospace, 6 1000-10 (with diagrams, pictures, table)
Gower, Pauline
Women in aerospace, **14** 2495
Careers, **3** 411, 413, (table) 414
Grab
Catapult, **3** 423
Graf Zeppelin
Airships, **1** 112, 113
Aviation, **2** 290
Commemorative stamps and medals, **3** 494
Dirigibles, **4** 631
Eckener, Hugo, **4** 668
Post, Wiley, **10** 1839
World records and round-the-world flights, **14** 2497
Zeppelins, **14** (picture) 2550, 2552
Graham, Harry
Barnstormers, **2** 333
Grahame-White, Claude (1879-1959, British aviator and aircraft builder), **6** 1010
Grain
Propellants, **10** 1859
Rocket propulsion systems, **11** 1968
Gramma
Photogrammetry, **10** 1779
Grand Baltiski (airplane)
First World War aircraft, **5** 825
Grand Old Lady
Commercial air transports, **3** 521

Grand Old Lady (book)
Douglas DC-3, **4** 648
Grant, Mary Griffin
Haise, Fred Wallace, Jr., **6** 1046
Graphite, 6 1010
Carbon, **3** 407
Graticule
Astronauts, 216, 218, 219, 222 (with picture)
Maps and mapping, **8** 1476
Gravitational attraction
Precession, **10** 1843
Gravitational body
Orbital velocity, **10** 1737
Gravitational deflection of light
Relativity theory, **11** 1953
Gravitational field
Earth, **4** 662
Kepler's laws, **7** 1275
Mercury, **8** 1527
Orbits and trajectories (with illustration),
10 1743-45
Gravitational force
Ballistic missile, **2** 313
Interplanetary travel, **7** 1208 (with diagram)
Kepler's laws, **7** 1275
Orbits and trajectories, **10** 1742-43
Re-entry vehicles, **11** 1931
Gravitational motions
Leverrier, Urbain, J. J., **7** 1334
Gravitational navigation
Orbits and trajectories, **10** 1747
Gravitational pull
Precession, **10** 1843
Gravitation, Universal law of
Astronomy, **2** 238
Relativity theory, **11** 1952
Gravity, 6 1011-13 (with diagram)
Acceleration, **1** 2-3
Kinetic energy, **7** 1277
Launch vehicles, **7** 1314
Newton, Sir Isaac, **9** 1693
Pusher propeller, **10** 1866
Spaceflight principles, **12** 2105, 2106
Space tools, **12** 2135
Stars, **12** 2160, 2162
Weight and balance, **13** 2472
Weightlessness, **13** 2472-73
Gravity-assist
Interplanetary travel, **7** 1208
Gravity feed
Jumbo jets, **7** 1255
Gravity gradient
Applications Technology Satellites, **2** 189
Explorer satellites, **5** 772
Guidance and control systems, **6** 1039
Gray, Colin
World War II (table), **14** 2517
Gray, Hawthorne
Balloons, **2** 324
Gray, H. B.
Distance and distance records, **4** 640
Gray, Stephen (1670-1736)
Electricity, **4** 683
Grayout, 6 1013
Centrifuge, **3** 437
Great Balloon Hoax
Mason, Thomas Monck, **8** 1498
Great Balloon of Nassau
Balloons (picture), **2** 318
Great Bear Lake
Bush flying, **3** 392
Great Britain (see also United Kingdom)
Ace, **1** 4
Aircraft carriers, **1** 48-49
Aircraft propulsion systems, **1** 58
Airfield, **1** 61
Automatic landing, **2** 287
Blimps, **2** 364, 365
Commercial air transports, **3** 530
World War II, **14** 2512
Great circle
Celestial sphere, **3** 431
Course plotting, **4** 579
Earth, **4** 663

Ecliptic, **4** 669
Equator, **4** 729
Latitude and longitude, **7** 1307
Meridian, **9** 1546
Great collection
Constellations, **3** 561
Great Comet of 1843
Comets, **3** 490
Great Dividing Range
Australia's aviation, **2** 279
Great Galaxy
Radio astronomy (contour map), **10** 1891
Greater Magellanic Clouds
Astronomy, **2** 253
Great Nebula of Andromeda
Ewen, Harold Iriving **4** 759
Great Race
Balloons, **2** 315
Great Red Spot
Astronomy, **2** 245
Greece
Commemorative stamps and medals,
3 493-94
European aerospace activities, **4** 746
NATO, **9** 1703-04
World War II, **14** 2515
Greek mythology
Aircraft propulsion systems, **1** 52
Mythology, **9** 1644
Green, Charles (1785-1870), British
balloonist), **6** 1013
Balloons, **2** 317, 318
Mason, Thomas Monck, **8** 1498
Greenhouse effect, 6 1013
Atmosphere, **2** 266
Venus, **13** 2408-09
Greenland
Air defense systems, **1** 60
Ballistic Missile Early Warning System,
2 313
Greenland Patrol
Coast Guard aviation, **3** 479
Greenwich, England
Celestial sphere, **3** 433
Greenwich mean time, 6 1013
Instrument panels, **7** 1177
Zulu time, **14** 2552
Greenwich meridian, 6 1014
Latitude and longitude, **7** 1307
Greenwich Star Catalogue
Astronomy, **2** 242
Gremlin, 6 1014 (with picture)
Grenades
Bombs, **3** 377
Greyhound, see C-2A Greyhound
Grid
Electronics, **4** 693
Grid pattern
Crop dusting, **4** 590
Griffith, Alan Arnold (1893-1963, British
scientist), **6** 104-15
Grissom, J. R.
Distance and distance records, **4** 641
Grissom, Virgil I. (1926-1967), **6** 1015
Apollo, **1** 168 (with picture)
Astronauts, **2** 215, 217, 218, 219, 224,
228, 229, 232 (with picture)
Blockhouse, **2** 367
Gemini,**5** 931-34, (picture) 933
Manned spaceflight, **8** 1461 (table)
Mercury program, **9** 1533, 1537, (data table)
1544
Ranger, **10** 1909
Recovery, **11** 1928
Gromov, Mikhail
Distance and distance records, **4** 640
Polar flights, **10** 1830
Ground-adjustable
Propeller, **10** 1862
Ground antennas, 6 1015-17 (with diagram,
pictures)
Ground clutter
Doppler effect, **4** 645

Ground control
Air traffic control, **1** 133
Charts, **3** 455
Control tower, **3** 564
Instrument flight techniques, **7** 1167
Maps and mapping, **8** 1479
Radio communications, **10** 1894
Ground control approach, 6 1018-20 (with
diagram)
Airports, **1** 97
Air traffic control, **1** 129
Electronics, **4** 704
Government in aerospace, **6** 1003
radar
Berlin airlift, **2** 352
Ground crew, 6 1020-21 (with pictures)
Agricultural aviation, **1** 41
Noise exposure, Acoustics, **1** 5
Ground-effect cushion
Supersonic transports, **12** 2185
Ground-effect machines, 6 1023-26 (with
diagrams, pictures)
Aircraft, **1** 45
Ground equipment
Instrument landing system, **7** 1171
Radar, **10** 1876
Ground handling
Airships, **1** 110-111
Ground instructor
Careers, **3** 417
Ground maneuvering
Piloting techniques, **10** 1801
Ground personnel
Jet aircraft, **7** 1235
Ground radar
Radar, **10** 1879
Ground roll
Piloting techniques, **10** 1801
Ground school
Pilot training, **10** 1810-11
Preflight training, **10** 1846
Ground Self-Defense Force
Japan's aerospace activities, **7** 1229
Ground service and maintenance, 6 1027-29
(with pictures)
Ground crew, **6** 1020
Groundspeed, 6 1029
Airspeed, **1** 116
Ground state
Masers, **8** 1496-97
Ground stations
Call signs, **3** 398
Ground support equipment, 6 1029-31
(with pictures)
Inflight emergency procedures, **7** 1155
Launch complex, **7** 1307
Launch facilities, **7** 1307
Ground sweeps
Crash trucks, **4** 583
Ground-to-air emergency code distress signals
Emergency signals, **4** 709
Panel code, **10** 1755
Ground training
High-altitude flight training, **6** 1085
Groups
Elements, **4** 705
Grover Loening Aircraft Co.
Loening, Grover Cleveland, **8** 1369
GRS 625A, West German satellite
International projects, **7** 1198
Grumman A-6 Intruder, see A-6 Intruder
Grumman Agcat
Agricultural aviation, **1** 40
Crop dusting, **4** 589
Grumman Aircraft Co.
Apollo, **1** 165
Grumman Aircraft Company
Orbiting observatories, **10** 1740
Grumman Albatross, see HU-16 Albatross
Grumman C-1A, see C-1A Trader
Grumman C-2A, see C-2A Greyhound
Grumman E-1B, see E-1B Tracer
Grumman F-6, see F-6 Hellcat
Grumman F-11 Tiger, see F-11 Tiger

Grumman F-111, see F-111
Grumman G-134 Mohawk, see G-134 Mohawk
Grumman Gulfstream
  Avionics (diagram), 2 307
  Business aviation (picture), 3 396
Grumman Gulfstream I
  Military air transports (table), 9 1578
Grumman Gulfstream II
  Avionics, 2 307
  Cockpit, 3 485
  General aviation aircraft (picture), 6 968
Grumman HU-16, see HU-16 Albatross
Grumman J2F amphibian
  Coast Guard aviation (picture), 3 477
Grumman, Leroy Randle (1895-   , American
    aviator, airplane designer), 6 1032
Grumman OV-1, see OV-1 Mohawk
Grumman SA-16 Albatross, see HU-16
    Albatross
Grumman TBF Avenger
  Second World War aircraft (with picture),
    11 2035
Grumman Tracker, see S-2 Tracker
GS, see Groundspeed
G-suit, 6 1033
G-switch
  Biosatellites, 2 357
G-value
  Centrifuge, 3 438
Guatemala
  Crop dusting, 4 587
  South and Central America's aviation,
    11 2090
Guerrilla
  Intelligence, military, 7 1180
Guggenheim, Daniel
  Airmail, 1 77
Guggenheim Fund for the Promotion of
    Aeronautics, 6 1033
  Instrument panels, 7 1173
Guggenheim Harry F.
  Medals and decorations (table), 8 1526
Guggenheim Medal
  Boeing, William Edward, 2 370
  Douglas, Donald Wills, 4 649
Guggenheim Trophy
  Fedden, Sir Roy, 5 792
Guidance, 6 1033
  Computers, 3 558
  Spacecraft design, 11 2100
Guidance and control systems, 6 1033-43 (with
    diagrams, pictures)
  Air-to-air missiles, 1 119-21, 122
  Apollo, 1 177-78
  Asteroids, 2 207
  Attitude and attitude control, 2 276
  Cybernetics, 4 602
  Gyroscope, 6 1044
  Homing devices, 6 1128
  Intercontinental ballistic missiles, 7 1182
  Jumbo jets, 7 1255
  Launch vehicles, 7 1316
  Military aviation, 9 1587
  Missiles, 9 1613-16
  Polaris missiles, 10 1831
  Poseidon missile, 10 1839
  Silos, 11 2052
  Surface-to-air missiles, 12 2199
Guided missiles, 6 1043
  Air-to-air missiles, 1 120
  Battlefield missile systems, 2 340
  Bombs, 3 377
  History of aviation, 6 1118
  Launch vehicle, 7 1322
  Missiles, 9 1610-16 (with diagram, pictures
    and data table)
  Transponder, 13 2309
  United Kingdom aerospace activities,
    13 2353
  World War II, 14 2519-20
Guided torpedo
  Antisubmarine missiles, 1 160
Guided weapons trials
  Woomera rocket range, 14 2496

Guinea
  Commemorative stamps and medals, 3 495
Gulf Stream
  Air masses, 1 80
Gulfstream (aircraft), see Grumman
    Gulfstream
Gulliver (experimental device)
  Extraterrestrial life, 5 781
Gunnery
  Azimuth, 2 308
  Kites, 7 1278
Guns
  Armament, 2 193
Guppy Aircraft Series (performance chart)
  Outsize cargo aircraft, 10 1750
Gusmao (GOOZ mow), **Bartholemeu**
    Lorenco de (1685-1724, Brazilian
    priest, inventor), 6 1043
  Balloons, 2 321
  Man-powered flight, 8 1464
Gustafson, Nancy
  Bull, John Sumter, 3 389
Gust lock, 6 1043
Gusts, 6 1043-44
Guynemer, Georges
  World War I, 14 2505, 2506, (table) 2507
GY-80 Horizon (airplane)
  France's aerospace activities, picture, 5 889
Gypson, Richard
  Balloons, 2 317
Gyro
  Attitude indicator, 2 276
  Compasses, 3 550
Gyrocompass
  Directional gyro, 4 628
  Gyroscope, 6 1044
Gyro Direction Indicator
  Manufacturing, 8 1469
Gyrodyne
  Fairey, Sir Charles, 5 790
Gyro flux gate compass systems
  Compasses, 3 546, 549
Gyroplane
  Breguet, Louis Charles, 3 388
Gyroscope, 6 1044 (with diagram, pictures)
  Attitude and attitude control, 2 275
  Intertial guidance, 7 1152, 1153
  Manufacturing, 8 1469
  Oceanographic research, 10 1734
  Photography, 10 1789
Gyrostabilized rocket
  Rockets and rocketry, 11 1979

H

H-1 (airplane)
  Hughes, Howard Robert, 6 1131
Haas, Patricia
  McDivitt, James A., 8 1518
Hack
  Terminology of aerospace (table), 12 2272
Hadley, George
  Meteorology, 9 1556
Haenlein, Paul (1835-1905, German engineer),
    6 1045
  Airships, 1 111
Hahn, Otto
  Manhattan Project, 8 1442
  Radiation, 10 1880
Hail, 6 1045
  Aviation weather, 2 301, (diagram) 302

  Precipitation, 10 1844
Haise, Fred Wallace, Jr. (1933-   ), 6 1046
  Astronauts, 2 217, 218, 219 (with picture)
Haizlip, Jimmy
  Air racing, 1 103
Halaby, Najeeb E. (HAL a bee) (1915-   ,
    American aviation consultant), 6 1046
Halberg, Dr. Franz
  Circadian rhythm, 3 460
Halberstadt (airplane)
  First World War aircraft, 5 816
Hale reflecting telescope
  Astronomy (picture) 2 239
  Glass, 6 983
  Radio astronomy, 10 1892
  Telescopes and astronomical instruments,
    12 2251, (picture) 2251
Haley, Andrew G. (1904-   , American
    aerospace leader), 6 1046-47
Hallam, Nebraska, Nuclear Power Facility
  Nuclear energy (picture), 9 1712
Hall, Bert
  Lafayette Escadrille, 7 1295
Hall, Chester Moor
  Astronomy, 2 242
  Telescopes and astronomical instruments,
    12 2247
Halley, Edmund (1656-1742, English
    astronomer), 6 1047
  Astronomy, 2 238, 242
  Comets, 3 491
Halley's Comet
  Astronomy, 2 238
  Bessel, Friedrich Wilhelm, 2 354
  Comets, 3 490-91 (with pictures and
    diagram)
  Retrograde motion, 11 1961
Hall method
  Lunar bases, 8 1387
Hall, Norman B.
  Coast Guard aviation, 3 476
Hall of Fame commemorative medal
  Commemorative stamps and medals, 3 494
Halo, 6 1047
Ham (chimpanzee)
  Animals in space, 1 155
Hamilton, Harriet E.
  Eisele, Donn F., 4 681
Hamilton, W. R.
  Celestial mechanics, 3 428
  Orbits and trajectories, 10 1742
Hancock
  Aircraft carriers (data table), 1 51
  United States Naval Aviation (pictures),
    13 2383, 2387
Hancock, John
  Speed and speed records, 12 2142
Hand brake
  Airplane, 1 90
Handheld maneuvering unit
  Maneuvering in space, 8 1429-30, (picture)
    1429
Handley Page Dart Herald
  Africa's aviation (picture), 1 36
  First World War aircraft, 5 817, 821
  Mainland China's aerospace activities,
    8 1428
Handley Page Halifax
  Bomber aircraft, 2 375
  World War II, 14 2518
Handley Page HP. 42 Hannibal
  History of aviation (picture), 6 1106
Handley Page Jetstream
  General aviation aircraft (picture), 6 967
  United Kingdom aerospace activities,
    13 2352
Handley Page Limited
  United Kingdom aerospace activities,
    13 2352
Handley Page 0/400
  World War I (picture), 14 2502, 2509
  First World War aircraft, 5 821
Handley Page, Sir Frederick (1885-1963,
    British aircraft designer), 6 1048

Handley Page transport
Commercial airlines, 3 506
Handley Page V/1500
Bomber aircraft, 2 374
World War I, 14 2509
Handley Page Victor B.Mk-2
Air forces of the world, 1 66
Bomber aircraft (picture), 2 375
Handley Page W8F
Commercial airlines (picture), 3 506
Handlines
Crash trucks, 4 583
Handling
Oxidizers, 10 1752
Propellants, 10 1860
Handoff
Air traffic control, 1 131
Hanes, H. A.
Speed and speed records (table), 12 2141
Hangar decks
Aircraft carriers, 1 47
Hangars, 6 1048-49 (with pictures)
Hanging engine pods
Landing gear, 7 1299
Hanner, Colleen
Truly, Richard H., 13 2313
Hannover CL-3 (airplane)
World War I, 14 2510
Hanroit HD-1 (airplane)
World War I, 14 2508
Hansa (airplane)
General aviation aircraft (picture), 6 966
Hanson, Robert
World War II (table), 14 2517
Hardened site, 6 1050
Hardesty, Huntington
Speed and speed records (table), 12 2141
Harding, Lawrence M.
Coast Guard aviation, 3 479
Hard landing, 6 1050
Hard landing probe
Lunar exploration (diagram), 8 1405
Hard point targets
Battlefield missile systems, 2 342
Hard stand, 6 1050
Hard suit
Space suits, 12 2134
Hardware, 6 1050
Terminology of aerospace (table), 12 2272
Hare (aircraft)
U.S.S.R. aerospace activities (table),
13 2337
Hare-and-hounds race
Balloons, 2 323
Hargrave, Lawrence (1850-1915, Australian
aeronautics pioneer), 6 1050
Australia's aviation, 2 278-79
History of aviation, 6 1099, (table) 1119
Kites, 7 1279
Ornithopter, 10 1748
Pilcher, Percy Sinclair, 10 1793
Hargraves, J.
Astronomy, 2 242
Harmon Trophy
Airmail, 1 74
Doolittle, James Harold, 4 643
Earhart, Amelia, 4 658
Lovell, James A., Jr., 8 1373
Trophies and awards (table), 13 2312
Harmonic law
Astronomy, 2 242
Kepler's laws, 7 1275
Harp, see Kamov KA-20
Harrier, see Hawker Siddeley Harrier
Harris, Cecil
World War II (table), 14 2517
Harris, Grace M.
Medals and decorations (table), 8 1526
Harris, Harold
Parachutes, 10 1758
Harr, Karl G., Jr.
Aerospace industry, 1 33
Careers, 3 411
Hart (aircraft)
Camm, Sir Sidney, 3 398

Hartford, Connecticut
Careers (table), 3 414
Hartmann, Erich
Ace, 1 4
World War II (table), 14 2517
Hartsfield, Henry W., Jr. 1933-　,
Aerospace research pilot), 6 1051
Manned Orbiting Laboratory, 8 1456
Harvard College Observatory
Telescopes and astronomical instruments,
12 2247, (picture) 2253
Hasselblad camera
Photography (picture), 10 1786
Hatches and doors, 6 1051-52 (with pictures)
Hat-in-Ring (insignia)
World War I, 14 2505 (with picture)
Haughland, Vern
Medals and decorations (table), 8 1526
Havoc
Attack aircraft, 2 (picture) 271, 273
Hawaii
Airports, 1 94, 98
Hawk
Battlefield missile systems, 2 342
Surface-to-air missiles, 12 2201, (picture)
2202, (table) 2204
NORAD, 9 1701
Hawk 75A, see Curtiss Hawk 75A
Hawker Cygnet
Camm, Sir Sydney, 3 398
Hawker, Harry G.
Commemorative stamps and medals, 3 495
Hawker Hunter (aircraft)
Air forces of the world, 1 64, 66
Camm, Sir Sydney, 3 398
United Kingdom aerospace activities,
13 2347
Hawker Hurricane, 6 1052-53 (with chart
and diagram)
Battle of Britain, 2 344
Camm, Sir Sydney, 3 398
History of aviation (picture), 6 1111
Second World War aircraft (with picture),
11 2030-31
Hawker Siddeley 748
Asia's aviation, 2 204
Hawker Siddeley Argosy
Cargo aircraft, 3 419
Military air transports (picture), 9 1577
Hawker Siddeley Aviation Ltd.
Camm, Sir Sydney, 3 398
Eurospace, 4 756
International projects, 7 1200
Hawker Siddeley Buccaneer
Air Forces of the world, 1 166
Attack aircraft, 2 272
Military aircraft (picture), 9 1568
Military aviation (picture), 9 1586
Naval aviation, worldwide, 9 1669
Hawker Siddeley DH-125 jet
Business aviation (picture), 3 395
General aviation aircraft (picture), 6 968
Hawker Siddeley DHC-5 Buffalo
Military air transports (picture), 9 1577
Hawker Siddeley Dove
DeHavilland Dove, 4 619
Italy's aerospace activities (picture), 7 1221
Hawker Siddeley Dynamics
EUROPA 1, 4 741
Hawker-Siddeley flying boats
Coast Guard aviation, 3 477
Hawker Siddeley Group Limited
United Kingdom aerospace activities,
13 2351, 2355
Hawker Siddeley Harrier
Air forces of the world, 1 63
Fighter aircraft, 5 811
United Kingdom aerospace activities,
13 2350
V/STOL aircraft, 13 2442
Hawker Siddeley Nimrod
Reconnaissance aircraft (with picture),
11 1923

Hawker Siddeley P-1127 Kestrel, see
P-1127 Kestrel
Hawker Siddeley Sea Vixen, see Sea Vixen
Hawker Siddeley Shackleton MR. Mk3
Air forces of the world, 1 66
Hawker Siddeley Trident, 3 527, 528, 529
(with picture and diagram)
Commercial air transports (picture), 3 529
Hawker Siddeley Vulcan, see BMk 2 Vulcan
Hawker Typhoon
World War II (picture), 14 2513
Hazards
Psychological factors of flight, 10 1864
Haze, 6 1053
Weather, 13 2451
Hazelton Company
Australia's aviation, 2 282
H-bomb, see Hydrogen bomb
HC-97, see C-97 Stratofreighter
He-51, see Heinkel He-51
He-III, see Heinkel-III
He-173, see Heinkel He-173
He-177, see Heinkel 177
He-178, see Heinkel 178
Head
Comets, 3 490
Heading, 6 1053
Compasses, 3 546-47, 551
Heading indicator
Instrument flight techniques, 7 1167
Heading references
Jumbo jets, 7 1252
Headquarters Command
United States Air Force, 13 2371
Headset, 6 1053
Heads-up instrument flight display
Human engineering, 6 1135
Head wind, 6 1053-54
Jet streams, 7 1242
Hearing Examiners, Bureau of
Civil Aeronautics Board, 3 465
Heat accumulation
Intercontinental ballistic missiles, 7 1183
Heat balance
Earth science, 4 667
Heat chambers
Cosmonauts, 4 570
Heat energy, 6 1054-55 (with picture)
Chemical energy, 3 456
Energy, 4 712
Mechanical energy, 8 1521
Plasma, 10 1822
Reciprocating engines, 11 1913
Sound, 11 2077
Heat exchangers, 6 1055
Airships (picture), 1 109
Apollo Applications, 2 186
Space stations, 12 2127
Temperature control, 12 2265
Heath, Lady Mary
Women in aerospace, 14 2494
Heath Parasol (airplane)
Homebuilt aircraft, 6 1124
Heating
X-15 research program, 14 2530
Heat radiation
Paints, 10 1754
Planck, Max K. E. L., 10 1816
X-rays, 14 2533
Heat-seeking homing guidance
Air-to-air missiles, 1 119-21
Homing devices, 6 1128
Heat-seeking missiles
Infrared detection devices, 7 1159
Heat shields, 6 1055-59 (with pictures)
Ablation, 1 1 (with picture)
cone
Lamination, 7 1297
Italy's aerospace activities, 7 1225
Launch vehicles, 7 1325
Re-entry, 11 1930-31, 1935
Plastics, 10 1823
Heat sink, 6 1059

(Continued)

Heat sink (Cont.)
Brakes, **3** 385
Electronics, **4** 703
Heat shields, **6** 1056
Intercontinental ballistic missiles, **7** 1183
Re-entry vehicles, **11** 1931
Temperature control, **12** 2268
Termal barrier, **12** 2282
Heat stability
Ceramics, **3** 439
Heat transfer
Atmosphere, **2** 266
Jumbo jets, **7** 1254
Re-entry vehicles, **11** 1932
Heat-transfer gas
Kosmos satellites, **7** 1293
Heavier-than-air craft, 6 1059
Heaviside-Kennelly
Atmosphere, **2** 264
Heavy hydrogen
Urey, Harold Clayton, **13** 2393
Heavy water
Radiation, **10** 1881
Hegenberger, Albert F.
United States Air Force, **13** 2362
Height-finding
Radar, **10** 1877
Heinemann, Edward H.
Medals and decorations (table), **8** 1526
Heinkel, Ernst Heinrich (1888-1958, German airplane designer), **6** 1059-60
Jet aircraft, **7** 1235
Heinkel He-III (chart, diagram), **6** 1060
Battle of Britain (picture), **2** 344
History of aviation, **6** 1112
Luftwaffe, **8** 1377
World War II (picture), **14** 2513
Heinkel He-51
Spanish Civil War, **12** 2139
Heinkel He-173
Manufacturing, **8** 1472
Heinkel He-177
Second World War aircraft, **11** 2033
Heinkel He-178
Aircraft propulsion systems, **1** 57
Heisenberg, Werner
Quantum theory, **10** 1869
Helicopter cover
Launching, **7** 1312
Helicopter observer
Plane spotter, **10** 1817
Helicopter patrols
Police and fire services, **10** 1835
Helicopter pilot
Scott, Sheila, **11** 2021
Helicopters, 6 1061-77 (with diagrams, pictures, table)
Aerodyne, **1** 25
Aerospace industry, **1** 31, 33
Aircraft, **1** 45
Aircraft carriers, **1** 47
Air forces of the world, **1** 64
Airmail, **1** 78
Air transports, **1** 139
Army aviation, **2** 195, 197
Auto-rotation, **2** 290
Bird flight, **2** 362
Cierva, Juan de la, **3** 460
Coast Guard aviation (pictures), **3** 478-79
Cockpit, **3** 487
Crop dusting, **4** 588, 590
Gas turbine engines, **5** 924
Heliports, **6** 1078
History of aviation, **6** 1094, 1117
Manufacturing, **8** 1475
Marine Corps Aviation, **8** 1482-1483, (pictures) 1482
Mechanical energy, **8** 1522
Military aircraft, **9** 1571
Naval aviation, worldwide, **9** 1667-72
Pararescue, **10** 1760
Parawing, **10** 1761
Penaud, Alphonse, **10** 1774
Police and fire services, **10** 1834-35
Reconnaissance, airborne, **11** 1920

Reconnaissance aircraft (with picture), **11** 1922
Recovery, **11** 1928
Refueling, **11** 1941
Rotary-wing aircraft, **11** 1991
Stability, **12** 2156
United Kingdom aerospace activities, **13** 2353
United States Naval Aviation, **13** 2390
Utility aviation, **13** 2394
Vietnam, **13** 2414, 2416-18, (pictures) 2415, 2419, 2421
Visual Flight Rules, **13** 2425
V/STOL aircraft, **13** 2438, 2444
Whirly Girls, **13** 2481
Helicopter Scheduled Airlines (table)
Commercial airlines, **3** 500
Heliocentric, 6 1078 (with diagram)
Heliocentric flight path
Orbits and trajectories, **10** 742, 1747
Heliocentric interplanetary magnetic field
Kosmos satellites, **7** 1293
Heliocentric parallax
Astronomy, **2** 249
Heliocentric theory
Aristarchus of Samos, **2** 193
Astronomy, **2** 242
Copernicus, Nicolaus, **3** 566
Helio Courier
Army aviation, **2** 197
Helio H-295 Super Courier
Army aviation, **2** 197
Heliopolis Air Works
Africa's aviation, **1** 37
High-lift devices, **6** 1088
Helios program
Balloons, **2** 328
Helio Stallion Model 550 (aircraft)
V/STOL aircraft (table), **13** 2443
Helipads
Heliports, **6** 1078
Heliports, 6 1078-79 (with pictures)
Airports, **1** 93, (pictures) 94
Economic implications of aerospace, **4** 670
Helicopters, **6** 1071
Helistops
Heliports, **6** 1078
Helitankers
Forest fire control, **5** 880
Helium, 6 1079-80
Aerostat, **1** 35
Air, **1** 42
Airships, **1** 108, 113
Atoms, **2** 271
Balloons, **2** 317
Gases, **5** 916
Stars, **12** 2160, 2161, 2162
Sun, **12** 2172
Helium ions
Radiation, **10** 1882
Helium magnetometer
Mariner probes, **8** 1488
Helium nucleus
Alpha particle, **1** 145
Helix principle
Man-powered flight, **8** 1463
Hellcat, see F-6 Hellcat
Helmets
Agricultural aviation, **1** 41
Personal equipment, **10** 1774
Pressure suit, **10** 1851
Rocket sled, **11** 1986
Helwan Air Works
Africa's aviation, **1** 37
Hemisphere rules, 6 1080-81 (with diagram)
Hemispherical theater
Planetarium, **10** 1818
Henize, Dr. Karl G. 1926-   , Scientist-astronaut, **6** 1081-82
Astronauts, **2** 218-19, 223 (with picture)
Henry Dreyfuss Associates
Human engineering, **6** 1133
Henry, James P. (1914-   , Aerospace medical pioneer), **6** 1082

Henry, Joseph
Electromagnetism, **4** 689
Henson, William Samuel (1812-1888, English engineer), **6** 1082
Aircraft propulsion systems, **1** 56-57
History of aviation, **6** 1095, (table) 1119
Stringfellow, John, **12** 2170
Heraclides Ponticus (Her a CLI dees PONT i cus)
Astronomy, **2** 235
Herbicides
Crop dusting, **4** 588
Hercules, Constellations, 3 562
Hercules (aircraft), see C-130 Hercules
Hercules (missile)
Surface-to-air missiles, **12** 2201
Hercules 8 (flying boat)
History of aviation, **6** 1116
Herlihy, Florence
Finley, John L., **5** 812
Hermes
Aircraft carriers, **1** 48, 49
Naval aviation, worldwide (United Kingdom), **9** 1669, (picture) 1668
Hermetically isolated surfaces
Oceanographic research, **10** 1734
Hero (C.100 B.C.)
Aeolipile, **1** 7
Aircraft propulsion systems, **1** 52, 57
Jet aircraft, **7** 1234
Rockets and rocketry, **11** 1971
Herodotus (Heh ROD o tus)
Apollo, **1** 163
Astronomy, **2** 234
Hero of Socialist Labor
Korolev, Sergei, **7** 1290
Heroes of the Soviet Union
Ace, **1** 4
Heroine of the Soviet Union
Nikolayeva-Tereshkova, Valentina, **9** 1697
Herres, Robert T. (1932-   , Aerospace research pilot), **6** 1082-83
Manned Orbiting Laboratory, **8** 1456
Herrick, Samuel (1911-   , American astronomer), **6** 1083
Herschel, Caroline (1750-1848)
Astronomy, **2** 238
Herschel family (Herschel, Sir William, 1738-1882, Herschel, Sir John Frederick William, 1792-1871, English astronomers), **6** 1083-84
Astronomy, **2** 238, 239, 242, 247
Celestial mechanics, **3** 428
Telescopes and astronomical instruments, **12** 2250
Uranus, **13** 2392
Hershey, Henry Blanchard
Balloons, **2** 322
International competitions, **7** 1191
Hertz, 6 1084
Electronics, **4** 700
Kilocycle, **7** 1276
Noise measurement, **9** 1700
Sound, **11** 2077
Hertz, Heinrich
Astronomy, **2** 242
Electromagnetism, **4** 689
Microcircuitry, **9** 1562
Radar, **10** 1872
Hertzsprung, Ejnar (HURTS sproong, EYE nar)
Astrophysics, **2** 257
Stars, **12** 2160
Hertzsprung-Russell (diagram)
Astronomy, **2** 250
Astrophysics, **2** 256
Stars, **12** 2161, (diagram) 2161
Heterosphere
Atmosphere, **2** 263
HF, see High Frequency
HH-3 helicopter (Sikorsky) (Jolly Green Giant)
Helicopters, **6** 1074
United States Air Force (picture), **13** 2369

HH-52 (Sikorsky)
  Coast Guard aviation (picture), **3** 478, 479
Hibbs, Albert Roach (1924-   , American
    aerospace engineer), **6** 1084
Hidalgo
  Asteroids, **2** 209
High, see High-pressure area
High-altitude bombing
  Bomber aircraft, **2** 376
  Bombs, **3** 378
High-altitude flight, 6 1084-85
  Aviation medicine, **2** 293-94
  Decompression, **4** 613
  Escape systems, **4** 734
  Launch vehicles, **7** 1328
High-altitude flight training, 6 1085-86
    (with picture)
High-altitude phenomena
  International Geophysical Year, **7** 1194
High-altitude rocket
  Radio astronomy, **10** 1890
  Woomera rocket range, **14** 2496
High-altitude tank
  Environmental simulators, **4** 728
High-aspect-ratio wing
  U-2, **13** 2396
High bays
  Kennedy Space Center, **7** 1269
High clouds
  Clouds, **3** 472
High-density microcircuit
  Solid-state physics (with drawing), **11** 2073
High flotation landing gear
  Jumbo jets, **7** 1254
**High-Frequency Communications Systems
    Provisions**
  Radio communications (diagram), **10** 1896
High-frequency noise
  Acoustics, **1** 4-5
High-frequency radio, 6 1086
  Airborne antennas, **1** 43
  Jumbo jets, **7** 1255
  Phonetic alphabet, **10** 1778
High-gain antennas
  Space communications, **11** 2099
High-intensity radiation
  Kosmos satellites, **7** 1293
Highlands
  Moon, **9** 1635
High-lift devices, 6 1086-88 (with diagrams)
High-performance aircraft, 6 1088-89
High-pressure area, 6 1089
  Air masses, **1** 80
  Anticyclone, **1** 159
  Isobar, **7** 1216
  Meteorology, **9** 1555
  Preflight training, **10** 1848
  Shock tubes and tunnels, **11** 2047
High-pressure gas storage room
  Kennedy Space Center, **7** 1273
High-pressure gas systems
  Apollo Applications Program, **2** 186
High-pressure testing
  Kennedy Space Center, **7** 1267
Highs (anticyclones)
  Weather, **13** 2450
High-speed aerodynamics
  Aerodynamics, **1** 24-25
  Parawing, **10** 1761
  Partial pressure suit, **10** 1763
High-speed surface transportation, 6 1098-92
    (with diagrams)
  Systems engineering, **12** 2226
High-stress applications
  Precious metals, **10** 1843
High-temperature materials
  Jumbo jets, **7** 1249
  Refractory metals, **11** 1936
High vacuum
  Environmental simulators, **4** 726
High wing
  Airplane (picture), **1** 86
  Wings, **14** 2492
Hill, Dudley
  Lafayette Escadrille, **7** 1295

Hill, Earl W.
  Alpha Eta Rho, **1** 145
Hill, E. J.
  Balloons, **2** 322
Hiller Aircraft
  X-series aerospace vehicles, **14** 2542
Hiller OH-23, see OH-23 Raven
Hiller rotorcraft
  Crop dusting, **4** 590
Hiller X-18, see X-18
Hill, Maynard L.
  Medals and decorations (table), **8** 1526
Hill, Virginia E.
  Crippen, Robert L., **4** 584
Hilton, Walter
  Coast Guard aviation, **3** 476
Himalayas (mountains)
  Hump airlift, **6** 1136
Hindenburg
  Airships, **1** 112-13 (with picture)
  Commemorative stamps and medals, **3** 494
  Dirigibles, **4** 631
  Zeppelins, **14** 2549, 2552
Hindus
  Astronomy, **2** 234
Hinkler, Bert
  Medals and decorations (table), **8** 1526
Hipparchus (Hip PARK us) (160-125 B.C.,
    Greek astronomer), **6** 1092
  Astronomy, **2** 235, 242
  Celestial mechanics, **3** 426
  Maps and mapping, **8** 1478
  Moon, **9** 1633
  Ptolemy, Claudius, **10** 1864
Hiroshima, Japan
  Atomic bomb, **2** 269
Hirth, Wolf
  Medals and decorations (table), **8** 1526
Hiryu
  Aircraft carriers, **1** 49
Hiscock, Thorp (1892-1934, American
    aeronautical engineer), **6** 1092
  Radio communications, **10** 1895
Historia Coelestis (se LES tis) (1712)
  Flamsteed, John, **5** 828
History of aviation, 6 1093-1121 (with
    diagrams, pictures, tables)
Hitchcock, Frank H.
  Airmail, **1** 69
Hitch-Hiker 1
  Environmental research satellites, **4** 723
Hittorf, Johann
  Electronics, **4** 693
HJT-18
  Asia's aviation (India), **2** 204
HL-10
  Lifting-body vehicles, **8** 1350
HMR-161 helicopter
  Marine Corps Aviation (picture), **8** 1482
HMS, see name of ship
Ho Chi Minh trail
  Vietnam, **13** 2422
Hog (aircraft)
  U.S.S.R. aerospace activities (table),
    13 2337
Hohmann orbits, 6 1122
  Launch vehicles, **7** 1317
Hohmann transfer ellipse, see Hohmann
    orbits
Hohmann, Walter
  Interplanetary travel, **7** 1207
Hold
  Countdown, **4** 576
  Terminology of aerospace (table), **12** 2272
Holding pattern, 6 1122
  Air traffic control (diagram), **1** 126
    138, 134
  Instrument flight techniques, **7** 1168
Holding point
  Federal airways systems, **5** 792
  Instrument flight techniques, **7** 1168
Holding stack
  Air traffic control, **1** 134
Hole current
  Electronics, **4** 701

Holland
  Airmail, **1** 75
  World War II, **14** 2512
Holloman Air Force Base
  Animals in space, **1** 154
Holmquist, Donald Lee (1939-   ), **6** 1122
  Astronauts, **2** 218, 219, 223 (with picture)
Holography
  Lasers, **7** 1306
Home
  Terminology of aerospace (table), **12** 2272
Homebuilt aircraft, 6 1123-27 (with pictures)
  Experimental aircraft, **4** 760
  Experimental Aircraft Association, **4** 760
  Sport flying, **12** 2148
Homing All-the-Way Killer, see Hawk
Homing devices, 6 1128 (with diagram)
  Guidance and control systems, **6** 1037
  Missiles, **9** 1613
  Surface-to-air missiles, **12** 2199
Homing signals
  Recovery, **11** 1928
Homosphere
  Atmosphere, **2** 263
Honduras
  Crop dusting, **4** 587
  South and Central America's aviation,
    11 2091
H-1 (rocket engine)
  Space propulsion systems, **12** 2122
Honest John
  Battlefield missile systems, **2** 341
  Missiles, **9** 1616
Honeycomb construction, 6 1128-29
  Materials, **8** 1503
Hong Kong
  Commercial airlines, **3** 509
Honorary Group Diploma
  Medals and decorations, **8** 1524
**Honor Award for Distinguished Service in
    Aeronautical Engineering**
  Johnson, Clarence Leonard, **7** 1242
Hook, see Mi-6
Hooker reflector telescope
  Astronomy, **2** 240
Hook-up
  Refueling, **11** 1940
Hopi Indians
  Boomerang, **3** 380
Hopkins, Phillip S.
  Medals and decorations (table), **8** 1526
Horbaczewski, E.
  World War II (table), **14** 2517
Horizon, 6 1129
  Astronomy, **2** 240
  Celestial sphere, **3** 431
Horizon System of Coordinates
  Celestial sphere, **3** 431
Horizontal accelerometers
  Inertial guidance, **7** 1153
Horizontal drag
  Launch vehicles, **7** 1314
Horizontal flight
  Convertiplane, **3** 565
Horizontally opposed engine
  Aircraft propulsion systems, **1** 56
Horizontal stabilizers, 6 1129
  Airplane, **1** 86
  Empennage, **4** 709
Horizontal velocity vector
  Inertial guidance, **7** 1153
Horizontal visibility
  Instrument landing categories, **7** 1169
Hornet
  Aircraft carriers, **1** 49
  Air-to-surface missiles, **1** 124
  Battlefield missile systems, **2** 343
  Doolittle, James Harold, **4** 643
  United States Naval Aviation, **13** 2380
  World War II, **14** 2522
Horn, Martha
  Chaffee, Roger B., **3** 445
Horse
  U.S.S.R. aerospace activities (table),
    13 2337

Horsehead Nebula
Astronomy, **2** 252
Nebula (picture), **9** 1688
Horse latitudes, 6 1129
Horsepower, 6 1129-30
Measurement of power, **8** 1518, (diagram)
8 1519
Propellers, **10** 1863
Reciprocating engines, **11** 1916
Hosho
Aircraft carriers, **1** 49
Hospital heliport
Airports, **1** 100
Hospitals
Police and fire services, **10** 1835
HOT
International projects, **7** 1201
Hot air
Aviation weather, **2** 305
Hot-air balloons, 6 1130
Aeronautics, **1** 26
Hot air ducts
Interiors of aircraft, **7** 1184
Hot-bleed cycle
NERVA, **9** 1691, (diagram) 1692
Hotchkiss machine gun
World War I, **14** 2505
"Hot wing" method
Deicing equipment, **4** 620
Hotz, Robert B.
Medals and decorations (table), **8** 1526
Houdini, Harry
Australia's aviation, **2** 279
Hound, see Mi-4
Hound Dog
Air-to-surface missiles, **1** 122-24
Bomber aircraft, **2** 376
Guidance and control systems, **6** 1041
Hovercar
Ground-effect machines, **6** 1026
Hovercraft
Ground-effect machines, **6** 1023
History of aviation, **6** 1117
United Kingdom aerospace activities,
13 2355, (picture) 2355
Howard, Ben Odell (1904- , American
aviator), **6** 1130
Medals and decorations (table), **8** 1526
Howard, Jean Ross
Whirly Girls, **13** 2481
Howe, C. D.
Canada's aviation, **3** 401
Howze, Hamilton H.
Vietnam, **13** 2416
Hoyle, Fred (1915- , British astronomer),
6 1130-31
HP.2, see Handley Page HP.2 Halifax
HR diagram, see Hertzsprung Russell diagram
Hs.748 (airplane)
United Kingdom aerospace activities,
13 2352
H II regions
Milky way, **9** 1605, 1607
Hubbard, Edward
Airmail, **1** 76-78
Commercial air transports, **3** 517
International airmail (picture), **7** 1188
Hubble, Edwin (1889-1953, American
astronomer), **6** 1131
Astronomy, **2** 242, 254
Galaxies, **5** 910
Hubble's constant
Hubble, Edwin, **6** 1131
Quasar, **10** 1871
Huber, E.
Medals and decorations (table), **8** 1526
Huch, W. F.
Balloons, **2** 330
Hudson Bay
Bush flying, **3** 392
Huey (helicopter), see HU-1 (Huey)
HueyCobra, see AH-1G HueyCobra
Huff-Daland crop dusting planes
Crop dusting, **4** 586

Huggins, William
Astronomy, **2** 242
Hughes AIM-47A missile
Air forces of the world, **1** 66
Hughes Aircraft Company
Air-to-air missiles, **1** 121
Applications Technology Satellites, **2** 189
Communications satellites, **3** 537
Electric propulsion, **4** 685
International Telecommunications
Satellite Consortium, **7** 1202
Surveyor, **12** 2210, 2212
Hughes Hot Cycle (V/TOL aircraft)
Helicopters, **6** 1068
Hughes, Howard Robert (1905- , American
aviator, aircraft manufacturer),
6 1131-32
Lockheed Constellation, **8** 1366
Speed and speed records (table), **12** 2141
World records and round-the-world
flights, **14** 2497
Hughes OH-6A, see OH-6a Cayuse
Hughes Phoenix
Missiles (picture), **9** 1613
Hull
Airships, **1** 106
Human centrifuge
Centrifuge, **3** 437 (with pictures)
Human engineering, 6 1132-35 (with pictures)
Aviation medicine, **2** 297
Human fatigue, 6 1135-36
Humidity, 6 1136
Meteorology, **9** 1555
Weather, **13** 2449
Hummingbirds
Bird flight, **2** 362
Hump airlift, 6 1136-37 (with pictures)
Hungary
Commemorative stamps and medals,
3 493
Crop dusting, **4** 587
European aerospace activities, **4** 746
International competitions, **7** 1192
Hunter, see Hawker Hunter
Hunter's Sword
Nebula, **9** 1689
HU-1 (Huey) (helicopter)
Coast Guard aviation (picture), **3** 475
Vietnam, **13** 2416
Hurel, Maurice
Medals and decorations (table), **8** 1526
Hurricane, see Hawker Hurricane
Hurricane Beulah
Weather (picture), **13** 2453
Weather satellites (picture), **13** 2467
HU-16 Albatross (Grumman)
Continental Air Command, **3** 563
Flying boats, **5** 861
Grumman Albatross, **6** 1031-32 (with
chart, picture)
Hustler, see B-58 Hustler
Huth, Heinz
Medals and decorations (table), **8** 1526
Huygens, Christian (Hy gens)
Aircraft propulsion systems, **1** 53
Astronomy, **2** 246
Quantum theory, **10** 1868
Hyatt, John and Isaiah
Plastics, **10** 1823
Hybrid
Air-to-surface missiles, **1** 122
Sounding rockets, **11** 2079
Hybrid systems, 6 1138
Hydra-Iris
Sounding rockets (with picture), **11** 2082
Hydraulic brake pressure
Brakes, **3** 387
Hydraulic jacking system
Kennedy Space Center, **7** 1272
Hydraulic pressure
Pressure gauges, **10** 1849
Hydraulic starters
Aircraft carriers, **1** 51

Hydraulic systems, 6 1138-40 (with diagram)
Cockpit, **3** 483
Jumbo jets, **7** 1252
Materials, **8** 1510
Preflight inspection, **10** 1846
Pressure gauges, **10** 1850
Hydrocarbons
Fuels, **5** 897, 898, 901
Hydrodynamic booster
Pontoons (with diagram), **10** 1838
Hydrodynamics, 6 1140
Oceanographic research, **10** 1734
Hydroecology
Mars, **8** 1492
Hydrofoils, 6 1140-41 (with picture)
Hydrogen, 6 1141
Air, **1** 42
Atoms, **2** 269
Balloons, **2** 316, 321
Cavallo, Tiberius **3** 424
Cryogenic propellants, **4** 595
Extraterrestrial life, **5** 775
Gases, **5** 915
Jupiter, **7** 1260
Montgolfier brothers, **9** 1632
Ozma project, **10** 1753
Plasma propulsion, **10** 1823
Propellants, **10** 1861
Space propulsion systems, **12** 2124
Stars, **12** 2160, 2161, 2162
Hydrogen atom
Lasers, **7** 1303
Quantum theory, **10** 1868-69, (diagram)
1870
Hydrogen bomb, 6 1141
Bombs, **3** 378
Nuclear energy, **9** 1711 (with picture)
Radiation, **10** 1881
Teller, Edward, **12** 2264
Hydrogen-fueled engine
Launch vehicles, **7** 1324-25
Hydrogen ions
Radiation, **10** 1882
Hydrogen-peroxide engines
Centaur, **3** 433, 434
Hydrogen-peroxide jets
Astronaut maneuvering unit, **2** 213
Hydrogen service tower
Kennedy Space Center, **7** 1272
Hydrographic Office
Charts, **3** 455
Hydrometers
Aviation weather, **2** 299
Hydroplane
Breguet, Louis Charles, **3** 388
Fabre, Henri, **5** 785
Hydroponics, 6 1141
Hydrosphere
Atmosphere, **2** 261
Hydrostatics, 6 1141
Hydyne
Explorer satellites, **5** 763
Hynek, Dr. J. Allen
Orbits and trajectories, **10** 1742, 1743,
1745
Unidentified flying objects, **13** 2322
Hyperbolic flight path
Interplanetary travel, **7** 1212 (with diagram)
Hyper Diamant
Launch vehicles, **7** 1327
Hypergolic fueling
Kennedy Space Center, **7** 1272
Oxidizers, **10** 1751
Hypergolic propellants, 6 1141
Launching, **7** 1312
Lunar Module, Apollo, **1** 173
Propellants, **10** 1861
Surveyor, **12** 2211
Titan III, **12** 2292
Hypergolic test facility
Kennedy Space Center, **7** 1267
Hypersonic aircraft
X-series aerospace vehicles, **14** 2539,
2542

Hypersonic flight, 6 1142-44 (with diagrams)
  Ablation, **1** 1
  Aerodynamics, **1** 25
  History of aviation, **6** 1121
Hypersonic shock tunnel
  Cornell Aeronautical Laboratory, **3** 566
Hypersonic speeds
  Langley Research Center, **7** 1302
Hypersonic wind tunnel
  Aerodynamics (picture) **1** 22
  Aerospace industry (picture), **1** 32
Hypoxia, 6 1144
  Aerospace medicine, **1** 34
  Aviation medicine, **2** 293, 294, 296
  Decompression, **4** 613
  Illusions, **7** 1148
  Man in flight, **8** 1444-45, (diagram and
    data table) 1444, (graph) 1445
Hysteresis error
  Altimeter, **1** 146

I

I-16 Mosca (fighter)
  Spanish Civil War, **12** 2139
IAS, see Indicated airspeed
IAS, see Institute of Aerospace Sciences
IATA, see International Air Transport
  Association
Iberia
  European aerospace activities, **4** 749
IBM Corporation
  Launch vehicles, **7** 1325
IBM 1800 computer
  Italy's aerospace activities, **7** 1222
IBM punched card
  Computer (picture), **3** 555
IBM System 360
  Computers, **3** 353, (picture) 559
IBM System/4 Pi computer
  Computers (picture), **3** 555
ICAO, see International Civil Aviation
  Organization
Icarus (IK uh rus)
  Asteroids, **2** 207
Icarus (mythology)
  Commemorative stamps and medals, **3** 493
  Ornithopter, **10** 1748
ICBM, see Intercontinental ballistic missile
Ice crystal process
  Precipitation (with diagram), **10** 1844
Iceland
  Commemorative stamps and medals, **3** 494
  NATO, **9** 1703-04
Iceland spar
  Crystallography, **4** 599
Ice pellets
  Precipitation, **10** 1844
Ice sheet
  Poles, **10** 1834
Icing, 7 1145-46
  Aviation weather, **2** 301
  Radio altimeter, **10** 1888
Iconoscope
  Electronics, **4** 699
IDCSP, see Initial Defense Communications
  Satellite Project
Identical-frequency photon
  Lasers, **7** 1303
Identification of space vehicles
  Legal implications of aerospace, **7** 1331

Idle air bleed
  Carburetion, **3** 409
Idling
  Carburetion, **3** 409
IFF coders
  Invader, Douglas, A-26, B-26, **7** 1214
IFR, see Instrument Flight Rules
Ignition systems, 7 1146
  Aircraft propulsion systems, **1** 54
  Propellants, **10** 1860
  Reciprocating engines, **11** 1917
Igniting energy
  Ignition systems, **7** 1146
Ignitrons
  Electronics, **4** 700
IGY, see International Geophysical Year
Il-2 Stormavik
  Second World War aircraft (with picture),
    11 2032
  World War II, **14** 2515
Il-12 (Ilyushin)
  Mainland China's aerospace activities,
    8 1426, 1428
Il-14 transport (Ilyushin)
  Mainland China's aerospace activities,
    8 1426, 1428
Il-18 Moskva (Ilyushin)
  Air forces of the world (Russia), **1** 64
  Mainland China's aerospace activities,
    8 (picture) 1428
  U.S.S.R. aerospace activities, **13** 2332,
    (table) 2337
Il-28 Beagle (Ilyushin)
  Asia's aviation, **2** 204, 205
  Bomber aircraft, **2** 373
  Naval aviation, worldwide, **9** 1670-71
  U.S.S.R. aerospace activities (talbe),
    13 2337
Il-62 (Ilyushin)
  Jet aircraft (picture), **7** 1234
  U.S.S.R. aerospace activities, **13** 2332, 2333,
    (picture) 2330
Ilijiuchin, Vladimir
  Altitude and altitude records, **1** 147
Illumination, law of intensity
  Light, **8** 1351
Illusions, 7 1147-48
Illustrious
  Aircraft carriers, **1** 50
ILS, see Instrument Landing System
Iltchenko, V.
  Medals and decorations (table), **8** 1526
Ilya Mourometz (airplane)
  First World War aircraft, **5** 825
Ilyushin aircraft, see Il-2, Il-12, Il-14, Il-18,
  Il-28, Il-62
Ilyushin, Sergei Vladimirovich (1894-   ,
  Russian aircraft designer), **7** 1148
  U.S.S.R. aerospace activities, **13** 2330,
    (picture) 2327
Image converter tube
  Telescopes and astronomical instruments,
    12 2255, 2258
Image intensifier
  Electronics, **4** 699
Image-matcher
  Celestial navigation, **3** 431
Image motion compensation
  Aerial photography, **1** 10
Image orthicon
  Tube, Television, **12** 2258
Immelmann, Max (1890-1918, German
  aviator and ace) **7** 1148
Immelmann (maneuver)
  Barnstormers, **2** 333
  World War I, **14** 2506
IMP, see Interplanetary Monitoring Platform
Impact
  Ranger (picture), **10** 1910
Impenetrability
  Matter, **8** 1515
Imperial Airways
  Cobham, Sir Alan, **3** 480
  Commercial airlines, **3** 506
Imperial Oil

Bush flying, 3 392
Implications of aerospace (with historical
  chart), **7** 1149-51
  Economic implications of aerospace,
    4 670-72
  Educational implications of aerospace,
    4 673-78
  Government in aerospace, **6** 1000-10
  Legal implications of aerospace, **7** 1331
  Military implications of aerospace,
    9 1588-89
  Political implications of aerospace,
    10 1836-37
  Social implications of aerospace, **11** 2066-67
  Space law, **12** 2119-20
Incandescent
  Light, **8** 1351
Incendiary bombs
  Bombs, **3** 378
Incident ray
  Light, **8** 1351
Inclination, 7 1151
  Compasses, **3** 546
  Earth, **4** 661
Inconel X (nickel alloy)
  X-15 research program, **14** 2532
Increased flow velocity
  Jet engines, **7** 1239
Increased workload factors
  Manned spaceflight, **8** 1462
Increase pitch attitude
  Maneuvers, **8** 1433
Independence (aircraft carrier)
  United States Naval Aviation, **13** 2382, 2383
Independencia (aircraft carrier)
  Naval aviation, worldwide (Argentina),
    9 1672
India
  Air forces of the world, **1** 64
  Asia's aviation, **2** 203, 204
  Astronomy, **2** 234
  Boomerang, **3** 380
  Crop dusting, **4** 587
  Naval aviation, worldwide, **9** 1671
Indian National Committee for Space Research
  International projects, **7** 1198
Indicated airspeed
  Airspeed, **1** 116
  Airspeed indicator, **1** 116 (with picture)
Indicated altitude
  Altimeter, **1** 145
Indicated horsepower
  Measurement of power, **8** 1518, (diagram)
    1519
Indicated Mach number
  Air speed, **1** 116
Indicated readings, 7 1151
Indirectly heated cathode
  Electronics, **4** 695
Indochina
  Air forces of the world, **1** 64
Indonesia
  Asia's aviation, **2** 205
  Naval aviation, worldwide, **9** 1671
Induced drag
  Aerodynamics, **1** 23
  X-series aerospace vehicles, **14** 2543
Induction system
  Reciprocating engines, **11** 1917
Industrial airpark
  Airports, **1** 93, (picture) 94
Industrial area
  Blockhouse, **2** 368
  Kennedy Space Center, **7** 1266
Industrial engineering
  Human engineering, **6** 1133
Industry in space
  Legal implications of aerospace, **7** 1331
  Technological projections, **12** 2237
Inertia
  Astronomy, **2** 242
  Matter, **8** 1515
Inertial guidance, 7 1152-55
  Accelerometer, **1** 3
  Air-to-surface missiles, **1** 124

(Continued)

Inertial guidance (Cont.)
Antisubmarine missiles, **1** 161
Attitude and attitude control, **2** 275
Battlefield missile systems, **2** 340
Dead reckoning, **4** 612
Guidance and control systems, **6** 1036
Jumbo jets, **7** 1252
Launch vehicles, **7** 1316
Missiles, **9** 1615
Navigation systems, **9** 1674
Peenemuende, **10** 1770
PRIME, **10** 1853
Radio navigation, **10** 1899
X-15 research program, **14** 2530
Inertial gyro platforms
Avionics, **2** 307
Inertial navigation
Gyroscope, **6** 1044
Instrument panels, **7** 1177
Jumbo jets, **7** 1252
Navigation systems (diagram), **9** 1677, 1680
Inertial reference sensors
Inertial guidance, **7** 1154 (with picture)
Inferior conjunction
Conjunction, **3** 560
Inferior planets
Astronomy, **2** 241
Inferior spheres
Astronomy, **2** 235, 242
Infernal machines
Bombs, **3** 377
Inflammable air
Montgolfier brothers, **9** 1632
Inflatoplane
Fabrics, **5** 786
Inflight communications
Space communications (with drawing),
11 2098
Inflight emergency procedures, 7 1155-56
Emergency landing procedures, **4** 707
Inflight refueling
Refueling, **11** 1937
Inflight service
Passenger services, **10** 1765
Information collecting
Intelligence, military, **7** 1181
Information systems, 7 1156-59
Kennedy Space Center, **7** 1267
Radar, **10** 1876
Social implications of aerospace, **11** 2067
Infrared camera
Photography (picture), **10** 1787
Infrared detection devices, 7 1159-62
Infrared film
Crop dusting, **4** 593
Infrared homing missiles
Air-to-air missiles, **1** 119-21
Infrared detection devices, **7** 1161
Missiles, **9** 1613-14
Infrared light
Orbiting observatories, **10** 1738
Infrared maps
Infrared detection devices, **7** 1159
Infrared radiation, 7 1162
Light, **8** 1350
Radiation, **10** 1880
Tracking systems and networks, **13** 2300
X-rays, **14** 2533
Infrared rays
Atmosphere, **2** 266
Observatories, **10** 1726
Infrared reconnaissance system
Reconnaissance aircraft, **11** 1920
Infrared seekers
Guidance and control systems, **6** 1037
Infrared tracker
Infrared detection devices, **7** 1160
Inhibited red fuming nitric acid
Delta rocket, **4** 622
**Initial Defense Communications Satellite
Project**
Communications satellites, **3** 531
Defense communication satellites, **4** 616
Military space program, **9** 1596-97 (with
picture)

Initial velocity
Inertial guidance, **7** 1154
Inject
Terminology of aerospace (table), **12** 2272
Injection
Launch vehicles, **7** 1316
Injection of payload
Launch vehicles, **7** 1319 (with diagram)
Injun (satellite)
Explorer satellites, **5** 771
NASA (drawing), **9** 1651
In-line engine
Aircraft propulsions systems, **1** 55 (with
diagram)
Reciprocating engine, **11** 1913
Input
Computers, **3** 552
Information systems, **7** 1157
Input axis
Inertial guidance, **7** 1152
Input-output devices
Computers, **3** 556
Insect control
Crop dusting, **4** 585
Insecticides
Crop dusting, **4** 588
Insects
Biosatellites, **2** 356
Insert
Terminology of aerospace (table), **12** 2272
Insertion tracking, 7 1162
Insignia, aircraft (with pictures), **7** 1163
In situ composites
Materials, **8** 1504
Insolation
Atmosphere, **2** 265
Inspections
Airworthiness, **1** 141
Careers, **3** 417
Ground service and maintenance, **6** 1027
Inspector authorization
Mechanic ratings, **8** 1523
Installation error
Altimeter, **1** 146
Institute for Space Studies
Goddard Space Flight Center, **6** 992
Institute for Telecommunication Sciences
Environmental Science Services
Administration, **4** 725
Institute of Aerospace Sciences
American Institute of Aeronautics and
Astronautics, **1** 150
Instrument approach
Radio altimeter, **10** 1888
Instrument Approach Chart
Charts, **3** 454
Instrumentation
Jumbo jets, **7** 1252
Kennedy Space Center, **7** 1267, 1271, 1273
Lunar Module, **8** 1410
Instrument Flight Charts
Charts, **3** 450
Instrument Flight Rules (with chart), **7** 1164-68
Airports, **1** 96
Air traffic control, **1** 126-28
Australia's aviation, **2** 284
Aviation weather, **2** 300
Charts, **3** 450
Control tower, **3** 564
Course plotting **4** 579
Flight plan, **5** 847
Hemisphere rules, **6** 1081
IFR flight plans
Air traffic control, **1** 130-31
IFR room
Air traffic control, **1** 128, 133
National Airspace System, **9** 1660
Radio communications, **10** 1897
Instrument flight techniques (with charts),
7 1166-71
Instrument landing categories (with diagram),
7 1168-72
Instrument landing system, 7 1170-71
Airborne antennas, **1** 43
Airports, **1** 96, 98

Attitude indicator, **2** 276
Automatic landing, **2** 287
Avionics, **2** 307
Beacon, radio, **2** 345
Flight director, **5** 840
Flight simulators, **5** 855
Instrument landing categories, **7** 1168
Invader, Douglas A-26, B-26, **7** 1214
Radio communications, **10** 1895
Radio navigation, **10** 1899
Instrument navigation systems
Distance Measuring Equipment, **4** 642
Instrument panels, 7 1172-80
Airplane, **1** (diagram) 85, 91
Cockpit, **3** 485
Link trainer, **8** 1361, (picture) 1361
Instrument procedure chart
Instrument Flight Rules, **7** 1164
Launch vehicles, **7** 1325
Insulators
Electricity, **4** 683
Electronics, **4** 694
Insurance, aviation, 7 1178-80
International Air Transport Association,
7 1189
Intake scoops
Jet engines, **7** 1238
Intake stroke
Aircraft propulsion systems, **1** 53
Integrated circuit
Circuit, **3** 461
Electronics, **4** 703
Miniaturization, **9** 1608 (with picture)
Solid-state physics, **11** 2073
Integrated instrument training
Pilot training, **10** 1810
Integrated vehicle checkout
Kennedy Space Center, **7** 1269
Integrity, 7 1180
Intelligence, military, 7 1180-81
Reconnaissance aircraft, **11** 1920-21
INTELSAT, 7 1201-05
Communications satellites, **3** 532, 538, 539
Intelsat II and III (with diagram)
International Telecommunications
Satellite Consortium, **7** 1202
Italy's aerospace activities, **7** 1222
Military space program (picture), **9** 1590
Intensity-modulated display
Radar, **10** 1875
Inter-Agency Cartographic Committee
Charts, 450
Inter-American Observatory
Telescopes and astronomical instruments,
12 2253
Interceptor aircraft, 7 1182
Air Defense Command, **1** 59
Air defense systems, **1** 60
Air forces of the world, **1** 64
Intercom, 7 1182
Intercontinental ballistic missiles, 7 1182-83
Air forces of the world, **1** 66
Antiballistic missile defense, **1** 158
Atlas missile and launch vehicle, **2** 259
Bumper Project, **3** 389
Drone aircraft, **4** 652
Fighter aircraft, **5** 808
Guidance and control systems, **6** 1041
Heat shields, **6** 1056, 1057
Inertial guidance, **7** 1152, 1154
Launch facilities, **7** 1307
Infrared detection devices, **7** 1159
Military aviation, **9** 1587
Missiles, **9** 1611-12, 1616, (data table) 1616
NORAD, **9** 1701
Orbits and trajectories, **10** 1746
Pioneer, **10** 1812
Polaris missiles, **10** 1832
Program management, **10** 1857-59
Propellants, **10** 1860
Radar, **10** 1874, 1876-77
Reconnaissance satellites, **11** 1925
Rockets and rocketry, **11** 1983-84
Schriever, Bernard A., **11** 2016
Silos, **11** 2052

Strategic Air Command, **12** 2167
Surface-to-surface missiles, **12** 2204
Titan rockets, **12** 2289
United States Air Force, **13** 2366
Interconversion of energy
Energy, **4** 714
Interface material
Materials (diagram), **8** 1501
Interference
Light, **8** 1352
Interference patterns
Lasers, **7** 1306
Interferometers
Astronomy, **2** 240
Ground antennas, **6** 1017
Radio astronomy, **10** 1893
Tracking systems and networks, **13** 2301
Intergalactic space, 7 1184
Intergranular corrosion
Materials, **8** 1512
Interior ballistics
Ballistics, **2** 314
Interiors of aircraft, 7 1184-87
Interline agreements
Commuter airlines, **3** 544
International Air Transport Association, **7** 1189
Intermediate range ballistic missiles, 7 1187
Air forces of the world, **1** 66
Explorer satellites, **5** 765
Jupiter rockets, **7** 1261
Missiles, **9** 1611-12, (data table) 1616
Surface-to-surface missiles, **12** 2205, 2206
Thor rockets, **12** 2283
Internal air pressure
Pressurization, **10** 1851
Internal combustion engines, 7 1187
Aircraft propulsion systems, **1** 53
Lanchester, Frederick William, **7** 1298
Reciprocating engines, **11** 1913
Temperature control, **12** 2267
Internal energy
Energy, **4** 714
Internal explosion engine
Cayley, Sir George, **3** 425
Internal supercharger
Power management, **10** 1842
International Affairs Bureau
Civil Aeronautics Board, **3** 465
International Agricultural Aviation Centre, 7 1187-88
Agricultural aviation, **1** 41
Crop dusting, **4** 593
International aircraft
Reconnaissance aircraft (data table), **11** 1923
International airmail, 7 1188
International airports
Mainland China's aerospace activities, **8** 1426
International airspace
Airspace, **1** 116
International Air Transport Agreement
Five Freedoms, **5** 826
International Air Transport Association, 7 1188-89
Commercial airlines, **3** 497, 513
International Astronautical Federation
Durant, Frederick Clark, III, **4** 655
International Astronomical Union
Constellations, **3** 561
International aviation and space agreements, 7 1189-90
Five Freedoms, **5** 826
Space law, **12** 2119
International Ballooning Committee
Medals and decorations, **8** 1526
International Civil Aviation Organization, 7 1190-91
Aircraft, **1** 45
Aviation medicine, **2** 295
Commercial airlines, **3** 513
Crash investigation, **4** 579, 583

Educational implications of aerospace, **4** 678
European air traffic control, **4** 752
Federation Aeronautique Internationale, **5** 804
Government in aerospace, **6** 1009
History of aviation, **6** 1114
Lighting facilities, **8** 1353-54
United Nations, **13** 2357
International communication
Communications satellites, **3** 531
Implications of aerospace, **7** 1151
International cooperation
International aviation and space agreements, **7** 1189
Sounding rockets, **11** 2080
International Council of Scientific Unions, 7 1193
International Geophysical Year, **7** 1195
International flight agreements
International aviation and space agreements, **7** 1189
International Flying Farmers, 7 1193
International Geophysical Year, 7 1193-1201
Berkner, Lloyd Viel, **2** 351
Explorer satellites, **5** 762
Jet Propulsion Laboratory, **7** 1240
Military space program, **9** 1592
Orbits and trajectories, **10** 1746
Polar flights, **10** 1830
NASA, **9** 1650
Weather satellites, **13** 2459
International Ice Patrol
Coast Guard aviation, **3** 479
International law
Implications of aerospace, **7** 1150
International aviation and space agreements, **7** 1189
International League of Aviators
Cochran, Jacqueline, **3** 481
International Phonetic Alphabet
Phonetic alphabet, **10** 1778
International projects, 7 1197
International relations
Implications of aerospace, **7** 1150
International Satellite for Ionospheric Studies, 7 1201
Alouette satellites, **1** 144
Explorer satellites, **5** 772
International Telecommunications Satellite Consortium, see INTELSAT
International Years of the Quiet Sun (with data table), 7 1204
Interplanetary communications systems
Lasers, **7** 1304
Interplanetary Explorer (satellite)
Explorer satellites, **5** 769
Interplanetary Flight (book)
Clarke, Arthur Charles, **3** 467
Interplanetary Monitoring Platform satellites, 7 1205
Explorer satellites, **5** 773
International Year of the Quiet Sun, **7** 1204
Interplanetary probes
Pioneer, **10** 1813
Interplanetary space, 7 1206
Matter, **8** 1513
Interplanetary spacecraft trajectories
Kepler's laws, **7** 1275
Orbits and trajectories, **10** 1746
Interplanetary space ship
Interplanetary travel, **7** 1213 (with diagram)
Interplanetary study
Earth science, **4** 666
Interplanetary travel, 7 1207-13
Orbits and trajectories, **10** 1747
Technological projections, **12** 2240
Inter-Range Instrumentation Group
Telemetry, **12** 2242
Interrogation, Recording and Location System, see IRLS technique

Interrupter gear
World War I, **14** 2505
Interstate Commerce Commission
Civil Aeronautics Board, **3** 462, 465
Interstellar dust, see Interstellar matter
Interstellar journeys
Interplanetary travel, **7** 1207
Interstellar matter, 7 1214
Astrophysics, **2** 258
Cosmic dust, **3** 568
Observatories, **10** 1726
Radiation, **10** 1882
Interstellar messages
Ozma project, **10** 1753
In trajectory
Pioneer, **10** 1813
Intrastate carriers
Charter flying, **3** 449
Intrepid
Balloons (picture), **2** 323
Intrinsically variable stars
Astrophysics, **2** 257
Intruder, see A-6 Intruder
Inverse Mercator projection
Maps and mapping (table), **8** 1479
Investigator-in-charge
Crash investigation, **4** 581-82
Invisible light
Light, **8** 1350
Io
Astronomy, **2** 245
Jupiter, **7** 1261
Ion, 7 1215
Ion engine
Careers (picture), **3** 415
Electric propulsion (picture), **4** 686
Ion, **7** 1215
Ionization
Electric propulsion, **4** 686
Stars, **12** 2160
Ionization chamber
Data acquisition and processing, **4** 609
Ionization chamber/particle flux detector
Mariner probes, **8** 1488
Ionization radiation levels
Kosmos satellites, **7** 1293
Ionized atom
Quantum theory, **10** 1870
Ionized gas
Plasma, **10** 1822
Ionized nitrogen
Aurora, **2** 277
Ionized plasma
Re-entry vehicles, **11** 1932
Ionosphere, 7 1215
Alouette satellites, **1** 144
Ariel satellites, **1** 192
Atmosphere, **2** 264
Explorer satellites, **5** 767, 770, 772
International Geophysical Year, **7** 1197
Kosmos satellites, **7** 1290, 1294
Mariner probes, **8** 1489
Military space program, **9** 1595
Orbiting observatories, **10** 1741
Radar, **10** 1873-74
Radio, **10** 1885
Space communications, **11** 2098
Sputniks, **12** 2153
Venus, **13** 2406
Ionospheric sounding stations
Berkner, Lloyd Viel, **2** 350
Ion propulsion (with picture and diagram), 7 1215
Ion propulsion facility
Careers (picture), **3** 415
Ions
Plasma, **10** 1823
Iran
Crop dusting, **4** 587
Iraq
Crop dusting, **4** 587

IRBM, see Intermediate range ballistic missile
Irby, Lo Ella
    Cunningham, R. Walter, **4** 600
Ireland
    Communications satellites, **3** 538
    European aerospace activities, **4** 751
    European air traffic control, **4** 752
IRFNA, see Inhibited red fuming nitric acid
IRLS technique
    Oceanographic research, **10** 1732
Iron, 7 1216
    Materials, **8** 1508
    Steels, **12** 2164
Iron bomb
    Bombs, **3** 378
Iron Cross
    World War I, **14** 2505
Iron meteorites
    Meteors, meteorites, and meteoroids, **9** 1561
Iroquois helicopter, see UH-1 Iroquois
Irregular galaxies
    Astronomy, **2** 253
Irvin, Leslie
    Parachutes, **10** 1758
Irvine, C. S.
    Distance and distance records, **4** 640
Irwin, James Benson (1930-   ), **7** 1216
    Astronauts, **2** 217, 218, 219 (with picture)
Islander (Britten-Norman)
    United Kingdom aerospace activities,
    13 2352
ISIS-X, see International Satellite for
    Ionospheric Studies
I-16 turbojet engine
    Aircraft propulsion systems, **1** 58
Island carrier
    Aircraft carriers, **1** 48
Isobar, 7 1216
    Anticyclone, **1** 159
    Aviation weather, **2** 299
Isochronal maintenance
    Preventive maintenance, **10** 1852
Isogonic lines, 7 1216-17
    Compasses, **3** 547
    Poles, **10** 1834
Isolation, 7 1217
    Psychological factors of flight, **10** 1864
Isolation chamber
    Cosmonauts, **4** 572
Isotopes
    Elements, **4** 704
    Radioisotope, **10** 1899
Israel
    Air forces of the world, **1** 64
    Communications satellites, **3** 538
Israeli-Arab Conflict—1967, 7 1217-18
Italia (airship)
    Amundsen, Roald, **1** 151
    Nobile, Umberto, **9** 1699
Italy's aerospace activities, 7 1219-25
    Air forces of the world, **1** 64-65
    Air raid, **1** 104
    Air-to-air missiles, **1** 120
    Bomber aircraft, **2** 374
    Commemorative stamps and medals,
    3 493, 494
    Crop dusting, **4** 587
    European Launcher Development
    Organization, **4** 754
    European Space Research Organization,
    4 755
    International Agricultural Aviation Centre,
    7 1187
    International projects, **7** 1198-99
    Launch vehicles, **7** 1327
    NATO, **9** 1703-04
    Naval aviation, worldwide, **9** 1670-71
    Second World War aircraft, **11** 2031
    World War II, **14** 2516-17
Ivans, William, Jr.
    Medals and decorations (table), **8** 1526

J

J.1, see Junkers J.1
J-2 engine
    Metals and metallurgy (picture), **9** 1550
    Space propulsion systems, **12** 2124
J-3 Cub, see Piper Cub
J-4, see Junkers J-4
J.10, see Junkers J.10
J-32, 35A, 37
    Air forces of the world (Sweden), **1** 65-65
J79 GE
    Jet engines, **7** 1239
J85 turbojet
    Aircraft propulsion systems (picture), **1** 58
J-1800 rubber balloons
    Meteorology (picture), **9** 1556
Jabara, James (1923-1966, American
    jet ace), **7** 1126
    United States Air Force, **13** 2366
Jackson, Barbara Ward
    Political implications of aerospace, **10** 1837
Jacquet, F.
    World War I (table, Top Aces), **14** 2507
Jagdstaffels
    World War I, **14** 2506, 2508
Jaguar (aircraft) (SUD-BAC)
    International projects (picture), **7** 1200
James Gordon Bennett Cup
    Curtiss, Glenn Hammond, **4** 600
    International competitions, **7** 1191
Jamming
    Electronic countermeasures, **4** 691
    Radar, **10** 1879
    Reconnaissance aircraft, **11** 1922
Janik, Francizen
    Medals and decorations (table), **8** 1526
Jansky, Karl Guthe (1905-1950, American
    founder of radio astronomy), **7** 1126
    Astronomy, **2** 242
    Observatories, **10** 1726
    Radiation, **10** 1882
    Radio astronomy, **10** 1889
Janssen, Pierre
    Astrophysics, **2** 255
Janssen Medal
    Lowell, Percival, **8** 1374
Japan's aerospace activities, 7 1227-31
    Aircraft carriers, **1** 48-51
    Aircraft propulsion systems, **1** 59
    Air raid, **1** 104
    Air-to-air missiles, **1** 120
    Asia's aviation, **2** 203
    Communications satellites, **3** 538
    Crop dusting, **4** 587, 593
    International Agricultural Aviation
    Centre, **7** 1187
    International projects, **7** 1199
    Jet streams, **7** 1241
    Launch vehicles, **7** 1326
    Naval aviation, worldwide, **9** 1671
    Pearl Harbor, **10** 1769-70
    Rockets and rocketry, **11** 1982
    Science Council
        Japan's aerospace activities, **7** 1231
    Second World War aircraft, **11** 2033-34
    Space Program
        Japan's aerospace activities, **7** 1230
    World War II, **14** 2512, 2520-23
Japan Air Lines
    Asia's aviation, **2** 204
    Commercial airlines, **3** 506
    Japan's aerospace activities, **7** 1127
Japanese Naval Air Force
    Kamikaze, **7** 1262
    Naval aviation, worldwide, **9** 1671

Japanese naval code
    World War II, **14** 2522
Jasta
    Fighter aircraft, **5** 811
JATO, see Jet-assisted takeoff
Jean, James
    Extraterrestrial life, **5** 782
Jeffries, Dr. John J.
    Airmail, **1** 69
    Aviation medicine, **2** 293
    Balloons, **2** 318
    Blanchard, Jean Pierre, **2** 363
Jenny, see Curtiss JN-4D Jenny
Jet aerobatic team
    Olds, Robert, **10** 1735
Jet aircraft (with pictures and data table),
    7 1232-36
    Ace, **1** 4
    Aerospace industry, **1** 29, 31
    Aircraft carriers, **1** 50-51
    Aircraft propulsion systems, **1** 57
    Airports, **1** 99
    Air traffic control, **1** 136
    Air transports, **1** 139
    Aviation weather, **2** 305
    Catapult, **3** 424
    Commercial air transports, **3** 524
        DeHavilland Comet I, **4** 617
    High-altitude flight training, **6** 1085
    High-performance aircraft, **6** 1088
    History of aviation, **6** 1114
    Manufacturing, **8** 1470
    Marine Corps Aviation, **8** 1482-83,
        (pictures) 1483
    Military aviation, **9** 1585-87 (with pictures)
    noise level
        Acoustics, **1** 4-5
    Penetration, **10** 1774
    Second World War aircraft, **11** 2037
    World War II, **14** 2519-20
    United States Air Force, **13** 2365
Jet aircraft propulsion
    Aeolipile, **1** 7
Jet-assisted takeoff, 7 1236
    American Rocket Society, **1** 151
    Jet aircraft, **7** 1236
    Polar flights, **10** 1830
    Rocket propulsion systems, **11** 1966
    Rockets and rocketry, **11** 1982
    Rocket sled, **11** 1986
Jetavators
    Polaris missiles, **10** 1832
Jet bomber
    Aerospace industry, **1** 31
    simulator
        Link, Edwin A., **8** 1361
Jet engines (with pictures and data chart),
    7 1237-39
    Aircraft propulsion systems, **1** 57, 58, 59
    Axial flow, **2** 308
    Combustion chamber, **3** 489
    Engines, **4** 717
    exhaust
        Afterburner, **1** 38
    Nozzles, **9** 1707
    Oceanographic research, **10** 1731
    Patents, **10** 1766
    Pod, **10** 1828
    Power management, **10** 1842
    Reaction engines, **10** 1912
    sound suppressors
        Boeing 2 707, 370
    Temperature control, **12** 2268
    United Kingdom aerospace activities,
    13 2347
Jet helicopter
    Police and fire services, **10** 1835
Jet Instrument Trainer, see C-11 Jet
    Instrument Trainer
Jetliners
    Airliners, **1** 67
    Boeing 2 707, 370
    Instrument panels, **7** 1176

Jet Navigation Chart
  Charts (picture), **3** 452
Jetports
  Airports, **1** 95
Jet propulsion, 7 1240
  Jet aircraft, **7** 1234
  Ramjet engines, **10** 1900
  Rocket propulsion systems, **11** 1966
Jet Propulsion Laboratory, 7 1240
  Bumper Project, **3** 390
  Data acquisition and processing, **4** 609
  Deep Space Network, **4** 615
  Dunn, Louis G., **4** 655
  Explorer satellites, **5** 763
  Mariner probes, **8** 1485
  NASA, **9** 1650, 1655
  Parks, Robert Joseph, **10** 1763
  Program management, **10** 1857
  Ranger, **10** 1905
  Sagan, Carl, **11** 2002
  Surveyor, **12** 2210, 2212
  Tracking systems and networks, **13** 2305
JetRanger helicopter, see Bell JetRanger
Jet reaction control system
  X-series aerospace vehicles, **14** 2541
Jet Route System
  Air traffic control, **1** 129
  Federal airways system, **5** 792
Jet shoes
  Maneuvering in space, **8** 1430, (picture)
  1431
JetStar, see Lockheed JetStar
Jetstream, see Handley Page Jetstream
Jet streams (with weather map), **7** 1241-42
  Acoustics, **1** 5
  Drift, **4** 652
  Weather maps and charts, **13** 2458
Jet syndrome
  Aviation medicine, **2** 292-97
  Circadian rhythm, **3** 461
Jettison, 7 1242
Jet trainer simulator
  Link, Edwin A., **8** 1361
Jet-vectored thrust principle
  X-series aerospace vehicles, **14** 2542
Jet-ways, enclosed
  Passenger services, **10** 1764
Jindivik (drone)
  Woomera rocket range, **14** 2497
JN-4D, see Curtiss JN-4D Jenny
Jodel D-9 (airplane)
  Homebuilt aircraft, **6** 1125, (picture) 1125
Jodrell Bank Observatory
  Communications satellites, **3** 533
John F. Kennedy International Airport
  Airports, **1** 99
  Flight, (picture) **5** 830
  Helicopters, **6** 1071
  Jumbo jets, **7** 1257
John F. Kennedy Space Center, see Kennedy
  Space Center
John J. Montgomery Award
  Armstrong, Neil A., **2** 193
Johnson, Amy (1903-1941, British pioneer
  aviatrix) **9** 1631
  Women in aerospace, **14** 2494
Johnson, Clarence Leonard, (1910-   ,
  American aircraft designer), **7** 1242
Johnson, Howard C.
  Altitude and altitude records, **1** 147
Johnson, James E.
  Ace, **1** 4
  World War II (table), **14** 2517
Johnson, K. Richard
  Medals and decorations (table), **8** 1526
Johnson, Major Richard L.
  Speed and speed records (table), **12** 2141
Johnson, Robert
  World War II (table), **14** 2517
Johnson, Roy W.
  Mercury program, **9** 1530
Johnston, Tex
  X-series aerospace vehicles, **14** 2535

Johnstone, Ralph
  Altitude and altitude records, **1** 147
Joining
  Production techniques, **10** 1856
Joint Chiefs of Staff, 7 1242
  Department of Defense, **4** 627
Joint ownership groups
  Australia's aviation, **2** 283
Joint Strategic Planning Staff
  Strategic Air Command, **12** 2168
Jolly Green Giant (helicopter), see HH-3
Jones, Katherine
  Overmyer, Robert F., **10** 1751
Jordan Airlines
  Mountain, desert, and jungle flying, **9** 1642
Jordan, Joe B.
  Altitude and altitude records, **1** 147, 148
Joule
  Energy, **4** 712
  Mechanical energy, **8** 1521
**Journal for the Institute of the Aeronautical
  Sciences**
  Dryden, Hugh Latimer, **4** 654
**Journal of the American Aviation Historical
  Society**
  American Aviation Historical Society, **1** 150
Journal of the Astronautical Sciences
  American Astronautical Society, **1** 149
Joy stick
  Control stick, **3** 563
  Kamikaze, **7** 1264
JP-4
  Fuels, **5** 901
JRM Mars, see Martin JRM Mars
JT3D-3 jet engines
  Jet engines, **7** 1239
Judicial process
  Implications of aerospace, **7** 1150
Jugoslovenski Aerotransport
  European aerospace activities, **4** 751
Jullien, Pierre
  Dirigibles, **4** 629
Julliot, Henri
  Lebaudy, Paul, **7** 1330
Jumbo jets (with maps, charts, diagrams
  and pictures), **7** 1243-58
  Airbus, **1** 44
  Airliner, **1** 67
  Air traffic control (picture), **1** 136
  Aviation medicine, **2** 297
  Commercial airlines, **3** 515
  Commercial air transports, **3** 530
  Jet aircraft, **7** 1236
  Preventive maintenance, **10** 1852
June Bug (airplane)
  Aerial Experiment Association (with
  picture), **1** 8
  Bell, Alexander Graham, **2** 347
  Curtiss, Glenn Hammond, **4** 600
Jungle Survival School
  Astronauts, **2** 227
  Mountain, desert, and jungle flying,
  9 1642-43
Junkers aircraft
  Airmail, **1** 71
  First World War aircraft, **5** 818, 824,
  (picture) 825
Junkers, Hugo, (1859-1935, German airplane
  designer and manufacturer), **7** 1258
  History of aviation, **6** 1107
  Manufacturing, **8** 1468
  Reciprocating engines, **11** 1918
Junkers J.1
  World War I, **14** 2510
Junkers J-4, 7 1258
Junkers J.10
  History of aviation (picture), **6** 1105
Junkers JU-87 Stuka
  Bomber aircraft, **2** 373
  Second World War aircraft (picture), **11** 2028
  World War II, **14** 2512, (picture) 2513, 2514
Junkers Ju bombers
  History of aviation (picture), **6** 1112
  Luftwaffe, **8** 1377

Second World War aircraft, 11 2033
Junkers Luftverkehr
  Commercial airlines, **3** 505
Juno
  Asteroid, **2** 208
  Astronomy, **2** 245
Juno rockets, 7 1259-1260
  Juno I
    Explorer satellites, **5** 761, 763
  Juno II, **7** 1259, 1260
    Launch vehicles, **7** 1325-26
  Juno V, **7** 1260
Jupiter (ship)
  Aircraft carriers, **1** 48
Jupiter (balloon)
  Airmail, **1** 69
Jupiter (planet), **7** 1260-61
  Astronomy, **2** 235, 237, 241, 252, 245
  Atmosphere, **2** 265
  Bessel, Friedrich Wilhelm, **2** 354
  Earth, **4** 663
  Extraterrestrial life, **5** 777
  Interplanetary travel, **7** 1208, 1209
  Launch vehicles, **7** 1314, 1329
  Legal implications of aerospace, **7** 1331
  Planets, **10** 1820
  Radar, **10** 1878
  Retrograde motion, **11** 1961
Jupiter rockets (with picture), **7** 1261
  Explorer satellites, **5** 763
  Intermediate range ballistic missiles, **7** 1187
  Juno rockets, **7** 1259
  Launch vehicles, **7** 1325
  Missiles, **9** 1611
  Re-entry vehicles, **11** 1931
Jurisdiction
  International aviation and space
  agreements, **7** 1190
Jutland, Battle of
  Aircraft carriers, **1** 50
Juutilainen, Eino
  World War II (table), **14** 2517

K

KA-3B Skywarriors
  United States Naval aviation, **13** 2387
Kaga
  Aircraft carriers, **1** 49
Kahn, Roger Wolfe
  Medals and decorations (table), **8** 1526
Kai-Feng-Fu, Battle of
  Aviation, **2** 290
Kai Kawus
  Mythology, **9** 1646, (picture) 1645
Kain, Edgar
  World War II (table), **14** 517
Kaiser, Albert R.
  Biosatellites, **2** 358
Kakol, Stanley J.
  X-series aerospace vehicles, **14** 2544
Kaman helicopters
  Aircraft carriers, **1** 47
  Crop dusting, **4** 588
  Helicopters, **6** 1066, (picture) 1066,
    (table) 1068
  Rescue and Recovery Service, **11** 1959
Kamikaze (with pictures and diagram),
  7 1262-64
  Air-to-surface missiles, **1** 123
  Marine Corps Aviation, **8** 1482
  World War II, **14** 2523

Kaminsky, Beverly M.
Michel, F. Curtis, **9** 1562
Kamov
Autogiros, **2** 285
Kamov Ka-20
U.S.S.R. aerospace activities (table), **13** 2337
Kamov KA-25
Helicopters (picture), **6** 1077
Kangaroo
Air-to-surface missiles, **1** 123
Kant, Emmanuel
Extraterrestrial life, **5** 782
Kaolinite
Ceramics, **3** 439
Kaplan, L.
Astronomy, **2** 242
Karel Doorman (aircraft carrier)
Naval aviation, worldwide (Netherlands), **9** 1670, (picture) 1671
Karman vortex trail theory
Von Karman, Theodore, **13** 2431
Kaulen, H.
Balloons, **2** 322
Kawasaki Aircraft Co.
Asia's aviation, **2** 204
Japan's aerospace activities, **7** 1231
Kawasaki GK-210
Naval aviation, worldwide, **9** 1671
Kawasaki Ki-45
World War II (picture), **14** 2519
Kayaba Corporation
Autogiros, **2** 286
Kazakov, Alexander
World War I, **14** 2501, (table) 2507, 2508
KB-50, see B-50
K-band radar
Jumbo jets, **7** 1255
KC-97, see C-97
KC-130F, see C-130 Hercules
KC-135 Stratotanker (Boeing)
Boeing 707, **2** 372
Military aircraft (picture), **9** 1566
Refueling (picture), **11** 1941
Kellet, R.
Distance records, **4** 640
Kelly, Clyde
Airmail, **1** 75
Kelly, Lt. Oakley (1891-1966, American army aviator), **8** 1417-18
Distance records, **4** 640
United States Air Force, **13** 2362
Kelvin, Lord
Computers, **3** 558
Kelvin scale
Temperature scales, **12** 2271
Kennedy International Airport
Airports (picture), **1** 93
Kennedy Space Center (with pictures and diagrams), **7** 1265-73
Apollo, **1** 178
Blockhouse, **2** 368
Launch Complex 39
Blockhouse, **2** 367, 368, 369
Launch facilities, **7** 1307
Launching, **7** 1308-09
Launch window, **7** 1329
NASA, **9** 1650, 1655
Outsize cargo aircraft, **10** 1749
Pioneer, **10** 1812
Range safety, **10** 1911
Recovery, **11** 1929
Saturn rockets, **11** 2011
Testing, **12** 2275
Kennel
Air-to-surface missiles, **1** 124
Keoeeit
Aurora, **2** 277
Kepler, Johannes, (1571-1630, German astronomer), **7** 1274
Astronomy, **2** 237, 242
Brahe, Tycho, **3** 385
Celestial mechanics, **3** 427
Earth science, **4** 665
Telescopes and astronomical instruments, **12** 2245

Kepler's laws (with chart), **7** 1274-75
Bessel, Friedrich Wilhelm, **2** 354
Orbits and trajectories, **10** 1742
Kerosene, 7 1276
Fuels, **5** 901
Launch vehicles, **7** 1315
Liquid-fuel rockets, **8** 1363
Power units, auxiliary, **10** 1843
Saturn rockets, **11** 2011
Kerwin, Joseph P. (1932-), **7** 1276
Astronaut, **2** 216, 218, 219, 222, 227 (with picture)
KE-28 reconnaissance camera
Photography (picture), **10** 1786
Keying
Metals and metallurgy, **9** 1553
Kick stage burn
Launch vehicles, **7** 1318
Kill Devil Hill
History of aviation, **6** 1099, 1100
Kiln
Ceramics, **3** 439
Kilocycle, 7 1276
Kilohertz, 7 1276
Kimball Cup
Trophies and awards (table), **13** 2312
Kincheloe, Iven C.
Altitude and altitude records, **1** 148
X-series aerospace vehicles, **14** 2537
Kindley, Field
World War I (table, Top Aces), **14** 2507
Kindling, Paul
Balloons, **2** 324
Kinesthetic sense, 7 1276-77
Kinetic energy, 7 1277
Brakes, **3** 385
Energy, **4** 712
Landing gear, **7** 1298
Mechanical energy, **8** 1520, (diagrams) 1520, 1521
Orbits and trajectories, **10** 1743
Potential energy, **10** 1840
Radiation, **10** 1881
King, Jacquelyn K.
Taylor, James M., **12** 2235
King, Miles
Cloud seeding, **3** 474
King, S. A.
Balloons, **2** 318
King's Cup
Trophies and awards (table), **13** 2312
Kingsford-Smith, Charles (1897-1935, Australian pilot), **7** 1277
Commemorative stamps and medals, **3** 495
Kipfer, H.
Medals and decorations (table), **8** 1526
Kipfer, Paul
Balloons, **2** 326
Piccard family, **10** 1790
Kipling, Rudyard
Aviation, **2** 292
Kirchoff, Gustav
Astrophysics, **2** 255
Kiss, Josef
World War I (table, Top Aces), **14** 2507
Kites, 7 1277-80
Aerial Experiment Association, **1** 7-8
Aircraft, **1** 45
Bell, Alexander Graham, **2** 347
Hargrave, Lawrence, **6** 1050
History of aviation, **6** 1099
Photogrammetry, **10** 1779
Rockets and rocketry, **11** 1972
Santos-Dumont 14 bis, **11** 2006
Sport flying, **12** 2150
Kittinger, Joseph W., Jr.
Bailout (picture), **2** 311
Gondolas, **6** 995
Kitting inspection
Quality control, **10** 1867
Kitt Peak National Observatory
Telescopes and astronomical instruments, **12** 2253, (picture) 2254
Kitty Hawk
Aircraft carriers (data table), **1** 51

Kitty Hawk, see P-40
Kitty Hawk (airplane)
Homebuilt aircraft, **6** 1123
Wright Flyer, **14** 2527
Kitty Hawk, North Carolina, 7 1280-81
History of aviation, **6** 1099
Kiwi, 7 1281
Launch vehicles, **7** 1328
NERVA, **9** 1691
Rover project, **11** 1993-94
U.S. Atomic Energy Commission, **13** 2375
KLM Royal Dutch Airlines
Airmail, **1** 75
European aerospace activities, **4** 748
Klystron
Electronics, **4** 700
Radar, **10** 1874
Knight, James H. (1893-1945, American aviator), **7** 1281-82
Airmail, **1** 73, 75
Knight of the skies
Barnstormers, **2** 336
Knight, William J.
X-15 research program, **14** 2530, (picture) 2531, 2533
Knot, 7 1282
Mile, **9** 1565
Koch chart, 7 1282
Kokkinaki, Vladimir
Medals and decorations (table), **8** 1526
Kollsman, Paul
Instrument panels, **7** 1173
Komarov, Vladimir M. (1927-1967), **7** 1282
Cosmonauts, **4** (pictures) 570, 571, 572, (table) 574
Manned spaceflight (table), **8** 1461
Medals and decorations (table), **8** 1524
U.S.S.R. aerospace activities, **13** 2344
Voskhod, **13**, 2433
Komet, see Messerschmitt Me-163 Komet
Komet D
Air-to-surface missiles, **1** 123
Korea
Air raid, **1** 104
Sabre, North American F-86, **11** 2000
Korean Air Lines
Asia's aviation, **2** 205
Korean war, 7 1283-89
Ace, **1** 4
Air-to-surface missiles, **1** 123
Army aviation, **2** 195
Aviation medicine, **2** 296
Helicopters, **6** 1066
History of aviation, **6** 1118
Marine Corps Aviation, **8** 1482, (picture) 1481
Super Sabre, North American F-100, **12** 2176
United States Air Force, **13** 2365
Korolev, Sergei (1906- , Russian aircraft engineer, rocket designer), **7** 1290
Kosmos satellites, 7 1290
Reconnaissance satellites, **11** 1927
U.S.S.R. aerospace activities, **13** 2339
Kozhedub, Ivan
Ace, **1** 4
World War II (table), **14** 2517
Kraft, Christopher C., Jr. (1924- , Flight director, NASA), **7** 1294
Gemini, **5** 936, 937, 952
Launching, **7** 1310, (picture) 1311
Mercury program, **9** 1537
Krebs, A. C.
Airships, **1** 111
Dirigibles, **4** 631
Krower, Ernst
Medals and decorations (table), **8** 1526
Kruetz, Kathleen Ann
England, Dr. Anthony W., **4** 717
Krypton
Air, **1** 42
KS-87 reconnaissance camera
Photography (picture), **10** 1786

K-type blimp
Blimps (picture), 2 365
KU-band
Jumbo jets, 7 1255
Kuettner, Joachim P.
Medals and decorations (table), 8 1526
Kuiper, Gerard
Astronomy, 2 246 247
Mars, 8 1491

L

L-19 and L-20 aircraft
Army aviation, 2 197
L-29 Delphin (airplane)
U.S.S.R. aerospace activities (table),
13 2337
L-49
Zeppelins (picture), 14 2550
La-7
World War II, 14 2515
Labine, Gilbert
Bush flying, 3 392
Laboratory vehicle
Manned Orbiting Laboratory, 8 1454
Labor market areas, Careers (table), 3 414
LABS, see Low Altitude Bombing System
Labyrinth-seal machine
Ground-effect machines, 6 1023
Lacquers
Paints, 10 1754
Lady Hay-Drummond Trophy
Trophies and awards (table), 13 2312
Lafayette Escadrille, 7 1295
World War I, 14 2505, 2506
LaFrance
Dirigibles, 4 631
Lagg-3
World War II, 14 2515
Lagrange, Joseph Louis (1736-1813)
Astronomy, 2 238
Celestial mechanics, 3 428
Orbits and trajectories, 10 1742
Lahn Cup
Trophies and awards (table), 13 2312
Laika, 7 1295
Animals in space, 1 154
Commemorative stamps and medals,
3 495
Explorer satellites, 5 762
Sputniks, 12 2153
U.S.S.R. aerospace activities, 13 2338
Lairds
Air racing (picture), 1 103
Commercial air transports, 3 517
Lake (airplane)
General aviation aircraft, 6 961
Lake Hood, Alaska
Airports (picture), 1 94
Lally, V.
GHOST program, 6 979
Lambda sounding rocket
Japan's aerospace activities (picture),
7 1230
Lambert, Charles de
Altitude and altitude records, 1 147
Lambert, Heinrich
Maps and mapping, 8 1478
Lambert projection, 7 1296
Charts, 3 450
Maps and mapping, 8 1478, (table) 1479

Laminar flow (with diagram), 7 1296
X-series aerospace vehicles, 14 2544
Lamination, 7 1296-97
LaMountain, John
Airmail, 1 69
Lana, Francesco de (1631-1687, Italian
Jesuit monk; inventor), 7 1297
Lancaster bomber (Avro)
Second World War aircraft (picture), 11 2031
World War II (picture), 14 2514
Lance
Battlefield missile systems, 2 341
Surface-to-surface missile, 12 2207,
(picture) 2207, (table) 2208
Lanchester, Frederick William (1868-1946,
English scientist), 7 1298
History of aviation, 6 1109
Land cruisers
Lunar bases, 8 1391
Land distances, survey
Radar, 10 1879
Land erosion
Aerial photography, 1 11
Landing
Airfield, 1 61
Air traffic control, 1 129
automatic
Radio altimeter, 10 1888
Bird flight, 2 359
Boeing 707, 2 370
Instrument Flight Rules, 7 1165
Instrument flight techniques, 7 1168
Brakes, 3 387
emergency fields
Airmail, 1 74
Manned spaceflight, 8 1463
procedures
Airships, 1 110
Emergency landing procedures, 4 707
Radar, 10 1878
Snow, 11 2062
Landing engine
Lunar Module
Apollo, 1 173-74
Landing gear, 7 1298-1300
Airframe, 1 66
Airplane (diagram), 1 89
Airships, 1 109
Bicycle gear, 2 354
Cross wind landing, 4 595
Hydraulic systems, 6 1139
Jumbo jets, 7 (picture) 1247, 1253
Pontoons, 10 1837
position-indicator
Instrument panels, 7 1176
Wheels, 13 2480
Landing roll distances
Performance charts, 10 1774
Landing techniques, 7 1300-02
helicopters
Auto-rotation, 2 290
Landing Signal Officer
Aircraft carriers, 1 47
Landry, Jules
Distance records, 4 640
Langley
Aircraft carriers, 1 48-49
United States Naval Aviation, 13 2380,
(picture) 2379
Langley Aerodrome (airplane)
Aircraft propulsion systems (picture), 1 52
National Air and Space Museum (picture),
9 1659
Langley Aeronautical Laboratory
Mercury program, 9 1530
Langley Air Force Base
Air University, 1 140
Astronauts, 2 224
Langley, Edward L.
Airmail (picture), 1 70
Langley Medal
Trophies and awards (table), 13 2312
Langley Research Center, 7 1302
Lunar Orbiter, 8 1411
NASA, 9 1655

Spinoff, 12 2143
Langley, Samuel Pierpont (1834-1906,
American aviation pioneer), 7 1302
Aircraft propulsion systems, 1 54, 57
Gliders, 6 985
History of aviation, 6 1098, (table) 1119
Manly, Charles Matthews, 8 1452
Manufacturing, 8 1466
National Air and Space Museum, 9 1659
Wright brothers, 14 2524
Langmuir, Irving
Plasma, 10 1822
Lansche, Jane
Williams, Clifton C., Jr., 13 2485
Lansen
Air forces of the world (Sweden), 1 64-65
Lansen 32A
Attack aircraft (picture), 2 272
Lanphier, Thomas G., Jr.
Medals and decorations (table), 8 1526
Laos
Asia's aviation, 2 203-04
Laplace, Pierre (1749-1827)
Aerodynamics, 1 24
Astronomy, 2 238
Celestial mechanics, 3 428
Orbits and trajectories, 10 1742
La Pression Barometrique
(Lah PRESS ee OWN Bar o met TREEK)
Aviation medicine, 2 293
Lasers (with pictures and diagrams),
7 1303-06
beam
Crop dusting, 4 593
Data acquisition and processing, 4 610
Electronics, 4 693, 704
Extraterrestrial life, 5 784
Geodetic satellites, 6 975
Human engineering, 6 1135
Manned spaceflight, 8 1462
Masers, 8 1497
Modulation, 9 1630
Precision measurements, 10 1845
Radiation, 10 1883
Terminology of aerospace (table), 12 2272
Tolerances, 12 2295
Lason (airplane)
U.S.S.R. aerospace activities (table),
13 2337
Lassiter, O. F.
Distance records, 4 641
Last quarter
Moon, 9 1634 (with picture)
L'Astronautique (book)
Esnault-Pelterie, Robert, 4 739
Latches
Cargo aircraft, 3 421
Latecoere-521 (lah-tih COUR) (airplane)
France's aerospace activities (picture),
5 886
Lateral axis
Airplane, 1 87
Attitude and attitude control, 2 275
Axes of rotation, 2 308
Pitch, 10 1816
Lateral separation
Air traffic control, 1 127
Lateral stability
Aerodynamics, 1 24
Latham, Hubert (1883-1912, French-
English aviator), 7 1306
Altitude and altitude records, 1 146-47
Distance records, 4 640
Rheims Air Meet, 11 1963
Latin America
Air forces of the world, 1 64
Latin Cross
World War I, 14 2505
Latitude and longitude, 7 1306-07
Celestial navigation, 3 429
Earth, 4 663
Greenwich meridian, 6 1014
Maps and mapping, 8 1476
Poles, 10 1833

Latitude drive motor
Planetarium, 10 1820
Launch angle
Recovery, 11 1929
Launch azimuth
Launching, 7 1309
Launch complex, 7 1307
Kennedy Space Center, 7 1266, 1272
Apollo, 1 178
Lunar bases (picture), 8 1380
Launch Control Center
Blockhouse, 2 (picture) 366, 368
Kennedy Space Center, 7 1272-73
Launching, 7 1308-10, 1312 (with picture)
Manned Orbiting Laboratory, 8 1455
Launch direction
Rendezvous and docking, 11 1956
Launch equipment
Reconnaissance aircraft, 11 1924
Launch escape system
Apollo, 1 166, 174-75 (with picture)
Launch escape tower
Apollo, 1 180 (picture)
Kennedy Space Center, 7 1267
Launch facilities, 7 1307
Launching, 7 1308-12
Antisubmarine missiles, 1 160
Applications Technology Satellites, 2 190
space vehicles
Legal implications of aerospace, 7 1331
Launch modes
Kennedy Space Center, 7 1267
Launch Operations Center
NASA, 9 1650
Launch pad
Launch complex, 7 1307
Orbiting observatories, 10 1741
Launch shroud
Aerospace Research Support Program
(picture), 1 35
Launch umbilical tower
Launch complex, 7 1307
Launch vehicles, 7 1313-30
Atlas missile and launch vehicle, 2 260
NASA, 9 1653, (table, Major Launchings)
1652
Retrorocket, 11 1962
Rockets and rocketry, 11 1982
Titan III, 12 2291
Launch velocity
Orbits and trajectories, 10 1746
Launch window, 7 1329
Insertion tracking, 7 1162
Interplanetary travel, 7 1209-10 (with data
table)
Launching, 7 1309
Rendezvous and docking, 11 1956
Laurence, E. O.
Radiation, 10 1882
Laussedat, Aime (Lohss DAH Ay MAY)
Aerial photography, 1 9
Photogrammetry, 10 1779
Lavatories
Interiors of aircraft, 7 1186
Lawrence, Mary Catherine
Engle, Joe Henry, 4 718
Lawrence Radiation Laboratory
Nuclear energy, 9 1711
Lawrence, Robert H., Jr. (1935-1967,
Aerospace research pilot), 7 1329
Lawrence Sperry Award
Engle, Joe Henry, 4 718
Johnson, Clarence Leonard, 7 1242
Trophies and awards (table), 13 2312
Law of conservation of energy
Mechanical energy, 8 1520
Law of conservation of matter
Matter, 8 1515
Law of inertia
Astronomy, 2 242
Law of universal gravitation
Earth, 4 662
Laws
Implications of aerospace, 7 1150

Laws of celestial mechanics
Celestial navigation, 3 430
Laws of motion
Astronomy, 2 238, 242
Celestial mechanics, 3 426
Laws of planetary motion
Celestial mechanics, 3 427
Newton's laws of motion, 9 1694
Lawyer, Richard E. (1932-   , Aerospace
research pilot), 7 1330
Manned Orbiting Laboratory, 8 1456
Lazy eight
Maneuvers, 8 1437, (diagram) 1439
LCC, see Launch Control Center
Lead
Radiation shield, 10 1884
Lead-acid battery
Battery, 2 339
Leading edge
Aerodynamics, 1 21
Airfoil, 1 61
Leading-edge flaps
Boeing 707, 2 370
Leading-edge slats
Jumbo jets, 7 1254
Leakproof seal
Reciprocating engines, 11 1916
Leaning mixtures
Mixture control, 9 1623
Power management, 10 1840
Lear Jet (airplane)
General aviation aircraft, 6 961, 967,
(picture) 968
High-altitude flight training (picture),
6 1085
Lebanon
Aircraft carriers, 1 51
Airlift, 1 67
Lebaudy (Ler boh DEE), dirigible
Lebaudy, Paul, 7 1330
Lebaudy, Paul, (1858-1937, French
industrialist, airship pioneer), 7 1330
Lebaudy, Pierre
Lebaudy, Paul, 7 1330
Lebouchere, Rene (Ler boo SHERE, Ray NAY)
Distance records, 4 640
LeBris, Jean-Marie (Ler BREE, Zhan-Ma REE)
History of aviation, 6 1095
Man-powered flight, 8 1464
Sailplanes, 11 2002
LeBrix (Ler BREE), **Joseph**
Distance and distance records, 4 641
Lecointe, Sadi (Ler KWANT, Sa DEE)
Altitude and altitude records, 1 147
Speed and speed records (table), 12 2141
Lefebvre (Ler FEV reh), **Eugene** (1878-1909,
French aviator), 7 1330
Wright brothers (picture), 14 2526
Le Flesseilles (Ler Fless AY)
Balloons (picture), 2 316
Legacy of Hiroshima, The (book)
Teller, Edward, 12 2265
Legagneaux (Ler ga NYOH), **George**
Altitude and altitude records, 1 147
Legal implications of aerospace, 7 1331
Legend
Maps and mapping, 8 1478
Lehmann, Ernst
World War I, 14 2509
Leibniz, Gottfried W.
Computers, 3 557
Lei Kung
Mythology, 9 1646
LeMay, Curtis Emerson, (1906-   , USAF
Chief of Staff), 7 1331
Astronaut wings, 2 232
Military aviation, 9 1585
United States Air Force, 13 2364
World War II, 14 2523
Lemoine, G.
Altitude and altitude records, 1 147

Lend-lease aircraft (Russia)
World War II, 14 2516
Length-to-diameter ratio
Sonic boom, 11 2075
Lenin
Commemorative stamps and medals, 3 494
Lenin Prize
Korolev, Sergei, 7 1290
Lenoir, Jean Joseph Etienne
Aircraft propulsion systems, 1 53-54
History of aviation (table), 6 1119
Lenoir, William B. (1939-   ), **7** 1332
Astronauts, 2 218, 219 (with picture)
Lens
Photography, 10 1782, 1783, 1785
Radar, 10 1876
Leo
Constellations, 3 562
Leonov, Alexei A. (1934-   ), **7** 1333
Belyayev, Pavel, 2 349
Cosmonauts, 4 569, 572, 574, (pictures)
570-71, 573, 575, (table) 574
Manned spaceflight (table), 8 1461
Medals and decorations (table), 8 1524
Ranger, 10 1909
U.S.S.R. aerospace activities, 13 2344
Voskhod, 13 2433
Leopard Air Ltd.
Africa's aviation, 1 36
Le Rhone engine
Aircraft propulsion systems, 1 55
Fokker, D-8, 5 867
World War I, 14 2502
LES, see Launch escape system
Lesser Megallanic Galaxies
Astronomy, 2 253
Letter Against Werner (treatise)
Copernicus, Nicolaus, 3 566
Leucippus (loo SIP us)
Atoms, 2 269
Levavasseur, Leon (Ler va vas SUR,
Lay OWN) (1863-1922, French
engineer), **7** 1333
Aircraft propulsion systems, 1 55
History of aviation, 6 1103, (table) 1119
Level-off, 7 1333
Level turns
Maneuvers, 8 1434
Leverrier, Urbain, J. J. (Ler very AY,
Oor BAN) (1811-1877; French
astronomer), **7** 1334
Astronomy, 2 242, 247
Celestial mechanics, 3 428
Neptune, 9 1690
LeVier, Tony
Air races, 1 103
Levine, C. A.
Distance records, 4 640
Lewis, Albert L.
Medals and decorations (table), 8 1526
Lewis, Lee
Balloons, 2 331
Lewis machine gun
World War I, 14 (picture), 2502, 2503, 2504
Lewis Research Center, 7 1334-35
Centaur, 3 433
Cryogenics, 4 597
NASA, 9 1657
Lexell's Comet
Comets, 3 491
Lexington
Aircraft carriers, 1 49
United States Naval Aviation, 13 2380, 2382
Ley, Willy (1906-   , German-American
author), **7** 1335
Peenemuende, 10 1770
Rockets and rocketry, 11 1979
LF
Low-frequency radio, 8 1374
Phonetic alphabet, 10 1778
Radio communications, 10 1894
LFC, see Lunar Flightcraft
LF/MF
Instrument panels, 7 1173

Liability
International Air Transport Association, **7** 1189
International aviation and space agreements, **7** 1190
Legal implications of aerospace, **7** 1331
Liability limitations
Insurance, aviation, **7** 1179
Libby, Frederick
World War I (table, Top Aces), **14** 2507
Liberator, see B-24 Liberator
Liberty Bell 7 (spacecraft)
Manned spaceflight (table), **8** 1461
Mercury program, **9** 1537, (table) 1544
NASA (table, Major Launchings), **9** 1652
Recovery, **11** 1928
Liberty engine
Aircraft propulsion systems, **1** 55, (picture) 53
First World War aircraft, **5** 819
World War I, **14** 2507
Libra
Constellations, **3** 562
Licensing of pilots
Balloons, **2** 319
Pilots and pilot certificates, **10** 1802
Lick Observatory
Telescopes and astronomical instruments, **12** 2253
Lidar gun
Crop dusting, **4** 593
Liechtenstein
Commemorative stamps and medals, **3** 493-94
European aerospace activities, **4** 751
Life raft, 7 1336
Life, search for
Interplanetary travel, **7** 1212
Life-support systems (with pictures and diagrams), **8** 1337-44
Cockpit, **3** 483
laboratory
Manned Spacecraft Center, **8** 1458
Manned Orbiting Laboratory, **8** 1452
Oxygen, **10** 1752
Photosynthesis, **10** 1790
Pressurization, **10** 1851
Radiators, **10** 1885
test facility
Kennedy Space Center, **7** 1267
Life-sustaining environment
Closed ecological system, **3** 469
Lift, 8 1344
Aerodynamics, **1** 20 (with diagram)
Bernoulli's principle, **2** 353
Bird flight, **2** 358, 360-61
Soaring (with sketch), **11** 2063
Stall, **12** 2158
Wings, **14** 2489-91
Lift-drag ratio, 8 1344
Lifting-body vehicles, **8** 1346-47
Piloting techniques, **10** 1802
Sailplanes, **11** 2002
Lift-fan aircraft
Helicopters, **6** 1069
Lifting-body vehicles (with pictures and diagrams), **8** 1345-50
Apollo Applications Program, **2** 187
Dyna-Soar program, **4** 657
Re-entry vehicles, **11** 1934
Lifting capacities
Kites, **7** 1278-80
Liftoff, 8 1350
Apollo (picture), **1** 179
Launching, **7** 1309, 1312
Terminology of aerospace (table), **12** 2272
Light (with diagram), **8** 1350-52
Atmosphere, **2** 266
Einstein, Albert, **4** 680
Magnitude, **8** 1420
Mechanical energy, **8** 1521
Photosynthesis, **10** 1789
Quantum theory, **10** 1868
Relativity theory, **11** 1951
Resolution, **11** 1961

Light aircraft, 8 1352
Light amplification
Lasers, **7** 1303
Light beam
Relativity theory, **11** 1952
Light conditions
Photography, **10** 1788
Light dot
Photogrammetry, **10** 1780
Lighted airways
Airmail, **1** 74
Light energy
Photosynthesis, **10** 1789-90
Lightening holes
Airships, **1** 106
Lighter-than-air craft, 8 1352-53
Helium, **6** 1080
Ornithopter, **10** 1748
Light gun, 8 1352
Emergency signals, **4** 709
Lighting facilities (with pictures and diagrams), **8** 1353-57
Light metals
Materials, **8** 1507
Lightning (with picture), **8** 1357
Plasma, **10** 1822
Lightning fighter (American), see P-38 Lightning
Lightning fighter (British), see P-11 Lightning
Lightning discharge
Jupiter, **7** 1260
Light photon
Solar cells (with diagram), **11** 2068
Light reflection
Light, **8** 1350
Radar, **10** 1872
Light refraction
Light, **8** 1350
Light-sensing pen
Information systems (picture), **7** 1157
Light-sensitive photo tubes
Sensors, **11** 2042
Light waves
Radar, **10** 1872
Radiation, **10** 1882
Light year, 8 1358
Astronomy, **2** 249
Quasar, **10** 1871
Lignin
Wood, **14** 2496
Lilienthal, Gustav
Ornithopter, **10** 1748
Lilienthal Medal
Medals and decorations, **8** 1524, (table) 1526
Lilienthal, Otto (1848-1896, German engineer and inventor), **8** 1358
Aviation medicine, **2** 293
Chanute, Octave, **3** 446
Gliders, **6** 985
History of aviation, **6** 1098, (table) 1119
Manufacturing, **8** 1466
Objects of art, **10** 1723
Ornithopter, **10** 1748
Pilcher, Percy Sinclair, **10** 1792
Sailplanes, **11** 2002
Wright brothers, **14** 2524
Lilienthal Ring
Fedden, Sir Roy, **5** 792
Limitations
Photography, **10** 1783
Radar, **10** 1879
Limiting airspeed, 8 1358
Lindbergh, Charles Augustus (1902- , American aviator), **8** 1359-60
Aerospace industry, **1** 30
Airmail, **1** 75
Barnstormers, **2** 336
Commemorative stamps and medals, **3** 495
Distance and distance records, **4** 640
History of aviation, **6** 1109, (picture) 1107
Instrument panels, **7** 1173
Medals and decorations (table), **8** 1526
Objects of art, **10** 1723
Parachutes, **10** 1758

Paris Air Shows, **10** 1762
Radio communications, **10** 1895
Ryan, T. Claude, **11** 1999
Spirit of St. Louis, **12** 2144
United States Air Force, **13** 2362
Lind, Don Leslie (1930-), **8** 1358-59
Astronauts, **2** 217, 218, 219, 222 (with picture)
Linear acceleration
Acceleration, **1** 2
Linear translation
Transponders, **13** 2310
Line of sight (with diagram), **8** 1360
Air traffic control, **1** 128
Ballistic Missile Early Warning System, **2** 314
Communications satellites, **3** 532
Microwave communications, **9** 1563
Space communications, **11** 2097
Linnekogel, Gino
Altitude and altitude records, **1** 147
Lines-of-position
Celestial navigation, **3** 429
Ling-Temco-Vought, see LTV
Ling-Temco-Vought C-142
Military air transports, **9** 1578 (with table)
Linke-Crawford, Frank
World War I, **14** (table) 2507, 2508
Link, Edwin A. (1904- , American aeronautical inventor), **8** 1360-61
Link Flying School
Link, Edwin A., **8** 1360
Link Mark IV Visual System
Flight simulators, **5** 855
Link trainer (with pictures), **8** 1361-62
Flight simulators, **5** 852, 853
Lippershey, Hans
Telescopes and astronomical instruments, **12** 2245
Lippisch, A.
Rockets and rocketry, **11** 1978
Lipsner, Benjamin F.
Airmail (with picture), **1** 70
Liquefied gases
Cryogenic propellants, **4** 595
Liquid-column gauge
Pressure gauges, **10** 1849
Liquid-cooled engine
Temperature control, **12** 2267
Liquid-fuel rockets, 8 1362-63
Launch vehicles, **7** 1316
Missiles, **9** 1611, (data table) 1616
Oberth, Hermann, **10** 1721
Liquid hydrogen
Centaur, **3** 433
Launch vehicles, **7** 1315
Liquid-fuel rockets, **8** 1363
NERVA, **9** 1691
Liquid lasers
Lasers, **7** 1303
Liquid metals
Metals and metallurgy, **9** 1554-55
Liquid oxygen, 8 1363
Carbon dioxide, **3** 407
Delta rocket, **4** 622
Kennedy Space Center, **7** 1267
Launch vehicles, **7** 1315
Liquid-fuel rockets, **8** 1363
Oxidizers, **10** 1752
Oxygen, **10** 1752
Propellants, **10** 1860
Rocket propulsion systems, **11** 1969
Rockets and rocketry, **11** 1977
Saturn rockets, **11** 2011
Liquid-propellant engines
American Rocket Society, **1** 151
Liquid-propellant rocket
Aerobee, **1** 17
Liquid propellants, 8 1363
Propellants (with data chart), **10** 1861
Liquids
Heat exchangers, **6** 1055
Matter, **8** 1513
Liquid water
Spacecraft sterilization, **11** 2104

Lithium, 8 1363
Atoms, **2** 271
Lithosphere
Atmosphere, **2** 261
Little Fox
Astronomy, **2** 248
Little Joe (with picture), **8** 1364
Apollo, **1** 166
Mercury program, **9** 1533, 1535, (picture) 1533
Little John
Battlefield missile systems, **2** 341
Surface-to-surface missiles, **12** 2206, (picture) 2207
Living matter
Bioastronautics, **2** 355
Living quarters
Lunar exploration, **8** 1407
Llewellyn, John Anthony (1933-   ), **8** 1364-65
Astronauts, **2** 216, 218, 219 (with picture)
Lloyd Luftdienst
Commercial airlines, **3** 505
L/MF Radio Range
Air traffic control, **1** 128-29
Federal airways system, **5** 792
LM&SS, see Lunar-mapping and survey system
LMS, see Lunar Module Shelter
Load
Electricity, **4** 685
Load change
Piloting techniques, **10** 1801
Load factor
Preflight training, **10** 1849
Load tests
Wings, **14** 2491
Lobes
Instrument landing system, **7** 1170
Local airline serivce
Regional airlines (with map), **11** 1943
Local scientific survey module
Lunar exploration, **8** 1403, (drawing) 1403
Localizer beam
Automatic landing, **2** 287
Instrument flight techniques, **7** 1168
Instrument landing system, **7** 1170
Localizer receiver
Instrument landing system, **7** 1170
Lockheed AH-56A Cheyenne, see AH-56A Cheyenne
Lockheed C-5A, see C-5A Galaxy
Lockheed C-130, see C-130 Hercules
Lockheed C-141, see C-141 Starlifter
Lockheed CL-475, see CL-475
Lockheed Constellation (with picture), **8** 1365-66
Cargo aircraft, **3** 418-19
Commercial air transports (picture), **3** 523
Empennage, **4** 710
History of aviation, **6** 1115
L-1649 Starliner, **8** 1366
Military air transports (table), **9** 1578
Reconnaissance aircraft, **11** 1922
Lockheed Corporation
Commercial airlines, **3** 515
Commercial air transports, **3** 519, 523
General aviation aircraft, **6** 961, 967
Jumbo jet, **7** 1245, 1246
Lockheed Electra
Commercial air transports, **3** 519, (pictures) 520, 524, 525
Johnson, Clarence Leonard, **7** 1242
Lockheed F-80, see F-80 Shooting Star
Lockheed F-94, see F-94 Starfire
Lockheed F-104, see F-104 Starfighter
Lockheed helicopters
Helicopters, **6** 1067, 1076, (picture) 1069, (table) 1068
Lockheed Jetstar
General aviation aircraft (picture), **6** 968
Military air transports (picture), **9** 1576, (table) 1578

Lockheed L-500, see C-5A Galaxy
Lockheed L-2000 (supersonic transport)
Supersonic transports, **12** 2190, (picture) 2190
Lockheed Missiles and Space Company
Agena rockets, **1** 38-39
Lockheed Orion transport
Commercial air transports (picture), **3** 520
Poseidon missiles, **10** 1838
Lockheed P-38 Lightning, see P-38 Lightning
Lockheed P-80 Shooting Star, see F-80 Shooting Star
Lockheed SR-71, see SR-71 reconnaissance aircraft
Lockheed U-2, see U-2
Lockheed Vega
Commercial air transports, **3** 519
History of aviation, **6** 1108, (picture) 1108
Winnie Mae, Lockheed Vega, **14** 2493
Lockheed WV-2
Reconnaissance aircraft, **11** 1922
Lockheed X-7, see X-7
Lockheed X-17, see X-17
Locklear, Oman
Barnstormers (picture), **2** 334, 335, 336
Lockyer, Joseph Norman
Astrophysics, **2** 255
Lodge receiver
Radio (with diagram), **10** 1887
Loening, Grover Cleveland (1888-   , American aircraft designer, manufacturer), **8** 1368-69
Aerospace industry, **1** 29
Loening Aeronautical Engineering Co.
Loening, Grover Cleveland, **8** 1369
Loening Amphibian (with picture and data chart), **8** 1369
Coast Guard aviation, **3** 476
Loerzer, Bruno
World War I (table, Top Aces), **14** 2507
Log books (with illustration), **8** 1369-70
Preflight inspection, **10** 1846
Logistics of aerospace, 8 1370
Lome, Dupuy de
Airships, **1** 111
London, England
Airports, **1** 95
London Daily Mail prize
Bleriot, Louis, **2** 363
Paulhan, Louis, **10** 1768
Roe, Alliott Verdon, **11** 1989
Lone Eagle
Lindbergh, Charles Augustus, **8** 1359
Lone Eagle (glider)
Gliders (picture), **6** 985
Long Beach, California
Careers (table), **3** 414
Long Beach (cruiser)
Nuclear energy, **9** 1713
Long count
Terminology of aerospace (table), **12** 2272
Long-distance pilot
Operational fatigue, **10** 1737
Long, George Ernest
Medals and decorations (table), **8** 1526
Longhorn (airplane)
First World War aircraft, **5** 822
Long Island Air Route Traffic Control Center
Air traffic control (picture), **1** 127
Longitudinal axis
Airplane, **1** 87
Attitude and attitude control, **2** 275
Axes of rotation, **2** 308
Landing gear, **7** 1298-99
Pitot-static system, **10** 1816
Roll, **11** 1990
Longitudinal separation
Air traffic control, **1** 127
Longitudinal stability
Aerodynamics, **1** 24
Celestial navigation, **3** 429
Earth, **4** 663
Maps and mapping, **8** 1476
Long-line interferometry
Earth, **4** 661

Long Look (Project)
General aviation, **6** 958
Long-period comets
Comets, **3** 490
Long-Range Aviation (Russia)
World War II, **14** 2515-16
Long-Range Missile
Rockets and rocketry, **11** 1984
Long range navigation, see Loran
Long-range surveillance
Radar, **10** 1874
Loon
Seaplanes, **11** 2023
Loop, 8 1371
Barnstormers, **2** 333
Beachey, Lincoln, **2** 345
Maneuvers, **8** 1440-41
Loop antenna
Airborne antennas, **1** 43-44
Loop range
Navigation systems, **9** 1674
Loran (with chart and diagrams), **8** 1371-72
Airborne antennas, **1** 44
Air traffic control, **1** 135
Astronomy, **2** 240
Avionics, **2** 307
Charts, **3** 450
Coast Guard aviation, **3** 479
Invader, Douglas A-26, B-26, **7** 1214
Navigation instruments, **9** 1673
Navigation systems, **9** 1679-80
Navigation techniques, **9** 1687 (with map)
Radio navigation, **10** 1899
Loridan, Marcel
Altitude and altitude records, **1** 147
Los Alamos Scientific Laboratory
Kiwi, **7** 1281
Nuclear detection satellites, **9** 1707-08
U.S. Atomic Energy Commission, **13** 2375
Los Angeles (dirigible)
Airships, **1** 111
Dirigibles, **4** 631, (data table) 631
Eckener, Hugo, **4** 668
United States Naval Aviation, **13** 2379
Zeppelins, **14** 2552
Los Angeles, California
Careers (table), **3** 414
Los Angeles, California, Polytechnic High School
Educational implications of aerospace, **4** 673
Los Angeles International Airport
Airports (pictures), **1** 93, 99
Loss of communications
Instrument Flight Rules, **7** 1165
Loss of lift
Laminar flow, **7** 1296
Lost Ball
Biosatellites, **2** 357
Lost Battalion
World War I, **14** 2510
Loudness
Noise measurement, **9** 1700
Louis W. Hill Space Transportation award
Gilruth, Robert Rowe, **6** 981
Lousma, Jack Robert (1936-   ), **8** 1372
Astronauts, **2** 217, 218, 219 (with picture)
Love, Bonnie R.
Peterson, Donald H., **10** 1776
Lovelace Clinic
Astronauts, **2** 220
Lovell, James A., Jr. (1928-   ), **8** 1372-73
Aerospace medicine (picture), **1** 34
Astronauts, 216, 217, 219, 221, 224, 231 (with picture)
Distance records, **4** 641
Gemini, **5** 940, 949-50, 952
Manned spaceflight (table), **8** 1461
Medals and decorations (table), **8** 1524
Spaceflight training (picture), **12** 2117
Love, Nancy Harkness
Women in aerospace, **14** 2495
Low altitude chart
Charts, **3** 451

Low-altitude flight, 8 1373
Low-altitude navigation
  Oil burner routes, **10** 1735
Low-altitude orbit
  Orbits and trajectories, **10** 1747
Low bays
  Kennedy Space Center, **7** 1269
Lowe, Jack G.
  Medals and decorations (table), **8** 1526
Lowe, Thaddeus S. C. (1832-1913, American aeronaut and meteorologist), **8** 1373
  Army aviation, **2** 194
Lowell Observatory
  Lowell, Percival, **8** 1374
Lowell, Percival (1855-1916, American astronomer), **8** 1374
  Extraterrestrial life, **5** 778
  Mars, **8** 1490
Low-energy particles
  Kosmos satellites, **7** 1290
Lower atmosphere
  Launch vehicles, **7** 1328
Lower camber, airfoil
  Airplane, **1** 85
Lowenhardt, Erich
  World War I (table, Top Aces), **14** 2507
Low fluid viscosity
  Oxidizer, **10** 1752
Low Frequency, see LF
Low frequency/medium frequency, see LF/MF
Low-frequency noise
  Acoustics, **1** 4-5
Low frequency radio, 8 1374
Low-frequency radiocompass
  Navigation instruments, **9** 1672
Low-hanging utility lines
  Outsize cargo aircraft, **10** 1748
Low-level bombing
  Air raid, **1** 104
  Bomber aircraft, **2** 376
Low-level ejection seat
  Escape systems, **4** 735
Low-level turbulence
  Aviation weather, **2** 303
Low/Medium Frequency Radio Range
  Air traffic control, **1** 128-29
  Beacon, radio, **2** 345
Low-noise traveling-wave tubes
  Radar, **10** 1874
Low-pressure area, 8 1374
  Anticyclone, **1** 159
  Aviation weather, **2** 303
  Isobar, **7** 1216
  Meteorology, **9** 1555
Lows (cyclones)
  Weather, **13** 2450
Low temperatures
  Aviation medicine, **2** 293
Low thrust
  Ion propulsion, **7** 1215
Low wing loading
  Sailplanes, **11** 2003
Low wings
  Wings, **14** 2492
LOX, see Liquid oxygen
LPM, see Lunar Payload Module
LSSM, see Local scientific survey module
LSSSD, see Lunar survey system staff device
LSV, see Lunar Surface Vehicle
LTV A-7 Corsair II, see A-7 Corsair II
LTV Aerospace Corporation
  Astronaut maneuvering unit, **2** 213
  Battlefield missile systems, **2** 341
LTV F-8, see F-8 Crusader
L-200 (Czechoslovakia)
  European aerospace activities, **4** 745
Lubricants, 8 1374-75
  Materials, **8** 1510
  Preventive maintenance, **10** 1852
Lubrication system
  Reciprocating engines, **11** 1918
Lufbery, Raoul
  Lafayette Escadrille, **7** 1295
  World War I, **14** 2506, (table) 2507

Lufthansa German Airlines
  Aerospace industry, **1** 32
  West Germany's aerospace activities, **13** 2475
Luftschiffbau L31
  Military aviation (picture), **9** 1579
Luftwaffe, 8 1375-77
  Ace, **1** 4
  Air-to-air missiles, **1** 120
  Battle of Britain, **2** 343
  Dornier, Claude, **4** 647
  Heinkel He 111, **6** 1060
  Messerschmitt Me-109, **9** 1546
  Military aviation, **9** 1582-85
  Rockets and rocketry, **11** 1980
  Royal Air Force, **11** 1995
  Second World War aircraft, **11** 2028
  Spanish Civil War, **12** 2139
  Survival and rescue, **12** 2218
  World War II, **14** 2512, 2514-15, 2516, 2518
Luke, Frank
  World War I, **14** 2507 (with table)
Luminosity, 8 1377
  Astronomy, **2** 249
  Light, **8** 1351
Luna (Mechta) (spacecraft)
  U.S.S.R. aerospace activities, **13** 2340, (pictures) 2341
Luna probes (with pictures and table), **8** 1377-79
Lunar-anchored Interplanetary Explorers
  Earth science, **4** 666
  NASA (drawing), **9** 1651
Lunar bases (with charts, diagrams and pictures), **8** 1380-95
  Closed ecological system (picture), **3** 470
Lunar calendar
  Astronomy, **2** 233
Lunar charts (with diagram, charts and picture), **8** 1396-1400
  Charts, **3** 455
Lunar colony
  Lunar bases, **8** 1389
Lunar craters
  Astrogeology, **2** 211
Lunardi, Vincent (1759-1806, Italian balloon pioneer), **8** 1401
  Balloons, **2** 317
Lunar drill
  Apollo Applications Program, **2** 188
  Lunar exploration, **8** 1404
Lunar eclipse
  Eclipse, **4** 668
Lunar exploration (with chart, diagrams, drawing, and picture), **8** 1401-07
  Apollo Applications Program, **2** 188
  Saturn rockets, **11** 2011
Lunar flightcraft
  Lunar bases, **8** 1391, 1393, (data table) 1394, (drawings) 1394
  Lunar exploration, **8** 1401-03
Lunar gardens
  Closed ecological system, **3** 469
Lunar geologic mapping
  Astrogeology, **2** 210
Lunar geology
  Astrogeology, **2** 212
Lunar landing mission
  Apollo, **1** 169-70
    cost, **1** 163
  Astronaut, **2** 232
  Electrical systems, **4** 682
  Launch window, **7** 1329
  Manned Spacecraft Center, **8** 1458
  Spaceflight principles, **12** 2108
  Spaceflight training, **12** 2117
Lunar landing research vehicle
  Edwards Air Force Base, **4** 678
Lunar landing sites
  Moon (picture), **9** 1636
  Surveyor, **12** 2209-16
Lunar Landing Training Vehicle
  Spaceflight training, **12** 2117

Lunar mapping and survey
  Lunar exploration, **8** 1404, (diagram) 1406
Lunar Module (with diagrams and picture), **8** 1409-10
  Airlock, **1** 67
  Aluminum, **1** 148
  Apollo, **1** 162, 170-75 (with pictures and diagrams)
  Apollo Applications Program, **2** 185
  Instrument panels, **7** 1178
  Kennedy Space Center, **7** 1267
  Lunar bases, **8** (diagrams) 1382, (table) 1383, (drawing) 1389
  Lunar exploration, **8** 1402, 1404, 1407
  Module, **9** 1630
  Radar, **10** 1878
  Space propulsion systems, **12** 2124, 2125
Lunar Module shelter
  Lunar exploration, **8** 1407
Lunar Module simulator
  Link, Edwin A., **8** 1361
  Manned Spacecraft Center, **8** 1458
  Spaceflight training, **12** 2117
Lunar motion
  Planetarium, **10** 1819
Lunar near-space exploration
  Lunar probes, **8** 1379
Lunar orbit
  Apollo Applications Program, **2** 187
  Interplanetary Monitoring Platform satellites, **7** 1206
  Rendezvous and docking, **11** 1956
Lunar Orbiter (with diagrams, pictures, and table), **8** 1410-14
  Aerospace industry (picture), **1** 28
  Agena rockets, **1** 38
  Aluminum, **1** 149
  Apollo, **1** 169, (picture) 170
  Astrogeology, **2** 211 (with picture)
  Atlas missile and launch vehicle, **2** 260
  Earth science, **4** 666
  Langley Research Center, **7** 1302
  Launch vehicles, **7** 1324
  Lunar bases, **8** 1380
  Moon (pictures), **9** 1633, 1635
  NASA (drawing), **9** 1651, (table) 1652
Lunar orbit rendezvous
  Apollo, **1** 164-84 (with diagram)
Lunar payload module
  Lunar exploration, **8** 1407
Lunar phase
  Planetarium, **10** 1819
Lunar probes
  U.S.S.R. aerospace activities, **13** 2340
Lunar Receiving Laboratory (with diagram), **8** 1414-15
  Manned Spacecraft Center, **8** 1459
Lunar surface
  Astrogeology (picture), **2** 211
  Astronomy, **2** 237
  Launch window, **7** 1329
  Lunar bases (tables), **8** 1385, 1386, 1390, 1387, 1389
  Oceanographic research, **10** 1734
  Photography, **10** 1783
  SNAP, **11** 2060
Lunar surface vehicle
  Lunar bases, **8** 1391, (data table) 1392, (drawings) 1393
Lunar survey system staff device
  Lunar exploration, **8** 1404
Lunar trajectory
  Launch vehicles, **7** 1325
Lunik II
  Astronomy, **2** 242
Luni-solar calendar
  Astronomy, **2** 235
Lunney, Marjorie
  Slayton, Donald K., **11** 2057
Luukkanen, Eino
  World War II (table), **14** 2517
Luxembourg
  European aerospace activities, **4** 751
  European air traffic control, **4** 752
  NATO, **9** 1703-04

M

Lydia (city)
  Astronomy (picture), 2 234, 235
Lynch, Bernard
  Escape systems, 4 731
Lyons, Harry W.
  Kingsford-Smith, Charles, 7 1277
Lyra
  Nebula, 9 1688 (with picture)
LZ-1—LZ-4
  Zeppelins, 14 2549, (picture) 2550

M-12 flying boat, see Beriev M-12
M-130 Clipper, see Martin M-130
M2-F1 and F2
  Lifting-body vehicles, 8 1350, (picture) 1345
M31 (Andromeda galaxy)
  Baade, Walter, 2 309
M-60 main battle tank
  Battlefield missile systems, 2 342
MA-2 propulsion system
  Atlas missile and launch vehicle, 2 260
Maan, W. J.
  International Agricultural Aviation Centre, 7 1187
MAC, see Military Airlift Command
MacArthur, Douglas
  Kamikaze, 7 1262
  World War II, 14 2522
Macchi M.39 racer (with picture), 8 1416
Macchi MB326H
  Australia's aviation, 2 280
MacCracken, William P.
  Medals and decorations (table), 8 1526
MacCready, Paul B., Jr.
  Medals and decorations (table), 8 1526
MacDonald, Charles
  World War II (table), 14 2517
Mace tactical missile
  NATO, 9 1704
  Surface-to-surface missiles, 12 2205, (picture) 2208
Mach cone
  Sonic boom, 11 2074
Mach (Mock), Ernst (1838-1916, Austrian physicist), 8 1416
  Mach number, 8 1417
Mach indicator
  Airspeed indicator, 1 117
Machine gun
  Maxim, Sir Hiram S., 8 1515
  World War I, 14 2505
Machining industry
  Precision measurements, 10 1845
Mach number, 8 1417
  Aerodynamics, 1 24
  Airspeed, 1 116
  Mach, Ernst, 8 1416
  MiG aircraft, 9 1565
  Wind tunnels, 13 2488
Mackay Trophy
  Arnold, Henry Harley, 2 201
  Doolittle, James Harold, 4 643
  Trophies and awards (table), 13 2312
Mackenzie Air Service
  Bush flying, 3 392
Mackie, E. D.
  World War II (table), 14 2517

Macleay, Lachlan (1931-   , Aerospace research pilot), 8 1417
  Manned Orbiting Laboratory, 8 1456
MacMillan Expedition
  Bennett, Floyd, 2 350
  Byrd, Richard Evelyn, 3 397
Macon
  Airships, 1 106, (picture) 109, 110, 113
  Dirigibles, 4 631
  United States Naval Aviation, 13 2380, (picture) 2380
Macready, Lt. John (1887-1966, American army aviator), 8 1417-18
  Altitude and altitude records, 1 147
  Distance and distance records, 4 640
  United States Air Force, 13 2362
Macroscopic physical processes
  Quantum theory, 10 1870
MADAR
  Jumbo jets, 7 1256
Maddalena, Umberto
  Distance and distance records, 4 640
Madden, Martin B.
  Airmail, 1 70
Madge (Beriev) (airplane)
  U.S.S.R. aerospace activities (table), 13 2337
Madon, Georges
  World War I (table, Top Aces), 14 2507
Mae West, 8 1418
Magellanic clouds
  Astronomy, 2 253
Magellans of the Air
  Douglas World Cruiser, 4 649
Magister
  Counter-insurgency aircraft, 4 577
Magnesium (with diagram), 8 1418-19
  Alloys, 1 144
  Bombs, 3 378
  Materials, 8 1507-08
Magnetic bearings
  Bearing, 2 346
Magnetic compass
  Compasses, 3 546, 547
  Polar flights, 10 1828
Magnetic cores
  Computers, 3 553
  Data acquisition and processing, 4 610
Magnetic course, 8 1419
  Automatic direction finder, 2 287
  Jumbo jets, 7 1255
  Omni navigation, 10 1737
Magnetic dip
  Compasses, 3 547
  Inclination, 7 1151
Magnetic energy
  Energy, 4 712
Magnetic field, 8 1419
  Aerobee, 1 18
  Aerospace Research Support Program, 1 35
  Argus project, 2 191
  Astronomy, 2 243
  Balloons, 2 324
  Earth, 4 662, 663 (with diagram)
  Electromagnetism, 4 688
  International Geophysical Year, 7 1197
  Interplanetary Monitoring Platform satellites, 7 1205
  Mariner probes, 8 1487, 1489
  Milky Way, 9 1605
  Piccard family, 10 1791
  Pioneer, 10 1813
  Plasma, 10 1823
  Radiation, 10 1881, 1883
  Stars, 12 2159, 2160
  Van Allen radiation belts, 13 2399
  Variometers, 13 2405
  Venus, 13 2406-07, 2409
Magnetic Heading Reference System
  Navigation systems (diagram), 9 1677
Magnetic line of force
  Electromagnetism, 4 689
Magnetic materials
  Materials, 8 1512
Magnetic north
  Omni navigation, 10 1737

Magnetic particle testing
  Materials, 8 1512
Magnetic pole
  Poles, 10 1833-34
Magnetic rays
  Astronomy, 2 249
Magnetic storms, 8 1420
Magnetic tape
  Data acquisition and processing, 4 610
  Reaction engines, 10 1912
Magnetic variation
  Isogonic lines, 7 1216
Magnetism
  Compasses, 3 546
Magnetism sunspots
  Kepler, Johannes, 7 1274
Magneto, 8 1420
  Ignition systems, 7 1147
  Reciprocating engines (with diagram), 11 1917
Magnetograph
  Variometers, 13 2405
Magnetohydrodynamics, 8 1420
  Aurora, 2 277
Magnetometer
  Mariner probes, 8 1487, 1488
Magnetosphere
  Atmosphere, 2 264
  Earth, 4 662
  measurement of, Pioneer, 10 1814
  Solar winds (with diagram), 11 2071
Magnetron
  Electronics, 4 700
Magnetron tube
  Radar, 10 1874
Magnets and magnetism
  Electromagnetism, 4 688-91
  Tape recording, 12 2234
Magnitude, 8 1420
  Astronomy, 2 249
Magnitude ratio
  Magnitude, 8 1420
Mail (Beriev) (airplane)
  U.S.S.R. aerospace activities (table), 13 2337
Main display console
  Apollo, 1 176, (picture) 177
Main geomagnetic field
  Geomagnetic field, 6 977
Mainland China's aerospace activities (with map and pictures), 8 1421-29
Maintenance and repair
  Careers, 3 416
Maintenance facilities
  Jumbo jets, 7 1251
Maitland, Lester J.
  United States Air Force, 13 2362
Majewska, Pelagia (mah YEWS ka)
  Medals and decorations (table), 8 1526
Making of a Moon (book)
  Clarke, Arthur Charles, 3 467
Makula, Edward
  Medals and decorations (table), 8 1526
Malathion
  Agricultural aviation, 1 40
Malaysia
  Crop dusting, 4 587
MALEV
  European aerospace activities, 4 748
Malfunction detection
  Launch facilities, 7 1307
  Maneuvering in space, 8 1430
Malfunction Insert Unit
  Flight simulators, 5 852
Malina, Frank J.
  Rockets and rocketry, 11 1982
Mallow (airplane)
  U.S.S.R. aerospace activities (table), 13 2337
Malta
  European aerospace activities, 4 751
  World War II, 14 2516
Management training seminar
  National Aviation Trades Association, 9 1663

Man-carrying gondola
  Pilatre de Rozier, Jean Francois, **10** 1792
Mandatory instruments
  Instrument panels, **7** 1176
Mandrake, see Yakovlev Mandrake
Maneuverable re-entry vehicle
  Surface-to-surface missiles, **12** 2204
Maneuvering in space (with pictures and
    diagrams), **8** 1429-31
  Apollo Applications Program (picture),
    2 188
Maneuvering instructions
  Collision avoidance system, **3** 488
Maneuvers (with diagrams and pictures),
    8 1433-41
  Preflight training, **10** 1849
Maneuvering speed, 8 1431
Manganese
  Magnesium, **8** 1419
Mangrove (airplane), see YAK-25 fighter
Manhattan Project, 8 1442
  Einstein, Albert, **4** 681
  Nuclear energy, **9** 1710
  Program management, **10** 1857
Manifold, 8 1442
  Intake
    Reciprocating engines, **11** 1916-17
Manifold pressure gauge
  Engine instruments, **4** 715
  Instrument flight techniques, **7** 1167
  Power management, **10** 1841
  Pressure gauges, **10** 1850
Man in flight (with chart, diagrams and
    graph), **8** 1443-51
Manly, Charles Matthews (1876-1927,
    American mechanical engineer and
    inventor), **8** 1452
  Manly engine
    Aircraft propulsion systems,
    1 (picture), 52, 54
Manly Gold Medal
  Fedden, Sir Roy, **5** 792
Man-machine interface
  Human engineering, **6** 1132
Manmade satellite, first
  Celestial mechanics, **3** 427
  Sputniks, **12** 2152
Man-monitored consoles
  Launch facilities, **7** 1307
Manned capsules
  Precision measurements, **10** 1845
Manned glider flight
  Lilienthal, Otto, **8** 1358
Manned interceptor aircraft
  Semi-Automatic Ground Environment,
    11 2039
Manned Orbiting Laboratory (with pictures),
    8 1452-57
  Abrahamson, James A., **1** 2
  Aerospace research pilot, **1** 34
  Airlock, **1** 67
  Bobko, Karol J., **2** 369
  Crews, Albert H., Jr., **4** 584
  Crippen, Robert L., **4** 584
  Douglas, Donald Wills, **4** 649
  Lawrence, Robert H., **7** 1329
  Lawyer, Richard E., **7** 1330
  Lifting-body vehicles, **8** 1346-47
  Macleay, Lachlan, **8** 1417
  Maneuvering in space, **8** 1430
  Military implications of space, **9** 1589
  Military space program, **9** 1591, 1601-02,
    1604
  Mitchell, Edgar Dean, **9** 1620
  Neubeck, Francis G., **9** 1692
  Overmyer, Robert F., **10** 1751
  Reusable launch vehicles, **11** 1962
  Titan III, **12** 2293
  United States Air Force, **13** 2369
  Vandenberg Air Force Base, **13** 2402
Manned Spacecraft Center (with pictures),
    8 1457-59
  Astronauts, **2** 215
  Computers, **3** 558
  Kennedy Space Center, **7** 1266

Launching, **7** 1308
Mission Control Center, **9** 1617-20
  (with picture)
NASA, **9** 1650, 1654, 1657
Recovery, **11** 1929
Spaceflight training, **12** 2116
Manned spaceflight (with table and
    diagrams), **8** 1460-63
  Borman, Frank, **3** 381
  Military space program, **9** 1600-01, (table)
    1604
  Radio, **10** 1885, 1887
Manned Space Flight Network
  International Geophysical Year, **7** 1197
  Interplanetary travel, **7** 1212
  Jet Propulsion Laboratory, **7** 1240
  Military space program, **9** 1604
  NASA, **9** 1653
  Tracking systems and networks, **13** 2303
Mannock, Edward
  Ace, **1** 4
  World War I, **14** 2506, (table) 2507
Man on the moon
  Apollo, **1** 162-84
Man/plant cycle
  Closed ecological system, **3** 469
Man-powered flight (with diagrams and
    picture), **8** 1463-65
Mantle
  Earth, **4** 660
Mantz, Paul
  Air races, **1** 103
Manual leaning
  Power management, **10** 1842
Manual mixture controls
  Power management, **10** 1840
Manufacturers Aircraft Association
  Manufacturing, **8** 1468
Manufacturing (with pictures and diagrams),
    8 1466-75
  Aerospace industry, **1** 29
  Occupations (with tables), **10** 1728-30
  Production techniques (with chart and
    diagram), **10** 1855
  Reliability and quality assurance, **11** 1954
**Man Will Never Fly Memorial Society
    Internationale, 8** 1476
Map-matcher
  Celestial navigation, **3** 431
  Missiles, **9** 1616
Maps and mapping (with table, maps and
    pictures), **8** 1476-80
  Gnomonic projection, **6** 991
  mapmaking experiments
    Orbiting observatories, **10** 1738
  map scale calibrations
    Plotter, **10** 1827
  Mercator projection, **8** 1527
  Photogrammetry, **10** 1780
  Photography, aerial, **10** 1785
  Pilot training, readings, **10** 1810
  Reconnaissance, airborne, **11** 1920
  Utility aviation, **13** 2395
Maraging steels
  Steels, **12** 2164
  Tensile strength, **12** 2271
Marauder, see B-26 Marauder
Marconi, Guglielmo (1874-1937, Italian-
    English inventor), **8** 1480, (picture),
    10 1887
  Radio (diagram), **10** 1887
  Transmitters, **13** 2308
Mare
  Astronomy, **2** 243
  Moon, **9** 1635
Mare Acidalium
  Mars, **8** 1490
Maria, see Mare
Mare Imbrium
  Lunar exploration (picture), **8** 1407
Marianas Turkey Shoot
  World War II, **14** 2523
Marine Corps Aviation (with pictures),
    8 1481-83
  Aerospace research pilot, **1** 34
  Korean war, **7** 1286

United States Naval Aviation, **13** 2388
Marineflieger der Bundeswehr
  Air forces of the world, **1** 66
Marine research
  Oceanographic research, **10** 1731
Mariner probes (with diagram, pictures, and
    table), **8** 1484-90
  Agena rockets, **1** 38
  Atlas missile and launch vehicle, **2** 260
  Guidance and control systems, **6** 1039
  Interplanetary travel, **7** 1208
  Jet Propulsion Laboratory, **7** 1240
  Launch vehicles, **7** 1324
  Mariner II, **8** 1486-87, (picture) 1487
    Astronomical unit, **2** 232
    Astronomy, **2** 242, 243, 247
    Interplanetary travel, **7** 1208 (with
      drawing)
  Mariner IV, **8** 1487-89, (table) 1486,
    (pictures) 1484, 1489, (trajectory
    diagram) 1488
    Astronomy, **2** 242, 244
    Data acquisition and processing,
      4 605, 606, 608
    Extraterrestrial life, **5** 780
    Interplanetary travel, **7** 1208 (with
      drawing)
  Mars, **8** 1490, 1492-93, (picture) 1492
  Mariner V, **8** 1489, (table) 1486,
    (picture) 1489
  NASA, **9** 1653 (table, Major Launchings)
    1652
  Observatories, **10** 1726
  Sagan, Carl, **11** 2002
  Orbits and trajectories, **10** 1747
  Parks, Robert Joseph, **10** 1763
  Pioneer, **10** 1812
  Testing (picture), **12** 2276
  Venus, **13** 2408
  Voyager, **13** 2436
Marine tactical data systems
  Carr, Gerald Paul, **3** 422
Marine technology
  Oceanographic research, **10** 1734
Marino, Grace
  Crews, Albert H., Jr., **4** 584
Maritime communications
  Communications satellites, **3** 543
Maritime Self-Defense Force
  Japan's aerospace activities, **7** 1229
Marius, Simon
  Astronomy, **2** 253
Mark I Relay Calculator
  Computers, **3** 557
Mark 46 antisubmarine torpedo
  Antisubmarine missiles, **1** 161
Marker beacon, 8 1490
  Airborne antennas, **1** 44
  Instrument flight techniques, **7** 1168
Marketing
  Careers, **3** 416
  Occupations (with tables), **10** 1729-30
Marlin, see Martin P5M-1 Marlin
Marquardt Corporation
  Ramjet engines, **10** 1901
Mars (with maps and pictures), **8** 1490-94
  Agena rockets, **1** 38
  Astronomy, **2** 235, 241, 242, 244, 245
  Atmosphere, **2** 265, 266
  Celestial mechanics, **3** 427
  Earth, **4** 659, 663, 666
  Extraterrestrial life, **5** 776
  Guidance and control systems, **6** 1041
  Infrared radiation, **7** 1162
  Interplanetary travel, **7** 1208-09, 1212
  Kepler's laws, **7** 1275
  Launch vehicles, **7** 1314
  Lowell, Percival, **8** 1374
  Mariner probes, **8** 1484-90, (picture) 1484,
    (table) 1486, (trajectory diagram) 1488
  Orbits and trajectories, **10** 1742, 1746-47
  Pickering, William Henry, **10** 1791
  Pioneer, **10** 1812
  Planets, **10** 1820
  Quantum theory, **10** 1870

(Continued)

Mars (Cont.)
Radar, **10** 1878
Solar system, **11** 2070
Spacecraft sterilization, **11** 2103
U.S.S.R. aerospace activities, **13** 2342
Voyager, **13** 2436
Mars biology
Mars, **8** 1490
Marshall Space Flight Center, 8 1494-95
Astronauts, **2** 223
NASA, **9** 1650, 1654, 1657
Pegasus, **10** 1773
Saturn rockets, **11** 2011
Testing, **12** 2275
Martian environmental medicine
Mars, **8** 1490, 1493
Martian life theory
Mars, **8** 1493
Martian organisms
Spacecraft sterilization, **11** 2104
Martin 167
Second World War aircraft, **11** 2029
Martin 2-0-2 and 4-0-4
Commercial air transports, **3** 524, 526
(with picture)
Martin B-10, see B-10
Martin B-57, see B-57 Canberra
Martin, Glenn L. (1886-1955, American
aircraft manufacturer), **8** 1495-96
Aerospace industry, **1** 29
Barnstormers, **2** 333
Martin, Jack
Polar flights, **10** 1831
Martin JRM Mars
Flying boats, **5** 860
Martin M-130
China Clipper (table, pictures), **3** 457-58
Commercial airlines, **3** 509
Flying boats, **5** 859
Martin Marietta Corp.
Air-to-surface missiles, **1** 124
Antiballistic missile defense, **1** 159
Battlefield missile systems, **2** 341
Manned Orbiting Laboratory, **8** 1452
Martin Mariner
Flying boats, **5** 860
Martin MB-2 bombers, see MB-2 bombers
Martin P5M-1 Marlin
Flying boats, **5** 861
Martin Sp-5M
Flying boats (picture), **5** 859
Martinsyde Co.
Camm, Sir Sydney, **3** 398
Martin XP6M-1 Seamaster
Flying boats, **5** 861
Mascot (airplane) (Ilyushin)
U.S.S.R. aerospace activities (table),
13 2337
Masers (with diagram and picture),
8 1496-97
Electronics, **4** 693, 704
Radar, **10** 1874
Mason, Thomas Monck (1803-89, English
aeronaut), **8** 1498
Airships, **1** 111
Mass, 8 1498
Gravity, **6** 1011
Kinetic energy, **7** 1277
Matter, **8** 1515
Relativity theory, **11** 1950
Massey, Frances
Hartsfield, Henry W., Jr., **6** 1051
Mass-luminosity law
Eddington, Arthur S., **4** 673
Mass production
Aerospace industry, **1** 29-33
Manufacturing, **8** 1470
Mass spectrometer
Extraterrestrial life, **5** 781
Mass transportation systems
Aerospace industry, **1** 32
Master sequence console
Blockhouse, **2** 367
Master station
Loran, **8** 1371-72, (diagram) 1372
Radio navigation, **10** 1899

Matador
Materials, **8** 1503
Material fatigue, 8 1498
Materials (with diagrams and pictures),
8 1499-1513
Advanced Research Project Agency, **1** 7
Jumbo jets, **7** 1251
Materials-handling area
Kennedy Space Center, **7** 1273
Mathematics
Careers, **3** 416
Mathews, Charles W.
Gemini, **5** 952
Matra/Hawker Siddeley Dynamics Martel
Missiles (picture), **9** 1613
Matrix metal
Metals and metallurgy, **9** 1553
Matsu
Nationalist China's aviation, **9** 1664
Matter (with pictures), **8** 1513-15
Matthews, Thomas
Quasar, **10** 1870
Mattingly, Thomas Kenneth, II (1936-   ),
8 1515
Astronauts, **2** 218, 219, (with picture)
Mauchly, John W.
Computers, **3** 557
Electronics, **4** 693
Maughan, Kathleen
Lind, Don Leslie, **8** 1359
Maughan, R. L.
Speed and speed records (table), **12** 2141
Maule (airplane)
General aviation aircraft, **6** 961
Maverick
Air-to-surface missiles, **1** 124
MAW
Battlefield missile systems (picture), **2** 342
Mawson, Douglas
Polar flights, **10** 1830
Max (airplane), see YAK-18
Maxim, Sir Hiram S. (1840-1916,
American-British scientist and inventor),
8 1515-16
Maximotor engine
Aircraft propulsion systems, **1** 55
Maximum allowable airspeed indicator
Airspeed indicator, **1** 116
Maximum value
Orbital velocity, **10** 1738
Maximum velocity
Burnout, **3** 390
Maximum winds
Jet streams, **7** 1241
Max Q
Terminology of aerospace (table), **12** 2272
Maxwell Air Force Base
Air University, **1** 140
Civil Air Patrol, **3** 466
Maxwell, James Clerk (1831-79)
Electromagnetism, **4** 689
Quantum theory, **10** 1868
Radar, **10** 1872
Maxwell's equations
Electromagnetism, **4** 689
Mayday, 8 1516
Emergency signals, **4** 708
Inflight emergency procedures, **7** 1155
Terminology of aerospace (table), **12** 2272
Mayflower
Airships (picture), **1** 108
Mazza, Vince
Escape systems, **4** 731
MB-2 bombers (Martin)
Bomber aircraft, **2** 374
MCC, see Mission Control Center
McCampbell, David
World War II (table), **14** 2517
McCandless, Bruce, II (1937-   ), **8** 1516
Astronauts, **2** 215, 217, 218, 219
(with picture)
McConnell, James W.
Lafayette Escadrille, **7** 1295
McConnell, John Paul (1908-   , USAF
officer), **8** 1516-17

NATO, **9** 1705
United States Air Force, **13** 2370
McConnell, Joseph, Jr. (1922-54, USAF,
pilot), **8** 1517
McCudden, James T. B.
World War I (table, Top Aces), **14** 2507
McCurdy, John A. Douglas
Aerial Experiment Association, **1** 7-8
(with picture)
McDivitt, James A. (1929-   ), **8** 1517-18
Astronauts, **2** 216, 217, 219, 223, 224,
231 (with picture)
Commemorative stamps and medals,
3 495
Escape systems (picture), **4** 737
Gemini, **5** 935-37
Maneuvering in space, **8** 1429
Manned spaceflight (table), **8** 1461
Re-entry vehicles, **11** 1934
Rendezvous and docking, **11** 1956
McDonald Observatory
Astronomy, **2** 246
McDonnell Aircraft Company
Asset Program, **2** 206
Instrument panels, **7** 1177
Gemini, **5** 926, 927, 933
Mercury program, **9** 1531
McDonnell Douglas Corporation
Aircraft carriers, **1** 46
Air-to-air missiles, **1** 121
Air-to-surface missiles, **1** 124
Antiballistic missile defense, **1** 159
Battlefield missile systems, **2** 342
Collision avoidance system, **3** 488
Douglas C-54, **4** 647
Douglas DC-3, **4** 649
Douglas, Donald Wills, **4** 649
Environmental simulators, **4** 728
Firepower, **5** 813
Jumbo jets, **7** 1246
Launching, **7** 1311
Manned Orbiting Laboratory, **8** 1452
McDonnell, James Smith, Jr., **8** 1518
McDonnell F-4 Phantom, see F-4 Phantom
McDonnell F-101, see F-101 Voodoo
McDonnell, James Smith, Jr. (1899-   ,
American aircraft designer and
manufacturer), **8** 1518
McGuire, Thomas
World War II (table), **14** 2517
McIntyre, Malcolm
Commercial airlines, **3** 502
McKay, John B.
Test pilots and test flying (picture), **12** 2279
X-15 research program, **14** (picture)
2531, 2533
McKinley, William
Aircraft propulsion systems, **1** 54
McMillan, Edwin M.
Nuclear energy, **9** 1711
McNamara, Robert S.
Government contracts, **6** 999
MDA
Radio altimeter, **10** 1888
Me-163, see Messerschmitt Me-163 Komet
Me-210, see Messerschmitt Me-210
Mean distance
Celestial mechanics, **3** 428
Mean sea level
Altitude and altitude records, **1** 146
Mean solar day
Time, **12** 2286
Means, James
History of aviation, **6** 1099
Measurement of power (with diagrams),
8 1518-20
Horsepower, **6** 1129
Measurements by photography
Photogrammetry, **10** 1779
Mechanical astronaut
Mercury program, **9** 1537
Mechanical energy (with diagrams),
8 1520-22
Energy, **4** 712

Mechanical engineering
Careers, **3** 416
Mechanical errors
Altimeter, **1** 146
Mechanical power
Measurement of power, **8** 1518-19, (diagrams) 1519
Mechanic ratings, 8 1523
Mechanics (with picture), **8** 1523-24
Planck, Max K. E. L., **10** 1816
Mechanization
Cybernetics, **4** 602
Mechta (spacecraft), see Luna
Medal of Recognition
Trophies and awards (table), **13** 2312
Medal for Humane Action
Medals and decorations (picture), **8** 1525
Medal of Honor
Medals and decorations (picture), **8** 1525
Medals and decorations (with pictures and tables), **8** 1524-26
Medes
Astronomy, **2** (picture) 234, 235
Medical application
Implications of aerospace, **7** 1151
Medical benefits
Communications satellites, **3** 542
Cyrogenics, **4** 598
Man in flight, **8** 1451
Medical certificate
Pilot training, **10** 1809
Medical examiner, 8 1526-27
Aviation medicine, **2** 294
Medical field
Radiation, **10** 1883
Medical mission
Police and fire services, **10** 1835
Medical oxygen bottle
Oxygen masks, **10** 1752
Medical research
Life-support systems, **8** 1338-39
Medical Service Corps
Personal equipment, **10** 1774
Medium-altitude flight, 8 1527
Medium Antitank Weapon, see MAW
Medium turns
Maneuvers, **8** 1434, (diagram) 1434
Meerwein, Karl Frederick (1737-1810)
Ornithopter, **10** 1748
Megacycle, 8 1527
Megahertz, 8 1527
Megacycle, **8** 1527
Radar, **10** 1874
Megale Syntaxis
Constellations, **3** 561
Meigs Field
General aviation (picture), **6** 953
Melbourne (aircraft carrier)
Australia's aviation (picture), **2** 281
Melbourne Museum
Australia's aviation, **2** 279
Melting point
Boron, **3** 382
Memory
Terminology of aerospace (table), **12** 2272
Mendeleev, Dmitri I. (men DALE yeff, dee MEE tree)
Elements, **4** 704, 705
Mental fitness
Cosmonauts, **4** 572
Man in flight, **8** 1449
Mercator, Gerhard
Maps and mapping, **8** 1478
Mercator projection, 8 1527
Maps and mapping, **8** 1478, (table) 1479
Mars (map), **8** 1491
Mercedes engine
World War I, **14** 2508
Merchant Marine Academy
Service academies, **11** 2044
Mercurial days
Mercury, **8** 1528
Mercury (planet), **8** 1527-28 (with picture)
Astronomy, **2** 235, 241, 242, 243
Celestial mechanics, **3** 428
Conjunction, **3** 560

Earth, **4** 659, 664
Extraterrestrial life, **5** 777
Leverrier, Urbain, J. J., **7** 1334
Planets, **10** 1820
Relativity theory, **11** 1953
Mercury astronauts
Atlas missile and launch vehicle, **2** 260
launch center
Kennedy Space Center, **7** 1273
Personal equipment, **10** 1775
Mercury-Atlas
Mercury program, **9** 1534, 1535, 1537, (picture) 1535
Mercury barometer
Barometer (diagram), **2** 337
Mercury-pool rectifiers
Electronics, **4** 700
Mercury program (with pictures, diagrams, map, and table), **9** 1529-45
Animals in space, **1** 154-55
Apollo, **1** 162, 164
Astronautics, **2** 212
Capsule, **3** 406
Environmental control systems, **4** 718
Escape systems, **4** 735, 736 (with diagram)
Instrument panels, **7** 1177-78
Interplanetary travel, **7** 1208, 1210
Lewis Research Center, **7** 1334
Manned spaceflight, **8** 1460, 1462, (table) 1461, (diagram) 1462
Radar, **10** 1878
Spacecraft design (with engineering sketch), **11** 2102
Control Center, **9** 1534, 1539, 1540, 1542, 1545
Faget, Maxime, **5** 788
Langley Research Center, **7** 1302
Launch vehicles, **7** 1322, 1324
Life-support systems, **8** 1338-41, (diagram) 1341
Military space program, **9** 1600-01
NASA, **9** 1650, (table, Major Launchings) 1652
Parawing, **10** 1761
Powers, John A., **10** 1842
Pressure suit (with picture), **10** 1851
Reaction control systems, **10** 1911-12
Recovery, **11** 1927
Re-entry vehicles, **11** 1932
Spacecraft design, **11** 2101
Spacesuits, **12** 2130
Temperature control, **12** 2265
Testing, **12** 2275
Mercury-Redstone 3
Launch vehicles (picture), **7** 1323
Mercury program, **9** 1533, 1535, 1536, (picture) 1536
Spacecraft
Attitude and attitude control, **2** 275
Gas jet propulsion, **5** 918
Heat shields, **6** 1057
Honeycomb construction, **6** 1129
Mercury vapor tubes
Electronics, **4** 700
Meridian, 9 1546
Celestial sphere, **3** 433
Latitude and longitude, **7** 1307
Maps and mapping, **8** 1476, (table) 1478-79
Mermoz, Jean
Distance records, **4** 640
Medals and decorations (table), **8** 1526
Merritt Island
Kennedy Space Center, **7** 1266
Launching, **7** 1310
Mesa transistors
Electronics, **4** 703
MESH
International projects, **7** 1199
Meshchersky, I. V.
U.S.S.R. aerospace activities, **13** 2338
Meson
Radiation, **10** 1880, 1882

Mesosphere
Atmosphere, **2** 264
Ionosphere, **7** 1215
Messerschmitt Me-109 (table, picture), **9** 1546-47
History of aviation (picture), **6** 1111
Messerschmitt, Willy, **9** 1546
Spanish Civil War, **12** 2139
World War II, **14** 2514, 2515
Messerschmitt Me-110
Luftwaffe (picture), **8** 1376
Second World War aircraft (picture), **11** 2028
World War II, **14** 2514
Messerschmitt Me-163 Komet
Luftwaffe, **8** 1377
Messerschmitt, Willy, **9** 1546
Military aviation, **9** 1585
Rockets and rocketry, **11** 1981
Second World War aircraft (picture), **11** 2037
World War II, **14** 2519
X-series aerospace vehicles, **14** 2535
Messerschmitt Me-210
Second World War aircraft, **11** 2033
Messerschmitt Me-262 (table, picture), **9** 1547-48
Luftwaffe, **8** 1377
Military aviation, **9** 1585
World War II, **14** 2515, 2519
Messerschmitt, Willy (1898-   , German engineer and airplane manufacturer), **9** 1546
Metabolism
Extraterrestrial life, **5** 775
Metal fatigue
Supersonic transports, **12** 2198
Vibration, **13** 2413
Metallic materials
Materials, **8** 1507
Metalloid
Boron, **3** 382
Metals and metallurgy (with pictures and diagrams), **9** 1548-55
Elements, **4** 705
Lunar bases, **8** 1387
Matter, **8** 1513
Semiconductors, **11** 2041
Meteor Crater
Meteors, meteorites, and meteoroids, **9** 1561
Meteor F-8
Air racing, **1** 103
Korean war (picture), **7** 1287
Meteorologica (book)
Meteorology, **9** 1555
Meteorological observation
Military implications of space, **9** 1589
Meteorological studies
Balloons, **2** 324
Kites, **2** 1279
Kosmos satellites, **7** 1292
Meteorologists
Aviation weather, **2** 306
Launching, **7** 1311
Meteorology (with pictures), **9** 1555-59
Aerology, **1** 25
Airflow, **1** 61
Atmosphere, **2** 263
Atmospheric pressure, **2** 268
Geophysics, **6** 978
GHOST program, **6** 978
International Years of the Quiet Sun, **7** 1204
Piccard family, **10** 1790
Preflight training, **10** 1847
Technological projections, **12** 2236
Weather, **13** 2452
Weather satellites, **13** 2459
Meteors, meteorites, and meteoroids, 9 1559-61
Astrogeology, **2** 212
Atmosphere, **2** 263
Comets, **3** 492
Craters, **4** 584
Detection satellites

(Continued)

Meteors, meteorites, and meteoroids (Cont.)
  Pegasus, **10** 1771
  Explorer satellites, **5** 763
  Extraterrestrial life, **5** 781
  Interplanetary travel, **7** 1212
  Meteoric dust
    Aerospace Research Support Program,
    1 35
Meteor 1 (sounding rocket)
  European aerospace activities, **4** 748
  Orbits and trajectories, **10** 1744
  Radar, **10** 1879
  Radiation, **10** 1883
  Swarms
Metering jet
  Carburetion, **3** 408
Methane
  Air, **1** 42
  Balloons, **2** 317
  Gases, **5** 916
  Jupiter, **7** 1260
  Thermal barrier, **12** 2282
  Unidentified flying objects, **13** 2325
Method of Reaching Extreme Altitudes (book)
  Rockets and rocketry, **11** 1975
Metron
  Photogrammetry, **10** 1779
Metropolitan airports
  Airports, **1** 99
Meulemeester, Andre de
  World War I (table, Top Aces), **14** 2507
Meusnier, Jean Baptiste Marie
  Airships, **1** 111
  Dirigibles, **4** 629
Mexican Astronomical Society Medal
  Lowell, Percival, **8** 1374
Mexico
  Commemorative stamps and medals, **3** 495
  Crop dusting, **4** 587
  Mexico City Airport, **1** 95
  Naval aviation, worldwide, **9** 1672
  South and Central America's aviation,
  11 2091
Meyer, C. H.
  Astronomy, **2** 242
Meyer, John
  World War II (table), **14** 2517
Meyer, Lothar
  Elements, **4** 704
M-4A3 tank
  Blockhouse, **2** 367
MGM-29A, 31A and 52A
  Battlefield missile systems, **2** 341
MHD, see Magnetohydrodynamics
MHz frequency
  Air traffic control, **1** 128
Mi-4 helicopters
  European aerospace activities, **4** 744
  Naval aviation, worldwide (Indonesia),
  9 1671
  U.S.S.R. aerospace activities (table),
  13 2337
Michel, F. Curtis (1934- , American
  scientist-astronaut), **9** 1561-62
  Astronaut, **2** 216-19 (with picture)
Michelson-Morley experiment
  Piccard family, **10** 1790
Michoud Operations
  NASA, **9** 1654, 1657
Micro-algae cultivator
  Photosynthesis, **10** 1790
Microcircuitry (with picture), **9** 1562-63
Microlock
  Ground antennas, **6** 1016
Micrometeoroid impacts
  Ariel satellites, **2** 192
Micrometeoroids
  Meteors, meteorites, and meteoroids,
  9 1559-60
  Pegasus, **10** 1771
Microminiature circuits
  Computers, **3** 557
Micronaire
  Crop dusting, **4** 594
Microphone (with picture), **9** 1563

Microprobe swarm
  Interplanetary travel, **7** 1212
Microscope studies
  Lasers, **7** 1306
Microscopic dust particle
  Orbiting observatories, **10** 1738
**Microwave Amplification by Stimulated
  Emission of Radiation,** see Masers
Microwave communications, 9 1563
  Electronics, **4** 700
  Satellites, **3** 532
Microwave Early Warning
  Microwave communications, **9** 1563
Microwave radio frequencies
  Ewen, Harold Irving, **4** 759
Microwave relays
  Radio, **10** 1888
Microwave tubes
  Electronics, **4** 699
Midas
  Military space program, **9** 1593-94
  (with picture)
  Reconnaissance satellites, **11** 1925-26
Mid-Canada Line
  Air defense systems, **1** 60
Midcourse corrections
  Mariner probes, **8** 1485, 1488
Middle clouds
  Clouds, **3** 473
Middle East
  Agricultural aviation, **1** 41
  Air forces of the world, **1** 64
  Israeli-Arab conflict—1967, **7** 1216-17
Middle latitudes
  Jet streams, **7** 1241
Middle markers
  Instrument landing system, **7** 1170
Midget (Mikoyan) (airplane)
  U.S.S.R. aerospace activities (table),
  13 2337
Midget aircraft races
  Air races, **1** 103
Midnight Sun
  Poles, **10** 1834
Midway
  Aircraft carriers, **1** 50, (data table) 51
Midwings
  Wings, **14** 2492
MiG aircraft, 9 1564-65
  History of aviation (picture), **6** 1117
MiG-3
  World War II, **14** 2515
MiG-6
  U.S.S.R. aerospace activities (table),
  13 2337
MiG-15 (picture), **9** 1565
  Air forces of the world, **1** 64
  Korean war, **7** 1284, 1287
  Naval aviation, worldwide (China), **9** 1671
  Sabre, North American F-86, **11** 2000
  Yakovlev, Aleksander, **14** 2547
MiG -17
  Ace (picture), **1** 4
  Air forces of the world, **1** 64
  Air-to-air missiles, **1** 121
  Asia's aviation, **2** 203, 204, 205
  Military aviation (picture), **9** 1586
  Naval aviation, worldwide (China), **9** 1671
  U.S.S.R. aerospace activities (table),
  13 2337
MiG-19
  Air forces of the world, **1** 64
  Asia's aviation, **2** 203, 204, 205
  Military aircraft (picture), **9** 1569
  U.S.S.R. aerospace activities (table),
  13 2337
MiG-21 (picture), **9** 1565
  Air forces of the world, **1** 64, 65
  Asia's aviation, **2** 203, 204, 205
  European aerospace activities, **4** 745
  U.S.S.R. aerospace activities (table),
  13 2337
MiG-23
  MiG aircraft, **9** 1565
  Olds, Robert, **10** 1735

  U.S.S.R. aerospace activities (table),
  13 2337
Mikhail Mil Mi-4P Hound (helicopter)
  Helicopters (table), **6** 1068
MILAN
  International projects, **7** 1201
Mile, 9 1565
Military
  Occupations (with table), **10** 1730
Military Academy
  Service academies, **11** 2044
Military aeronautics
  Doppler effect, **4** 645
Military aerospace activities
  Careers, **3** 411, 413, (table) 414, 417
  Government in aerospace, **6** 1000-03
  Industry, **1** 30-33
Military aircraft (with pictures), **9** 1566-71
  Air forces of the world, **1** 64-65
  Airships, **1** 113-14
  Attack aircraft, **2** 271-74
  Bomber aircraft, **2** 373-76
  Call signs, **3** 398
  Fighter aircraft, **5** 806-11
  Military air transports, **9** 1574-78
  Military aviation, **9** 1579-87
  Reconnaissance aircraft, **11** 1920-24
Military Air Demonstration Teams
  Barnstormers, **2** 336
Military Airlift Command (with pictures),
  9 1571-74
  Airlift, **1** 67
  National emergency airlift plans, **9** 1663
  Rescue and recovery service, **11** 1958-61
  United States Air Force, **13** 2370
Military airports 1 93
  Pilot's information file, **10** 1809
Military air traffic
  European air traffic control, **4** 752
Military air transports (with pictures and
  table), **9** 1574-78
  United States Air Force, **13** 2373
  Vietnam, **13** 2415
Military Air Transport Service
  Military Airlift Command, **9** 1571-72
Military Assistance Advisory Group
  Nationalist China's aviation, **9** 1665
Military aviation (with pictures), **9** 1579-87
Military censorship
  Intelligence, military, **7** 1180
Military connotations
  Political implications of aerospace, **10** 1837
Military flight maneuvers
  Maneuvers, **8** 1439-41
Military implications of space, 9 1588-89
Military launch vehicles
  Military space program, **9** 1601-02
Military mapping
  Discoverer Project, **4** 634
  Observation platform
    Lowe, Thaddeus S. C., **8** 1373
Military operations
  Plane spotter, **10** 1817
Military procedures
  Radio communications, **10** 1898
Military reconnaissance
  Aerial photography, **1** 9-11
  Discoverer Project, **4** 634
  Infrared detection devices, **7** 1159
Military rockets
  Propellants, **10** 1859
Military role
  Commercial airlines, **3** 504
Military satellites
  Astronautics, **2** 212
Military secrecy
  Intelligence, military, **7** 1180-81
Military space program (with diagrams,
  pictures and table), **9** 1591-1605
Military test pilots
  Astronauts, **2** 220
Military uses
  Police and fire services, **10** 1835
Milk-bottle balloons
  Balloons, **2** 330

Milky Way (with diagram and picture),
9 1605-07
Astronomy, 2 237, (table) 242, 251 (with
picture)
Baade, Walter, 2 309
Cosmic dust, 3 568
Earth, 4 660
Extraterrestrial life, 5 782
Galaxies, 5 910
Milky Way Galaxy
Planets, 10 1821
Nebula, 9 1688-89
Nova, 9 1707
Quasars, 10 1871
Radiation, 10 1882
Radio astronomy, 10 1889, 1892
Space, 11 2093
Universe, 13 2391
X-ray stars, 14 2533
Miller, Stanley
Extraterrestrial life, 5 775
Millibar
Atmospheric pressure, 2 268
Barometer, 2 336
Millikan, Robert (1868-1953)
Balloons, 2 325
Milliken, W. W.
Medals and decorations (table), 8 1526
Millionth comparator
Precision measurement, 10 1845
MIN-23A (Hawk)
Battlefield missile systems, 2 342
Minas Gerais (aircraft carrier)
Naval aviation, worldwide (Brazil), 9 1672
Mineral lubricants
Lubricants, 8 1375
Minetti, G. Joseph
Civil Aeronautics Board, 3 463
Miniaturization (with pictures), 9 1607-08
Minigun helicopter
Army aviation, 2 198
Mini Guppy
Outsize cargo aircraft, 10 (table, picture),
1750
Minimal escape velocities
Launch vehicles, 7 1314
Minimum controllable airspeeds
Maneuvers, 8 1435
Piloting techniques, 10 1801
Minimum decision altitude, see MDA
Minimum dual time
Pilot training, 10 1810
Minimum energy trajectory
Orbits and trajectories, 10 1746
Minimum equipment list
Certification procedures, 3 443
Minimum standards
Lighting facilities, 8 1353
Pilot training, 10 1809
Minimum value
Orbital velocity, 10 1738
Mining
Bush flying, 3 392
Minispring systems
Crop dusting, 4 594
Minitrack Network
Command and data acquisition, 3 493
Military space program, 9 1592-93
Woomera rocket range, 14 2497
Minitrack radio telemetry
International Geophysical Year, 7 1196
Minkowski, Hermann
Relativity theory, 11 1951
Minuteman missile
Aerospace Research Support Program,
1 35
Atlas missile and launch vehicle, 2 260
Dunn, Louis G., 4 655
Inertial guidance, 7 1152
Information systems, 7 1157
Intercontinental ballistic missiles,
7 1182-83
Jumbo jets, 7 1256

Launch vehicles, 7 1314
Military space program (picture), 9 1602
Missiles (table), 9 1616
Silos (with picture), 11 2053
Surface-to-surface missiles, 12 2206
United States Air Force, 13 2369
(picture), 2367
Mirage aircraft
Bomber aircraft (table), 2 373
France's aerospace activities, 5 889,
(picture) 891
Mirage III
Africa's aviation, 1 37
Air forces of the world (France), 1 65
Australia's aviation, 2 280 (with picture)
Fighter aircraft, 5 811
France's aerospace activities, 5 889
Mirage IV
Air forces of the world (France), 1 66
Mirage IV (with data table, diagram and
picture), 9 1609
Bomber aircraft, 2 373
Mirages
Poles, 10 1834
Mira the Wonderful
Astrophysics, 2 258
Mirror landing system
Aircraft carriers, 1 47, 51
Misrair
Africa's aviation, 1 37
Missile alarm
Reconnaissance satellites, 11 1925
Missile Defense Alarm System (Midas)
Military space program, 9 1594
Missiles (with diagram, pictures, and table),
9 1610-16
Aeronautical engineering, 1 26
Aerospace employment,
Careers (table), 3 412
Antiballistic missile defense, 1 159
Arrow, 2 202
Atlas missile and launch vehicle, 2 259-60
Glass, 6 983
Guidance and control systems, 6 1041
Hardened site, 6 1050
Honeycomb construction, 6 1129
Inertial guidance, 7 1152
Intercontinental ballistic missiles, 7 1182
International projects, 7 1201
Launch facilities, 7 1307
Liquid oxygen, 8 1363
Mainland China's aerospace activities,
8 1428
Military aviation, 9 1587, (picture) 1586
Oceanographic research, 10 1734
Penetration, 10 1774
Poseidon missile, 10 1839
Strategic Air Command, 12 2168
United States Air Force, 13 2366, 2373
U.S.S.R. aerospace activities, 13 2336
(table) 2337
Vanderberg Air Force Base, 13 2402
Vietnam, 13 2423
V-2 rocket missile, 13 2445
West Germany's aerospace activities,
13 2479
White Sands Missile Range, 13 2482-83
Missile test ranges, 9 1617
Mission, 9 1617
Mission Control Center (with pictures and
diagram), 9 1617-20
Computers, 3 558
Electronics (picture), 4 692
Insertion tracking, 7 1162
Kennedy Space Center (pictures),
7 1272, 1273
Launching, 7 1308-09
Manned Spacecraft Center, 8 1458
Radio communications, 10 1894-98
Rendezvous and docking, 11 1957
Spaceflight safety, 12 2111
Spaceflight training, 12 2116
Mission profile
Interplanetary travel, 7 1209

Mississippi Test Facility
NASA, 9 1654, 1657
Missouri (ship)
Kamikaze (picture), 7 1262
Mitchell (aircraft) see B-25 Mitchell
Mitchell, Edgar Dean (1930-   ,
Astronaut), 9 1620
Astronaut, 2 217, 218, 219, 226 (with
picture)
Mitchell, North American B-25 (with data
table, diagram and picture), 9 1621-22
(see also B-25 Mitchell)
Mitchell, William (1879-1936, American
military aviator), 9 1620-21
Air raid, 1 104
Bomber aircraft, 2 374
DeSeversky, Alexander Procofieff, 4 627
History of aviation, 6 1108
Manufacturing, 8 1468
Military aviation, 9 1580, 1582
Speed and speed records (table), 12 2141
Spitfire, 12 2146
United States Air Force, 13 2361-62
World War II, 14 2512
MITRE Corp.
Program management, 10 1858-59
Mitsubishi Heavy Industries
Asia's aviation, 2 204
Japan's aerospace activities, 7 1230-31
Mitsubishi 97 Sally
Second World War aircraft (picture),
11 2034
Mitsubishi A6M Zeke
Mitsubishi Zero-Sen (picture), 9 1622
Second World War aircraft, 11 2033
Mitsubishi G4M Betty, see Betty bomber
Mitsubishi Zero-Sen, 9 1622 (with picture,
table, diagram)
Zero, 14 2552
Mixture control, 9 1622-23
Power management, 10 1842
Mizar
Astrophysics, 2 257
Mi-1,-2,-8 (helicopters)
General aviation (picture), 6 957, 965, 1071
MOBEX, see Mobile exploration vehicle
Mobile bases
Lunar bases, 8 1391
Mobile blockhouses
Blockhouse, 2 367
Mobile control towers
Aeronautical Center, 1 26
Mobile exploration vehicle
Lunar exploration, 8 1403, (drawing) 1403
Mobile geological laboratory
Astrogeology, 2 212
Mobile laboratory vehicle
Lunar exploration, 8 1403, (drawing) 1403
Mobile launcher
Blockhouse, 2 368
Kennedy Space Center, 7 1268-69,
1271-72
Mobile service structure
Kennedy Space Center, 7 1272, (pictures)
1267, 1271
Manned Orbiting Laboratory, 8 1455
Mock, Geraldine C. (1925-   , American
aviatrix), 9 1623-24
Women in aerospace, 14 2496
Mockups
Spacecraft design, 11 2103
Testing, 12 2273
Model Aeronautic Association
Australia's aviation, 2 282
Model aircraft (with pictures), 9 1624-26
Academy of Model Aeronautics, 1 2
International competitions, 7 1191, 1193
Model Airways System
Airports, 1 97
Model Comet (airplane
Cessna, Clyde V., 3 445
Model engines
Model aircraft, 9 1626
Model rocketry (with diagrams and pictures),
9 1626-29

Modulated beam
  Lasers, **7** 1304
Modulated signal
  Beam-rider guidance, **2** 346
Modulation (with graph), **9** 1629-30
  Noise measurement, **9** 1700
  Radio, **10** 1887
Module, 9 1630
  Launch vehicles, **7** 1328
  Terminology of aerospace (table), **12** 2272
Mohawk, see G-134 Mohawk
Mohawk, see OV-1 Mohawk
Mohawk Airlines
  Charter flying, **3** 448
  Commercial airlines, **3** 513
Mohorovicic discontinuity
  Earth, **4** 660
Moist lapse rate
  Adiabatic process, **1** 6-7
Moisture
  Rain, **10** 1900
Mojave helicopter, see CH-37 Mojave
MOL, see Manned Orbiting Laboratory
MOLAB, see Mobile laboratory vehicle
Molecular energy
  Energy, **4** 712
Molecular generator
  Kosmos satellites, **7** 1294
Molecule, 9 1631
  Matter, **8** 1513
  Ozone, **10** 1753
  Quantum theory, **10** 1868
  Sound (with graph), **11** 2078
Mollison, James (1905-1959, British pioneer
    aviator), **9** 1631
  Bellanca, Giuseppe, **2** 349
Molly Brown (spacecraft)
  Gemini, **5** 933
Molniya satellite
  Communications satellites, **3** 543
  International projects (picture), **7** 1199
  U.S.S.R. aerospace activities, **13** 2340,
    (picture) 2338
Molybdenum
  Materials, **8** 1507
Moment of forces
  Aerodynamics, **1** 23
Momentum, 9 1631
Monarch of the Moon
  Craters, **4** 584
Monge, Marcy
  Man-powered flight, **8** 1464
Mongol (airplane), see MiG-21
Mong Sport (airplane)
  Homebuilt aircraft, **6** 1125
Monitor
  Instrument landing system, **7** 1171
  Remote control, **11** 1954
Monitoring station
  Regional space centers, **11** 1946
Monkeys
  Biosatellites, **2** 356
Monochromatic
  Lasers, **7** 1303
Monocoque and semimonocoque design
    (with diagram), **9** 1631-32
  Airplane, **1** 83
  Fuselage, **5** 908
  History of aviation, **6** 1105
  Intercontinental ballistic missiles, **7** 1183
Monoline
  Model aircraft, **9** 1624
Monolithic materials
  Metals and metallurgy, **9** 1554
Monomail
  Boeing, William Edward, **2** 370
Monomer
  Plastics, **10** 1825
Monoplane, 9 1632
  Airplane, **1** 86
  Biplane, **2** 358
  History of aviation, **6** 1106
Monoplane vs. biplane
  Bleriot, Louis, **2** 363
Monopoly
  Patents, **10** 1766

Monopropellant
  Oxidizers, **10** 1751
Monopulse radar
  Radar, **10** 1877
Monorail
  High-speed surface transportation, **6** 1090
Monostatic
  Radar, **10** 1874
Monroe, Mary Ellen
  Irwin, James Benson, **7** 1216
Montgolfier brothers, 9 1632
Montgolfier, Jacques Etienne (1745-1799,
    French inventor), **9** 1632
Montgolfier, Joseph Michel (1740-1810,
    French inventor) **9** 1632
  Balloons, **2** 315, 318, 321
  Cavallo, Tiberius, **3** 425
  Charles, Jacques Alexandre Cesar, **3** 447
  History of aviation, **6** 1094
  Lunardi, Vincent, **8** 1401
  Parachutes, **10** 1756
  Pilatre de Rozier, Jean Francois, **10** 1792
Montgolfier Diploma
  Medals and decorations, **8** 1526
    (with table)
Montgolfier hot-air balloon
  Objects of art, **10** 1721
Montgolfier, Marianne
  Balloons, **2** 320
Monthly window
  Launch window, **7** 1329
Moon (with diagrams and pictures),
    9 1633-38
  Apollo, **1** 178-84
  Astronauts, **2** 228
  Astronomy, **2** 233, 243
  bright side
    Astronomy (picture), **2** 244
  Celestial mechanics, **3** 427
  Earth, **4** 663
  Explorer satellites, **5** 772
  Extraterrestrial life, **5** 777
  Far Side (project)
    Lunar charts, **8** 1400
  Launch vehicles, **7** 1314
  Luna probes, **8** 1377-79
  Orbits and trajectories, **10** 1744
  Pickering, William Henry, **10** 1791
  Planetarium, **10** 1818-19
  Precession, **10** 1843
  Radar, **10** 1878
  Radiation, **10** 1882, 1884
  Rendezvous and docking, **11** 1956
  Satellites, **11** 2006
  Space, **11** 2092-93
  Surface
    Parabola, **10** 1756
    Ranger, **10** 1909
  Surveyor, **12** 2209
  Technological projections, **12** 2235, 2238
  U.S.S.R. aerospace activities, **13** 2340,
    2342
Moonbooster
  Launch vehicles, **7** 1325
Moon echoes
  Astronomy, **2** 242
Mooney (aircraft)
  General aviation aircraft, **6** 961, 966, 968,
    (picture) 963
Moon houses
  Fabrics, **5** 787
Moon probe
  Astronomy, **2** 242
Moon slopes
  Ranger, **10** 1911
Moonwatch
  International Geophysical Year, **7** 1196
  Tracking systems and networks, **13** 2300
Moore, Betty L.
  Grissom, Virgil I., **6** 1015
Moore-Brabazon, J.T.C. (1864-1964,
    British aviator), **3** 384
Moorehead Planetarium
  Astronauts, **2** 223
Moore, Robert
  Barnstormers (picture), **2** 333

Moose (Yakovlev) (airplane)
  U.S.S.R. aerospace activities (table),
    13 2337
Morane (aircraft)
  World War I, **14** 2502
Morane Bullet (airplane)
  World War I, **14** 2505
Morane, Leon
  Altitude and altitude records, **1** 147
Morane Monoplane
  First World War aircraft, **5** 818, 823
Morane-Saulnier (airplane)
  General aviation (picture), **6** 959
  Second World War aircraft, **11** 2029
Morehouse's Comet of 1908
  Comets (picture), **3** 491
Morning stars
  Astronomy, **2** 242
Morrow Board
  Military aviation, **9** 1582
Morse code (with table), **9** 1639
  Instrument panels, **7** 1173
  Lasers, **7** 1304
  Radio, **10** 1887
Morse, Philip M.
  Program management, **10** 1857
Mortar shells
  Bombs, **3** 377
Mosaic photography, 9 1639-40
Moseley, Wendell F.
  Douglas DC-3, **4** 648
Mosely, C. C.
  Air racing, **1** 102
Mosher, Samuel B.
  Flying Tigers, **5** 865
Mosquito, DeHavilland DH-98 (with table,
    diagram, and picture), **9** 1640 (see also
    DH-98 Mosquito)
  Bomber aircraft (table), **2** 373
Mossolov, Gueorgiu
  Altitude and altitude records, **1** 147, 148
  Speed and speed records (table), **12** 2141
Motion, 9 1640
Motion, Law of
  Aerodynamics, **1** 20
  Aircraft propulsion systems, **1** 52
  Astronomy, **2** 242
Motion sickness
  Aviation medicine, **2** 293
Motivation
  Psychological factors of flight, **10** 1864
Mountain, desert, and jungle flying (with
    pictures), **9** 1641-43
Mount Palomar Observatory
  Astronomy **2** (picture), 239, (table), 242
    10 1723 (picture)
  Baade, Walter, **2** 309
  Observatories, **10** 1725
  Telescopes and astronomical instruments,
    12 2247, 2251, 2253
Mount Wilson Observatory
  Baade, Walter, **2** 309
  Telescopes and astronomical instruments,
    12 2250
Movable tail
  Empennage, **4** 711
Movable wingtips
  Aerial Experiment Association, **1** 8
Moving pictures
  Passenger services, **10** 1765
Moving target
  Radar, **10** 1876-78
Mozhaiski, Alexander
  History of aviation, **6** 1097, (table) 1119
Mp-1 (flying boat)
  Flying boats (picture), **5** 860
MQM-34D
  Drone aircraft, **4** 653
MQM-57A (Northrop)
  Reconnaissance aircraft, **11** 1924
Mrkos Comet
  Comets (picture), **3** 492
MSL, see Mean sea level
M-type airship
  Airships, **1** 110-11

Blimps, **2** 365
Multicolored filter
Schlieren photography, **11** 2016
Multiengine airplanes
Piloting techniques, **10** 1801
Propellers, **10** 1863
Reciprocating engines, **11** 1919
Multifunction array radar
Antiballistic missile defense, **1** 159
Multigun, trench-strafing model
Jumbo jets, **7** 1258
Multimode radar
Jumbo jets, **7** 1255
Multiple Array Radar
Radar, **10** 1876
Multiple balloons
Balloons, **2** 327
Multiple burn upper stage
Launch vehicles (with diagram), **7** 1319
Multiple disc brakes
Airplane, **1** 90
Multiple Independent Re-entry Vehicle
Surface-to-surface missiles, **12** 2204
Multiple kite flights
Kites, **7** 1280
Multiple satellite system
Navigation satellites, **9** 1674
Multiple signals
Data acquisition and processing, **4** 606
Multiplexed signals
Modulation, **9** 1630
Receivers, **10** 1912
Multiplexing
Data acquisition and processing, **4** 607
Telemetry, **12** 2242
Multirow radial engine
Reciprocating engines, **11** 1918
Multistage rockets
Rockets and rocketry, **11** 1977
Munch, Guido
Astronomy, **2** 242, (picture) 250
Murchison crater
Apollo (picture), **1** 170
Murphy, Charles S.
Civil Aeronautics Board, **3** 463
Murphy, Michael C.
Medals and decorations (table), **8** 1526
Murphy, Robert T.
Civil Aeronautics Board, **3** 463
Murray, Arthur
Altitude and altitude records, **1** 148
Murray, W.
Astronomy, **2** 242
Mu satellite launcher
Japan's aerospace activities (picture),
7 1230
Musee de l'Air
Demoiselle, **4** 623
Musgrave, Franklin Story (1935-   ,
American scientist-astronaut), **9** 1643
Astronaut, **2** 218, 219 (with picture)
Musketeer 19, see Beech Musketeer
Muskrat
Meteorology (picture), **9** 1556
Mustang
Homebuilt aircraft, **6** 1125, 1126
Mustang, North American P-51 (with data
table, diagram, and picture), **9** 1643
(see also P-51 Mustang)
Mutation
Extraterrestrial life, **5** 775
Muttniks
Animals in space, **1** 154
Muuss, Ada
Givens, Edward Galen, Jr., **6** 981
MX-324 (Northrop)
X-series aerospace vehicles, **14** 2535
MX-524 (Bell Aircraft)
X-series aerospace vehicles, **14** 2536
MX-774
Atlas missile and launch vehicle, **2** 259
My-4, see Bison
Mya (airplane)
U.S.S.R. aerospace activities, **13** (picture)
2335, (table) 2337

Mylar
Airships, 1 108
Balloons, **2** 331
Communications satellites, **3** 533
Fabrics, **5** 786
Geodetic satellites, **6** 976
Mystere IV
Air forces of the world (France), **1** 65
Asia's aviation, **2** 204
Mysteres, Super, see Super Mystere aircraft
Mysterium Cosmographicum (book)
Kepler, Johannes, **7** 1274
Mythology (with pictures), **9** 1644-46

N

N3N (aircraft)
Crop dusting, **4** 588
N-9 seaplanes
Coast Guard aviation, **3** 476
N2S-5, see Stearman PT-17
NA-300 (North American)
Counter-insurgency aircraft, **4** 576
NAA, see National Aeronautic Association
NACA, see National Advisory Committee for
Aeronautics
NACATS, see North American Clear Air
Turbulence Tracking System
Nacelle (with diagram), **9** 1647
Airframe, **1** 66
Airplane, **1** 91
Nadir
Celestial sphere, **3** 431
NAEC, see National Aerospace Education
Council
Nagumo, Admiral
Pearl Harbor, **10** 1770
Nairobi Airport
Airports (picture), **1** 100
NAP, see National Airport Plan
Napalm
Air raid, **1** 104
Bombs, **3** 378
Vietnam, **13** 2415-23
Weaponry, **13** 2448-2449
Napoleonic Wars
Balloons, **2** 323
Narrow-beam detector
Infrared detection devices, **7** 1159
Narsarsuaq Air Base
Balchen, Bernt, **2** 312
NASA, see National Aeronautics and
Space Administration
NASA Distinguished Public Service Medal
Berkner, Lloyd Viel, **2** 351
NASA Distinguished Service Medal
Cooper, L. Gordon, Jr., **3** 566
Gilruth, Robert Rowe, **6** 981
Glenn, John Herschel, Jr., **6** 984
Grissom, Virgil I., **6** 1015
NASA Exceptional Service Medal
Astronauts, **2** 230
Borman, Frank, **3** 382
Cernan, Eugene Andrew, **3** 440
Collins, Michael, **3** 488
Conrad, Charles, Jr., **3** 561
Cooper, L. Gordon, Jr., **3** 566
Gordon, Richard F., Jr., **6** 996
Grissom, Virgil I., **6** 1015
McDivitt, James A., **8** 1518
Stafford, Thomas P., **12** 2157

NASA Outstanding Leadership Medal
Debus, Kurt Heinrich, **4** 612
Faget, Maxime, **5** 789
Speed and speed records (table), **12** 2141
National Academy of Science
Astronauts, **2** 222
Explorer satellites, **5** 762
International Geophysical Year, **7** 1194
Jet-assisted takeoff, **7** 1236
Lunar exploration, **8** 1401
**National Advisory Committee for
Aeronautics, 9** 1647
Commercial air transports, **3** 520
Crossfield, Albert Scott, Jr., **4** 594
Doolittle, James Harold, **4** 644
Dryden, Hugh Latimer, **4** 654
Government in aerospace, **6** 1004
Manufacturing, **8** 1467, 1468, 1470, 1472
Mercury program, **9** 1530
Military aviation, **9** 1582
NASA, **9** 1650
Re-entry vehicles, **11** 1932
National Aeronautic Association, 9 1647-48
Academy of Model Aeronautics, **1** 2
Aero clubs, **1** 18
Air racing, **1** 102
Balloons, **2** 319
Distance and distance records, **4** 639
Endurance and endurance records, **4** 711
Federation Aeronautique Internationale,
5 804
Model aircraft, **9** 1626
National Pilots Association, **9** 1666
Speed and speed records, **12** 2140
**National Aeronautics and Space Act of 1958,
9** 1648
National Aeronautics and Space Council,
9 1657
**National Aeronautics and Space Administra-
tion** (with diagrams, pictures, and tables),
9 1649-1657
Apollo, **1** 162-84
Apollo Applications Program, **2** 185-88
Astronauts, **2** 215-31
Balloons, **2** 331
Biosatellites, **2** 356
Careers, **3** 413, (table) 416, 417
Cobb, Geraldyn, **3** 480
Communications satellites, **3** 533, 536
Computers, **3** 558-59
Crash investigation, **4** 579, 582-83
Data acquisition and processing, **4** 606
Debus, Kurt Heinrich, **4** 612
Department of Defense, **4** 627
Discoverer Project, **4** 634
Agena rockets, **1** 38-39
Dryden, Hugh Latimer, **4** 654
Dynamic soaring, **4** 656
Economic implications of aerospace, **4** 672
Explorer satellites, **5** 765, 773
Faget, Maxime, **5** 788
Geodetic satellites, **6** 971, 974-76
Gilruth, Robert Rowe, **6** 980-81
Goddard Space Flight Center, **6** 992
Aerobee, **1** 18
Lasers, **7** 1304
Government in aerospace, **6** 1005
International projects, **7** 1198-99
Italy's aerospace activities, **7** 1223-24
International Satellite for Ionospheric
Studies, **7** 1201
Jet Propulsion Laboratory, **7** 1240
Kennedy Space Center, **7** 1265-66,
1268, 1273
Launching, **7** 1310-11
Kiwi, **7** 1281
Kraft, Christopher C., Jr., **7** 1294
Langley Research Center, **7** 1302
Launch vehicles, **7** 1319, 1322-23, 1328
Centaur, **3** 433
Delta rocket, **4** 622
Juno rockets, **7** 1259-60
Jupiter rockets, **7** 1261
Lewis Research Center, **7** 1334-35

(Continued)

National Aeronautics and Space Administration (Cont.)
Life-support systems, **8** 1338-43
Lifting-body vehicles, **8** 1350
Lunar charts, **8** 1400
Lunar exploration, **8** 1401-07
Manned Spacecraft Center, **8** 1457
  Lunar Receiving Laboratory, **8** 1414-15 (with diagram)
Mariner probes, **8** 1484-88
Marshall Space Flight Center, **8** 1494
Mercury program, **9** 1529, 1533, 1534, 1540, 1542
Military implications of space, **9** 1588-89
Military space program, **9** 1591-1605
Mission Control Center, **9** 1617-20
NERVA, **9** 1691
Oceanographic research, **10** 1734-41
Orbiting observatories, **10** 1741
Outsize cargo aircraft, **10** 1750
Parawing, **10** 1761
Parker, Robert A. R., **10** 1763
Pegasus, **10** 1773
Photography, **10** 1787
Photosynthesis, **10** 1790
Piccard family, **10** 1791
PILOT, **10** 1784
Pioneer, **10** 1812, 1814
Pressure suit, **10** 1851
Program management, **10** 1857-58
RAND Corporation, **10** 1903
Ranger, **10** 1905, 1911
Reconnaissance satellites, **11** 1924
Re-entry vehicles, **11** 1932, 1934
Research Flight Center
  Edwards Air Force Base, **4** 678
Reusable launch vehicles, **11** 1962
Robots, **11** 1966
Satellites, **11** 2008
SNAP, **11** 2061
Sounding rockets, **11** 2083
Surveyor, **12** 2209
Tiros Operational Satellite System
  ESSA spacecraft, **4** 739
Tracking systems and networks, **13** 2303
X-15 research program, **14** 2529-2533
XB-70, North American Valkyrie, **14** 2529
National Aeronautics and Space Council, **9** 1657-58
  National Aeronautics and Space Act of 1958, **9** 1648
National Aerospace Education Council, **9** 1658
  Aerospace, **1** 97
  National Aeronautic Association, **9** 1648
National Air and Space Museum (with pictures), **9** 1658-60
  Durant, Frederick Clark, III, **4** 655
  Loening Amphibian, **8** 1369
  Ninety-Nines, **9** 1698
  Wright brothers, **14** 2526
  X-series aerospace vehicles, **14** 2537
National Airlines
  Boeing 707, **2** 370
  Commercial airlines, **3** 498
National Airport Plan
  Federal Aviation Administration, **5** 801
National Air Races
  Air racing, **1** 102
National Air Shows
  Air shows, **1** 115
National Airspace System (with diagrams), **9** 1660-62
  Airman's Information Manual, **1** 80
  Careers, **3** 413, 416
  NOTAM, **9** 1706
  Preflight training, **10** 1846
National Air Taxi Conference, **9** 1662
  Charter flying, **3** 449
National Air Transport
  Airmail (picture), **1** 76
  Commercial airlines, **3** 498, 509, 510
National Association of Rocketry
  Model rocketry, **9** 1626-29
National Association of State Aviation Officials, **9** 1662-63

National Association of Third Level Airlines
  Commuter airlines, **3** 544
National Aviation Education Council
  Aerospace, **1** 27
National Aviation Facilities Experimental Center
  Federal Aviation Administration, **5** 796, 801
National Aviation Trades Association, 9 1663
National Business Aircraft Association
  Business aviation, **3** 396
National Business Aircraft Show
  Air shows, **1** 115
National Capital Airports, Bureau of
  Airports, **1** 98
National Center for Atmospheric Research
  Balloons, **2** 321, 330
  Berkner, Lloyd Viel, **2** 351
National Championship Air Races
  Air racing, **1** 103
National Defence Headquarters
  Ballistic Missile Early Warning System, **2** 314
National Defense Education Act
  Educational implications of aerospace, **4** 674
National emergency airlift plans, 9 1663
National Environmental Satellite Center, 9 1664
  Environmental Science Services Administration, **4** 724
National Geographic Society
  Balloons, **2** 321
National Hurricane Research Laboratory
  Environmental Science Services Administration, **4** 725
National Intercollegiate Flying Association, 9 1664
National Investigations Committee for Aerial Phenomena
  Unidentified flying objects, **13** 2322
Nationalist China's aviation (with pictures), **9** 1664-66
National Model Airplane Championships
  Academy of Model Aeronautics, **1** 2
National Model Rocket Championship Meet
  Model rocketry, **9** 1628
National Notice to Airmen System, see NOTAM
National Pilots Association, 9 1666-67
  Cobb, Geraldyn, **3** 480
National Radio Astronomy Observatory
  Berkner, Lloyd Viel, **2** 351
National Science Foundation
  Berkner, Lloyd Viel, **2** 351
  Explorer satellites, **5** 762
National Security Act Amendments
  Department of Defense, **4** 626
National Security Council
  Department of Defense, **4** 627
National Supersonic Transport Program
  XB-70, North American Valkyrie, **14** 2529
National Transportation Safety Board, 9 1667
  Civil Aeronautics Board, **3** 462, 464
  Crash investigation, **4** 579, (team chart) 580
NATO, see North Atlantic Treaty Organization
Natural gas
  Balloons, **2** 317
  Helium, **6** 1079
Natural satellite, 9 1667
Natural shape balloon
  Balloons, **2** 330
Nature of the Universe, The (book)
  Hoyle, Fred, **6** 1131
Nausea
  Airsickness, **1** 115
Nautical charts
  Charts, **3** 455
Nautical mile
  Mile, **9** 1565
Nautilus (submarine)
  Nuclear energy, **9** 1713
Navaids, see Navigation aids

Naval Academy
  Service academies, **11** 2044
Naval Appropriation Act of 1916
  Coast Guard aviation, **3** 475
Naval Aviation Museum, 9 1672
Naval aviation
  United States, **13** 2376-90
  Worldwide, **9** 1667-72
Naval Oceanographic Office
  Charts, **3** 455
Naval Ordnance Development Award
  Draper, Charles Stark, **4** 651
Naval Research Laboratory
  Aerobee, **1** 17
  International Years of the Quiet Sun, **7** 1204
Naval Test Center
  Bull, John Sumter, **3** 389
Navigating
  Pilot training, **10** 1810
  Preflight training, **10** 1848
Navigation
  Airborne antennas, **1** 43
  Azimuth, **2** 308
  Bush flying, **3** 392
  Careers, **3** 416
  Jumbo jets, **7** 1252
  Occupations (with tables), **10** 1729-30
  Spacecraft design, **11** 2100
Navigation aids (Navaids)
  Federal Aviation Administration, **5** 800
  Federal airways system, **5** 792
  Instrument panels, **7** 1173
Navigational requirements
  Orbits and trajectories, **10** 1742
Navigation application
  Radar, **10** 1878
Navigation-communication instruments
  Cockpit, **3** 485
Navigation instruments, 9 1672
  Instrument flight techniques, **7** 1167
  Instrument panels, **7** 1176
  Sextant (diagram), **11** 2045
Navigation lights
  Charts, **3** 450
Navigation satellites (with picture), **9** 1673-74
Navigation systems (with diagrams), **9** 1674-81
  Legal implications of aerospace, **7** 1331
  Inertial guidance, **7** 1152
  Military aviation, **9** 1587
Navigation techniques (with diagrams, maps and pictures), **9** 1681-87
Navigator
  Aircrew, **1** 59
  Observers, **10** 1726
Navy Blue Angels
  Precision flying, **10** 1845
Navy Curtiss (airplane)
  Coast Guard aviation, **3** 477
Navy pilots
  Aerospace research pilot, **1** 34
Near-zero visibility
  Instrument panels, **7** 1173
Nebel, Rudolf
  Rockets and rocketry, **11** 1979
Nebula (with pictures), **9** 1688-89
  Astronomy, **2** 238, 251
  Astrophysics, **2** 258
  Galaxies, **5** 910, (picture) 911
  Planetarium, **10** 1820
Nebular hypothesis
  Astronomy, **2** 238
Nebulosities
  International Geophysical Year, **7** 1197
Needle mixture control
  Mixture control, **9** 1623
Negative
  Photography, **10** 1782
Negative acceleration
  Deceleration, **4** 612
Negative electricity
  Electricity, **4** 684
Negative-g, 9 1689
  Acceleration, **1** 3

Negative plate
Battery, **2** 338
Negative semiconductor
Electronics, **4** 701
Negative shadow
Masers, **8** 1496
Negatrons
Beta particle, **2** 354
Negligible mass
Orbits and trajectories (diagrams), **10** 1743
Neon
Air, **1** 42
Neoprene
Airships, **1** 108
Nephanalysis
National Environmental Satellite Center, **9** 1664
Weather satellites, **13** 2461
Neptune (planet) (with picture), **9** 1689-90
Adams, John Couch, **1** 6
Astronomy, **2** 242, 243
Atmosphere, **2** 265
Bessel, Friedrich Wilhelm, **2** 354
Earth, **4** 663
Extraterrestrial life, **5** 777
Legal implications of aerospace, **7** 1331
Leverrier, Urbain, J. J., **7** 1334
Planets, **10** 1820
Retrograde motion, **11** 1961
Solar system, **11** 2070
Neptune P-2, see P-2 Neptune
Asia's aviation, **2** 204
Ne reid
Astronomy, **2** 247
Neptune, **9** 1690, (picture) 1689
NERVA (with pictures and diagram), **9** 1691-92
Electric propulsion, **4** 685
Launch vehicles, **7** 1328
Propellants, **10** 1862
Nuclear energy, **9** 1714
Rover project, **11** 1993-94
U.S. Atomic Energy Commission, **13** 2375
Netherlands
Communications satellites, **3** 538
Crop dusting, **4** 587
European aerospace activities, **4** 748
European air traffic control, **4** 752
European Launcher Development Organization, **4** 754
European Space Research Organization, **4** 755
International Agricultural Aviation Centre, **7** 1187
Launch vehicles, **7** 1327
NATO, **9** 1703-04
Naval aviation, worldwide, **9** 1670, (picture) 1671
Neubeck, Francis G. (1932-   , American aerospace research pilot), **9** 1692-93
Manned Orbiting Laboratory, **8** 1456
Neuenhofen, Willi
Altitude and altitude records, **1** 147
Neurophysiology
Cybernetics, **4** 602
Neutral atmosphere
Atmosphere, **2** 265
Neutron, 9 1693
Atoms, **2** 269
Kiwi, **7** 1281
Matter, **8** 1513
Nuclear energy, **9** 1710
Proton, **10** 1863
Radiation shield, **10** 1884
Radioisotope, **10** 1899
Neutron detectors
Nuclear detection satellites, **9** 1709
Neutron stars
Radio astronomy, **10** 1892
Stars, **12** 2162
New England Airlines
Nichols, Ruth Rowland, **9** 1696
New environment
Lunar bases, **8** 1385, (table) 1384

Newfoundland
Commemorative stamps and medals, **3** 495
Newhouse, R. C.
Electronics, **4** 693
New, Harry S.
Airmail, **1** 75
New jobs
Social implications of aerospace, **11** 2066
New moon
Moon, **9** 1634
Newton, Sir Isaac (1642-1727, English scientist and mathematician), **9** 1693
Aircraft propulsion systems, **1** 52
Atoms, **2** 269
Celestial mechanics, **3** 426, 428
Earth, **4** 662
Earth science, **4** 666
Fluid mechanics, **5** 857
Gravity, **6** 1012
Jet aircraft, **7** 1234
Kepler's laws, **7** 1274-75
Momentum, **9** 1631
Observatories, **10** 1725
Quantum theory, **10** 1868
Relativity theory, **11** 1951-52
Rockets and rocketry, **11** 1971
Telescopes and astronomical instruments, **12** 2249
Newtonian telescope
Telescopes and astronomical instruments, **12** 2249
Newton, Maurice
Airmail (picture), **1** 70
Newton's laws of motion (with diagrams), **9** 1694-95
Acceleration, **1** 2
Aerodynamics, **1** 19-20
Aircraft propulsion systems, **1** 52
Gravity, **6** 1012
Jet engines, **7** 1237
Jet propulsion, **7** 1240
Launch vehicles, **7** 1314
Quantum theory, **10** 1868
Newton's third law of motion
Reaction engines, **10** 1912
New York Airways
Helicopters, **6** 1070
New York, New York
Careers (table), **3** 414
New York, Rio and Buenos Aires Air Lines
Commercial airlines, **3** 508
New Zealand
Crop dusting, **4** 587
New Zealand Air Force
Second World War aircraft, **11** 2034
Nicaragua
Crop dusting, **4** 587
South and Central America's aviation, **11** 2091
Nicholetts, C. E.
Distance records, **4** 640
Nichols, Ruth Rowland (1901-   , American Aviatrix), **9** 1696
Altitude and altitude records, **1** 148
Women in aerospace, **14** 2494
Nicholson's Journal (1809-1810)
Cayley, Sir George, **3** 425
Nickel, 9 1695-96
Materials, **8** 1508
Steels, **12** 2164
Nickel-base alloys
Alloys, **1** 144
Nickel-cadmium
Battery, **2** 339
Nieuport (airplane)
First World War aircraft, **5** 822, 824, (pictures) 815, 823
History of aviation (picture), **6** 1105
World War I (picture), **14** 2503, 2506, 2508
Nigerian Airways
Africa's aviation, **1** 36
Night flying
Airmail, **1** 73-74
Korean war, **7** 1286

Night operations
Aircraft carriers (picture), **1** 50
Night photography
Infrared radiation, **7** 1162
Night reconnaissance missions
Photography, **10** 1789
Nike
Douglas, Donald Wills, **4** 649
Nike Ajax
Missiles (table), **9** 1616
Nike Apache
Aerospace Research Support Program, **1** 35
Nike Cajun
Aerospace Research Support Program, **1** 35
Nike Hercules missiles
Air defense systems, **1** 61
Guidance and control systems, **6** 1041
Missiles (table), **9** 1616
NORAD, **9** 1701
Surface-to-air missiles, **12** 2201, (picture) 2201
Nike Javelin
Aerospace Research Support Program, **1** 35
Nike-X
Atlas missile and launch vehicle, **2** 260
Government in aerospace, **6** 1006
Nike-Zeus program
Antimissile missiles, **1** 159
Nikolayev, Andrian G. (1929-   , Russian cosmonaut), **9** 1696-97
Cosmonauts, **4** 574, (pictures) 570, 573, (table) 574
Manned spaceflight (table), **8** 1461
Popovich, Pavel, **10** 1838
Medals and decorations (table), **8** 1524
Rendezvous and docking, **11** 1958
U.S.S.R. aerospace activities, **13** 2343
Nikolayeva-Tereshkova, Valentina (1937-   , Russian cosmonaut), **9** 1697
Cosmonauts, **4** 574, (pictures) 570, 573, 575, (table) 574
Medals and decorations (table), **8** 1524
U.S.S.R. aerospace activities, **13** 2344
Vostok, **13** 2435
Nimbostratus clouds
Clouds, **3** 473
Nimbus
Clouds, **3** 472
Command and data acquisition, **3** 493
Earth science, **4** 667
Gas jet propulsion, **5** 918
Infrared detection devices, **7** 1159
Oceanographic research, **10** 1732
National Environmental Satellite Center, **9** 1664
SNAP (with picture), **11** 2060
Weather satellites, **13** 2461, 2462, (pictures) 2462 2463, (table) 2470
Nimitz, Chester W.
World War II, **14** 2522
Nimrod, see Hawker Siddeley Nimrod
Ninety-Nines, 9 1697-98
Women in aerospace, **14** 2495
Nishizawa, Hiroyashi
World War II (table), **14** 2517
Nissan Motor Co., Ltd.
Japan's aerospace activities, **7** 1231
Nitric acid
Launch vehicles, **7** 1315
Liquid-fuel rockets, **8** 1363
Nitrification
Nitrogen, **9** 1698
Nitrogen, 9 1698
Air, **1** 42
Atmosphere, **2** 261
Gases, **5** 916
Nitrogen bubbles
Aviation medicine, **2** 297
Bends, **2** 349
Nitrogen cycle
Atmosphere, **2** 263
Nitrogen, **9** 1698

Nitrogen fixation
  Nitrogen, **9** 1698
Nitrogen tetroxide
  Apollo, **1** 173
  Launch vehicles, **7** 1315
  Liquid-fuel rockets, **8** 1363
Nitrous oxide
  Air, **1** 42
NLM
  European aerospace activities, **4** 748
Nobel prize
  Einstein, Albert, **4** 680
  Nuclear energy, **9** 1711
  Planck, Max K. E. L., **10** 1816
Nobile, Umberto (1885-   , Italian airship
    designer), **9** 1698-99
  Airships, **1** 112
  Amundsen, Roald, **1** 151
  Dirigibles, **4** 631
  Polar flights, **10** 1829
Noble gases
  Helium, **6** 1079
Noise (with data table), **9** 1699-1700
  Acoustics, **1** 4-5
  Sonic boom, **11** 2074
  Supersonic transports, **12** 2178
Noise measurement, 9 1700
Noise suppressors
  Acoustics (picture), **1** 5
Nolde, Francis W.
  Medals and decorations (table), **8** 1526
Nominal
  Terminology of aerospace (table), **12** 2272
Nonapproved schools
  Pilot training, **10** 1809
Nonconductors
  Electronics, **4** 694
Nondestructive landing
  Reusable launch vehicles, **11** 1962
Nonflammable components
  Lamination, **7** 1296
Nonmetals
  Elements, **4** 705
Nonreturning boomerang
  Boomerang, **3** 380
Nonrigid construction
  Airships, **1** 106, 109, (drawing) 112
Nonscheduled airlines
  Commercial airlines, **3** 513
Nonslaved system
  Compasses, **3** 549
Nonstructural materials
  Materials, **8** 1501
Nonuniform motion
  Motion, **9** 1640
NOO, see Naval Oceanographic Office
NORAD (with pictures), **9** 1700-03
  Air Defense Command, **1** 59
  Air defense systems, **1** 60
  Air forces of the world, **1** 64
  Ballistic Missile Early Warning System,
    2 313
  Blimps, **2** 366
  Canada's aviation, **3** 404
  Information systems, **7** 1157
  Interceptor aircraft, **7** 1182
  Semi-Automatic Ground Environment,
    11 2039
  Space Defense Center
    Biosatellites, **2** 357
  Space garbage, **12** 2119
  Tracking systems and networks, **13** 2305
Nord 2501 (transport)
  France's aerospace activities (picture),
    5 885
Nord-Aviation
  France's aerospace activities, **5** 889, 890
Norden bombsight
  Military aviation, **9** 1585
Norge (airship)
  Airships, **1** 112
  Amundsen, Roald, **1** 151
  Ellsworth, Lincoln, **4** 707
  Nobile, Umberto, **9** 1698-99

Norstad, Lauris (1907-   , American Air
    Force general), **9** 1703
North accelerometer
  Inertial guidance, **7** 1153
North Africa
  World War II, **14** 2516
North America
  Air Defense Command, **1** 59
  Air defense systems, **1** 60
  Air forces of the world, **1** 64
  Air masses (map), **1** 81
  Aurora, **2** 277
  Crop dusting, **4** 587
North American A-5 Vigilante,
    see A-5 Vigilante
North American AT-6, see AT-6 Texan
North American F-100 Super
    Sabre, see F-100 Super Sabre
North American Air Defense Command,
    see NORAD
North American Aviation
  Air-to-surface missiles, **1** 124
  Apollo, **1** 164
  Canada's aviation, **3** 404
  Launching, **7** 1311
  X-15 rocket engines
    Aircraft propulsion systems, **1** 59
North American Clear Air Turbulence
    Tracking System
  Clear air turbulence, **3** 468
North American B-25, see B-25 Mitchell
North American F-86, see F-86 Sabre
North American NA-300, see NA-300
North American OV-10A, see OV-10A Bronco
North American P-51 Mustang,
    see P-51 Mustang
North American Rockwell Corporation
  Clean room, **3** 468
  Crossfield, Albert Scott, Jr., **4** 594
  Little Joe, **8** 1364
  XB-70, North American Valkyrie, **14** 2528
North American Sabreliner
  General aviation aircraft (picture), **6** 967
  History of aviation (picture), **6** 1115
North American X-10, see X-10 test vehicle
North American X-15, see X-15 research
    program
North American XB-70 Valkyrie, see XB-70
North arrow
  Maps and mapping, **8** 1476
North Atlantic Command
  Air forces of the world (U.S.A.F.), **1** 65
North Atlantic Ocean
  Air masses, **1** 80
North Atlantic Treaty Organization, 9 1703-05
  Air forces of the world, **1** 65, 66
  Berkner, Lloyd Viel, **2** 351
  International projects, **7** 1201
  Italy's aerospace activities, **7** 1220
  United States Air Force, **13** 2359
  West Germany's aerospace activities,
    13 2475
North celestial pole
  Celestial sphere, **3** 431
Northeast Air Lines
  Commercial airlines, **3** 498
Northerly turning error
  Compasses (with diagram), **3** 548-49
Northern aerial mineral explorations
  Bush flying, **3** 392
Northern Fleet
  Air forces of the world (Russia), **1** 65
Northern Hemisphere
  Anticyclone, **1** 159
  Constellations, **3** 562
Northern Territory
  Australia's aviation, **2** 281
North Korean Air Force
  Korean war, **7** 1284
North magnetic pole
  Compasses, **3** 546
  Geomagnetic field, **6** 977
  Poles, **10** 1834

North Pacific Halibut Patrol
  Coast Guard aviation, **3** 479
North Pole
  Air defense systems, **1** 60
  Amundsen, Roald, **1** 151
  Bennett, Floyd, **2** 350
  Byrd, Richard Evelyn, **3** 397
  Polar flights, **10** 1828
  Poles, **10** 1833
Northrop CF-5 Freedom Fighter,
    see F-5 Freedom Fighter
  Canada's aviation, **3** 404
  History of aviation, **6** 1118
Northrop Corporation
  Northrop F-5 Freedom Fighter, **9** 1705
Northrop F-5, see F-5 Freedom Fighter
Northrop MQM-57A, see MQM-57A
Northrop SM62 Snark, see SM62 Snark
Northrop Snark
  Missiles (picture), **9** 1613
Northrop T-38 Talon, see T-38 Talon
Northrop X-4, see X-4
Northrop X-21, see X-21
North Star (airplane)
  Canada's aviation, **3** 401
North Star
  Planetarium, **10** 1819
  Polaris star, **10** 1833
North Vietnam
  Asia's aviation, **2** 203-4
  Vietnam, **13** 2414
Northwest Airlines
  Commercial airlines, **3** 512
Northwest Orient Airlines
  Commercial airlines, **3** 497
Norway
  Communications satellites, **3** 538
  Crop dusting, **4** 587
  European aerospace activities, **4** 747
  International projects, **7** 1199
  NATO, **9** 1703-04
  World War II, **14** 2512
Norwegian Air Lines
  Balchen, Bernt, **2** 312
Nose cone (with picture), **9** 1705-06
  Atlas missile and launch vehicle, **2** 259
  Ceramics (picture), **3** 439
  Heat shields, **6** 1057
  Jupiter rockets, **7** 1261
  Missiles, **9** 1610
Nose cone fairing
  Communications satellites (picture), **3** 534
Nose gear steering
  Jumbo jets, **7** 1254
Nose-up attitude
  Landing techniques, **7** 1301
Nose wheel
  Landing gear, **7** 1299
  Wheels, **13** 2480
NOTAM, 9 1706
Nova, 9 1706-07
  Stars, **12** 2159
Noyes, Blanche
  Women in aerospace, **14** 2494
Nozzles, 9 1707
  Jet engines, **7** 1239
NRX-A3 (NERVA Reactor Experiment)
  NERVA (picture), **9** 1691
NRX/EST
  NERVA (picture and diagram), **9** 1692
N. S. North Star (airship)
  First World War aircraft, **5** 821
N-square Law
  Lanchester, Frederick William, **7** 1298
NTSB, see National Transportation Safety
    Board
Nuclear analysis techniques
  Oceanographic research, **10** 1734
Nuclear arsenal
  Polaris missiles, **10** 1832
Nuclear bombs
  Argus project, **2** 191
  Bomber aircraft, **2** 376

(Continued)

Nuclear bombs (Cont.)
  Bombs, **3** 378
  Radiation, **10** 1883
Nuclear detection satellites (with pictures and diagrams), **9** 1707-09
  Military implications of space, **9** 1589
Nuclear deterrent weapon
  Poseidon missiles, **10** 1838
Nuclear energy (with pictures), **9** 1709-15
  Atomic bomb, **2** 269
  Energy, **4** 712
  Fission, **5** 826
  Interplanetary travel, **7** 1213
  Planets, **10** 1820
  Radiation, **10** 1883
  Rocket propulsion systems, **11** 1970
  SNAP program, **11** 2059
  Space power systems, **12** 2121
  Stars, **12** 2161
Nuclear Engine for Rocket Vehicle Applications, see NERVA
Nuclear engines
  Aircraft propulsion systems, **1** 52
  Kiwi, **7** 1281
  Launch vehicles, **7** 1328
  Space propulsion systems, **12** 2121
Nuclear fuel, 9 1715
Nuclear ground powerplants
  Kiwi, **7** 1281
Nuclear physics, 9 1715-16
  Nuclear energy, **9** 1709
  Quantum theory, **10** 1869-70
Nuclear power
  Aircraft propulsion systems, **1** 59
  Electric propulsion, **4** 685
  Interplanetary travel, **7** 1207-08, 1213
  Nuclear energy, **9** 1712, with pictures
Nuclear powers
  Air forces of the world, **1** 63
Nuclear propulsion (with pictures and diagrams), **9** 1716-20
  Aircraft propulsion systems, **1** 52
  Launch vehicles, **7** 1329
  Radiation shield, **10** 1884
  Space propulsion systems, **12** 2121
Nuclear-pulse engine
  Rocket propulsion systems, **11** 1970
Nuclear reactions
  Radiation, **10** 1880
  Rockets and rocketry, **11** 1985
Nuclear reactor
  Aircraft carriers, **1** 46-51
  Containment vessel
    Airlock, **1** 67
  Ion propulsion, **7** 1215
  Manhattan Project, **8** 1442
  Nuclear energy, **9** 1712-13, (pictures), 1710-14
  Nuclear fuel, **9** 1715
  Oceanographic research, **10** 1731
  Radiation, **10** 1882-83
  Radioisotope, **10** 1899
  Rocket propulsion systems, **11** 1970
  SNAP, **11** 2061
Nuclear Rocket Development Station
  NASA, **9** 1657
Nuclear rocket engines
  Rocket propulsion systems, **11** 1969
Nuclear rockets
  Launch vehicles, **7** 1328
  Rockets and rocketry, **11** 1985
Nuclear satellites
  Military space program, **9** 1597-98
Nuclear test detection
  Advanced Research Project Agency, **1** 7
  Nuclear detection satellites, **9** 1707
Nuclear war
  Polaris missiles, **10** 1832
Nuclear warheads
  Antiballistic missile defense, **1** 159
  Bomarc missiles
    Air defense systems, **1** 61
  Genie rocket
    Air-to-air missiles, **1** 121
  Missiles, **9** 1610
  Polaris missiles, **10** 1832

Surface-to-surface missiles, **12** 2204
Nuclear weapons
  Aircraft carriers, **1** 47
  Air forces of the world, **1** 65
  NATO, **9** 1704
Nucleating agents
  Ceramics, **3** 439
Nuclei
  Quantum theory, **10** 1870
Nucleus
  Atoms, **2** 269
  Comets, **3** 490
  Electronics, **4** 694
Null
  Navigation systems, **9** 1675
Null point
  Automatic direction finder, **2** 286
Number One (insignia)
  World War I, **14** (picture) 2505
Numerical control
  Precision measurements, **10** 1846
Nungesser, Charles
  World War I, **14** 2504, 2506, (table) 2507, 2508, 2510
"Nursing" crew
  Agricultural aviation, **1** 41
Nutrients
  Algae, **1** 143
Nychthemeral
  Circadian rhythm, **3** 460
Nylon
  Airships, **1** 108

O-1 Bird Dog (Cessna)
  Army aviation (picture), **2** 197
  Asia's aviation, **2** 204
O-2 spotter planes (Cessna)
  Marine Corps Aviation, **8** 1483
Oak Ridge National Laboratory
  Nuclear energy, **9** 1711-12
OAO, see Orbiting Astronomical Observatory
OAR, see Office of Aerospace Research
Oberth, Hermann, (1894-   , Rumanian-German rocket scientist), **10** 1721
  Dornberger, Walter Robert, **4** 646
  Electric propulsion, **4** 685
  Peenemuende, **10** 1770
  Rockets and rocketry, **11** 1977, 1985
Oberursel UR II (airplane engine)
  Fokker D-8, **5** 867
  World War I, **14** 2502
Objects of art, 10 1721
Oblate spheroid
  Earth, **4** 660
  Precession, **10** 1843
Observation balloons
  Balloons, **2** 323-24
  World War I, **14** 2503, (picture) 2504
Observation planes (see also Reconnaissance aircraft)
  Military aircraft, **9** 1568 (with pictures)
Observation satellites
  Reconnaissance satellites, **11** 1924
Observatories, 10 1723-26
Observatory construction
  Observatories, **10** 1723
Observer, 10 1726
Obstruction altitude
  Piloting techniques, **10** 1801-02

Obstruction lighting
  Lighting facilities, **8** 1354
Occluded front
  Aviation weather, **2** 305
  Front, **5** 894 ·
  Weather, **13** 2450
Occupations, 10 1726-30
  Careers, **3** 411
Ocean currents
  Oceanographic research, **10** 1732
Oceanic or maritime surface
  Air masses, **1** 80
Oceanic traffic control
  Air traffic control, **1** 135
Ocean of Storms
  Luna probes, **8** 1378
  Moon, **9** 1635
  Surveyor, **12** 2213
Oceanographic observations
  Satellites, **11** 2008
Oceanographic research, 10 1731-34
  Implications of aerospace, **7** 1151
Oceanography
  International Geophysical Year, **7** 1195
  Oceanographic research, **10** 1731
Oceans
  Reconnaissance, airborne, **11** 1920
Ocean Systems, Inc.
  Link, Edwin, A., **8** 1361
Ocean technology
  Oceanographic research, **10** 1734
Octane rating
  Fuels, **5** 898
Octet truss
  Geodesics, **6** 970
Oelerich, Harry
  Altitude and altitude records, **1** 147
Oepik, H. G.
  Mars, **8** 1491
Oersted, Hans Christian, (1777-1851)
  Electromagnetism, **4** 688
Office of Aerospace Research, 10 1735
  United States Air Force, **13** 2371
Office of Life Sciences
  Life-support systems, **8** 1339
Office of Military Aeronautics
  Arnold, Henry Harley, **2** 201
Office of Strategic Services
  Intelligence, military, **7** 1180
Offut Air Force Base
  Strategic Air Command, **12** 2167
Oficinas Tecnicas Dornier
  Dornier, Claude, **4** 647
OGO, see Orbiting Geophysical Observatory
OH-6A Cayuse helicopter (Hughes)
  Army aviation, **2** 197, (picture) 198
  Reconnaissance aircraft, **11** 1923
OH-13 Sioux helicopter (Bell)
  Agricultural aviation (picture), **1** 40
  Army aviation, **2** 197
  General aviation (picture), **6** 953
OH-23 Raven helicopter (Hiller)
  Army aviation, **2** 197
O'Hare Airport
  Air traffic control, (diagram) **1** 126, 137-39
  Commercial airlines, **3** 503
  Government in aerospace (diagram), **6** 1009
Ohio Agricultural Experimental Station
  Crop dusting, **4** 586
Ohm, Georg Simon
  Electricity, **4** 684
Ohm's Law
  Electricity, **4** 684
Oil burner routes, 10 1735
Oil-canning
  propeller noise
    Acoustics, **1** 4-5
Oil pressure gauge
  Engine instruments, **4** 715
  Instrument panels, **7** 1176
  Pressure gauges, **10** 1850
Oil temperature gauge
  Instrument panels, **7** 1176
  Temperature gauges, **7** 2269-70

O

Old Charley
World War I, **14** 2505
Oldfield, Barney
Air shows, **1** 115
Olds, Robert, (1922-   , American Air
Force officer) **10** 1735-36
Ace (picture), **1** 4
Astronauts 218, 219 (with picture)
Oleo strut landing gear
Airplane, **1** 89
Olieslagers, Jan
Altitude and altitude records, **1** 147
Distance records, **4** 640
World War I (table, Top Aces), **14** 2507
Oliver, Ruth Law, (1877-   , American
aviatrix), **10** 1736
Women in aerospace, **14** 2494
Olson, Edith
Women in aerospace, **14** 2496
Olson, Trudy
Cooper, L. Gordon, Jr., **3** 566
Olympic Airways
European aerospace activities, **4** 746
Omicron Ceti
Astrophysics, **2** 258
Omlie, Phoebe Fairgrave
Women in aerospace, **14** 2494
Omnidirectional antenna
Ground antennas, **6** 1015
Surveyor, **12** 2210
Omni navigation (with picture), **10** 1736-37
Omni range
Air traffic control, **1** 128
Beacon, radio, **2** 345
Cockpit, **3** 485
Navigation systems, **9** 1674, 1675, 1678,
(diagram), 1677
Visual omni range, **13** 2426
On Aerial Navigation (article)
Cayley, Sir George, **3** 425
Onboard computers, 10 1737
Kosmos satellites, **7** 1292
One-burn upper stage
Launch vehicles, **7** 1317
100-hour inspection
Preventive maintenance, **10** 1852
Ong, William A.
Medals and decorations (table), **8** 1526
Onnes, Heike Kamerlingh
Cryogenics, **4** 596
On-the-job training
Photogrammetry, **10** 1780
On the Phenomena (book)
Planetarium, **10** 1818
Oort, Jan H.
Comets, **3** 492
Opaque
Light, **8** 1351
Open cockpit
Airplane (picture), **1** 83
Open-loop control
Guidance and control systems, **6** 1034
Open sea rescues
Rescue and Recovery Service (with
pictures), **11** 1958
Open space sleds
Maneuvering in space, **8** 1431
Operating limitations
Certification procedures, **3** 443
Operating model
Prototype, **10** 1863
Operating Rights, Bureau of
Civil Aeronautics Board, **3** 465
Operational, 10 1737
Operational data
Airman's Information Manual, **1** 80
Operational fatigue, 10 1737
Operational navigation chart
Charts, **3** 450, 451, 455
Operation Barbarossa
World War II, **14** 2515-16
Operation Sea Lion
Battle of Britain, **2** 343
Operations Support Wing
Mission Control Center, **9** 1617

Operation Sunflare
Friedman, Herbert, **5** 894
Operation Torch
World War II, **14** 2516
Opposition
Conjunction, **3** 560
Optical alignments of critical guidance
Kennedy Space Center, **7** 1267
Optical axis
Orbiting observatories, **10** 1740
Optical detector
Nuclear detection satellites, **9** 1709
Optical equipment
Kosmos satellites, **7** 1292
Optical experiments
Relativity theory, **11** 1949, 1951
Optical glass
Glass, **6** 983
Optical illusions
Illusions, **7** 1147
Optical image
Photography, **10** 1781
Optical lenses
Celestial navigation, **3** 430
Optical observation
Reconnaissance, airborne, **11** 1919
Optical pyrometry
Temperature gauges, **12** 2270
Optical recorder (picture)
Photography, **10** 1786
Optical sight
Infrared detection devices, **7** 1161
Optical stereo-plotting instrument
Photogrammetry, **10** 1780
Optical telescope
Orbiting observatories, **10** 1738
Optical tracking
Battlefield missile systems, **2** 342
Optical tracking stations
International Geophysical Year, **7** 1196
Quantum theory, **10** 1870
Optical windows
Radio astronomy, **10** 1890
Planck, Max K. E. L., **10** 1816
Opticks (book)
Newton, Sir Isaac, **9** 1693
Optimal bomber design
RAND Corporation, **10** 1903
Oral Operational Examination
Pilot's training, **10** 1811
Oral temperature probe
Aerospace medicine (picture), **1** 34
Orbit (see also Orbits and trajectories)
Agena rockets, **1** 39
Applications Technology Satellites, **2** 189
Atoms, **2** 270
Celestial mechanics, **3** 427
Earth, **4** 660, 661
Launch vehicles, **7** 1314
Mercury program, **9** 1545
Planets, **10** 1821
Orbital altitudes
Launch vehicles, **7** 1313
Orbital animal flight
Animals in space, **1** 154
Orbital elements
Tracking systems and networks, **13** 2298
Orbital inclination
Orbits and trajectories, **10** 1747
Orbital launch vehicle
Sounding rockets, **11** 2080
Orbital maneuvering systems
Kennedy Space Center, **7** 1267
Orbital plane
Orbits and trajectories, **10** 1746-47
Orbital precession
Orbits and trajectories, **10** 1746
Orbital velocity, 10 1737-38
Launch vehicles, **7** 1314
Orbital workshop
Apollo Applications Program, **2** 185
Astronauts, **2** 215
Orbiter
Explorer satellites, **5** 762

Orbiting Astronomical Observatory
Agena rockets, **1** 38
Atlas missile and launch vehicle, **2** 260
Earth science, **4** 666
Guidance and control systems, **6** 1040
Orbiting observatories, (with picture and
diagram), **10** 1738-40
NASA, **9** 1653
Major Launchings, (table), **9** 1652
Orbiting Geophysical Observatory
Agena rockets, **1** 38
Atlas missile and launch vehicle, **2** 260
Cunningham, R. Walter, **4** 600
International Years of the Quiet Sun, **7** 1204
NASA, **9** 1653
Major Launchings (table), **9** 1652
Orbiting observatories, **10** 1741
Orbiting observatories, 10 1738-41
(OSCAR)
Orbiting satellite
Antiballistic missile defense, **1** 159
Orbiting Satellites Carrying Amateur Radios
Communications satellites, **3** 533-34,
(table) 543
Discoverer Project, **4** 639
Orbiting Solar Observatory
Delta rocket, **4** 622
Earth science, **4** 666
International Years of the Quiet Sun, **7** 1204
NASA, **9** 1653
Major Launchings (table), **9** 1652
Orbiting observatories, (with picture and
diagram), **10** 1738-39
X-ray stars, **14** 2533
Orbiting Vehicle spacecraft
Aeorspace Research Support Program,
1 35 (with picture)
Atlas missile and launch vehicle, **2** 260
Environmental research satellites, **4** 723
Military space program (picture), **9** 1595
Photography, **10** 1789
Orbits and trajectories, 10 1742-47
Orbits, Theory of
Orbits and trajectories, **10** 1742
Ordnance
Launch vehicles, **7** 1317
Organic chemical interpretations
Mars, **8** 1491
Organic substances, search for
Extraterrestrial life, **5** 774-84
Interplanetary travel, **7** 1212
Orientation
Man in flight, **8** 1446-48, (diagrams)
1447, 1448
Pioneer (with diagram), **10** 1814
Orion (o RY un)
Astronomy, **2** 252
Constellations, **3** 562
Nebula, **9** 1689
Milky Way, **9** 1605
Orion, see P-3 Orion
Orion transport, see Lockheed Orion
Orion (Wiley Post's airplane)
Johnson, Clarence Leonard, **7** 1232
Oriskany (ship)
Aircraft carriers (data table), **1** 51
Ornithopter, 10 1748
Bird flight, **2** 358
Da Vinci, Leonardo, **4** 611
History of aviation (picture), **6** 1094
Man-powered flight, **8** 1463-65
Penaud, Alphonse, **10** 1774
Orthographic projection
Maps and mapping, **8** 1478
Ortmans, V.
World War II (table), **14** 2517
Oscar Association
Communications satellites, **3** 534
Oscar I-III, see Orbiting Satellites Carrying
Amateur Radios
Oscillation
Electronics, **4** 695
Oscillation error
Compasses, **3** 549

Oscillation theory
Space, **11** 2093
Oscillator
Data acquisition and processing, **4** 605
Osler, M. S.
World War II (table), **14** 2517
Osoviakhlm-V-6
Dirigibles (picture), **4** 630
Ostfriesland (ship)
Bomber aircraft, **2** 374, (with picture)
Otter (aircraft)
Army aviation (picture), **2** 199
Canada's aviation, **3** 403
Otto cycle
Aircraft propulsion systems, **1** 54
Reciprocating engines, **11** 1914
Otto, Nikolaus August
Aircraft propulsion systems, **1** 54
History of aviation (table), **6** 1119
Reciprocating engines, **11** 1914
Our Air Force, the Keystone of National Defense (book)
Mitchell, William, **9** 1621
Our Nuclear Future (book)
Teller, Edward, **12** 2265
Outer casings
Launch vehicles, **7** 1316
Outer core
Geomagnetic field, **6** 977
Outer markers
Instrument landing system, **7** 1170
Outer space
International aviation and space agreements, **7** 1189-90
Kosmos satellites, **7** 1290
Legal implications of aerospace, **7** 1331
Space, **11** 2092-93
Outer Space Treaty
Space law, **12** 2119
Space, **11** 2092-93
Outgassing (oxygen)
Lunar bases, **8** 1387
Outline of History (book)
Wells, Herbert George, **13** 2474
Outpost
Lunar bases, **8** 1389, 1391
Output
Computers, **3** 553
Outriggers
Bicycle gear, **2** 354
Outsize cargo aircraft, 10 1748-50
OV-1 Mohawk (Grumman)
Army aviation, **2** 197
Military aircraft (picture), **9** 1568
Reconnaissance aircraft, **11** 1923
OV1 and OV3-3 satellites
Military space program (picture), **9** 1595
OV-10A Bronco (North American)
Counter-insurgency aircraft, **4** 576-77 (with picture)
Marine Corps Aviation, **8** 1483
Reconnaissance aircraft, **11** 1923
Overall mission time
Interplanetary travel, **7** 1210, (with diagram)
Over drainage pipes
Jumbo jets, **7** 1258
Over-exposure
Photography, **10** 1785
Overhead panel
Cockpit, **3** 486
Overlapping exposures
Photogrammetry, **10** 1780
Overmyer, Robert F. (1936-
Aerospace research pilot), **10** 1751
Manned Orbiting Laboratory, **8** 1456
Overpressure
Supersonic transports, **12** 2195
Overt propaganda
Intelligence, military, **7** 1180
Ovington, Earle
Airmail, **1** 69

OV satellite, see Orbiting Vehicle Spacecraft
Owl
NASA (drawing), **9** 1651
Owner's handbook
Pilot's handbook, **10** 1809
OX, see Standard SJ-1 "OX"
OX-5 Club, 10 1751
Aircraft propulsion systems, **1** 56
Oxidation reaction
Chemical energy, **3** 456
Oxidation-reduction and electrical energy
Chemical energy, **3** 456
Oxidizers, 10 1751-52
Jet engines, **7** 1237
Launch vehicles, **7** 1315
Lubricants, **8** 1375
Propellants, **10** 1859
Rocket propulsion systems, **11** 1967
Rockets and rocketry, **11** 1985
Oxidizing atmosphere
Atmosphere, **2** 265
Oxygen, 10 1752
Aerospace medicine, **1** 34
Air, **1** 42
Algae, **1** 143
Astronaut maneuvering unit, **2** 213
Atmosphere, **2** 261
Aviation medicine, **2** 293
Balloons, **2** 326
Carbon dioxide, **3** 407
Closed ecological system, **3** 470
Cryogenic propellants, **4** 595
Environmental control system, **4** 720
Extraterrestrial life, **5** 775
Gases, **5** 916
Hypoxia, **6** 1144
Life-support systems, **8** 1340-43, (diagrams) 1341, 1342, 1343, (pictures) 1342
Lunar bases, **8** 1387
Man in flight, **8** 1444-45, (diagram and data table) 1444, (graph) 1445
Oxidizers, **10** 1751
Oxygen toxicity, **10** 1753
Ozone, **10** 1753
Plasma, **10** 1822
Pressure suit, **10** 1851
Propellants, **10** 1861
Spacesuits, **12** 2129
Oxygen atmosphere
Ozone, **10** 1753
Oxygen, liquid, see Liquid oxygen
Oxygen masks, 10 1752-53
Life-support systems, **8** 1337, (diagrams and picture) 1341
Pressurization, **10** 1851
Rocket sled, **11** 1987
Soaring (picture), **11** 2064
World War I, **14** 2510 (with picture)
Oxygen regulators
Oxygen masks, **10** 1753
Oxygen substitute
Launch vehicles, **7** 1315
Oxygen system
Partial pressure suit, **10** 1763
Oxygen toxicity, 10 1753
Man in flight, **8** 1451
Ozma project, 10 1753
Extraterrestrial life, **5** 784
Ozone, 10 1753
Air, **1** 42
Extraterrestrial life, **5** 776
Ozone gases, **10** 1753
Polar flights, **10** 1831
Stratosphere, **12** 2170
Ozone concentrations
Ariel satellites, **2** 192
Ozone layer
Atmosphere, **2** 264
Ozonosphere
Atmosphere, **2** 264

P

P, see Polar air mass
P2-V Neptune (Lockheed)
Jet aircraft (picture), **7** 1236
Naval aviation, worldwide, **9** 1670-72
P2Y, see Consolidated P2Y
P-3 Orion (Lockheed)
Air forces of the world (picture), **1** 63
Australia's aviation, **2** 281
Naval aviation (picture), **9** 1671
P5M-1 Marlin, see Martin P5M-1 Marlin
P-11 Lightning (English Electric)
Air forces of the world, **1** 64, 66
Air racing, **1** 103
Fighter aircraft, **5** 811
History of aviation, **6** 1118
P-26 Peashooter (Boeing), **10** 1864-65
Fighter aircraft, **5** 811
P-36, see Curtiss P-36
P-38 Lightning (Lockheed), **8** 1368 (with picture and chart)
Bong, Richard Ira, **3** 379
Johnson, Clarence Leonard, **7** 1242
Pursuit airplane, **10** 1866
P-39 Airacobra (Bell)
Air races, **1** 103
Bell, Lawrence Dale, **2** 348
Second World War aircraft (with picture), **11** 2036
P-40 Tomahawk (Curtiss)
Fighter aircraft (picture), **5** 809
P-40 Curtiss (with picture and table), **10** 1776
Second World War aircraft, **11** 2031, (with picture) 2035
World War II, **14** 2520
P-47 Thunderbolt (Republic)
Pursuit airplane, **10** 1866
P-51 Mustang (North American)
World War II, **14** 2519
P-59, see XP-59
P-61
Cloud seeding, **3** 474
P-80, see F-80 Shooting Star
P-1127 Kestrel (Hawker Siddeley)
Camm, Sir Sydney, **3** 398
International projects, **7** 1199
V/STOL aircraft (table), **13** 2443
P-1157 vertical-riser fighter (Hawker Siddeley)
Air forces of the world, **1** 66
PA-11, see Piper Cub
PA-18, see Piper Cub
PA-25 Pawnee, see Piper Pawnee
PA-32 Cherokee, see Piper Cherokee Six
Pacer (airplane)
Piper, William T., **10** 1815
Pacific Aero Products Company
Boeing, William Edward, **2** 369
Pacific Air Forces
United States Air Force, **13** 2371
Pacific Airlines
Boeing, William Edward, **2** 369
Commercial airlines, **3** 513
Pacific Air Transport
Airmail, **1** 77
Commercial airlines, **3** 510
Pacific Command
Air forces of the world (USAF), **1** 65
Pacific Fleet
Air forces of the world (Russia), **1** 65
Pacific Launch Operations Office
NASA, **9** 1657
Pacific Ocean
Air defense systems, **1** 60

Pacific Oceanographic Laboratories
Environmental Science Services
Administration, **4** 725
Pacific 1 satellite
Communications satellites, **3** 539
Pack mule
Lunar bases, **8** 1391, (drawing) 1393
Paddlewheel (satellite)
Explorer satellites, **5** 767
Pad Terminal Connection Room
Kennedy Space Center, **7** 1273
Pad time
Kennedy Space Center, **7** 1268
Pageos (satellite)
Aluminum, **1** 149, (with picture)
Geodetic satellites, **6** 975-76 (picture)
976, (table) 973
Paillard, Anthoine
Distance records, **4** 640
Paint, 10 1754
Pakistan
Asia's aviation, **2** 203, 205
Crop dusting, **4** 587
Pakistan International Airlines
Mainland China's aerospace activities,
8 1425, (picture) 1425
Pallas
Asteroids, **2** 208
Astronomy, **2** 245
Pallet
Cargo aircraft, **3** 421
Pan
Emergency signals, **4** 708
Inflight emergency procedures, **7** 1155
PANAGRA
South and Central America's aviation,
11 2088
Panama
Commemorative stamps and medals, **3** 495
Pan American Airways
Charter flying, **3** 448
China Clipper, **3** 457
Flying boats, **5** 859
Commercial airlines, **3** 497, 508
Trippe, Juan Terry, **13** 2311
Pan American-Grace Airways
Commercial airlines, **3** 508
Pan American World Airways
Africa's aviation, **1** 36
Boeing 707, **2** 370
Jumbo jets, **7** 1246, 1257
Terminology of aerospace (table), **12** 2272
Pancake landing
Military aviation (pictures), **9** 1581
Panel code, 10 1755
Pangborn, Clyde
Bellanca, Giuseppe, **2** 349
Panoramic cameras
Aerial photography, **1** 9
Reconnaissance aircraft, **11** 1922
Panzer divisions
World War II, **14** 2512
Paper airplane
Jumbo jets, **7** 1246
PAR, see Precision Approach Radar
Parabellum machine gun
World War I, **14** 2504, 2505
Parabellum pistol
World War I (picture), **14** 2501
Parabola (with diagram), **10** 1755-56
Ballistic trajectory, **2** 314
Orbits and trajectories, **10** 1742
Parabolic flight
Launch vehicles, **7** 1319
Parabolic motion
Orbits and trajectories, **10** 1743
Parabolic orbit
Orbits and trajectories, **10** 1744
Parabolic receivers
Parabola, **10** 1756
Parabolic reflector
Ground antennas, **6** 1016
Radar, **10** 1877
Radio astronomy, **10** 1892-93

Parabolic-shaped figure
Area rule, **2** 190
Parabolic surface
Parabola, **10** 1756
Parabolic trajectory
Parabola, **10** 1756
Paraboloids (picture)
Radio astronomy, **10** 1892
Paracargo planes
Forest fire control, **5** 880
Parachute canopy
Parachutes, **10** 1757
Parchute Federation
Australia's aviation, **2** 282
Parachute jump training
Pararescue, **10** 1760
Parachute pack
Parachutes, **10** 1757
Parachutes (with pictures), **10** 1756-59
Bailout, **2** 310
Blanchard, Jean Pierre Francois, **2** 363
Escape systems, **4** 730
Fabrics, **5** 786, 787
First World War aircraft, **5** 817
Garnerin, Andre-Jacques, **5** 913, 914
Recovery, **11** 1928
Re-entry, **11** 1930
Skydiving (picture), **11** 2054
Soaring (picture), **11** 2064
Sport flying, **12** 2150
Wise, John, **14** 2493
World War I, **14** 2503
World War II, **14** 2512
Parachuting
International competitions, **7** 1191
Paraffin
Extraterrestrial life, **5** 781
Paraglider
Fabrics, **5** 786, 787
Parawing, **10** 1760
Sport flying (picture), **12** 2150
Paraguay
South and Central America's aviation,
11 2091
Parallax, 10 1760
Astronomy, **2** 249
Bessel, Friedrich Wilhelm, **2** 354
Jumbo jets, **7** 1256
Parsec, **10** 1763
Parallel of altitude
Celestial sphere, **3** 431
Parallels
Maps and mapping, **8** 1476, (table) 1478-79
Parallels of declination
Celestial sphere, **3** 433
Parallels of latitude
Celestial sphere, **3** 433
Parametric amplifier
Masers, **8** 1497
Radar, **10** 1874
Pararescue, 10 1760
Military aircraft, **9** 1570
Pararescuemen
Flickinger, Donald Davis, **5** 829
Pararescue, **10** 1760
Recovery, **11** 1928
Rescue and Recovery Service, **11** 1958-59
Parasailing, see Skysailing
Parasitic drag
X-series aerospace vehicles, **14** 2543
Parawing (with pictures), **10** 1760-61
Parawing program
Parawing, **10** 1761
Survival and rescue, **12** 2219
Paris
Airmail, **1** 69
Paris Air Shows (with pictures), **10** 1762
Commercial airlines, **3** 515
Paris Convention
Air Commerce Act, **1** 45
Parker, Alvin
Medals and decorations (table), **8** 1526
Parker, Robert A. R. (1936- , Scientist-
astronaut), **10** 1763
Astronauts, **2** 218 219 (with picture)

Parker, S. V.
Coast Guard aviation, **3** 476
Parking orbit
Orbits and trajectories, **10** 1746-47
Spaceflight principles, **12** 2106
Parking orbit coast mode
Launch vehicles, **7** 1318
Parks, Robert Joseph, (1922- , American
aerospace scientist), **10** 1763
Parrish, Wayne W.
Medals and decorations (table), **8** 1526
Parsec, 10 1763
Astronomy, **2** 249
Parsons, Edwin
World War I, **14** 2506
Parsons, William
Telescopes and astronomical instruments,
12 2250
Part 135, Federal Aviation Regulations
Charter flying, **3** 448
Partial pressure suit, 10 1763
Personal equipment, **10** 1775
Particles
Radiation shield, **10** 1884
Particulate
Radiation, **10** 1880
Pascal, Blaise
Computers, **3** 556
Jumbo jets, **7** 1249, 1251, 1255
Passenger Emergency Evacuation Standards
Certification procedures, **3** 444
Passenger-mile, 10 1764
Passengers
Airliner, **1** 67
Commercial airlines, **3** 503
Interiors of aircraft, **7** 1186
Passenger services, 10 1764-65
Passive communications satellite
Communications satellites, **3** 532
Passive reflector satellite, 10 1765
Patents, 10 1765
Patrick Air Force Base
Acquisition and tracking radar
(picture), **1** 6
Launching, **7** 1312
Patrouille de France
Demonstration teams, **4** 626
Patrol Bomber Squadron Six
Coast Guard aviation, **3** 479
Patterns
Lighting facilities, **8** 1353, (diagram and
picture) 1355
Patterson, William
Commercial airlines, **3** 502
Pattle, Marmaduke St. J.
World War II (table), **14** 2517
Patton, George
World War II, **14** 2517
Paulhan, Louis (1883- , French aviator),
10 1768-69
Altitude and altitude records, **1** 146, 147
Distance records, **4** 640
Pauli exclusion principle
Atoms, **2** 270
Pauli, Wolfgang
Atoms, **2** 270
Paul Tissandier Diploma
Medals and decorations, **8** 1524,
(table) 1526
Pavlovian dogs
Animals in space, **1** 154
Pawnee, see Piper Pawnee
Payload injection motors
Launch vehicles, **7** 1319
Payloads, 10 1769
Aerobee, **1** 17-18
Aerospace Research Support Program, **1** 35
Agena rockets, **1** 39
Centaur, **3** 434
Discoverer Project, **4** 639
Intercontinental ballistic missiles, **7** 1182
International projects, **7** 1198
Launch vehicle, **7** 1313-14, 1325
Missiles, **9** 1616

Nose cone, **9** 1705-06
  Rockets and rocketry, **11** 1977
  Sounding rockets (with diagram), **11** 2080
  Weight and balance, **13** 2471
Pazmany PL-1 (airplane)
  Homebuilt aircraft, **6** 1125
PBY, see Consolidated PBY
PE-2 attack bomber
  Second World War aircraft (with picture),
  11 2032
Peaceful uses of outer space
  International projects, **7** 1198
Peak horsepower
  Measurement of power, **8** 1519,
  (diagram) 1519
Peaking forecasts
  Jumbo jets, **7** 1257
Pearl Harbor, 10 1769-70
  United States Air Force, **13** 2363
  World War II, **14** 2520-21
Peary, Robert E.
  Amundsen, Roald, **1** 151
  Poles, **10** 1834
Peashooter, see P-26
Pectorals
  Bird flight, **2** 360
  Man-powered flight, **8** 1463-65
Peculiar A-stars
  Stars, **12** 2159
Peenemuende (Rocket Development Center),
  10 1770-71
  Debus, Kurt Heinrich, **4** 612
  Dornberger, Walter Robert, **4** 646
  Ehricke, Krafft Arnold, **4** 680
  Missiles, **9** 1611
  Rockets and rocketry, **11** 1978-79
  V-2 rocket missile, **13** 2445
  Von Braun, Wernher, **13** 2429
  World War II, **14** 2511
Pegasus (satellite), **10** 1771-73
  Aluminum, **1** 149
  Earth science, **4** 666
  Environmental research satellites, **4** 724
Pegasus (myth)
  Mythology (picture), **9** 1644
Pegoud, Adolphe (1889-1915, French
  aviator), **10** 1773
  Barnstormers, **2** 333
  Beachey, Lincoln, **2** 345
Peking National Defense Sports Association
  Mainland China's aerospace activities
  (picture), **8** 1427
Pellegrino, Ann
  Women in aerospace, **14** 2496
Penaud, Alphonse (1850-80, French
  aeronautical pioneer), **10** 1774
  History of aviation, **6** 1096, (table) 1119
Pencil beam
  Radar, **10** 1877
Penetration, 10 1774
Penn Central Railroad
  High-speed surface transportation, **6** 1091
Pennsylvania (ship)
  Aircraft carriers, **1** 48 (with picture)
Pentathos (book)
  Erathosthenes, **4** 729
Pentodes
  Electronics, **4** 697
Penumbra
  Eclipse, **4** 668
People's Republic of China
  Air forces of the world, **1** 63, 64
  Asia's aviation, **2** 203
  Mainland China's aerospace activities,
  8 1421
PEPP, see Planetary Entry Parachute Program
Pepper plants
  Biosatellites, **2** 356
Performance
  Telemetry, **12** 2241-42
  Testing, **12** 2272-76
Performance capability
  Launch window, **7** 1329

Performance characteristics
  Propellers (with picture), **10** 1863
Performance charts, 10 1774
  Pilot's handbook, **10** 1809
Performance data, see entries on individual
  aircraft
Performance test
  Preventive maintenance, **10** 1852
Periapsis
  Orbits and trajectories, **10** 1744
Pericynthion
  Rendezvous and docking, **11** 1957
Perigee, 10 1774
  Alouette satellites, **1** 144
  Ariel satellites, **2** 192
  International Satellite for Ionospheric
  Studies, **7** 1201
  Orbits and trajectories, **10** 1744
Perihelion, 10 1774
  Asteroids, **2** 207
  Comets, **3** 490
  Pioneer, **10** 1813
Perilune
  Explorer satellites, **5** 773
Period of rotation
  Jupiter, **7** 1260
Periodic comets
  Comets, **3** 490
Periodic maintenance
  Preventive maintenance, **10** 1852
Periodic table
  Elements, **4** 704-05
  Metals and metallurgy, **9** 1548-55
Peripheral jets
  Ground-effect machines, **6** 1023
Periscopes
  Blockhouse, **2** 369
Periscopic sextant
  Navigation instruments, **9** 1673
Perlite
  Liquid oxygen, **8** 1363
Perma-warm spots
  Mars, **8** 1492
Peroxide rocket controls
  X-15 research program, **14** 2530
Perreyon, Edouard
  Altitude and altitude records, **1** 147
Perrin, Jean B.
  Electronics, **4** 693
Perry, John, Jr.,
  Link, Edwin A., **8** 1361
Pershing missiles (picture), **9** 1610
  Battlefield missile systems (picture), **2** 341
  Missiles, **9** 1610-16
  NATO, **9** 1704
  Surface-to-surface missiles, **12** 2206
  (table), 2208
Personal equipment, 10 1774-75
  Oxygen masks, **10** 1752-53
  Pressure suit, **10** 1850-51
  Survival kit, **12** 2220
  Skydiving, **11** 2054
Personnel
  Blockhouse, **2** 366
Personnel decontamination station
  Decontamination, radiological, **4** 614
Persson, Per Axel
  Medals and decorations (table), **8** 1526
PERT
  Program management, **10** 1859
Perturbation theory
  Orbits and trajectories, **10** 1742
Perturbing attractions
  Kepler's laws, **7** 1275
Peru
  Crop dusting, **4** 587
  South and Central America's aviation,
  11 2091
Pescadores
  Nationalist China's aviation, **9** 1664
Pesticide dust
  Crop dusting, **4** 586
Peterson, Forrest S.
  X-15 research program, **14** 2533

Peterson, Donald H. (1933- , aerospace
  research pilot), **10** 1775-76
  Manned Orbiting Laboratory, **8** 1456
Pets
  Passenger services, **10** 1765
Peugeot, Armand (1849-1915, French
  aircraft engine manufacturer), **10** 1776
Pezzi, Mario
  Altitude and altitude records, **1** 147, 148
  Caproni, Count Gianni, **3** 406
P-factor
  Torque, **12** 2295
Pfalz aircraft
  First World War aircraft, **5** 824 (picture),
  825
Pfalz D-12 fighter
  History of aviation (picture), **6** 1105
Pfeffer, Wilhelm
  Circadian rhythm, **3** 460
Phantom station
  Omni navigation, **10** 1737
Phantom II, McDonnell Douglas F-4A, see
  F-4 Phantom
Phases
  Celestial mechanics, **3** 427
  Modulation, **9** 1630
  Moon, **9** 1634-35, with pictures
Phase shift
  Electromagnetism, **4** 691
Phenolic nylon
  Ablation, **1** 1
Philco-Ford Corp.
  Air-to-air missiles, **1** 121
  Battlefield missile systems, **2** 342
Philippine Air Lines
  Commercial airlines, **3** 506
Philippine Clipper, see Martin M-130
Philippine Islands
  Aircraft carriers, **1** 49
  World War II, **14** 2511
Philippine Sea (carrier)
  United States Naval Aviation (picture),
  13 2383
Philippine Sea, Battle of the
  Aircraft carriers, **1** 50
  World War II, **14** 2511
Phillips, Horatio F. (1845-1912, English
  aeronautical pioneer), **10** 1777-78
  History of aviation, **6** 1097, (table) 1119
Philolaus of Croton
  Astronomy, **2** 235, 242
**Philosophiae Naturalis Principia
  Mathematica** (book)
  Astronomy, **2** 238
  Newton, Sir Isaac, **9** 1693
Philosophical principles, effect
  Implications of aerospace, **7** 1150
Philologos (book)
  Erathosthenes, **4** 729
Phoebe
  Pickering, William Henry, **10** 1791
Phoebus (glider)
  West Germany's aerospace activities, **13**
  2477 (picture), 2476
Phoebus programs
  Rover project, **11** 1993-94
Phoebus reactor
  Launch vehicles, **7** 1328
  U.S. Atomic Energy Commission, **13** 2375
Phoenix
  Air-to-air missiles, **1** 121
  Phoenix I
  Sounding rockets, **11** 2084
Phobos
  Astronomy, **2** 244
Phonetic alphabet, 10 1778
  Preflight training, **10** 1848
  Radio communications, **10** 1897
Phosphorous
  Bombs, **3** 378
Photodetector
  Celestial navigation, **3** 430
Photoelectric cells
  Astrophysics, **2** 258

Photoelectric effect
Quantum theory (with diagram), **10** 1868
Photoelectric photometry
Astronomy, **2** 240
Photoelectric tubes
Electronics, **4** 699
Photoemission
Electronics, **4** 694
Photogeometric map
Maps and mapping (picture), **8** 1480
Photogrammetric technician
Photogrammetry, **10** 1780
Photogrammetry (with diagram and pictures), **10** 1779-1880
Aerial photography, **1** 9-14
Maps and mapping, **8** 1479-80
Reconnaissance, airborne, **11** 1919-20
Photographic magnitude
Astronomy, **2** 249
Magnitude, **8** 1420
Photographic observation
Reconnaissance, airborne, **11** 1919-20
Photography (with diagrams and pictures), **10** 1781
Aerial photography, **1** 9
Herschel family, **6** 1084
Resolution, **11** 1961
Telescopes and astronomical instruments, **12** 2253, 2255
Photography Applied to Surveying (book)
Aerial photography, **1** 10
Photography, Infrared
Infrared detection devices, **7** 1161
Infrared radiation, **7** 1162
Photometry
Pickering, William Henry, **10** 1791
Photomultipliers
Electronics, **4** 699
Telescopes and astronomical instruments, **12** 2255
Photon
Einstein, Albert, **4** 680
Lasers, **7** 1304
Light, **8** 1351
Masers, **8** 1496
Photogrammetry, **10** 1779
Quantum theory, **10** 1869
Photon engines
Electric propulsion, **4** 687
Photo-reconnaissance aircraft
Aerial photography, **1** 9-14
Fighter aircraft, **5** 807
Reconnaissance aircraft, **11** 1920-24
Photo-reconnaissance satellites
Discoverer Project, **4** 634
Intelligence, military, **7** 1180-81
Reconnaissance satellites, **11** 1924-27
Photosphere
Astronomy, **2** 241
Photosphere
Sun, **12** 2173
Photosynthesis, 10 1789-90
Air, **1** 42
Algae, **1** 143
Atmosphere, **2** 263
Carbon, **3** 406
Carbon dioxide, **3** 407
Closed ecological system, **3** 469
Life-support systems, **8** 1344
Phototransistor
Electronics, **4** 703
Physical condition
Man in flight, **8** 1449
Physical examinations
Astronauts, **2** 220
Physical fitness
Aviation medicine, **2** 292
Physical sciences
Apollo Applications Program, **2** 185
Legal implications of aerospace, **7** 1331
Physical states of matter
Matter, **8** 1513-14
Physical training
Astronauts, **2** 230
Cosmonauts, **4** 570-74

Physicians
Aerospace medicine, **1** 33
Flying doctor services, **5** 861-62
Flying Physicians Association, **5** 863-64
Physics
Careers, **3** 416
Physiologists
Aerospace medicine, **1** 33
Piaggio Douglas PD-808
Italy's aerospace activities (picture), **7** 1220
Piaggio P-116B Portofino
Italy's aerospace activities, **7** 1220
Piaggio P-166
General aviation aircraft (picture), **6** 957
Piantanida, Nicolas J.
Medals and decorations (table, Paul Tissandier Diploma), **8** 1526
Piazzi
Astronomy, **2** 244
Piccard, Auguste Antoine (1884-1962)
Balloons, **2** 325
Commemorative stamps and medals, **3** 493
Gondolas, **6** 995
Piccard family, **10** 1790
Piccard, Donald Louis (1926-   )
Balloons, **2** 318, 322, 330
Medals and decorations (table, Montgolfier Diploma Recipients), **8** 1526
Piccard family, **10** 1791
Piccard Effect
Piccard family, **10** 1790
Piccard family, 10 1790-91
Piccard, Jacques (1922)
Piccard family, **10** 1791
Piccard, Jean (1884-1963)
Balloons, **2** 325
Piccard, Jeannette (Ridlon) (1895-   )
Balloons **2** 320
Piccard, Jean Felix (1884-1963)
Piccard family, **10** 1790
Piccio, Pier Euggiero
World War I (table, Top Aces), **14** 2507
Pickering, William Henry, (1858-1938, American astonomer), **10** 1791
Pickoffs
Data acquisition and processing, **4** 605
Pictet, Raoul
Liquid oxygen, **8** 1363
Pictomaps
Maps and mapping, **8** 1480
Picture points
Maps and mappings **8** 1479
Picture tube
Television, **12** 2260
Piedmont Airlines
Commercial airlines, **3** 513
Piel Emeraude (airplane)
Homebuilt aircraft, **6** 1125
Pietenpol (airplane)
Homebuilt aircraft, **6** 1124
Pierce, John Robinson, (1910-   American electronic engineer), **10** 1791
Piezo-electric transducer
Data acquisition and processing, **4** 605
Piggyback spacecraft
Launch vehicles, **7** 1318
Pilatre de Rozier, Jean Francois (1756-1785, French chemist and first balloonist), **10** 1792
Commemorative stamps and medals, **3** 493
Pilatus Porter (airplane)
European aerospace activities (picture), **4** 751
General aviation (picture), **6** 957
Pilcher, Paul
Aviation medicine, **2** 293
Pilcher, Percy Sinclair, (1886-1899, English pioneer aviator and engineer), **10** 1792-93
Aircraft propulsion systems **1** 54
History of aviation, **6** 1098, (table) 1119
Pile
Nuclear energy (picture), **9** 1710

Pillow balloon
Balloons, **2** 330
PILOT, see Piloted Lowspeed Tests
Pilot, 10 1793-94
Aircrew, **1** 59
Army aviation, **2** 200
Aviation medicine, **2** 292
Crop dusting, **4** 592
Federal Aviation Administration, **5** 799
Flight instructor, **5** 842
Flight management, **5** 843
Flight simulators, **5** 851, 852, 854
High-altitude flight training, **6** 1085
Parachute, **10** 1759
Supersonic transports, **12** 2198
Test pilots and test flying, **12** 2277
Pilotage, 10 1794
Dead reckoning, **4** 612
Pilot training, **10** 1810
Pilotage navigation
Navigation techniques, **9** 1681
Pilot and crew wings, with illustration, **10** 1794-95
Pilot certification
Aviation medicine, **2** 295
Piloted Lowspeed Tests
Lifting-body vehicles, **8** 1349
Pilot Exhibition Schools
Barnstormers, **2** 332
Maneuvers, **8** 1435
Psychological factors of flight, **10** 1864
Seaplanes, **11** 2024
Piloting techniques (with diagrams, chart and pictures), **10** 1796-1800
Pilots and pilot certificates, 10 1802-08 (with qualifications charts)
Aeronautics, **1** 26
Air Commerce Act, **1** 45
Instrument Flight Rules, **7** 1165
Pilot's handbook, 10 1809
Pilot's information file, 10 1809
Pilot training, 10 1809-12
Pilot weather reports, 10 18-12
Military space program, **9** 1600
START, **12** 2163
X-series aerospace vehicles, **14** 2544
Pilurs, Mrs. Tracy
Women in aerospace, **14** 2496
Pinedo, Francesco de
Medals and decorations (table, FAI Gold Air Medal), **8** 1526
Pines, Battle of
Balloons, **2** 323
Pinetree Line
Air defense systems, **1** 60
Pinhole camera
Photography, **10** 1782 (with diagram)
Pioneer (with data table, diagrams and pictures), **10** 1813-14
Earth science, **4** 666
Interplanetary travel, **7** 1208
NASA (table, Major Launchings), **9** 1652
Pioneer I, **10** 1812
International Geophysical Year, **7** 1196
Launch vehicle, **7** 1322
Pioneer II, **10** 1812
Pioneer III, **10** 1812
International Geophysical Year, **7** 1196
Juno rockets, **7** 1260
Launch vehicles, **7** 1325
Pioneer IV
Juno rockets, **7** 1260
Pioneer VI
Astronomy, **2** 242
Satellites, **11** 2006
Pipeline patrol
Utility aviation, **13** 2394
Piper 140 (trainer)
Trainer aircraft, **13** 2307
Piper aircraft
Australia's aviation, **2** 283
Commuter airlines, **3** 545
Crop dusting, **4** 590
General aviation (pictures), **6** 957, 959
General aviation aircraft, **6** 961, 963, 966, (pictures) 962, 963

Piper Apache
  Piper, William T., **10** 1815
Piper Aztec
  Air taxis (picture), **1** 117
Piper Cherokee Six
  Air taxis (picture), **1** 117
  Pleasure flying (picture), **10** 1826
Piper Comanche
  General aviation aircraft (picture), **6** 963
  Radio communications, **10** 1894-98
Piper Cub, 10 1815 (with picture, table, diagram)
  Air shows (picture), **1** 115
  Crop dusting, **4** 588, 589
  Piper, William T., **10** 1815
  Pleasure flying, **10** 1825
Piper Pawnee
  Agricultural aviation, **1** 40
  Airplane, **1** 89
  Crop dusting, **4** 590
Piper Tri-Pacer
  Africa's aviation, **1** 36
  Counter-insurgency aircraft, **4** 577
Piper, William T. (1881- , American aircraft manufacturer), **10** 1814-15
  Medals and decorations (table, Paul Tissandier Diploma), **8** 1526
PIREPS
  Pilot weather reports, **10** 1812
Pirie, Robert B.
  Medals and decorations (table, Paul Tissandier Diploma), **8** 1526
Piston engine
  Power management, **10** 1842-43
  Reciprocating engine, **11** 1913-14
Pisces (PY sees)
  Constellations, 562
Piston aircraft
  Altitude and altitude records, **1** 148
Pitcairn-Cierva Autogiro Company
  Autogiros, **2** 285
Pitcairn, Harold
  Autogiros, **2** 285
Pitcairn J-5
  Commercial air transports (picture), **3** 517
Pitch, 10 1816
  Ailerons, **1** 41
  Axes of rotation, **2** 308
  Instrument flight techniques, **7** 1166
  Instrument panels, **7** 1173, 1177
  Jumbo jets, **7** 1255
  Noise measurement, **9** 1700
  Photography, **10** 1785
  Piloting techniques, **10** 1797, 1801
  Propellers, **10** 1863
  Radar, **10** 1872
  Reciprocating, **11** 1918
Pitch attitude
  Maneuvers, **8** 1433
Pitch axis
  Aerodynamics, **1** 23
  Airplane, **1** 87
  Attitude and attitude control, **2** 275
Pitot-static system (with diagram), **10** 1816
Pitot tube
  Icing, **7** 1145
  Pitot-static system, **10** 1816
Pitts Special (airplane)
  Homebuilt aircraft, **6** 1125, (picture) 1124
Planar transistors
  Electronics, **4** 703
Planck, Max K. E. L., (1858-1947, German physicist), **10** 1816-17
  Black body, **2** 362
  Einstein, Albert, **4** 680
  Quantum theory, **10** 1868
Planck's Law, 10 1817
  Black body, **2** 362
Plane spotter, 10 1817
Planetarium (with picture and diagram), **10** 1818-20
Planetary contamination
  Spacecraft sterilization, **11** 2103
Planetary Entry Parachute Program
  Balloons, **2** 331

Planetary environment
  Spacecraft sterilization, **11** 2103
Planetary escape velocity
  Launch vehicles, **7** 1314
Planetary formation
  Planetarium, **10** 1821
Planetary measurements
  Radar, **10** 1879
Planetary motion
  Laws of
    Brahe, Tycho, **3** 385
    Kepler's laws, **7** 1275
  Model
    Planetarium, **10** 1818-19
Planetary nebulae
  Astronomy, **2** 250
  Nebula, **9** 1688
Planetary orbits
  Astronomy, **2** 242
  Interplanetary travel, **7** 1211
Planetary photography
  Pickering, William Henry, **10** 1791
Planet hopping
  Interplanetary travel (with diagram), **7** 1211-12
Planetoids
  Asteroids, **2** 207
Planets, 10 1820-21
  Astronomy, **2** 233, 242
  Celestial mechanics, **3** 427
  Extraterrestrial life, **5** 774
  Interplanetary travel, **7** 1212
  Planetarium, **10** 1818
  Quantum theory, **10** 1870
  Radiation, **10** 1883
  Retrograde motion, **11** 1961
  Unidentified flying objects, **13** 2324
Planet X
  Mars, **8** 1493
Plankton
  Oceanographic research, **10** 1732
Planned Orbiting Solar Observatories
  Computers, **3** 560
Planophore (flying machine)
  History of aviation, **6** 1096
Plan position indicator, 10 1821-22
Plant life
  Biosatellites, **2** 358
Plant spores
  Air, **1** 42
Plasma, 10 1822-23
Plasma engine
  Rocket propulsion systems, **11** 1970
Plasma propulsion, 10 1823
  Electric propulsion, **4** 687
Plasma state
  Matter, **8** 1513, 1514
Plasma wall
  Re-entry vehicles, **11** 1934
Plastic-film balloon
  Balloons (diagram), **2** 327
  Piccard family, **10** 1791
Plastics, 10 1823-25
  Boron, **3** 382
  Production techniques, **10** 1854
Plate
  Electronics, **4** 695
Plate current
  Electronics, **4** 695
Plato
  Astronomy, **2** 235, 242
Platz, Reinhold
  Fokker D-8, **5** 867
  Fokker DR-1 triplane, **5** 868
Playback
  Readout, **10** 1912
Playing card
  Objects of art, **10** 1723
Pleasure flying, 10 1825-27
Pleiades (PLEE uh deez)
  Astronomy (picture), **2** 248
  Balloons, **2** 328
  Nebula, **9** 1689
  Piccard family, **10** 1791

Plenum-chamber machine
  Ground-effect machines, **6** 1023
Plexiglas
  Airplane, **1** 83
  Canopy, airplane, **3** 405
  Windows and windshields, **13** 2486
Plotter, 10 1827
  Navigation instruments, **9** 1672
Plotting boards
  Kennedy Space Center (picture), **7** 1273
Plotting system
  Photogrammetry, **10** 1779
PLSS, see Portable life-support system
Plum Brook Station
  NASA, **9** 1657
Plus count
  Countdown, **4** 576
Pluto, 10 1827-28
  Astronomy, **2** 242, 243, 245, (picture) 247
  Earth, **4** 659, 664
  Interplanetary travel, **7** 1210
  Launch vehicles, **7** 1314
  Mars, **8** 1490
  Planets, **10** 1820
  Solar system, **11** 2070
Plutonium
  Nuclear energy, **9** 1710-11
Plutonium production reactor
  Manhattan Project, **8** 1442
Plywood
  Wood, **14** 2496
Pneumatic deicing systems
  Deicing equipment, **4** 620
Pneumatic motors
  Jumbo jets, **7** 1252
Pneumatic system
  Cockpit, **3** 483
  Jumbo jets, **7** 1255
  Kennedy Space Center, **7** 1271
Poberezny, Paul H.
  Experimental Aircraft Association, **4** 760
Pod, 10 1828
Pogo (Bell)
  V/STOL aircraft, **13** 2439
Pogo stick
  Maneuvering in space, **8** 1431
  Terminology of aerospace (table), **12** 2272
Pogue, William Reid (1930-), **10** 1828
  Astronaut (with picture), **2** 217-19
Point defense aircraft
  Interceptor aircraft, **7** 1182
Pointer movement
  Pressure gauges (with diagram), **10** 1850
Pokryshkin, A. L.
  World War II (table), **14** 2517
Poland
  Commemorative stamps and medals, **3** 495
  Crop dusting, **4** 587
  European aerospace activities, **4** 747
  Luftwaffe, **8** 1376
  World War II, **14** 2512
Polando, J.
  Distance records, **4** 640
Poland PZL Gawron
  European aerospace activities (picture), **4** 748
Polar air masses
  Air masses, **1** 80-81
Polar aviation
  U.S.S.R. aerospace activities, **13** 2330
Polar axes, Earth's
  Precession, **10** 1843
Polar circumference
  Poles, **10** 1833
Polar flights, 10 1828-31
Polar gnomonic projection
  Maps and mapping (table), **8** 1478
Polaris missiles, 10 1831-32
  Faget, Maxime, **5** 789
  Government in aerospace, **6** 1006
  Inertial guidance, **7** 1152, 1154
  Materials, **8** 1506 (with picture)
  Missiles (table), **9** 1616
  Poseidon missiles, **10** 1838-39

(Continued)

Polaris missiles (Cont.)
Program management, **10** 1858
Rocket propulsion systems, **11** 1966
Surface-to-surface missiles, **12** 2206
Polaris star, 10 1833
Constellations, **3** 562
Planetarium, **10** 1819
Polaris submarine units
NORAD, **9** 1701
Polarization
Battery, **2** 339
Electromagnetism, **4** 691
Polar jet stream
Atmosphere, **2** 264
Stratosphere, **12** 2170
Polar landing
Polar flights, **10** 1830
Polar launches
Orbiting observatories, **10** 1741
Polar Orbiting Geophysical Observatory
Orbiting observatories, **10** 1738, 1741
Polar orbits
Orbiting observatories, **10** 1741, 1746
Polar regions
Air masses, **1** 80
International Geophysical Year, **7** 1197
Polar flights, **10** 1830
Polarity checker
Apollo (picture), **1** 166
Polar Star (airplane)
Ellsworth, Lincoln, **4** 707
Polar stereographic projection
Maps and mapping (table), **8** 1479
Poles, 10 1833-34
Pole Star
Polaris star, **10** 1833
Police and fire services, 10 1834-36
Utility aviation, **13** 2394
Polikarpov U-2 (airplane)
U.S.S.R. aerospace activities, **13** 2330,
(picture) 2329
Pollom, Janet Merle
Evans, Ronald Ellwin, **4** 757
**Political implications of aerospace,
10** 1836-37
Pollution detection
Infrared radiation, **7** 1162
Polskie Linie Lotnicze
European aerospace activities, **4** 748
Polyconic projection
Maps and mapping, **8** 1479, (table) 1479
Polyethylene
Airships, **1** 108
Polyethylene captive balloon
Balloons (picture), **2** 331
Polyethylene films
Balloons, **2** 328, (picture) 329
Polyot (spacecraft)
U.S.S.R. aerospace activities, **13** 2340
Pomilio (airplane)
First World War aircraft, **5** 822
Ponticus, Heraclides
Astronomy, **2** 235
Pontoons, 10 1837-38
Fabre, Henri, **5** 785
World War I, **14** 2503
Popovich, Pavel (1930-   ), **10** 1838
Cosmonauts, **4** 574, (pictures) 570, 572,
(table) 574
Manned spaceflight (table), **8** 1461
Medals and decorations (table), **8** 1524
Rendezvous and docking, **11** 1958
U.S.S.R. aerospace activities, **13** 2344
Vostok, **13** 2435
Polymers and polymerization
Plastics, **10** 1825
Population I and II stars
Baade, Walter, **2** 309
Stars, **12** 2159-63
Porphyrin
Extraterrestrial life, **5** 781
Porosity
Matter, **8** 1515
Portable launcher
Apollo (picture), **1** 165

Portable life-support system
Lunar Module, **8** 1409
Portugal
Crop dusting, **4** 587
European aerospace activities, **4** 748
International Agricultural Aviation Centre,
7 1187
NATO, **9** 1703-04
Poseidon missiles, 10 1838-39
Materials, **8** 1506
Surface-to-surface missiles, **12** 2206,
(table) 2208
Position
Air traffic control, **1** 132
Celestial navigation, **3** 429
Inertial guidance, **7** 1152
Instrument landing system, **7** 1170
Positive control areas, 10 1839
Positive dihedral
Wings, **14** 2491
Positive electricity
Electricity, **4** 684
Positive G force
Acceleration, **1** 3
Positive G tolerance limit
Acceleration, **1** 3
Positive ion
Electronics, **4** 694
Positive plate
Battery, **2** 338
Positive-pressure breathing
Life-support systems, **8** 1337-38
Positive print
Photography, **10** 1782
Positive semiconductor
Electronics, **4** 701
Positive transparency
Photography, **10** 1782
Positrons
Beta particle, **2** 354
Nuclear energy, **9** 1710
Postage stamps
Commemorative stamps and medals,
3 493
Postal rates
International airmail, **7** 1188
Post, Augustus
Aerial Experiment Association (picture),
1 8
Posters
Objects of art, **10** 1722
Post-launch conditions
Launch facilities, **7** 1307
Post meridiem
Meridian, **9** 1546
Post Office Department
Airmail, **1** 68-79
Airports, **1** 97
Civil Aeronautics Board, **3** 462
Post-solo phase
Pilot training, **10** 1810
Post, Wiley (1910-1935, American
pioneer aviator), **10** 1839
Aviation, **2** 290
Johnson, Clarence Leonard, **7** 1242
Manned spaceflight, **8** 1460
Medals and decorations (table), **8** 1526
Spacesuits, **12** 2129
Winnie Mae, **14** 2493
World records and round-the-world flights,
14 2497
Potential energy, 10 1840
Energy, **4** 712
Mechanical energy, **8** 1520, (diagrams)
1521, 1522
Orbits and trajectories, **10** 1743
Potentiometer
Data acquisition and processing, **4** 605
Potez 54
Second World War aircraft, **11** 2029
Potez 840
General aviation aircraft (picture), **6** 965
Potez Magister
Counter-insurgency aircraft, **4** 577
Potter, William C.
Aerospace industry, **1** 29

Potthast, Bruno
Medals and decorations (table), **8** 1526
Pour point
Lubricants, **8** 1375
Powder Puff Derby, 10 1840
Air racing, **1** 103
Ninety-Nines, **9** 1697
Women in aerospace, **14** 2495
Power
Horsepower, **6** 1129
Instrument flight techniques, **7** 1166
Power computer
Cruising flight, **4** 595
Power coordination
Piloting techniques, **10** 1797
Power distribution and controls
Cockpit, **3** 482
Electrical systems, **4** 681
Powered drive wheels
Jumbo jets, **7** 1253
Power generation
Electrical systems, **4** 681
Power Jets, Ltd.
Aircraft propulsion systems, **1** 57, 58
Power lever
Power management, **10** 1842
Power management, 10 1840-42
Power pedestal
Kennedy Space Center, **7** 1272
Powerplant
Aircraft propulsion systems (picture), **1** 57
Airplane, **1** 90-91
Airships **1** 105, 107
Jumbo jets, **7** 1252
Mechanics, **8** 1524
Nuclear energy, **9** 1712 (with pictures)
Power setting
Piloting techniques, **10** 1801
Power management, **10** 1840
Powers, Francis Gary
U-2, **13** 2396
Powers, John A. (1922-   , Voice of
Project Mercury), **10** 1842-43
Power stroke
Aircraft propulsion systems, **1** 53
Power supply
Kosmos satellites, **7** 1292
Power units, auxiliary, 10 1843
PPI scope
Plan position indicator, **10** 1821
Praeger, Otto
Airmail, **1** 70
Prandtl, L.
Aerodynamics, **1** 22
Fluid mechanics, **5** 858
Pravda
Commemorative stamps and medals, **3** 494
Precession, 10 1843
Planetarium, **10** 1819
Weather satellites, **13** 2463
Precession of the equinoxes
Astronomy, **2** 236
Hipparchus, **6** 1092
Precious metals, 10 1843
Precipitation, 10 1844-45
Plan position indicator, **10** 1821
Precipitation hardening
Metals and metallurgy, **9** 1553
Precise trajectory
Launch vehicles, **7** 1316
Precision Approach Radar
Air traffic control, **1** 129
Instrument landing system, **7** 1170
Precision flying, 10 1845
Precision injection
Launch vehicles, **7** 1319
Precision measurements, 10 1845-46
**Precision Recovery Including Maneuvering
Entry,** see PRIME
Precision skydiving
International competitions, **7** 1192
Precision timing
Collision avoidance system, **3** 488
Preddy, George
World War II (table), **14** 2517

Preflight inspection, 10 1846
  Piloting techniques, **10** 1801
  Preventive maintenance, **10** 1852
Preflight planning
  Flight planning, **5** 847
Preflight techniques
  Instrument flight techniques, **7** 1167
Preflight training, 10 1846-49
Pregnant Guppy
  Outsize cargo aircraft, **10** 1749, 1750
Prelaunch conditions
  Launch facilities, **7** 1307
Prelaunch fueling
  Launch vehicles, **7** 1315
Prelaunch testing
  Kennedy Space Center, **7** 1266
Prescott, Robert W.
  Flying Tigers, **5** 865
Preset guidance system
  Missiles, **9** 1615
Pressure
  Atmospheric pressure, **2** 268
  Density altitude, **4** 626
  Man in flight, **8** 1444-46
  Meteorology, **9** 1555
Pressure altimeter
  Altimeter, **1** 145
  Pressure altitude, **10** 1849
Pressure altitude, 10 1849
  Koch chart, **7** 1282
Pressure changes
  Man in flight, **8** 1448-49
Pressure cooker
  Manufacturing, **8** 1473
Pressure-demand system oxygen mask
  Life-support systems (diagram), **8** 1340
  Oxygen masks, **10** 1752
Pressure disturbances
  Sonic boom, **11** 2074
Pressure-fed systems
  Propellants (with diagram), **10** 1860
Pressure fueling
  Jumbo jets, **7** 1255
Pressure gauges, 10 1849-50
Pressure gradient force
  Wind, **13** 2485
Pressure level charts
  Aviation weather, **2** 299
  Sound (with table), **11** 2077
Pressure measurements, sensitive
  Pressure gauges, **10** 1850
Pressure suit, 10 1850-51
  Environmental control system, **4** 720
  Life-support systems, **8** 1338, (pictures
    and diagrams) 1341, 1342
  Manned spaceflight, **8** 1460
  Personal equipment, **10** 1775
  Pressurization, **10** 1851
  Spacesuit, **12** 2129
Pressure waves
  Sonic boom (with graph), **11** 2074
Pressurization, 10 1851-52
  Airplane, **1** 84
  Hypoxia, **6** 1144
  Temperature control, **12** 2266
Pressurized aircraft
  Aviation medicine, **2** 295
  Life-support systems, **8** 1338, (diagrams)
    1338, 1339
  Man in flight, **8** 1445-46, (diagram) 1446
  Manufacturing, **8** 1469,
  Pressurization, **10** 1851
Pressurized gondola
  Piccard family, **10** 1791
Pretakeoff checklist
  Preflight inspection, **10** 1846
Prevailing winds
  Airports, **1** 94
Preventive maintenance, 10 1852
Prevost, Maurice
  Air racing, **1** 102
Price, Rene Louise
  Carpenter, Malcolm Scott, **3** 422
Primary areas
  Recovery, **11** 1927

Primary attitude
  Jumbo jets, **7** 1252
Primary batteries
  Battery, **2** 339
Primary cosmic rays
  Cosmic rays, **3** 568
  Kosmos satellites, **7** 1293
**PRIME (Precision Recovery Including
    Maneuvering Entry), 10** 1852-53
  Military space program, **9** 1600 (with
    picture)
  START, **12** 2163
  Vehicle research spacecraft, **13** 2406
  X-series aerospace vehicles, **14** 2544
Prime meridian
  Celestial sphere, **3** 433
  Latitude and longitude, **7** 1307
Primeval fireball theory
  Astronomy, **2** 242
Prince, Norman
  Lafayette Escadrille, **7** 1295
Princeton (carrier)
  United States Naval Aviation (picture), **13**
    2382
Principia (book)
  Astronomy, **2** 238
  Celestial mechanics, **3** 426
  Newton, Sir Isaac, **9** 1693
Printed circuits
  Circuit, **3** 461
Prior art
  Patents, **10** 1766
Prisms
  Lasers, **7** 1305
Pritchard, John A.
  Coast Guard aviation, **3** 479
Private airplanes
  (see also General aviation aircraft)
  Call signs, **3** 398
Private airport
  Airports, **1** 93
Private Pilot Certificate
  Aircraft Owners and Pilots Association, **1** 52
  Pilot training, **10** 1809-11
Probables
  Ace, **1** 4
Probe and drogue system (fueling system)
  Cobham, Sir Alan, **3** 480
  Refueling (with picture), **11** 1938-39
  Tanker aircraft, **12** 2233
Pro bono publico
  Civil Aviation Medical Association, **3** 466
**Prodromo Overo Saggio di Alcune
    Invenzioni Nuove (book)**
  Lana, Francesco de, **7** 1297
Production Certificate
  Certification procedures, **3** 440
Production techniques, 10 1854-57
  Aerospace industry, **1** 29
  Manufacturing, **8** 1466-75
  Program management, **10** 1857
  Reliability and quality assurance, **11** 1954
Product quality
  Quality control, **10** 1867
Proficiency phase
  Pilot training, **10** 1810
Prognostic chart
  Aviation weather, **2** 300
Program
  Computers (with diagram), **3** 553-56
**Program Evaluation Review Technique
    (PERT)**
  Government contracts, **6** 999
Program management, 10 1857-59
Progress in Flying Machines (book)
  Chanute, Octave, **3** 446
  History of aviation, **6** 1099
Prohibited airspace
  Prohibited area, **10** 1859
Prohibited area, 10 1859
Project Blue Book
  Unidentified flying objects, **13** 2322
Project Emily
  Thor rockets, **12** 2285
Project Stratoscope
  Sun, **12** 2173

Projectiles
  Ballistics, **2** 314
Projections
  Maps and mapping, **8** 1478-79,
    (table) 1478-79
Projector, movable
  Planetarium, **10** 1818
Project System Definition Phase
  International projects, **7** 1201
Prolate spheroid
  Airships, **1** 105
Propagation
  Energy, **4** 715
Propellants, 10 1859-62
  Hybrid systems, **6** 1138
  Hypergolic propellants, **6** 1141
  Intercontinental ballistic missiles, **7** 1182
  Missiles (table), **9** 1616
  Oxidizers, **10** 1751
  Rocket propulsion systems, **11** 1969
  Spaceflight principles, **12** 2106 (table),
    2109
  Space propulsion systems, **12** 2121, 2122
  X-15 research program, **14** 2532
Propellant systems
  Kennedy Space Center, **7** 1271
Propellant tanks
  Launch vehicles, **7** 1317
Propellers, 10 1862-63
  Aircraft propulsion systems, **1** 53
  Airplane, **1** 90
  Airships (picture), **1** 109
  Gas turbine engines, **5** 918, 924
  Pitch, **10** 1816
  Pusher propeller, **10** 1866
  Reciprocating engines, **11** 1918
  Torque, **12** 2295
  Wood, **14** 2496
Propeller blades
  Airfoil, **1** 61
  Icing, **7** 1145
Propeller-driven aircraft
  Aircraft carriers, **1** 46
  Air transports, **1** 139
  Acoustics, **1** 5
  Ignition systems, **7** 1146, 1147
Propeller wash
  Slipstream, **11** 2058
Properties of materials
  Materials, **8** 1501-02, (diagram) 1501
Properties of matter
  Matter, **8** 1514-15
Proportionality
  Kepler's laws, **7** 1275
Proprioceptual sense
  Man in flight, **8** 1446-47, (diagram) 1447
Propulsion
  Aircraft propulsion systems, **1** 53
  Plasma propulsion, **10** 1823
  Spacecraft design, **11** 2101
  Gas jet propulsion, **5** 917
  Space propulsion systems, **12** 2121
Propulsion energy
  Interplanetary travel, **7** 1212
Propulsion requirements
  Interplanetary travel, **7** 1211
Propulsion sled
  Rocket sled, **11** 1987
Propulsion stage
  Apollo, **1** 173
  Jupiter rockets, **7** 1261
Propulsion systems
  Aircraft propulsion systems, **1** 53
  Government in aerospace, **6** 1003
  Ground-effect machines, **6** 1024
  Intercontinental ballistic missiles, **7** 1182
  Launch vehicles, **7** 1314, 1316
  Maneuvering in space **8** 1430,
    (picture) 1430
  Missiles, **9** 1612-13
  Solid-fuel rockets, **11** 2071
  Space propulsion systems, **12** 2121
Propulsive energy
  Launch vehicles, **7** 1313-14
Propulsive exhaust gas
  Launch vehicles, **7** 1328

Prospector program, 10 1863
Protection of country
Patents, **10** 1768
Protective coatings
Materials, **8** 1510-11
Protective drugs
Radiation sickness, **10** 1884
Proteins
Extraterrestrial life, **5** 775
Proton, 10 1863
Atoms, **2** 269
Interplanetary Monitoring Platform
satellites, **7** 1205
Matter, **8** 1513
Nuclear energy, **9** 1710
Radiation, **10** 1880
Radioisotope, **10** 1899
Proton nucleus
Quantum theory, **10** 1868
Proton satellites
Launch vehicles, **7** 1326
U.S.S.R. aerospace activities, **13** 2340,
(picture) 2338
Protoplanet hypothesis
Earth, **4** 663
Protoplasm
Plasma, **10** 1822
Prototype, 10 1863
Prototype flight test
Certification procedures, **3** 443
Protractor
Plotter, **10** 1827
Provider, see C-123 Provider
Provost (aircraft)
Air forces of the world (Sudan), **1** 64
Asia's aviation, **2** 205
Counter-insurgency aircraft, **4** 577
Proximity fuse
Antiaircraft weapons, **1** 157
PRPA, see Professional Race Pilots
Association
Pseudo-adiabatic lapse rate
Adiabatic process, **1** 6-7
Psychological factors of flight, 10 1864
Acoustics, **1** 5
Aerospace medicine, **1** 33
Aviation medicine, **2** 293
Flying safety, **5** 864
Ptolemy, Claudius (A.D. 100-200)
(2nd century, Astronomer and
geographer), **10** 1864
Astronomy, **2** 236, 237, 249
Celestial mechanics, **3** 426, 427
Constellations, **3** 561
Copernicus, Nicolaus, **3** 566
Kepler, Johannes, **7** 1274
Magnitude, **8** 1420
Public service
Careers, **3** 417
Occupations, **10** 1730 (with tables)
Puff the Magic Dragon, see C-47 Skytrain
Pulitzer Race
Air racing, **1** 102
Pulitzer trophy
Curtiss R2C racers, **4** 601
Trophies and awards (table), **13** 2312
Pulsars
Stars, **12** 2162
Pulsating stars (Pulsars)
Astrophysics, **2** 257
Pulse-amplitude modulation
Telemetry, **12** 2242
Pulse code modulation
Modulation, **9** 1630
Pulsed Doppler radars
Radars, **10** 1877
Pulse duration or width modulation
Telemetry, **12** 2242
Pulsejet engine, 10 1865-66
Aircraft propulsion systems, **1** 58-59
Engines, **4** 717
Jet engines, **7** 1237
Pulse modulation, 9 1630
Pulse position or time modulation
Telemetry, **12** 2242

Pulses
Radar, **10** 1872
Pulses of energy
Planck's Law, **10** 1817
Pumping
Lasers, **7** 1303
Purple Heart
Medals and decorations (picture), **8** 1525
Purser, see Steward
Pursuit airplane, 10 1866
Fighter aircraft, **5** 808
World War I, **14** 2506
Pusher propeller, 10 1866
Propellers, **10** 1862-63
PX-S flying boats
Asia's aviation, **2** 204
Pylon, 10 1866
Pylon eights
Maneuvers, **8** 1439, (diagram) 1440
Pyrotechnic device
Balloons (diagram), **2** 326, 327
Ignition systems, **7** 1147
Kennedy Space Center, **7** 1267
Oxidizers, **10** 1751
Pythagoras
Astronomy, **2** 235, 242

Q

Q
Terminology of aerospace (table), **12** 2272
Qantas
Australia's aviation, **2** 280
Commercial airlines, **3** 506
Quad Duct (aircraft)
Helicopters, **6** 1069
Quail
Air-to-surface missiles, **1** 124
Qualifications
Smokejumpers, **11** 2059
Quality assurance
Program management, **10** 1859
Quality control, 10 1867-68
Manufacturing, **8** 1470
Radioisotope, **10** 1899
Reliability and quality assurance, **11** 1954
Zero defects, **14** 2552
Quanta
Einstein, Albert, **4** 680
Planck's Law, **10** 1817
Quantity of motion
Momentum, **9** 1631
Quantum jump
Masers, **8** 1496
Quantum mechanics
Masers, **8** 1496
Quantum theory, **10** 1868, 1870
Quantum of energy
Quantum theory, **10** 1868
Quantum physics
Black body, **2** 362
Quantum state
Atoms, **2** 270
Quantum theory, 10 1868-71
Light, **8** 1350
Planck, Max K. E. L., **10** 1816
Semiconductors, **11** 2042
Quarles, Mrs. Donald
Women in aerospace, **14** 2496
Quartz
Ablation, **1** 1

Quartz flashtube
Lasers, **7** 1305
Quartz monochromator
Astrophysics, **2** 256
Quasar, 10 1870-71
Astronomy, **2** 240, 242, 254
Ground antennas, **6** 1017
Universe, **13** 2391, 2392
Quasipermanent Base
Lunar bases, **8** 1389, 1395
Quasi-stellar objects
Quasar, **10** 1870
Quasi-stellar radio source
Quasar, **10** 1871
Queen Air, see Beech Queen Air
Quemoy
Nationalist China's aviation, **9** 1664
Quersin, Phillippe
Medals and decorations (table, Montgolfier
Diploma Recipients), **8** 1526
Quesada, Pete
United States Air Force, **13** 2362
Question Mark (airplane)
United States Air Force, **13** 2362,
(picture) 2362
"Quick Change"
Cargo aircraft (picture), **3** 420
Quick Change loader
Cargo aircraft, **3** 421
Quick-dump device
Agricultural aviation (picture), **1** 39, 41
Quick-egress hatch
Apollo, 168
Quiet Birdmen, 10 1871
Quiet sun
Kosmos satellites, **7** 1293
Quimby, Harriet
Women in aerospace, **14** 2494

R

R4D, see C-47 Skytrain
R4D rocket engine
Rocket propulsion systems, with picture,
11 1969
R-6 twin-float torpedo planes
Coast Guard aviation, **3** 476
R-33
Airships, **1** 111
R-34
Airships, **1** 111
RAAF, see Australian Air Force, **2**
RA-5C Vigilante, see A-5 Vigilante
Raborn, W. F.
Program management, **10** 1858
Racetrack patterns, see Holding patterns
Radar, 10 1872-79
Acquisition and tracking radar, (color
picture) **1** 6
Air defense systems, **1** 60-61
Air-to-surface missiles, **1** 122
Air traffic control, **1** 129-30, 132
Astronomy, **2** 242
Aviation weather (with picture), **2** 300
Coast Guard aviation, **3** 479
Computers, **3** 557
Electronic countermeasures, **4** 691
Electronics, **4** 693, 704
European air traffic control, **4** 752
Government in aerospace, **6** 1002, 1003,
(picture) 1002

Ground antennas, **6** 1017
Ground control approach, **6** 1018
Guidance and control systems, **6** 1037
History of aviation, **6** 1114
Inflight emergency procedures, **7** 1155
Oceanographic research, **10** 1732
Plan position indicator, **10** 1821
Reconnaissance, airborne, **11** 1920-21
Refueling, **11** 1940
Sonar, **11** 2073
Space communications, **11** 2096
Surface-to-air missiles, **12** 2199
Terminology of aerospace (table), **12** 2272
Tracking systems and networks, **13** 2303
Transceivers, **13** 2307
Transponder, **13** 2309
Unidentified flying objects, **13** 2323
United States Air Force, **13** 2372
Radar altimeter
Radio altimeter, **10** 1888
Radar antenna
Airships, **1** 114
Ballistic Missile Early Warning System
(with picture), **2** 313
Radar beam
Beam-rider guidance, **2** 346
Crop dusting, **4** 593
Radar communications dome (picture)
Closed ecological system, **3** 469
Radar console
Console, **3** 561
Instrument flight techniques, **7** 1166
Radar coverage, blanket (diagram)
Air defense systems, **1** 60
Radar detection system
Ballistic Missile Early Warning System,
2 313
Battle of Britain, **2** 343
Radio, **10** 1888
Radar echo techniques
Acquisition and tracking radar, **1** 6
Astronomy, **2** 242
Radar evaluation pod
Gemini, **5** 938
Rendezvous and docking, **11** 1956
Radar frequencies
Radio, **10** 1888
Radar guide beam
Beam-rider guidance, **2** 346
Radar handoff
Instrument flight techniques, **7** 1168
Radar homing guidance
Air-to-air missiles, **1** 119-21
Radar microwave links (picture)
Air traffic control, **1** 127
Radar navigator
Observer, **10** 1726
Radar/radio emissions
Reconnaissance aircraft, **11** 1920
Radar set
Radar, **10** 1872
Radarscopes
Air traffic control (with picture), **1** 130, 132
Cockpit, **3** 485
Radar system
Instrument flight techniques, **7** 1168
Launch vehicles, **7** 1316
Radar warning system
Radar, **10** 1873
Radar waves
Infrared radiation, **7** 1162
Radial acceleration
Acceleration, **1** 2
Orbits and trajectories, **10** 1743
Radial beams
Service Module Apollo, **1** 173
Radial engine
Aircraft propulsion systems, **1** 56
(diagram) 55
Reciprocating engines, **11** 1914
Radial force
Orbits and trajectories, **10** 1743
Radial motion
Orbits and trajectories, **10** 1743
Radial velocity
Radio astronomy, **10** 1891

Radiating capacity
Kosmos satellites, **7** 1293
Radiant energy
Quantum theory, **10** 1868, 1870
Radio, **10** 1885
Radiation, 10 1880-84
Atmosphere, **2** 265
Bioastronautics, **2** 355
Biosatellites, **2** 356
Black body, **2** 362
Clouds, **3** 471
Explorer satellites, **5** 761, 765, 769
Gamma rays, **5** 913
Heat energy, **6** 1055
Jupiter, **7** 1260
Kosmos satellites, **7** 1292
Light, **8** 1350
Radioisotope, **10** 1899
Space biology, **11** 2094
Sputnik, **12** 2153, 2154
Sun, **12** 2172
Supersonic transports, **12** 2197
U.S. Atomic Energy Commission, **13** 2375
Radiation absorption
Observatories, **10** 1726
Radiation belts, see also Van Allen radiation
belts
Kosmos satellites, **7** 1290-91
Orbiting observatories, **10** 1741
Radiation danger
Kosmos satellites, **7** 1290
Radiation data
Launch vehicles, **7** 1325-26
Military space program (table), **9** 1604
Radiation emission
Quantum theory (with diagram), **10** 1870
Radiation engines
Electric propulsion, **4** 687
Radiation exposure
Radiation sickness, **10** 1884
Radiation shield, 10 1884
Radiation sickness, 10 1884
Radiation windows
Radiation, **10** 1883
Radiative equilibrium
Eddington, Arthur S., **4** 673
Radiators, 10 1884-85
Reciprocating engines, **11** 1917
Radio (with charts, diagrams and picture),
10 1885-88
Air traffic control, 128-29
High frequency radio, **6** 1086
Homing devices, **6** 1128
Panel codes, **10** 1755
Space communications, **11** 2096, 2099
Telemetry, **12** 2242
Tracking systems and networks, **13** 2300
Transceivers, **13** 2307
Transmitters, **13** 2308
Radio
Transponder, **13** 2309
Radioactive
Radiation, **10** 1881
Radioactive decay
Planets, **10** 1820
Radioactive isotopes
SNAPS, **11** 2060
Radioactive uranium
Kiwi, **7** 1281
Radio aids
Pilot training, **10** 1810
Radio altimeter, 10 1888
Automatic landing, **2** 288
Navigation instruments, **9** 1673
Radio antennas
Icing, **7** 1145
Radio astronomy, 10 1889-93
Astronomy, **2** 240
Baade, Walter, **2** 309
Earth, **4** 661
Observatories, **10** 1726
Stars, **12** 2159-63
Radio Astronomy Explorer (satellite)
Explorer satellites, **5** 773
NASA (drawing), **9** 1651

Radio bands
High frequency radio, **6** 1086
Low frequency radio, **8** 1374
Radio beacon, see Beacon, radio
Radio beam, see Beam, radio
Radio briefing
Briefing, **3** 388
Radio-command guidance system
Guidance and control systems, **6** 1036
Radio communications, 10 1894-98
Air traffic control, **1** 125-39
Headset, **6** 1053
Instrument Flight Rules, **7** 1165
Ionosphere, **7** 1215
Maneuvering in space, **8** 1430
Radio Compass System
Navigation systems (diagram), **9** 1676
Radio-controlled models
Model aircraft, **9** 1624, (picture), 1625
Radio difficulties
Inflight emergency procedures, **7** 1156
Radio-directed glide bombs
Air-to-surface missiles, **1** 123
Radio direction finder
Electronics, **4** 693
Navigation systems, **9** 1675
Radio emissions
Ewen, Harold Irving, **4** 759
Radio energy
Radar, **10** 1872
Radio facilities
Charts, **3** 450, 452, 454
Instrument flight techniques, **7** 1167
Radio frequency waves
Airborne antennas, **1** 42
Astronomy, **2** 242
Transmitters, **13** 2308
Radiography
Materials, **8** 1512
Radio guidance systems
Crop dusting, **4** 593
Radio impulses
Launch vehicles, **7** 1316
Radioisotope, 10 1899
Radio Magnetic Direction Indicator
Automatic direction finder, **2** 287
Navigation techniques (with pictures),
9 1683-1683
Radiometeorography
Meteorology, **9** 1557
Radiometers
Mariner probes, **8** 1487
Oceanographic research, **10** 1732
Radio navigation, 10 1899
Jumbo jets, **7** 1255
Loran, **8** 1371-72
Navigation techniques, **9** 1881-87
Radio noise,
Jupiter, **7** 1260-61
Radio observatories
Observatories, **10** 1726
Radio astronomy, **10** 1889-93
Radio Operator's Permit
Pilot's training, **10** 1811
Radio ranges
Beacon, radio, 345
Radio receiver
Instrument flight techniques, **7** 1168
Radio astronomy, **10** 1893
Radio reflections
Radar, **10** 1872
Radio signals
Ozma project, **10** 1753
Radiosonde balloon
GHOST program, **6** 979
Radiosonde units, 10 1899
Adiabatic process, **1** 6-7
Anemometer, **1** 152
Aviation weather, **2** 299
Jet streams, **7** 1242
Meteorology, **9** 1557
Weather maps and charts, **13** 2455
Radio spectral line
Radio astronomy, **10** 1891
Radio spectrum
Radiation, **10** 1880

Radio sun
Radio astronomy, **10** 1890
Radio telescopes
International Geophysical Year, **7** 1196
Parabola, **10** 1756
Radio astronomy, **10** 1889
Telescopes and astronomical instruments, **12** 2258
Radio tracking
Radio astronomy, **10** 1889
Recovery, **11** 1929
Tracking systems and networks, **12** 2297
Radio transceiver
Radio, **10** 1885
Transceivers, **13** 2307-08
Radio transmitter
Radio, **10** 1885
Transmitters, **13** 2308-09
Radio transmission
Radio, **10** 1885
Radio waves
Electromagnetism, **4** 688
Extraterrestrial life, **5** 784
Jansky, Karl Guthe, **7** 1126
Jupiter, **7** 1260
Observatories, **10** 1726
Orbiting observatories, **10** 1738
Radar, **10** 1872, 1878
Radio, **10** 1885
X-rays, **14** 2533
Radio window
Quantum theory, **10** 1870
Radium
Alpha particle, **1** 145
Radome, 10 1900
Airborne antennas, **1** 44
Glass, **6** 983
Radon
Atmosphere, **2** 263
RAF, see Royal Air Force
Railway Labor Act of 1926
Civil Aeronautics Board, **3** 462
Rain, 10 1900
Aviation weather, **2** 300
Precipitation, **10** 1844
Rall, Gunther
World War II (table), **14** 2517
Rallying
International competitions, **7** 1191, 1193
Ram air
Pitot-static system, **10** 1816
Ramjet
Aircraft propulsion systems, **1** 58-59
Engines, **4** 717, **10** 1900-02
Hypersonic flight, **6** 1142
Jet engines, **7** 1237
Missiles, **9** 1612
Pulsejet engine (with diagram), **10** 1865
Ramo, Simon, (1913-   , American
engineering executive), **10** 1902
Program management, **10** 1858
Ramp, 10 1903
Runways, **11** 1998
Ram rise
Icing, **7** 1146
Ramsey, William
Astrophysics, **2** 255
Rams horn VOR (with picture)
Airborne antennas, **1** 43
Randall, Louise Elizabeth
Mitchell, Edgar Dean, **9** 1620
RAND Corporation, 10 1903
Discoverer Project, **4** 633
Military implications of space, **9** 1588-89
Project RAND
Communications satellites, **3** 352
Discoverer Project, **4** 633
Program management, **10** 1857
Reconnaissance satellites, **11** 1926
R&D, see Research and Development
Random composite
Materials, 1504 (diagram), **8** 1504
Randrup, Michael
Altitude and altitude records, **1** 147
Range
Piloting techniques, **10** 1802

Plotter, **10** 1827
Ranger
Aircraft carriers (picture), **1** 46, 49-50
United States Naval Aviation, **13** 2380,
2381, (picture) 2385
Ranger (with pictures, data table and
diagrams) **10** 1905-11
Agena rockets, **1** 38
Aluminum, **1** 149
Astrogeology, **2** 211
Data acquisition and processing, **4** 607
Earth science, **4** 666
Launch vehicles, **7** 1324
Lunar bases, **8** 1380
NASA, **9** 1653, (table, Major Launchings)
1652
Parks, Robert Joseph, **10** 1763
Ranger VII—IX
Astronomy, **2** 242, 244
Range safety, 10 1911
Launching, **7** 1310
Rangoon, Burma
Mainland China's aerospace activities,
8 1425
Rankin, E. P.
Distance and distance records, **4** 640
Rankine scale
Temperature scales, **12** 2271
Rapelling
Survival and rescue, **12** 2218
Rare-earth metals
Elements, **4** 705
Magnesium, **8** 1419
Rarefraction
Sound, **11** 2077
Rascal
Dornberger, Walter Robert, **4** 646
Rated horsepower
Measurement of power, **8** 1518-19,
(diagram) 1519
Rate gyros
Automatic pilot, **2** 288
Rate of climb
Koch chart, **7** 1282
Performance charts, **10** 1774
Piloting techniques, **10** 1797
Pressure gauges, **10** 1849
Rate of turn
Maneuvers, **8** 1437
Rates
Airmail, **1** 77-78
Rats
Animals in space, **1** 153
Biosatellites, **2** 356
Raven helicopter, see OH-23 Raven
Rawdon T-1
Crop dusting, **4** 589
Rawinsonde
Meteorology, **9** 1557
Ray E. Tenhoff Award
Trophies and awards (table), **13** 2312
Rayleigh, Lord
Bird flight, **2** 361
Raymond Orteig prize
Spirit of St. Louis, **12** 2145
Raytheon Co.
Battlefield missile systems, **2** 343
Sparrow III
Air-to-air missiles, **1** 121
Raytheon Hawk
Missiles (picture), **9** 1613
Razon
Air-to-surface missiles, **1** 123
RB-57 (Martin-Marietta) see B-57
RC-121, see Lockheed Constellation
RCA 110A computers
Blockhouse, **2** 368
RCS, see Reaction control system
R.E. 8 (fighter)
First World War aircraft (picture), **5** 820
Reactants
Chemical energy, **3** 456
Reaction control systems, 10 1911-12
Apollo, **1** 177
Lunar Module, **8** 1408
X-15 research program, **14** 2532

Reaction engines, 10 1912
Jet engines, **7** 1237
Jet propulsion, **7** 1240
Reaction jet
Guidance and control systems, **6** 1040
Reaction Motors, Inc.
American Rocket Society, **1** 151
X-series aerospace vehicles, **14** 2536
Reactors, see Nuclear reactors
Read, A. C. (Putty)
Coast Guard aviation, **3** 476
Readout, 10 1912
Terminology of aerospace (table), **12** 2272
Real time
Space communications, **11** 2097
Terminology of aerospace (table), **12** 2272
Real Time Computer Complex
Mission Control Center, **9** 1617-18
Reaumur scale
Temperature scales, **12** 2271
Reber, Grote
Astronomy, **2** 242
Radio astronomy, **10** 1889
"Recce" aircraft
Aerial photography, **1** 11
Reconnaissance aircraft, **11** 1920
Receivers, 10 1912
Radar, **10** 1875, 1879
Radio, **10** 1885
Transceivers, **13** 2307
Receiving equipment
Omni navigation, **10** 1737
Rechkalov, G. A.
World War II (table), **14** 2517
Reciprocal policy of certification
Certification procedures, **3** 441
Reciprocating engines, 11 1913-19
Aircraft propulsion systems, **1** 53
Business aviation, **3** 394
Combustion chamber, **3** 489
Engines, **4** 717
Ignition systems, **7** 1147
Internal combustion engines, **7** 1187
Power management, **10** 1840
Radiators, **10** 1884
Revolution, **11** 1962
Rotating combustion engine, **11** 1992-93
Supercharger, **12** 2175
Reconnaissance, airborne, 11 1919-20
Photography, **10** 1785
Reconnaissance aircraft, 11 1920-24
First World War aircraft, **5** 816
Intelligence, military, **7** 1181
Military aircraft, **9** 1570, (pictures) 1568
SR-71, Lockheed and YF-12A, **12** 2155
U-2, **13** 2396
Reconnaissance and strike fighters
Air forces of the world, **1** 64
Reconnaissance balloons
Balloons, **2** 323
Reconnaissance camera
Photography, **10** 1785, 1788
Reconnaissance photographs
Photography, **10** 1785
Reconnaissance radar
Radar, **10** 1878
Reconnaissance satellites, 11 1924-29
Intelligence, military, **7** 1181
Political implications of aerospace, **10** 1837
Satellites, **11** 2006
Records
Altitude and altitude records, **1** 146
Distance and distance records, **4** 639
Endurance and endurance records, **4** 711
Speed and speed records, **12** 2140
World records and round the world flights,
14 2497
Recovery, 11 1927-29
Aircraft carriers, **1** 47
Launching, **7** 1311
Re-entry, **11** 1930
Terminology of aerospace (table), **12** 2272
Recovery capsule
Biosatellites, 356

Recovery communications
Radio communications, with diagram,
10 1898
Recovery from vertical flight
Maneuvers, 8 1439-40
Recovery Service
Pararescue, 10 1760
Recovery zones
Launching, 7 1309
Rectangular flight path
Landing techniques, 7 1300
Rectification
Electronics, 4 695
Rectifier
Semiconductors, 11 2041
Recurrent novae
Astrophysics, 2 258
Nova, 9 1706
Recycling oxygen system
Carbon dioxide, 3 407
Red alert, 11 1930
Red Arrows
Demonstration teams (picture), 4 624, 626
Redeye
Antiaircraft weapons, 1 158
Battlefield missile systems, 343
Surface-to-air missiles, 12 2202, (table)
2204
Red fuming nitric acid
Aerobee, 1 17
Red giant star
Astronomy, 251
Extraterrestrial life, 5 782
Stars, 12 2161
Red-lens test
Aviation medicine, 2 294
Redout, 11 1930
Negative-g, 9 1689
Red planet
Astronomy, 2 244
Mars, 8 1490
Red rope
Balloons, 2 317
Red shift
Astronomy, 2 250
Doppler effect, 4 644
Quasars, 10 1871
Relativity theory, 11 1952
Red spot (with picture)
Jupiter, 7 1260-61
Redstone Arsenal
Launch vehicles, 7 1325
Marshall Space Flight Center, 8 1494
Oberth, Hermann, 10 1721
Redstone missile
Explorer satellites, 5 762, 763
Juno rockets, 7 1259
Jupiter rockets, 7 1261
Rockets and rocketry, 11 1983
WRESAT, 14 2524
Reducing atmosphere
Atmosphere, 2 265
Reduction
Chemical energy, 3 456
Redundancy, 11 1930
Spaceflight safety, 12 2111
Supersonic transports, 12 2198
Redundant transmitters
Orbiting observatories, 10 1741
Red Wing (aircraft)
Aerial Experiment Association, 1 8
Reed, D. A., Jr.
Manufacturing, 8 1474
Reed, Lt. Henry A.
Aerial photography, 1 10
Re-entry, 11 1930
Ablation, 1 1
Launching, 7 1311
Launch vehicles, 7 1314
Parachutes, 10 1759
Plasma, 10 1823
PRIME, 10 1853
Re-entry angle
Re-entry vehicles, 11 1931
Re-entry body
Polaris missiles, 10 1832

Re-entry control systems
Kennedy Space Center, 7 1267
Re-entry corridor, 11 1930
Re-entry heating
Launch vehicles, 7 1316
Re-entry heat shields, see Heat shields
Re-entry of space vehicles
Legal implications of aerospace, 7 1331
Re-entry vehicles, 11 1931-36
Biosatellites, 2 356, 357
Heat shields, 6 1057
Intercontinental ballistic missiles, 7 1182
Rockets and rocketry, 11 1985
Temperature control, 12 2265
Reference beam
Lasers, 7 1306
Reference point
Polaris star, 10 1833
Reflected ray
Light, 8 1351
Reflected wave
Sonic boom, 11 2075
Reflecting paraboloidal dish
Radar, 10 1876-77
Reflecting telescope
Astronomy (with picture), 2 238-40
Telescopes and astronomical instruments,
12 2247
Reflection
Electromagnetism, 4 691
Light, 8 1351-52
Radio, 10 1885
Reflection, law of
Light, 8 1351-52
Reflection nebulae
Astrophysics, 2 258
Nebula, 9 1689
Reflector communication satellite
Communication satellites, 3 532
Reflector telescope
Astronomy, 2 242
Observatories, 10 1725
Telescopes and astronomical instruments,
12 2247
Reflex klystron
Electronics, 4 700
Refraction
Light, 8 1351-52
Refraction of starlight
Astronomy (with diagram), 2 237
Refractor telescope
Astronomy, 2 242
Telescopes and astronomical instruments,
12 2246
Refractory metals, 11 1936
Materials, 8 1507
Metals and metallurgy, 9 1553
Refueling, 11 1937-42
Tanker aircraft, 12 2232
Refueling envelope
Refueling, 11 1939
Refueling in flight, see Refueling
Regeneratively cooled rocket engine
American Rocket Society, 1 151
Regener, Eric (1881-1955)
Balloons, 2 325
Regia Aeronautica
Military aviation, 9 1583
Regional airlines, 11 1942-44
Commercial airlines, 3 498
Regional space centers, 11 1944-46
Registration marks
Registration of aircraft, 11 1946 (with
data table)
Registration of aircraft, 11 1946-48
Regulation of aviation
Federal Aviation Administration, 5 794
Reheat
Afterburner, 1 38
Aircraft propulsion systems, 1 57
Reid, W. S.
Distance and distance records, 4 640
Reinforced-monocoque fuselage design
Airplane, 1 83

Monocoque and semimonocoque design,
9 1632
Reinforced plastics
Materials, 8 1506
Plastics, 10 1825
Reinforcement
Materials, 8 1506
Reinsurance treaties
Insurance, aviation, 7 1179
Reitsch, Hanna
Helicopters, 6 1062
Relative bearings
Bearing, 2 346
Relative humidity
Humidity, 6 1136
Relative wind
Angle of attack, 1 152
Maneuvers, 8 1434
Relativity theory, 11 1948-53
Einstein, Albert, 4 680
Piccard family, 10 1790
Quasars, 10 1871
Radio astronomy, 10 1892
Sun, 12 2175
Universe, 13 2392
Relay
Communications satellites, 3 534, 543
Delta rocket, 4 622
International Telecommunications Satellite
Consortium, 7 1202
NASA, 9 1653, (table, Major Launchings)
1652
Satellites, 11 2007
Release mechanisms
Landing gear, 7 1298
Reliability and quality assurance, 11 1954
Relief features symbols
Charts, 3 454
Relief map
Maps and mapping, 8 1477
Reluctant Revolutionary, The (book)
Teller, Edward, 12 2265
Remote Air Intake facility
Kennedy Space Center, 7 1273
Remote compass transmitter
Compasses, 3 550
Remote control, 11 1954
Reconnaissance aircraft, 11 1924
Robots, 11 1965
Remote indicating compass
Directional gyro, 4 629
Renard, Charles (1847-1905, French
officer and engineer), 11 1954
Airships, 1 111
Dirigibles, 4 631
Renaux, Eugene
Farman, Henri and Maurice, 5 791
Rendezvous and docking, 11 1956-58
Gemini, 5 926
Refueling, 11 1940
Simulation
Manned Spacecraft Center, 8 1458
Regional space centers, 11 1946
Rendezvous apparatus
Kennedy Space Center, 7 1267
Rendezvous maneuver
Radar, 10 1878
Rendezvous target vehicle
Agena rockets, 1 38
Rental car
Passenger services, 10 1764
Rentschler, Frederick B.
Commercial airlines, 3 510
Repeater communications satellite
Communications satellites, 3 532
Repeater relay stations
Microwave communications, 9 1563
Repeaters
Navigation instruments, 9 1672
Reproducers
Receivers, 10 1912
Reproduction of life
Extraterrestrial life, 5 775
Republic Aviation Corporation
De Seversky, Alexander Procofieff, 4 628

Republic F-84, see F-84 Thunderstreak
Republic F-105, see F-105 Thunderchief
Republic P-47 Thunderbolt, see P-47 Thunderbolt
Republic of Korea Ground Forces, see ROKA
Repulsor rocket
    Peenemuende, **10** 1770
Requirements Committee
    Pilots and pilot certificates, **10** 1808
Rescue and Recovery Service, 11 1958-61
Rescue of astronauts
    Legal implications of aerospace, **7** 1331
    Pararescue, **10** 1760
Research and development
    Economic implications of aerospace, **4** 670, 672
    Federal Aviation Administration **5** 801
    Government in aerospace, **6** 1006
    History of aviation, **6** 1118
    Intelligence, military, **7** 1180-81
    Manned Orbiting Laboratory, **8** 1454
    Occupations (with tables), **10** 1727-30
    Spinoff, **12** 2142
    Photosynthesis, **10** 1789
Research applications
    Radar, **10** 1878
Research Flight Facility
    Environmental Science Services Administration, **4** 725
Research Satellite for Geophysics
    Environmental research satellites, **4** 723
Reservations
    Air terminals, **1** 118
Resistance activities
    Intelligence, military, **7** 1180
Resistance to heat
    Beryllium, **2** 354
Resnier, General
    Man-powered flight, **8** 1464
Resolution, 11 1961
    Photography, **10** 1785
Resonant frequency
    Lasers, **7** 1303
Resonator
    Electronics, **4** 700
Respiration
    Aviation medicine, **2** 293
Respirators
    Agricultural aviation, **1** 41
Respiratory system
    Bird flight, **2** 360
Restartable solids
    Propellants, **10** 1860
Restraint garment
    Pressure suit, **10** 1850
Restraints
    Launch window, **7** 1329
Restricted airspace, 11 1961
Retractable drive wheels
    Jumbo jets, **7** 1253
Retractable gear
    Airplane, **1** 89
    Bird flight, **2** 359
    Landing gear, **7** 1300
Retractable hooks
    Aircraft carriers, **1** 47
Retrieval applications
    Parachutes, **10** 1759
Retrograde motion, 11 1961
    Astronomy, **2** 235, 236
    Solar system, **11** 2069
Retrorocket, 11 1962
    Launch vehicles, **7** 1318
    Mercury program, **9** 1539, (drawing), 1531
    Re-entry, **11** 1930, 1933
    Surveyor, **12** 2211, 2213, 2215
Return boomerang
    Boomerang, **3** 380
Return of astronauts
    Legal implications of aerospace, **7** 1331
Reusable launch vehicles, 11 1962
    Launch vehicles, **7** 1328
Reuse capability
    Jumbo jets, **7** 1254

Reveals
    Jumbo jets, **7** 1251
Revenue mile, 11 1962
Reversal error
    Altimeter, **1** 146
Reverse biased
    Electronics, **4** 702
Revetment, 11 1962
Revolution, 11 1962
    Solar system (table), **11** 2069
Revolutionary period
    Astronomy, **2** 243
Rex Aviation Ltd.
    Australia's aviation, **2** 283
RF, see Radio frequency
RF-4 tactical missile
    NATO, **9** 1704
RF-101, see F-101
RF-104, see F-104
RF-4, see F-4 Phantom
RF-8, see F-8 Crusader
RF-111A, see F-111
RFACA, see Royal Federation of Aero Clubs
RF systems test facility
    Kennedy Space Center, **7** 1267
Rheims Air Meet, 11 1962-63
    History of aviation, **6** 1103
Rheinbote
    Missiles, **9** 1611
Rhein-Main Base
    Berlin airlift, **2** 351
Rhine, Bertrand
    Medals and decorations (table, Paul Tissandier Diploma), **8** 1526
Rhodes, E. S.
    Coast Guard aviation, **3** 476
Ribbon microphone
    Microphone, **9** 1563
Rib tests
    Wings, **14** 2491
Richardson, Holdren C.
    Catapult, **3** 424
Richardson seaplane
    Coast Guard aviation, **3** 475
Richter, John
    Ace, **1** 4
    United States Air Force, **13** 2362
Richthofen, Baron Manfred von, (1892-1918, German flying ace), **11** 1964
    Ace **1** 4
    Flying Circus, **5** 861
    Fokker DR-1 triplane, **5** 869
    Sopwith Camel, **11** 2076
    World War I (picture), **14** 2505, 2506, (table) 2507, 2508
Rickenbacker, Edward Vernon, (1890-American aviator and ace), **11** 1964-65
    Ace, **1** 4
    Aerospace industry, **1** 30
    Bong, Richard Ira, **2** 379
    Commercial airlines, **3** 502
    World War I, **14** 2505, 2507, 2510, (table) 2507
Ricker, Betty A.
    Lawyer, Richard E., **7** 1330
Riedel, Klaus
    Rockets and rocketry, **11** 1979
Right ascension
    Astronomy (with diagram), **2** 240
Right-to-exclude
    Patents, **10** 1766
Rigid construction
    Airships, **1** 106, 109-10
Rigid-frame aircraft
    Commemorative stamps and medals, **3** 493
Rigid rotor
    Helicopters, **6** 1067
    V/STOL aircraft, **13** 2444
Rignot, Georges
    Distance and distance records, **4** 630
Riley 400
    DeHavilland Dove, **4** 619

Rilles
    Moon, **9** 1636
Rime ice
    Aviation weather, **2** 301
    Icing, **7** 1145
Ring Nebula
    Nebula, **9** 1688 (with picture)
Ring system
    Astronomy, **2** 246
Rip cord
    Parachutes, **10** 1757
Rip-panel
    Balloons, **2** 317
    Wise, John, **14** 2493
Risztics, Johann
    Distance and distance records, **4** 640
Ritchey, George W.
    Telescopes and astronomical instruments, **12** 2250
RJ-1
    Delta rocket, **4** 622
    Discoverer Project, **4** 636
Road to Space Travel, The (book)
    Rockets and rocketry, **11** 1978
Robert brothers (A. J. and M.N.)
    Airships, **1** 111
    Balloons, **2** 316, 321
    Charles, Jacques Alexandre Cesar, **3** 447
Robert H. Goddard Memorial Trophy
    Gilruth, Robert Rowe, **6** 981
    Trophies and awards (table), **13** 2312
Robert J. Collier Trophy
    Trophies and awards (table), **13** 2312
Robert S. Ball award
    Clarke, Arthur Charles, **3** 467
Robertson (aircraft)
    High-lift devices, **6** 1088
Robertson Aircraft Corporation
    Airmail, **1** 75
Robertson Air Transport
    Commercial airlines, **3** 509
Robinson Anemometer
    Anemometer, **1** 152
Robinson, John
    Medals and decorations (table), **8** 1526
Robinson, R. W.
    Speed and speed records (table) **12** 2141
Robots, 11 1965-1966
ROC
    Air-to-surface missiles, **1** 123
Rochas, Beau de
    four-stroke cycle engines, Aircraft propulsion systems, **1** 53
Rocket, see Launch vehicles, Rockets and rocketry
Rocket assist
    Ramjet engines, **10** 1900
Rocket astronomy
    Friedman, Herbert, **5** 893
Rocket blasting
    Refractory metals, **11** 1936
Rocket burn
    Launch vehicles, **7** 1316
Rocket-carrying aviation
    Air forces of the world, **1** 65
Rocketdyne Division (North American)
    Launch vehicles, **7** 1325
    Space propulsion systems, **12** 2122, 2124
Rocket engines
    Aircraft propulsion systems, **1** 58-9
    Booster, **3** 381
    Combustion chamber, **3** 489
    Engines, **4** 717
    Ignition systems, **7** 1147
    Jet engines, **7** 1237
    Launch vehicle, **7** 1314
    Military space program (pictures), **9** 1603
    Missiles, **9** 1612
    Nozzles, **9** 1707
    Oceanographic research, **10** 1731
    Oxidizers, **10** 1751
    Reaction engines, **10** 1912
    Space propulsion systems, **12** 2121
Rocket experiment station
    Peenemuende, **10** 1770

Rocket flights, see Rockets and rocketry
Rocket into Interplanetary Space (book)
Rockets and rocketry, **11** 1977
Rocket motor
Model rocketry, **9** 1627
Rocket nose cones, see Nose cone
Rocket postal service
Objects of art, **10** 1722
Rocket-powered aircraft
World War II, **14** 2519-20
X-15 research program, **14** 2529-33
X-series aerospace vehicles, **14** 2534-44
Rocket-powered cars
Rockets and rocketry, **11** 1978
Rocket power series
Sounding rockets, **11** 2084
Rocket propellants
Cryogenics, **4** 597
Oxidizers, **10** 1752
Propellants, **10** 1859
Rocket propulsion
Aerospace industry, **1** 31
Goddard, Robert Hutchings, **6** 991-92
Rocket Propulsion Laboratory
Edwards Air Force Base, **4** 678
Test pilots and test flying, **12** 2280
Rocket propulsion systems, 11 1966-70
Quantum theory, **10** 1870
Rocket range
Range safety, **10** 1911
Rockets and rocketry, 11 1971-85
Air Defense Command, **1** 59
American Rocket Society, **1** 151
Armament, **2** 193
Arrow, **2** 202
Commemorative stamps and medals, **3** 495
Fireworks, **5** 814
Fuels, **5** 901
Goddard, Robert Hutchings, **6** 991
History of aviation, **6** 1109, 1114
Hydraulic systems, **6** 1140
Launching, **7** 1308
Launch vehicles, **7** 1313
Manned spaceflight, **8** 1460
Precision measurements, **10** 1845
Propellants, **10** 1862
Radiation, **10** 1884
Space propulsion systems, **12** 2121, 2122
Sputnik, **12** 2152
Surveyor, **12** 2211
Temperature control, **12** 2269
Thrust, **12** 2286
Tsiolkovsky, Konstantin Edwardovitch, **13** 2313-14
U.S.S.R. aerospace activities, **13** 2338
United Kingdom aerospace activities, **13** 2350, 2354
Von Braun, Wernher, **13** 2429
V-2 rocket missile, **13** 2445
Weather, **13** 2452
Rocket seats
Escape systems, **4** 735
Rocket sled, 11 1986-88
Rocketsondes
Meteorology, **9** 1557
Rockets, sounding, see Sounding rockets
Rocket system
Rockets and rocketry, with illustrations, **11** 1973
Rockwell, Kiffin
Lafayette Escadrille, **7** 1295
Rocky Mountains
lighted airways
Airmail, **1** 74
Rodd, H. C.
Coast Guard aviation, **3** 476
Rodenticides
Crop dusting, **4** 588
Rodgers, Calbraith Perry, (1879-1912, American aviator), **11** 1988
Aviation, **2** 292
Roe, Alliott Verdon (1877-1958, English aircraft manufacturer), **11** 1989

Commercial airlines, **3** 506
Roentgen, Wilhelm Konrad
X-rays, **14** 2533
Rogallo, Francis
Parawing, **10** 1760
Rogallo wing
Parawing, **10** 1760
Rogers Dry Lake
Edwards Air Force Base, **4** 678
Rogers, J. W.
Speed and speed records (table), **12** 2141
Rogers, Will, (1879-1935, American humorist and aviation enthusiast), **11** 1989
Post, Wiley, **10** 1840
Rohlf, Roland
Altitude and altitude records, **1** 147
Rohrbach, Adolf
History of aviation, **6** 1108
Manufacturing, **8** 1468
ROKA
Korean war, **7** 1284
ROLAND
International projects, **7** 1201
Roland (airplane)
First World War aircraft, **5** 824
Roll, 11 1990
Instrument panels, **7** 1177
Jumbo jets, **7** 1255
Maneuvers, **8** 1433
Roll axis
Aerodynamics, **1** 23
Airplane, **1** 87
Attitude and attitude control, **2** 275
Axes of rotation, **2** 308
Roller floors
Jumbo jets, **7** 1253
Roll film
Aerial photography, **1** 9
Photography, **10** 1784
Rolling
Metals and metallurgy, **9** 1550
Production techniques, **10** **1855**
Rolls, C. S.
Royce, Frederick Henry, **11** 1996
Rolls-Royce Limited
United Kingdom aerospace activities, **13** 2348, 2349-51
Rolls-Royce V-12 engine
Aircraft propulsion systems, **1** 55
Roma
Dirigibles, **4** 631
Romain, Pierre
Balloons, **2** 318
Romanet, Bernard de
Speed and speed records (table), **12** 2141
Roman, Nancy
Women in aerospace, **14** 2496, (picture), 2495
Rommel, Erwin
World War II, **14** 2516
Ronneau, Laurel
Women in aerospace, **14** 2496
R-100 dirigible
Airships (picture), **1** 111
R-101
Dirigibles, **4** 631
Roosa, Stuart Allen, (1933-   , astronaut), **11** 1990
Astronauts, **2** 217, 218, 219
Roosevelt, Franklin Delano
Aerospace industry, **1** 30
Aircraft carriers, **1** 50, 51
Airmail (picture), **1** 68, 73, 77
Arnold, Henry Harley, **2** 201
Civil Aeronautics Board, **3** 464
Ross, Malcolm D., (1919-   , American aerospace scientist), **11** 1990
Balloons, **2** 322, 330
Rossi, Aime
Distance and distance records, **4** 640
Rossi, Maurice
Distance and distance records, **4** 640, 641
Reciprocating engines, **11** 1914
World War I, **14** 2502

Rotary radial engine
Aircraft propulsion systems, **1** 55
Rotating combustion engine, **11** 1993
Rotary-wing aircraft, 11 1991-92
Rotating beacons, 11 1992
Rotating combustion engine, 11 1992-93
Wankel engine
Aircraft propulsion systems, **1** 59
Rotating cup anemometer
Anemometer (picture), **1** 152
Rotating stabilizer
Horizontal stabilizer, **6** 1129
Rotation, 11 1993
Earth, **4** 661
Guidance and control systems, **6** 1034
Solar system (table), **11** 2069
Rotation of atoms
Infrared radiation, **7** 1162
Rotational momentum
Atoms, **2** 270
Rotational period
Astronomy, **2** 243
Rotational speeds
Celestial mechanics, **3** 428
Rotocraft
Fairey, Sir Charles, **5** 790
Rotodyne
Fairey, Sir Charles, **5** 790
Rotor
Brakes, **3** 385, 386
Helicopters, **6** 1063, 1066-69
V/STOL aircraft, **13** 2439
Rougier
Altitude and altitude records, **1** 147
Route of flight
Instrument flight techniques, **7** 1167
Round-the-world flights
World records and round-the-world flights, **14** 2497
Route patterns
Airmail, **1** 77
Rover project, 11 1993-1994
Kiwi, **7** 1281
Launch vehicles, **7** 1328
Lunar bases, **8** 1391 (drawing), **8** 1393
NERVA, **9** 1691
Oceanographic research, **10** 1734
Space propulsion systems, **12** 2122
U.S. Atomic Energy Commission, **13** 2375
Royal Aeronautical Society, 11 1994
Balloons, **2** 319
Royal Air Cambodge of Cambodia
Mainland China's aerospace activities, **8** 1425
Royal Air Force, 11 1994-96
Autogiros, **286**
Bader, Douglas Robert Stuart, **2** 310
Balchen, Bernt, **312**
Ballistic Missile Early Warning System, **2** 314
Battle of Britain, **2** 343
International projects, **7** 1200-01
Jet engines, **7** 1238
Military aviation, **9** 1582-85
Naval aviation, worldwide (United Kingdom), **9** 1668-69
P-40, Curtiss, **10** 1777
Phonetic alphabet, **10** 1778
Spitfire, **12** 2146
Survival and rescue, **12** 2218
United Kingdom aerospace activities, **13** 2350
World War I, **14** 2500-10
World War II, **14** 2514
Royal Air Maroc
Africa's aviation, **1** 37
Royal Astronomical Society
Adams, John Couch, **1** 6
Royal Canadian Air Force
Bishop, William Avery, **2** 362
Canada's aviation, **3** 404
Royal Dutch Airlines (KLM)
Commercial airlines, **3** 506
European aerospace activities, **4** 748
Royal Federation of Aero Clubs
Australia's aviation, **2** 282

Royal Flying Corps
Cobham, Sir Alan, **3** 480
Royal Institution
Brabazon of Tara, Lord, **3** 384
Royal Khmer Aviation
Asia's aviation, **2** 205
Royal Thai Air Force
Asia's aviation, **2** 204
Royce, Frederick Henry, (1863-1933, British
engineer), **11** 1996
Rozier, Jean Francois Pilatre de
Aviation medicine, **2** 292
Balloons, **2** 318, 321
RR Lyrae
Stars, **12** 2160, 2162
Rubber, 11 1997
Rubber cord landing gear
Airplane, **1** 89
Rubber disc landing gear
Airplane, **1** 89
Rubis
Launch vehicles, **7** 1327
Ruby laser
Lasers, **7** 1303, 1304
Ruby maser
Masers (picture), **8** 1497
Rudder, 11 1998
Airplane, **1** 86, 87
Attitude and attitude control, **2** 275
Rudder action
Aerodynamics, **1** 23
Rudder control
Chanute, Octave, **3** 446
Piloting techniques, **10** 1796-97
Rudders
Empennage, **4** 709, 710
Rudder trim
Airplane, **1** 88
Ruddervators
Airplane, **1** 88
Rudolphine Tables, (1627)
Kepler, Johannes, **7** 1274
Ruel, Andrew
Lafayette Escadrille, **7** 1295
Ruffo di Calabria, Fulco
World War I (table, Top Aces), **14** 2507
Rumania
Commemorative stamps and medals,
3 495
European aerospace activities, **4** 749
Rumpler observation airplane
World War I (picture), **14** 2502
Rumsey, Lawrence
Lafayette Escadrille, **7** 1295
Rundstedt, Karl von
World War II, **14** 2518
Runup, 11 1998
Flight management, **5** 844
Preflight inspection, **10** 1846
Runway identification lights
Lighting facilities, **8** 1354
Runway lengths
Jumbo jets, **7** 1257
Runway lights
Lighting facilities, **8** 1356-57, (picture)
1353, (diagrams) 1355, 1356
Runway markings
Runways, **11** 1999
Runways, 11 1998-99
Airports (with picture), **1** 94, 95
Runway visibility range
Automatic landing, **2** 288
Instrument landing categories, **7** 1169
Rupture
Materials, **8** 1508
Rushworth, Robert A.
X-15 research program, **14** (picture)
2531, 2533
Russell, Henry Norris
Astrophysics, **2** 257
Stars, **12** 2160
Russia
Agricultural aviation, **1** 41
Air-to-air missiles, **1** 120-21
Air-to-surface missiles, **1** 123-24

Antiballistic missile defense, **1** 158
Apollo, **1** 165
Astronauts, **2** 217
Berlin airlift, **2** 351
Blimps, **2** 366
Bomber aircraft, **2** 374
Commemorative stamps and medals,
3 494, 495
Commercial airlines, **3** 507
Commercial air transports, **3** 530
Cosmonauts, **4** 569-75
Crop dusting, **4** 587, 593
Educational implications of aerospace,
4 674
International aviation and space
agreements, **7** 1190
International competitions, **7** 1192
Interplanetary travel, **7** 1208
Korean war, **7** 1284, 1287
Launch vehicles, **7** 1313, 1315, 1326
Life-support systems, **8** 1338
Mainland China's aerospace activities,
8 1424-26, 1428
military aircraft production
Air forces of the world, **1** 64-5
Missiles, **9** 1611-12
Naval aviation, worldwide, **9** 1670
nuclear powerplant
Aircraft propulsion systems, **1** 59
Orbits and trajectories, **10** 1746
P-40, Curtiss, **10** 1776
Photosynthesis, **10** 1790
Polar flights, **10** 1830
Political implications of aerospace, **10** 1836
Program management, **10** 1857
Reconnaissance aircraft, **11** 1921
Reconnaissance satellites, **11** 1926-27
Re-entry vehicles, **11** 1935
Rockets and rocketry, **11** 1978, 1982
Satellites, **11** 2006
Second World War aircraft, **11** 2031-32
Soyuz, **11** 2091
Supersonic transports, **12** 2179-99
World War I, **14** 2500-10
World War II, **14** 2515
Russian Academy of Sciences
Korolev, Sergei, **7** 1290
Russian aircraft
Air forces of the world, **1** 64
MiG aircraft, **9** 1564-65
YAK aircraft, **14** 2545-46
Russian Air Force
Air forces of the world, **1** 65
Second World War aircraft, **11** 2028
Russian An-22
Jumbo jets, **7** 1251
Russian fighter aircraft
Africa's aviation, **1** 37
Parachutes (pictures), **10** 1758
Russians
Antimissile missiles, **1** 159
Berlin airlift, **2** 352
International Geophysical Year, **7** 1196
Russian satellite nations
aircraft development
Air forces of the world, **1** 64
Russian space program
U.S.S.R. aerospace activities, **13** 2327
Russian Il-28's
Asia's aviation, **2** 203
Russia's jumbo jet
Jumbo jets, **7** 1256
Russia's spaceflight program
Cosmonauts, **4** 569-75
Kosmos satellites, **7** 1290
Russia's Vostok Station
Poles, **10** 1834
Rutherford, Lord
Atoms, **2** 269
RV (swept mid-wing monoplane)
YAK aircraft, **14** 2546
RVR, see Runway visual range

Ryan Aeronautical Corp.
Parawing, **10** 1761
X-series aerospace vehicles, **14** 2541
Ryan Firebee
Drone aircraft (picture), **4** 652
Reconnaissance aircraft, **11** 1923
Ryan, John D.
Aerospace industry, **1** 29
Ryan, T. Claude, (1898-   , American
aircraft manufacturer), **11** 1999
Ryan X-13, see X-13 Vertijet
Ryan XV-5A
Helicopters, **6** 1069
V/STOL aircraft (table), **13** 2443

S

S-2A, see Snow S-2A
S-2D
Crop dusting, **4** 591
S-2 Tracker (Grumman)
Asia's aviation, **2** 204
Australia's aviation, **2** 281
Naval aviation, worldwide, **9** 1670-72
S-IVB
Apollo Applications Program, **2** 185, 186
S-42 flying boat, see Sikorsky S-42
S-43 amphibian, see Sikorsky S-43
S-58 helicopter (picture)
Army aviation, **2** 199
S-61 helicopter, see SH-3 Sea King
S-62 helicopter, see HH-52A
S-64 helicopter, see CH-54 Skycrane
SA-16, see HU-16 Albatross
SA-321F, see Sud-Aviation SA 321F
SA-330 (helicopter)
Helicopters (picture), **6** 1076
SAAB-35 Draken, see Draken
SAAB-105 (picture)
Demonstration teams, **4** 624, 626
SAAB aircraft
Sweden's aviation, **12** 2224, (pictures)
2223, 2224
Saab factory
Air forces of the world (Sweden), **1** 65
SAAB Viggen, see Viggen 37 Thunderbolt
SABENA
Commercial airlines, **3** 506
European aerospace activities (Belgium),
4 743-44
Sabotage
Intelligence, military, **7** 1180
Sabre, see Canadair Sabre
Sabre, see F-86 Sabre
Sabrejet, see F-86 Sabre
Sabreliner, see North American Sabreliner
Sabreliner, see T-39 Sabreliner
Sabre, Super, see F-100 Super Sabre
SAC, see Strategic Air Command
Sachsen
Zeppelins, **14** 2550
Sachs, Henry
Rockets and rocketry, **11** 1977
Sacred Cow (airplane)
Commercial air transports, **3** 522
Saddle gun
Crop dusting (picture), **4** 585
Sadler, James
Balloons, **2** 317
Saenger, Eigen
Dynamic soaring, **4** 656, 657
Rockets and rocketry, **11** 1978

Saeta jet trainer
  Africa's aviation, 1 37
Safe control speed
  Piloting techniques, 10 1801
SAFEGE system (monorail)
  High-speed surface transportation, 6 1090
Safety
  Air Commerce Act, 1 45
  Flying safety, 5 854-55
  Interiors of aircraft, 7 1184
Safety belts, 11 2000-01
Safety statistics, 11 2001-02
Safonov, M.
  World War I (table, Top Aces), 14 2507
Sagan, Carl (1934- , American astronomer; astrophysicist), 11 2002
SAGE, see Semi-Automatic Ground Environment
Sage, Mrs. Letitia
  Balloons, 2 320
Sagittal G force
  Acceleration, 1 3
Sagittarius
  Astronomy, 2 251
  Constellations, 3 562
Sailplanes, 11 2002-05
  Canopy, airplane, 3 405
  Cockpit, 3 487
  France's aerospace activities, 5 891
  Gliders, 6 984
  Mechanical energy, 8 1522
  Soaring, 11 2062
Saint-Exupery, Antoine de (1900-1944, French aviator; author), 11 2005
St. Louis, Missouri
  Careers (table), 3 414
St. Petersburg-Tampa Airboat Line
  Commercial airlines, 3 504
  Commercial air transports, 3 517
Saipan
  Aircraft carriers, 1 51
Sakai, Saburo
  World War II (table), 14 2517
Salaries
  Astronauts, 2 231
Sales
  Careers, 3 416
  Occupations, 10 1729-30 (with tables)
Salinity
  Oceanographic research, 10 1732
Salley (airplane), see Mitsubishi 97 Sally
Salmson bomber
  World War I, 14 2510
Salvador
  Crop dusting, 4 593
Sam (monkey)
  Animals in space, 1 154
Samos
  Military space program, 9 1593-94 (with picture)
  Reconnaissance satellites, 11 1925
  Samos 3
    Reconnaissance satellites, 11 1924, 1926
Sample operations area
  Lunar Receiving Laboratory, 8 1414-15, (diagram) 1415
Samson, Charles R.
  Aircraft carriers, 1 48
  Naval aviation, worldwide (United Kingdom), 9 1667
Sandage, Allan R.
  Astronomy, 2 254
  Quasar, 10 1870
San Diego, California
  Careers (table), 3 414
San Francisco terminal
  Air terminals (picture), 1 118
Sandwich panel laminations
  Lamination, 7 1297
Sandwich structure
  Honeycomb construction, 6 1128
San Jose, California
  Careers (table), 3 414

San Marco
  Environmental research satellites, 4 723
  International projects, 7 1198
  Italy's aerospace activities, 7 1223, (picture) 1224
  NASA, 9 1653
Santa Ana, California
  Careers (table), 3 414
Santos-Dumont, Alberto (1873-1932, Brazilian aviation pioneer), 11 2005
  Airships, 1 111
  Distance records, 4 641
  History of aviation, 6 1101, (table) 1119
  Levavasseur, Leon, 7 1333
  Speed and speed records, 12 2142
  Objects of art, 10 1722-23
Santos-Dumont 14-bis, 11 2005-06
  Demoiselle, 4 623
Saratoga (ship)
  Aircraft carriers, 1 49, (data table) 51
  United States Naval Aviation, 13 2380, 2382
SAS, see Scandinavian Airlines System
Satellite and Missile Observation System
  Military space program, 9 1594
Satellite communications
  Oceanographic research, 10 1734
  Radio communications, 10 1896 (with diagram)
Satellite composite photos
  Meteorology (picture), 9 1558
Satellite Control Facility
  Manned Orbiting Laboratory, 8 1454
Satellite Link System
  South and Central America's aviation, 11 2088
Satellite orbit
  Orbits and trajectories, 10 1747
Satellite relay
  Avionics, 2 308
Satellite test vehicle
  Launch vehicles, 7 1327
Satellite tracking
  International Geophysical Year, 7 1196
Satellites, 11 2006-08
  Acquisition and tracking radar, 1 6
  Applications Technology Satellites, 2 189
  Commemorative stamps and medals, 3 495
  Communications satellites, 3 531-43
  Defense communications satellites, 4 615-17
  Discoverer Project, 4 634
  Earth science, 4 666, 667
  Explorer satellites, 5 761-73
  Geodetic satellites, 6 971
  Guidance and control systems, 6 1039
  Infrared detection devices, 7 1159
  International Telecommunications Satellite Consortium, 7 1202-04
  Jupiter, 7 1261
  Navigation satellites, 9 1672-74
  Nuclear detection satellites, 9 1707-9
  Oceanographic research, 10 1731
  Radio, 10 1885
  Reconnaissance satellites, 11 1924-27
  Tape recording, 12 2234
  Television, 12 2260
  Tracking systems and networks, 13 2297
  United Kingdom aerospace activities, 13 2354-55
  U.S.S.R. aerospace activities
  Vehicle research satellites
  Weather satellites
  West Germany's aerospace activities, 13 2479
Satre, Pierre
  Medals and decorations (table), 8 1526
Saturated air
  Evaporation and condensation, 4 757
Saturn (planet), 11 2009
  Astronomy, 2 235, 241, 245
  Atmosphere, 2 265
  Bessel, Friedrich Wilhelm, 2 354
  Earth, 4 659, 664
  Extraterrestrial life, 5 777

  Interplanetary travel, 7 1208-09
  Lowell, Percival, 8 1374
  Mythology, 9 1644
  Pickering, William Henry, 10 1791
  Retrograde motion, 11 1961
Saturn rockets (with chart), 11 2011-14
  Cornell Aeronautical Laboratory, 3 567
  Ground Computer Systems Blockhouse, 2 368
  Launch vehicles, 7 1319-24, 1329
  Marshall Space Flight Center, 8 1494
  NASA, 9 1653, 1654, (table) 1652
  Space propulsion systems, 12 2122
  Space stations, 12 2125
  Testing, 12 2275
  Saturn I, 11 2011
    Apollo, 1 164 (with picture)
    Launch vehicles, 7 1319-20, 1325
    Pegasus, 10 1773
  Von Braun, Wernher, 13 2429
Saturn IB-Centaur (launch vehicle)
  Model rocketry, 9 1627
  Voyager, 13 2436
Saturn I Workshop
  Space stations, 12 2126
Saturn V
  Acoustics, 1 5
  Aerospace industry, 1 28
  Aluminum, 1 148
  Apollo, 1 164-70 (with diagram and pictures)
  Apollo Applications Program, 2 185
  Astronautics, 2 212
  Centaur, 3 435
  Computers, 3 558
  Flight test programs, 5 857
  Honeycomb construction, 6 1129
  Juno rocket, 7 1260
  Kennedy Space Center, 7 1267, 1271
  Launch facilities, 7 1307, 1308
  Launching, 7 1309, 1312
  Launch vehicles, 7 1329, (table), 1319-20
  Manufacturing, 8 1474
  NERVA, 9 1692
  Propellants, 10 1860-61
  Reusable launch vehicles, 11 1962
Savannah (merchant ship)
  Nuclear energy, 9 1713
Savoia-Marchetti (aircraft manufacturer)
  Flying boats, 5 858
SB2C Hell Diver
  Second World War aircraft (with picture), 11 2026-27
SBD-1
  Attack aircraft, 2 273
Scandinavian Airlines System
  Commercial airlines, 3 506
  European aerospace activities, 4 745, 747
  Sweden's aviation, 12 2225
Scanning systems
  Infrared detection devices, 7 1159
Scaroni, Silvio
  World War I (table, Top aces), 14 2507
Scattering
  Electromagnetism, 4 691
Scheduled airline, 11 2015
Scheduled carriers
  Charter flying, 3 448
Scheduled flights
  Air taxis, 1 117
Schematic representation
  Shock tubes and tunnels, 11 2047
Schiaparelli, Giovanni
  Mars, 8 1490
Schirra, Walter M., Jr. (1923- , astronaut), 11 2015
  Apollo (picture), 1 171
  Astronauts, 2 215, 217, 219, 223, 225, 228, 229, 230, 232 (with picture)
  Atlas missile and launch vehicle, 2 260
  Gemini, 5 940-42
  Instrument panels, 7 1177
  Manned spaceflight (table), 8 1461
(Continued)

Schirra, Walter M., Jr. (Cont).
Mercury program, **9** 1533, 1540, 1542-43, (data table) 1544
Rendezvous and docking, **11** 1956
Telemetry (picture), **12** 2243
Schlieren photography, 11 2015-16
Schmetterling
Missiles, **9** 1611, **12** 2200
Schmidt, Bernhard
Telescopes and astronomical instruments, **12** 2253
Schmidt, Maarten
Quasar, **10** 1871
Schmidt, Otto J.
Polar flights, **10** 1829-30, (picture) 1829
Schmiedl, Friedrich
Rockets and rocketry, **11** 1978
Schmitt, Harrison H. (1935-   , Scientist-astronaut), **11** 2016
Astronauts, **2** 217, 218, 219, 222 (with picture)
Schneider, Jacques
History of aviation (table), **6** 1119
Trophies and awards (table), **13** 2312
Schneider Trophy
Air racing, **1** 102
Curtiss R2C racers, **4** 601
Doolittle, James Harold, **4** 643
History of aviation, **6** 1108
Macchi M.39 racer, **8** 1416
Royal Air Force, **11** 1995
Trophies and awards (table), **13** 2312
School of Aviation Medicine
Animals in space, **1** 154
School for Flight Surgeons
Aviation medicine, **2** 294
Schreder, Richard E.
Medals and decorations (table), **8** 1526
Schreiner Airways
European aerospace activities, **4** 747
Schriever, Bernard A. (1910-   , USAF General), **11** 2016
Manned Orbiting Laboratory, **8** 1452
Program management, **10** 1857
Reconnaissance satellites, **11** 1927
United States Air Force, **13** 2366
Schroeder, Rudolph
Altitude and altitude records, **1** 146, 147
Schroedinger, Erwin
Quantum theory, **10** 1869
Schutte-Lanz Company
Airships, **1** 111
Schweickart, Russell L. (1935-   , astronaut) **11** 2017
Astronauts, **2** 217, 218, 219, 224 (with picture)
Blockhouse (picture), **2** 368
Schweizer (glider)
Gliders (picture), **6** 984
Gliding, **6** 986, 991, (picture) 987, 988
Sailplanes, **11** 2003
Schweizer, Edward (1852-1931)
Balloons, **2** 317
Schweizer, Ernest
Medals and decorations (table), **8** 1526
Schweizer, Paul A.
Medals and decorations (table), **8** 1526
Science Abstracts (magazine)
Clarke, Arthur Charles, **3** 467
Science and Technology Series
American Astronautical Society, **1** 149
Science fiction, 11 2017-20
Science fiction magazines
Science fiction, **11** 2017
Scientific American Trophy
Aerial Experiment Association, **1** 8
Scientific Balloon Center
Balloons, **2** 330
Scientific Literature Information System
Information systems, **7** 1158
Scientific measurements
Kosmos satellites, **7** 1290
Scientific Passenger Pods
Aerospace Research Support Program, **1** 35

Scientist-astronauts
Astronauts, **2** 215
Scientists
Careers (table), **3** 412, 413
NASA
Careers (table), **3** 416
Scintillation counters
Explorer satellites, **5** 764
Score
Communications satellites, **3** 533, (table) 543
Defense communications satellites, **4** 615
Launch vehicles, **7** 1323
Military space program, **9** 1593
Scorpius
Aerobee, **1** 18
Constellations, **3** 562
Scorpius X-1
X-ray stars, **14** 2533
Scott, C. W. A.
Medals and decorations (table), **8** 1526
Scott, David M.
Medals and decorations (table), **8** 1526
Scott, David R. (1932-   , astronaut), **11** 2020
Astronauts, **2** 217, 218, 219, 224, 230 (with picture)
Gemini, **5** 942
Manned spaceflight (table), **8** 1461
Recovery, **11** 1928
Rendezvous and docking, **11** 1957-58
Scott, Robert Falcon
Polar flights, **10** 1830
Poles, **10** 1834
Scott, Sheila (1927-   , British aviatrix and actress), **11** 2021
Women in aerospace, **14** 2496
Scout, 11 2021-22
Aerospace Research Support Program, **1** 35
Explorer satellites, **5** 767
Langley Research Center, **7** 1302
Launch facilities, **7** 1307
Launch vehicles, **7** 1319-24
Military space program, **9** 1602
NASA, **9** 1653
Scoville, Curtis L.
PRIME, **10** 1853
Scrag (missile)
Surface-to-surface missiles, **12** 2205
Scramjet, 11 2022
Jet engines, **7** 1237
Screen grid
Electronics, **4** 696, 698
Scribing
Maps and mapping, **8** 1480
Scrub, 11 2022
Terminology of aerospace (table), **12** 2272
SCS, see Stabilization and control system
SCUBA
Rescue and Recovery Service, **11** 1958
S. E. 5 (picture)
Biplane, **2** 358
First World War aircraft (pictures), **5** 815, 816
World War I, **14** 2506, (picture) 2507, 2508
SE-210 Caravelle, see Caravelle transport
Seabat helicopter, see SH-34 Seabat
Seaboard World Airlines
Charter flying, **3** 448
Commercial airlines, **3** 514
Seaborg, Glenn T.
Nuclear energy, **9** 1711
Seacat
Missiles (table), **9** 1616
See Eagle flying boat (Vickers-Supermarine)
Flying boats (picture), **5** 860
Sea Fury
Asia's aviation, **2** 205
Seagull
European aerospace activities (picture), **4** 751
Sea Hawk (Hawker Siddeley)
Asia's aviation, **2** 204
Naval aviation, worldwide (India), **9** 1671
Sea King helicopter, see SH-3D Sea King
Sea Knight, see CH-46 Sea Knight

Sealab II
Carpenter, Malcolm Scott, **3** 422
Sealab III
Oceanographic research (picture), **10** 1733
Sea level
Atmospheric pressure, **2** 268
Pressure altitude, **10** 1849
Pressurization, **10** 1851
Seamans, Robert
Astronaut, **2** 232
Sea of Rains
Luna probes, **8** 1378
Moon, **9** 1636
Sea of Storms
Apollo, **1** 170
Sea of Tranquility
Moon, **9** 1635-36 (with picture)
Surveyor, **12** 2214
Seaplanes, 11 2022-25
Aircraft carriers, **1** 48
Fabre, Henri, **5** 785
First World War aircraft, **5** 819, 820
History of aviation, **6** 1105, 1109, 113, (picture) 1100
Naval aviation, worldwide (Russia), **9** 1670
seaplane bases
Airports, **1** 93
United States Naval Aviation, **13** 2377
Search and rescue, 11 2025
Airports, **1** 100
Civil Air Patrol, **3** 466
Flight service stations, **5** 851
Search coil magnetometer
Cunningham, R. Walter, **4** 600
Search radar
Navigation instruments, **9** 1673
Radar, **10** 1876
Sea rescue float
Survival and rescue, **12** 2218
Sea Scout
Blimp, **2** 364
Sea Sparrow (missile)
Surface-to-air missiles, **12** 2203
Sea Stallion helicopter, see CH-53 Sea Stallion
Seat-anchoring device
Interiors of aircraft, **7** 1184
SEATO, see South East Asia Treaty Organization
Seattle, Washington
Careers (table), **3** 414
Sea Venom
Australia's aviation, **2** 281
Sea Vixen jets (Hawker Siddeley)
Air forces of the world, **1** 66
Fighter aircraft (picture), **5** 809
Naval aviation, worldwide (United Kingdom), **9** 1669, (picture) 1668
Sea water
Oceanographic research, **10** 1731
Second
Parsec, **10** 1763
Secondary batteries
Battery, **2** 339
Secondary cosmic rays
Cosmic rays, **3** 568
Secondary emission
Electronics, **4** 694
Secondary landing area
Recovery, **11** 1928
2nd ATAF
NATO, **9** 1704
Second burn
Launch vehicles, **7** 1317-18
Second-stage engines
Apollo (pictures), **1** 166, 179
Second World War aircraft (with pictures), **11** 2026-38
Spitfire, **12** 2146
World War II, **14** 2511
SECOR
Earth, **4** 663
Geodetic satellites, **6** 972-74, (picture) 975, (table) 973

(Continued)

SECOR (Cont.)
Military space program, **9** 1595, 1598 (with picture)
Reconnaissance satellites, **11** 1926
Secrecy Order
Patents, **10** 1768
Secret
Classified information, **3** 467
Sectional Aeronautical Chart
Charts, **3** 450, 451
Sector
Air traffic control, **1** 127, 131, 132
Secular changes
Earth, **4** 662
Secular variation
Geomagnetic field, **6** 977
Sedatives
Drug effects, **4** 653
S.E. 5, 11 2039
See, Elliot M., Jr. (1927-1966, astronaut), **11** 2038
Astronauts, **2** 216, 217 (with picture)
Seguin, Augustin
Distance records, **4** 640
Seismic Sea Wave Warning System
Environmental Science Services Administration, **4** 725
Seismometer
Ranger, **10** 1906
Selective calling equipment
Radio communications, **10** 1896 (with diagram)
Self-luminous signs
Nuclear energy, **9** 1715
Selfridge, Thomas E.
Aerial Experiment Association, **1** 7-8 (with picture)
Army aviation, **2** 195
Self-sealing doors
Airlock, **1** 67
Self-sufficiency
Lunar bases, **8** 1395
Semiautomated baggage-handling system
Jumbo jets, **7** 1253
Semi-Automatic Ground Environment, 11 2039-41
Air Defense Command, **1** 59
Air defense systems, **1** 60
Computers, **3** 558
NORAD, **9** 1703
Program management, **10** 1858
Weaponry, **13** 2449
Semicantilever wings, 14 2491-92
Airplane, **1** 86
Semicircular canals
Man in flight, **8** 1447
Semiconductors, 11 2040-41
Electronics, **4** 692, 700, 704
Lasers, **7** 1303
Materials, **8** 1511
Solid-state physics, **11** 2073
Semi-monocoque design
Airplane, **1** 83
Aluminum, **1** 148
Monocoque and semimonocoque design, **9** 1632
Seminole, see U-8 Seminole
Semirigid construction
Airships, **1** 106
Semispherical protrusions
Kosmos satellites, **7** 1294
Semper Paratus
Coast Guard aviation, **3** 480
Seney, John S.
Man-powered flight, **8** 1465
Ornithopter, **10** 1748
Sense antenna
Automatic direction finder, **2** 287
Sensing circuits
Electric systems, **4** 681
Sensing devices
Data acquisition and processing, **4** 605
Sensors, **11** 2042

Sensitive axis
Inertial guidance, **7** 1152
Sensors, 11 2042-43
Aerial photography, **1** 10
Aerospace Research Support Program, **1** 35
Automatic pilot, **2** 289
Inertial guidance, **7** 1152
Military space program, **9** 1595
Modulation, **9** 1630
Nuclear detection satellites, **9** 1709
Surveyor, **12** 2211
Sensory deprivation, 11 2043
Sensory equipment
Reconnaissance aircraft, **11** 1922, 1924
Sensory panels
Interplanetary Monitoring Platform satellites (picture), **7** 1206
Sensory stimuli
Illusions, **7** 1147
Sentinel
Antiballistic missile defense, **1** 159
Missiles (table), **9** 1616
Surface-to-air missiles, **12** 2203
Separation
Aerodynamics, **1** 22
Air traffic control, **1** 127
Hemisphere rules, **6** 1080
Sequential Collation of Range, see SECOR
Serb
Missiles (table), **9** 1616
Surface-to-surface missiles, **12** 2205
SEREB
EUROPA 1, **4** 741
Eurospace, **4** 756
Sergeant
Battlefield missile systems, **2** 341, (picture) 340
Surface-to-surface missiles, **12** 2206, (table) 2208
Serpens
Nebula (picture), **9** 1688
Serpentine
Asbestos, **2** 202
Service academies, 11 2043-45
Service ceiling
Ceiling, **3** 426
Bomber aircraft, **2** 375
Service centers
Jumbo jets, **7** 1256
Service Module
Apollo, **1** 164-73 (with diagram and pictures)
Apollo Applications Program, **2** 185, 186
Module, **9** 1630
Propulsion system
Apollo, **1** 177
Space propulsion systems, **12** 2125
Servoactuators
Hydraulic systems, **6** 1140
Servomechanism, 11 2045
Radar, **10** 1877
Servo motor control loop
Automatic pilot, **2** 288, (diagram) 289
Servo motors
Seruomechanism, 11 2045
Orbiting observatories, **10** 1738
Seversky Aircraft Corporation
De Seversky, Alexander Procofieff, **4** 628
Seversky, Alexander de, see De Seversky, Alexander Procofieff
Severskys
Air racing, **1** 103
Sextant, 11 2045
SFOF, see Space Flight Operations Facility
SH-3 Sea King helicopter (Sikorsky) (S-61R)
Coast Guard aviation, **3** 478
Italy's aerospace activities, **7** 1221
Naval aviation, worldwide, **9** 1670-72
SH-34 Seabat helicopters (Sikorsky)
Naval aviation, worldwide, **9** 1670-71
West Germany's Bundesluftwaffe
Air forces of the world, **1** 66
Shackleton, see Hawker Siddeley Shackleton MR.Mk3

Shaft horsepower
Power management, **10** 1842
SHAPE, see Supreme Headquarters Allied Powers Europe
Shapley, Harlow (1885-   , American astronomer), **11** 2045
Shark fin
Airborne antennas, **1** 43 (with picture)
Sharp, William
Airmail, **1** 69
Shatter cones
Meteors, meteorites, and meteoroids, **9** 1561
Shawnee helicopter, see CH-21 Shawnee
Shear resistance
Fabrics, **5** 786
Shear, wind, 11 2046
Sheldon, Charles S., II
Reconnaissance satellites, **11** 1927
Sheldon, Dr. John
Aviation medicine, **2** 293
Shell
Atoms, **2** 270
Shenandoah (dirigible)
Airships, **1** 107-08, 112
Dirigibles, **4** 631
Gondolas, **6** 994
Shepard, Alan B., Jr., 1923-   ), 11 2046
Astronauts, **2** 215, 216, 217, 219, 225, 229, 232 (with picture)
Blockhouse, **2** 367
Manned spaceflight (table), **8** 1461
Mercury program, **9** 1533, 1536, (picture) 1536, (data table) 1544
Sheppard, Morris
Airmail, **1** 69
Shillelagh
Battlefield missile systems, **2** 342
Infrared detection devices, **7** 1161
Surface-to-surface missiles, **12** 2207, (picture) 2207, (table) 2208
Shin Meiwa Company
Asia's aviation, **2** 204
Shin Meiwa PX-S
Naval aviation, worldwide, **9** 1671
Shinn, Gus
Polar flights, **10** 1830
Shipment activities
Quality control, **10** 1867
Ships
Oceanographic research, **10** 1731, 1734
Shirt-sleeve environment, 11 2046-47
Shoals
Oceanographic research, **10** 1732
Shock, 11 2047
Environmental simulators, **4** 726
Shock absorption
Landing gear
Airplane, **1** 89
Shockley, William
Electronics, **4** 693
Shock tubes and tunnels, 11 2047-48
Shock tunnel
Shock tubes and tunnels, **11** 2048
Shock wave, 11 2048
Aerodynamics, **1** 24
Expansion waves, **4** 760
Shock tubes and tunnels, **11** 2047
Sonic boom, **11** 2074
Shoemaker, E. M.
Astrogeology, **2** 212
Shoemaker, Faye L.
Stafford, Thomas P., **12** 2157
Shoho
Aircraft carriers, **1** 49
Shokaku
Aircraft carriers, **1** 49
Shonk, Robert
Airmail (picture), **1** 70
Shooting Star, see F-80 Shooting Star
Shooting stars
Meteors, meteorites, and meteoroids, **9** 1559

Shoran
Navigation systems, **9** 1679-80
Short brothers, 11 2049
United Kingdom aerospace activities,
13 2353
Short Calcutta
Commercial airlines (picture), **3** 506
Short, Eustace (1875-1932)
Short brothers, **11** 2049
Short field takeoff
Piloting techniques, **10** 1797
Short, Horace (1869-1917)
Aircraft carriers, **1** 48
Short brothers, **11** 2049
Shorthorn (airplane)
First World War aircraft, **5** 822
Short, Hugh Oswald (1883-   )
Short brothers, **11** 2049
Short-period comets
Comets, **3** 490
Short-Range Attack Missile
Air-to-surface missiles, **1** 124
Short Scipio (flying boat)
Flying boats (picture), **5** 859
Short Stirling bomber
Bomber aircraft, **2** 375
World War II, **14** 2518
Short Sunderland S. 25 (flying boat)
Flying boats, **5** 860
History of aviation, **6** 1114
Short takeoff and landing aircraft, see STOL
Short wavelengths
Atmosphere (diagram), **2** 266
Shot
Terminology of aerospace (table), **12** 2272
Shoulder harnesses
Agricultural aviation, **1** 41
Shrike
Air-to-surface missiles, **1** 124
X-series aerospace vehicles, **14** 2540
Shrike test missile, see X-9 Shrike
Shroud
Firewalls, **5** 813
Nose cone, **9** 1705
Parachutes, **10** 1759
Satellites, **11** 2008
Shutter
Photography, **10** 1782-83
Pulsejet engine (with diagram), **10** 1866
Shuttle service
Airmail, **1** 78
Siai-Marchetti
Italy's aerospace activities, **7** 1220
Sial
Earth, **4** 660
Sicily
World War II, **14** 2516-17
Side guides
Jumbo jets, **7** 1253
Sidereal day
Earth, **4** 660
Sidereal Message (book)
Astronomy, **2** 237
Sidereal period
Astronomy, **2** 240, 243
Sidereal year
Earth, **4** 661
Sidereus Nuncius (book)
Astronomy, **2** 237
Sidewinder missile
Air Defense Command, **1** 59
Air defense systems, **1** 61
Air forces of the world, **1** 66
Air-to-air missiles, **1** 120-21 (with picture)
Battlefield missile systems, **2** 343
Homing devices, **6** 1128
Infrared detection devices, **7** 1160
Marine Corps Aviation, **8** 1482
Missiles (table), **9** 1616
Sight
Piloting techniques, **10** 1796
Sigma 7 (spacecraft)
Manned spaceflight (table), **8** 1461
Mercury program, **9** 1542-43, (table) 1544
NASA (table), **9** 1652

SIGMETS, 11 2049
Signal amplification
Receivers, **10** 1912
Signal Corps (airplane)
Wright brothers (picture), **14** 2526
Signal light guns
Air traffic control, **1** 133
Signalling
Survival and rescue, **12** 2217
Signal plate
Television, **12** 2258
Signals
Intercom, **7** 1182
Radar, **10** 1879
Receivers, **10** 1912
Signature
Re-entry vehicles, **11** 1935
Significant Meteorological Advisories, see
SIGMETS
Sikorsky 61N
Asia's aviation (picture), **2** 205
Sikorsky CH-34, see CH-34 Choctaw
Sikorsky CH-37, see CH-37 Mojave
Sikorsky CH-53, see CH-53 Sea Stallion
Sikorsky CH-54, see CH-54 Skycrane
Sikorsky Grand (with performance chart),
11 2050
Sikorsky helicopters
Helicopters, **6** 1063, 1069, 1074, (diagram)
1064, (pictures) 1070, 1072-73, 1075,
(table) 1068
Nationalist China's aviation (picture),
9 1666
Rescue and Recovery Service, **11** 1960
Sikorsky HH-52A, see HH-52A
Sikorsky, Igor I. (1899-   , Russian-American
aeronautical engineer), **11** 2049-50
Aerospace industry, **1** 29
Helicopters, **6** 1062-63
History of aviation, **6** 1105, (table) 1119
Medals and decorations (table), **8** 1526
Sikorsky, Ilya Mourometz
First World War aircraft, **5** 825
Sikorsky R4
Crop dusting, **4** 588
Sikorsky S-42 (with performance chart),
11 2050-51
Flying boats, **5** 859
Sikorsky S-43 amphibian
Commercial air transports (picture), **3** 518
Sikorsky S-61R, see SH-3 Sea King
Sikorsky S-64, see CH-54 Skycrane
Sikorsky SH-3D, see SH-3D Sea King
Sikorsky SH-34, see SH-34 Seabat
Sikorsky UH-19, see UH-19 Chickasaw
Sikorsky VS-300 (with performance chart),
11 2051
Silent chambers
Cosmonauts, **4** 570
Silica glass
Glass, **6** 982
Silicon, 11 2052
Plastics, **10** 1823
Semiconductors, **11** 2041
Silicon-controlled rectifier
Electronics, **4** 703
Silicon diode
Miniaturization, **9** 1608
Silicon solar cells
Electronics (picture), **4** 702
Silos, 11 2052-54
Silver City Airways
Commercial airlines, **3** 514
Silver Dart
Aerial Experiment Association, **1** 8
Silver iodide crystals
Cloud seeding, **3** 474
Silver Star
Medals and decorations (picture), **8** 1525
Sima
Earth, **4** 660
Simons, David G.
Medals and decorations (table), **8** 1526

Simplex communications
Radio communications, **10** 1895
Simulated flights
Kennedy Space Center, **7** 1268
Simulators, see Spaceflight simulators
Single disc brakes
Airplane, **1** 90
Single-engine plane
Instrument panels, **7** 1176
Single shell
Airplane, **1** 83
Sink rate
Gliders, **6** 984
Sintered
Iron, **7** 1216
Metals and metallurgy, **9** 1554
Sioux helicopter, see OH-13 Sioux
Sirius
Bessel, Friedrich Wilhelm, **2** 354
Binary stars, **2** 255
Sisakyan, N. M.
Cosmonauts (Selection; Training), **4** 570-71
Sivel, H. T.
Aviation medicine, **2** 293
Balloons, **2** 324
6th ATAF
NATO, **9** 1704
16th century rocket launcher
Rockets and rocketry (with illustrations),
11 1974
695th Aerospace Test Wing
Vandenberg Air Force Base, **13** 2402
Size requirements
Runways, **11** 1999
SK-4
Korolev, Sergei, **7** 1290
Skalski, S.
World War II (table), **14** 2517
Skeleton
Bird flight, **2** 359
Skid, 11 2054
X-15 research program, **14** 2532 (with
picture)
Ski-equipped plane
Airplane, **1** 90
Polar flights, **10** 1830
Skinner, Leslie
Rockets and rocketry, **11** 1982
Skin radiators
Radiators, **10** 1885
Skin-track
Space communications, **11** 2096
Skin trackers
Radar, **10** 1874
SKOGA, see Sovetski-Kitaysko Aktsionernoe
Obshestvo Grazhdanskoi Aviatsii
Sky, 11 2054
Skycrane helicopter, see CH-54 Skycrane
Skydiving, 11 2054-55
Parachutes, **10** 1759
Sport flying, **12** 2150
Skyhawk, see A-4 Skyhawk
Skyhawk, see Cessna 172 Skyhawk
Skyhooks
Balloons, **2** 327
Skyhopper (airplane)
Homebuilt aircraft, **6** 1125
Sky Knight
Helicopters, **6** 1075
Skylane, see Cessna 182 Skylane
Skylark (rocket)
Woomera rocket range, **14** 2496
Sky, map of
Radio astronomy, **10** 1891
Skymaster, see Cessna Skymaster
Skymaster transport, see C-54 Skymaster
Skyraider, see A-1 Skyraider
Sky sailing (parasailing)
Sport flying, **12** 2150
Sky-spy system
Reconnaissance satellites, **11** 1927
Skytrain, see C-47 Skytrain
Skytyping
Skywriting, **11** 2056

Skyward (book)
  Byrd, Richard Evelyn, 3 397
Skywarrior, see A-3 Skywarrior
Skywarriors, see KA-3B Skywarriors
Skyways, A Book on Modern Aeronautics
  (book), 9 1621
Skywriting, 11 2056-57
SLA, see Spacecraft LM-Adapter
Slab elevator
  Elevators, 4 706
Slar
  Radar, 10 1878
Slave
  Terminology of aerospace (table), 12 2272
Slaved system
  Compasses, 3 549
Slave station
  Loran, 8 1371-72, (diagram) 1372
  Radio navigation, 10 1899
Slayton, Donald K. (1924-   ), 11 2057
  Astronauts, 2 215, 217, 219, 225, 229, (with
    picture)
  Blockhouse (picture), 2 368
  Mercury program, 9 1533, 1537, 1540
SLC, see Space Launch Complex
SLC-3X
  Launch vehicles, 7 1324
Sleet, 11 2057-58
  Precipitation, 10 1844
Slick Airlines
  Commercial airlines, 3 514
Slip, 11 2058
  Terminology of aerospace (table), 12 2272
Slip bands
  Material fatigue, 8 1498
Slip landing
  Cross-wind landing, 4 594
Slippage
  Propellers, 10 1862
Slipstream, 11 2058
Slo-Scan display
  Aviation weather, 2 300
Slosh
  Gravity, 6 1011
  Launch vehicles, 7 1318
Slot
  High-lift devices, 6 1088
Slotted aileron and flap
  Airplane, 1 87-88
Slow flight, 11 2058
  Maneuvers, 8 1435, (diagram) 1437
Slurry
  Forest fire control, 5 881
SLV-3, see Standard Launch Vehicle-3
SLV-3C
  Atlas missile and launch vehicle, 2 260
SLVA-3A
  Atlas missile and launch vehicle, 2 260
SM62 Snark (Northrop)
  History of aviation, 6 1118
SM-64 Navaho surface-to-surface guided
    missile
  X-series aerospace vehicles, 14 2541
Small circle
  Earth, 4 663
  Equator, 4 729
Smeltzer, Gratia Kay
  Lousma, Jack Robert, 8 1372
Smirnoff, I.
  World War I (table, Top Aces), 14 2507
Smith, Cyrus Rowlett (1899-   , American
    airline executive), 11 2058
  Commercial airlines, 3 502, 512
Smith, Floyd
  Parachutes, 10 1757
Smith, Joan Merriam
  Women in aerospace, 14 2496
Smith, Lowell
  United States Air Force, 13 2362
Smith Miniplane
  Homebuilt aircraft, 6 1125
Smithsonian Institution
  Biplane, 2 358

National Air and Space Museum, 9 1658
  Durant, Frederick Clark, III, 4 655
Smithson, James (1765-1829)
  National Air and Space Museum, 9 1658
Smog, 11 2058-59
Smoke fires
  Panel code, 10 1755
Smoke inhalation
  Man in flight, 8 1450
Smokejumpers, 11 2059
  Parachutes, 10 1759
Smoke smeller
  Exhaust gas analyzer, 4 759
SNAP program, 11 2059-61
  U.S. Atomic Energy Commission, 13 2375
SNAP-7B, C, D, E,
  Nuclear energy, 9 1714
SNAP-8
  Metals and metallurgy (picture), 9 1555
  SNAPS (with diagram), 11 2061
SNAP-10A
  Nuclear energy, 9 1714 (with picture)
SNAP-18 nuclear generator
  Aerospace industry (picture), 1 28
SNAP-27 radioisotope thermoelectric
    generator
  Lunar exploration, 8 1407
Snark (airplane), see SM62 Snark
Snark
  Missiles (table), 9 1616
Snecker, Shirley Jean
  Herres, Robert T., 6 1083
SNECMA
  Australia's aviation, 2 280
Sniperscopes
  Infrared detection devices, 7 1159
SNJ (flight trainer)
  Flight simulators, 5 852
Snow, 11 2061-62
  Precipitation, 10 1844
  Rain, 10 1900
Snow S-2A
  Crop dusting, 4 589
SO-1221 Djinn (helicopter)
  France's aerospace activities (picture),
    5 890
Soaring, 11 2062-66
  Bird flight, 2 362
  Gliders, 6 984
  Sport flying, 12 2150
Soaring Society of America, 11 2066
  Armstrong, Neil A., 2 193
  Gliding, 6 986
  Pleasure flying, 10 1826
Social implications of aerospace, 11 2066-67
Sociedad Colombo-Alemana de Transportes
  Commercial airlines, 3 507
  South and Central America's aviation,
    11 2087-91
Society of Automotive Engineers
  Measurement of power, 8 1519
  Social implications of aerospace, 11 2067
Society of Experimental Test Pilots
  Test pilots and test flying, 12 2279, 2280
Soda-lime glass
  Glass, 6 982
Sod-field tires
  Northrop F-5 Freedom Fighter, 9 1705
Soft field landing
  Piloting techniques, 10 1797
Soft landing, 11 2068
  Apollo, 1 169
  Luna probes, 8 1378
  Terminology of aerospace (table), 12 2272
Soft metallic ferromagnets
  Materials, 8 1512
Software, 11 2068
  Terminology of aerospace (table), 12 2272
Soil analysis laboratory
  Crop dusting, 4 593
Soil samples
  Moon (picture), 9 1638

Soko Galeb (aircraft)
  European aerospace activities (picture)
    4 751
Solar astrophysics
  Astrophysics, 2 255
Solar calendar
  Astronomy, 2 234, 242
Solar cells, 11 2068-69
  Communications satellites, 3 533, 539
  Electricity, 4 685
  Electronics, 4 702, 703
  GHOST program, 6 979
  Oceanographic research, 10 1731
  Orbiting observations, 10 1738
  power supply
    Kosmos satellites, 7 1292
  Radiation, 10 1883
  Semiconductors, 11 2041
  Space power systems, 12 2120
  Sputniks, 12 2153
  Surveyor, 12 2210
  U.S.S.R. aerospace activities, 13 2339
  Weather satellites, 13 2460
Solar corona
  Interplanetary travel, 7 1212
Solar day
  Earth, 4 660
Solar eclipse
  Astronomy, 2 234
  Eclipse, 4 668, 669 (with diagram)
Solar-electric spacecraft
  Electric propulsion, 4 685
Solar emissions
  Radio astronomy, 10 1890
Solar energy
  Explorer satellites, 5 767
  Parabola, 10 1756
  Radiation, 10 1881
Solar flares
  International Years of the Quiet Sun, 7 1204
  Magnetic storms, 8 1420
  Matter (picture), 8 1514
  Pioneer, 10 1813
  Radiation, 10 1883
  Sun, 12 2174
  Supersonic transports, 12 2197
Solo flights
  Pilots and pilot certificates, 10 1808
  Pilot training, 10 1809
Solar flux
  Oceanographic research, 10 1731
Solar motion
  Planetarium, 10 1819
Solar observatory
  Apollo Applications Program, 2 186
Solar-oriented experiment package
  Orbiting observatories, 10 1741
Solar panels
  Orbiting observatories, 10 1741
Solar particles
  Poles, 10 1834
Solar plasma
  International Years of the Quiet Sun, 7 1204
  Mariner probes, 8 1487, 1488
Solar power
  Electric propulsion, 4 685
Solar radiation
  Aerobee, 1 18
  Atmosphere (picture), 2 266
  Planets, 10 1820
Solar rays
  Greenhouse effect, 6 1013
Solar simulators
  Cryogenics, 4 597
Solar system, 11 2069-70
  Aristarchus of Samos, 2 193
  Astronomy, 2 233, 247
  Earth, 4 663
  Extraterrestrial life, 5 774
  Kepler, Johannes, 7 1274
  Kepler's laws, 7 1275
  Leverrier, Urbain, J. J., 7 1334
  Orbiting observatories, 10 1740
  Orbits and trajectories, 10 1742
    (Continued)

Solar System (Cont.)
Parallax, **10** 1760
Perihelion, **10** 1774
Planetarium, **10** 1820
Planets, **10** 1820-21
Space, **11** 2093
Technological projections, **12** 2235, 2239, 2240
Solar time
Astronomy, **2** 240
Solar ultraviolet
Jupiter, **7** 1260
Solar wind, 11 2071
Astronomy, **2** 247
Earth, **4** 662
Comets, **3** 490
Geomagnetic field, **6** 977
International Years of the Quiet Sun, **7** 1204
Interplanetary Monitoring Platform satellites, **7** 1205
Magnetic storms, **8** 1420
Pioneer, **10** 1813
Radiation, **10** 1882-83
Space, **11** 2093
Space weather, **12** 2138
Sun, **12** 2174
Van Allen radiation belts, **13** 2401
Solar X-rays
Radiation, **10** 1882
Solberg, H.
Meteorology, **9** 1557
Solid-fuel motors
Kennedy Space Center, **7** 1267
Solid-fuel rockets, 11 2071
Launch vehicles, **7** 1315-16
Solid logic circuitry
Computers, **3** 557
Solid mass
Launch vehicles, **7** 1315
Solid-propellant rockets
Ignition systems, **7** 1146
Solid-fuel rockets, **11** 2071
Solid propellants
Propellants, **10** 1859
Solids
Matter, **8** 1513
Solid-state circuitry
Computers, **3** 557
Jumbo jets, **7** 1252
Microcircuitry, **9** 1562
Solid-state communications
Jumbo jets, **7** 1255
Solid-state electronics
Miniaturization, **9** 1608
Solid-state physics, 11 2071-73
Solrad
Explorer satellites, **5** 772, 773
Military space program, **9** 1595
Some Recent Researches in Solar Physics (book)
Hoyle, Fred, **6** 1131
Sonar, 11 2073-74
Electronics, **4** 704
S-1C Stage Saturn V
Aerospace industry (picture), **1** 28
Apollo, **1** 169
Launch vehicles (diagram), **7** 1323
Saturn rockets, **11** 2013
Sonic barrier
Government in aerospace, **6** 1005
Sonic boom, 11 2074-75
Acoustics, **1** 5
Shock wave, **11** 2048
Supersonic flight, **12** 2177
Supersonic transports, **12** 2195, 2196
Sonne camera
Aerial photography, **1** 10
Sophistication, 11 2075
Terminology of aerospace (table), **12** 2272
Sopwith Camel, 11 2076
Biplane, **2** 358
Fighter aircraft, **5** 811
First World War aircraft, **5** 816, 820, (picture) 816

History of aviation (picture), **6** 1105
World War I, **14** 2506, 2508
Sopwith, Thomas (1888- , British aircraft manufacturer), **11** 2075
Sopwith Tripe
World War I, **14** 2506, 2508
Sormovitch (hovercraft)
Ground-effect machines (picture), **6** 1026
Sortie, 11 2076
Soryu
Aircraft carriers, **1** 49
SOS, 11 2076
Mayday, **8** 1516
Soucek, Apollo
Altitude and altitude records, **1** 146-48
Sound, 11 2076-78
Acoustics, **1** 4-5
Noise, **9** 1699
Supersonic flight, **12** 2177
Sound barrier
United States Air Force, **13** 2365
Yaeger, Charles E., **14** 2547
Sounding balloon
Balloons, **2** 325
Sounding rockets, 11 2079-85
Aerobee, **1** 17
Aerospace Research Support Program, **1** 35
Argus Project, **2** 191
Earth science, **4** 666, 667
Goddard Space Flight Center, **6** 992
International Geophysical Year, **7** 1196
International projects, **7** 1199
Italy's aerospace activities, **7** 1225
Japan's aerospace activities, **7** 1231
Launch vehicles, **7** 1317
Rocket propulsion systems, **11** 1966
Scout, **11** 2021
Tracking systems and networks, **13** 2303
WRESAT, **14** 2524
Sound levels
Noise (data table), **9** 1699
Noise measurement, **9** 1700
Sound waves
Shock wave (with diagram), **11** 2048
Sonar, **11** 2073
Sound, **11** 2077
South Africa
Africa's aviation, **1** 37
Air forces of the world, **1** 64
South America
Boron, **3** 382
Crop dusting, **4** 587
South American anomaly
Pegasus, **10** 1773
South and Central America's aviation, 11 2087-91
South Atlantic magnetic anomaly
Explorer satellites, **5** 772
South celestial pole
Celestial sphere, **3** 431
Constellations, **3** 562
Southeast Asia
Agricultural aviation, **1** 41
Asia's aviation, **2** 203
Vietnam, **13** 2414
South East Asia Treaty Organization
Air forces of the world, **1** 65
United States Air Force, **13** 2359
Southerly turning error
Compasses, **3** 549-50 (with diagram)
Southern Cross
Astronomy, **2** 252
Southern Cross (aircraft)
Kingsford-Smith, Charles, **7** 1277
Southern Hemisphere
Anticyclone, **1** 159
Constellations, **3** 562
Southern Skylines
Commercial airlines, **3** 512
South Korean aviation
Asia's aviation, **2** 205
South magnetic pole
Compasses, **3** 546
Geomagnetic field, **6** 977
Poles, **10** 1834

South Pole
Amundsen, Roald, **1** 151
Byrd, Richard Evelyn, **3** 397
Polar flights, **10** 1829
Poles, **10** 1833
South Vietnam
Asia's aviation, **2** 203, 204
Vietnam, **13** 2414
Southwest Air Fast Express
Commercial airlines, **3** 512
Sovetski-Kitaysko Aktsionernoe Obshestvo Grazhdanskoi Aviatsii
Mainland China's aerospace activities, **8** 1424
Soviet Military Aviation Forces-VVS
U.S.S.R. aerospace activities, **13** 2335, 2336
Soviet Strategic Rocket forces
Rockets and rocketry (with picture), **11** 1983
Soviet Union, see Russia
Soyuz, 11 2091
Cosmonauts, **4** 574
Soyuz-1
Cosmonauts (table), **4** 574
Komarov, Vladimir, M., **7** 1282
U.S.S.R. aerospace activities, **13** 2344
Sp-5M flying boat, see Martin Sp-5M
Spaatz, Carl (1891- , American Air Force Officer), **11** 2092
United States Air Force, **13** 2362, 2364, (picture) 2365
Spaatz 55 (glider)
Gliders (picture), **6** 984
Space, 11 2092-93
Aerospace medicine, **1** 33-34
Agena rockets (picture), **1** 38
Earth, **4** 660
Escape systems, **4** 735
first woman in balloons, **2** 321
Implications of aerospace, **7** 1149, 1151
Metals and metallurgy, **9** 1549
Patents, **10** 1766
Quantum theory, **10** 1870
Rocket propulsion systems, **11** 1967
simulator
Environmental simulators, **4** 728
Space Act of 1958
Mercury program, **9** 1530
Space age
Aerospace industry, **1** 31
Agena rockets, **1** 38-39
Commemorative stamps and medals, **3** 495
Manufacturing, **8** 1472-73
Paints, **10** 1754
Space and Missile Systems Organization
Discoverer Project, **4** 632
Nuclear detection satellites, **9** 1707
Space-atmosphere gliders
Dynamic soaring, **4** 656
Space biology, 11 2094-95
Animals in space, **1** 154
Space booster
Launch facilities, **7** 1307
Nose cone, **9** 1705-06
Space cabin
Capsule, **3** 406
Space cameras
Aerial photography, **1** 9
Space capsule
Algae, **1** 143
Balloons, **2** 325
Space charge
Electronics, **4** 695
Space communications, 11 2096-99
Legal implications of aerospace, **7** 1331
Telemetry, **12** 2241
Spacecraft, 11 2100
Aeronautical engineering, **1** 26
Aerospace industry, **1** 29
Agena rockets, **1** 38-39
Alloys, **1** 143
Apollo, **1** 162
Attitude and attitude control, **2** 275
Carbon dioxide, **3** 407

Crash investigations, **4** 579, 582
Data acquisition and processing, **4** 610
Decompression, **4** 614
Doppler navigation, **4** 646
Gemini, **5** 926
Heat shields, **6** 1056
Hohmann orbits, **6** 1122
Human engineering, **6** 1134
Hydraulic systems, **6** 1140
Instrument panels, **7** 1177
International projects, **7** 1197-98
Launching
   Orbits and trajectories, **10** 1742
Launch vehicles, **7** 1313-14
Life-support systems, **8** 1337-44
maneuvers
   Orbital velocity, **10** 1738
   Mercury program, **9** 1529
noise level
   Acoustics, **1** 4-5
orbit
   Inclination, **7** 1151
Paints, **10** 1754
Radiation, **10** 1882
recovery
   PRIME, **10** 1853
return of
   International aviation and space
     agreements, **7** 1190
Satellites (with picture), **11** 2007
Temperature control, **12** 2265
Spacecraft design, 11 2100-03
Spacecraft safety, **12** 2111
Space stations, **12** 2127
Spacecraft-LM Adapter
Apollo, **1** 174
Lunar Module, **8** 1408
Spacecraft sterilization, 11 2103-04
**Spacecraft Technology and Advanced
Re-entry Test,** see START
Spacecraft weight
Spacecraft design, **11** 2102
Space Defense Center
Ballistic Missile Early Warning System,
2 313
Space Detection and Tracking System
NORAD, **9** 1702
Tracking systems and networks, **13** 2300,
2305
Space Disturbances Laboratory
Environmental Science Services
Administration, **4** 725
Space environment
Bioastronautics, **2** 355
simulation laboratory
   Lunar Module (picture), **8** 1409
   Manned Spacecraft Center, **8** 1458
Space biology, **11** 2094
Space equivalent altitude
Balloons, **2** 320
Launch vehicles, **7** 1328
Space exploration
Interplanetary travel, **7** 1212
Legal implications of aerospace, **7** 1331
Logistics of aerospace, **8** 1370
Photogrammetry, **10** 1780
Rockets and rocketry, **11** 1985
Space exploration costs
Implications of aerospace, **7** 1150
Spaceflight
Aerospace, **1** 27
Celestial navigation, **3** 429
Data acquisition and processing, **4** 604
Kosmos satellites, **7** 1294
Man in flight, **8** 1450
Manned spaceflight, **8** 1460
Navigation systems, **9** 1680-81
Oceanographic research, **10** 1734
Orbits and trajectories, **10** 1745
Pressure suit, **10** 1850
Sensors, **11** 2043
Space Flight Operations Facility
Deep Space Network, **4** 615
Jet Propulsion Laboratory, **7** 1240

Spaceflight principles, 12 2105-11 (with
diagrams, tables)
Spaceflight safety, 12 2111
Spaceflight simulators, 12 2112-13 (with
pictures)
Spaceflight training, **12** 2116
Spaceflight training, 12 2114-18 (with pictures)
Spaceflight simulators, **12** 2112
Space garbage, 12 2119
Tracking systems and networks, **13** 2297
Space gloves
Instrument panels, **7** 1177
Space helmets
Plastics, **10** 1824 (with pictures)
Space hothouse
Photosynthesis, **10** 1790
Space Launch Complex 6
Manned Orbiting Laboratory, **8** 1454-55
Space law, 12 2119-20
Implications of aerospace, **7** 1150
Legal implications of aerospace, **7** 1331
Space Law and Government (book)
Haley, Andrew G., **6** 1047
Space medicine, 12 2120
Aerospace medicine, **1** 33
Space biology, **11** 2094
Space navigation
Orbits and trajectories, **10** 1742
Space planes
Military aircraft, **9** 1571
Space power systems, 12 2120-21
Oxygen, **10** 1752
Space probes
Radio, **10** 1885, 1888
Sounding rockets, **11** 2080
Space biology, **11** 2095
Space projectile
Oberth, Hermann, **10** 1721
Space propulsion systems, 12 2121-25,
(with pictures)
Spaceflight principles, **12** 2110, (table) 2109
Space rendezvous
Astronauts, **2** 216
Rendezvous and docking, **11** 1955
Space Science Steering Committee
Biosatellites, **2** 356
Space scientists
Orbiting observatories, **10** 1741
Space segment
Communications satellites, **3** 538
Space stations (with pictures), **12** 2125-28
Aerospace, **1** 27
Fabrics, **5** 787
Marshall Space Flight Center, **8** 1494
Space study
Regional space centers, **11** 1946
Spacesuits (with pictures), **12** 2129-35
Apollo, **1** 176
Bottlesuits, **3** 382
Fabrics, **5** 787
Instrument panels, **7** 1177
Kerwin, Joseph P., **7** 1276
Maneuvering in space (pictures), **8** 1429,
1430
Oceanographic research, **10** 1734
Personal equipment, **10** 1775
Pressurization, **10** 1851
Rubber, **11** 1997
Space Support
Rescue and Recovery Service, **11** 1960
Space Surveillance System
NORAD, **9** 1701-02
Tracking systems and networks, **13** 2305
Space Task Group
Mercury program, **9** 1530
Space taxi
Bottlesuit, **3** 383
Space technology
Oceanographic research, **10** 1734
Space Technology Laboratory
Dunn, Louis G., **4** 655
Explorer satellites, **5** 765
Space tools (with pictures), **12** 2135-37
Spacetrack
Air Defense Command, **1** 59

Military space program, **9** 1603
Space Tracking and Data Acquisition Network
NASA, **9** 1653
Tracking systems and networks, **13** 2303
Space trajectories
Orbits and trajectories, **10** 1742
Space vehicles, see Spacecraft
Space walk
Astronauts, **2** 216
Collins, Michael, **3** 487
Cosmonauts, **4** 569
Walk in space, **13** 2447
Space weather, 12 2138
SPAD aircraft, 12 2138
First World War aircraft, **5** 816, 818, 822
(pictures), 816, 819
Lafayette Escadrille **7** 1295
History of aviation (picture), **6** 1105
World War I, **14** 2504, 2506, (pictures)
2505, 2508
SPADATS
Military space program, **9** 1602-03
Spain
Communications satellites, **3** 538
Crop dusting, **4** 587
European aerospace activities, **4** 749
European Space Research Organization,
4 755
International Agricultural Aviation Centre,
7 1187
International competitions, **7** 1192
Naval aviation, worldwide, **9** 1671
Spanish Civil War, **12** 2139
Spandau fighter
World War I, **14** 2504
Spandau machine gun
World War I, **14** 2508, (pictures) 2501, 2508
Spanish Civil War, 12 2139 (with pictures)
Air raid, **1** 104
Military aviation, **9** 1583
Spantax
European aerospace activities, **4** 749
Spark advance
Power management, **10** 1842
Sparrow
Air-to-air missiles, **1** 120-21
Marine Corps Aviation, **8** 1482
Sparrow III
   Air-to-air missiles (picture), **1** 119, 121
   Guidance and control systems, **6** 1041
Sparta (project)
WRESAT, **14** 2524
Spartan
Antiballistic missile defense, **1** 159
Surface-to-air missiles, **12** 2203, (picture)
2202
Spasur
Military space program, **9** 1603
Radar, **10** 1874
Spatial disorientation, 12 2140
Man in flight (diagrams), **8** 1448
Special and Tactical Air Warfare Centers
Elgin Air Force Base, **4** 678
Special circuits
Electrical systems, **4** 681
Special classification
Astrophysics, **2** 256
Special theory of relativity
Relativity theory, **11** 1948
Einstein, Albert, **4** 680-81
Specific gravity, 12 2140
Specific impulse
Launch vehicles, **7** 1315
Measurement of power, **8** 1519
Plasma propulsion, **10** 1823
Specified temperature
Power management, **10** 1842
Spectrograph, 12 2172
Spectrogram
Quasar, **10** 1871 (with drawing)
Spectroheliograms
Astronomy (picture), **2** 241
Spectroheliograph
Astronomy (picture) **2** 239, 240

Spectrometer
Quantum theory, **10** 1870
Spectroscope
Astronomy, **2** 238, 242
Telescopes and astronomical instruments, **12** 2255, (picture) 2255
Spectroscopic binary star
Astrophysics, **2** 257
Spectroscopic detectors
Oceanographic research, **10** 1732
Spectroscopic studies
Mars, **8** 1491
Spectroscopy
Infrared radiation, **7** 1162
Spectrum
Astrophysics, **2** 257
Sun, **12** 2172
X-rays, **14** 2533
Specular
Light, **8** 1352
Speed
Ballistic trajectory, **2** 314
Mach number, **8** 1417
Motion, **9** 1640
Sonic boom, **11** 2075
Speed and speed records, 12 2140-42
(with table)
Speed brakes
Cockpit, **3** 482
Speed of light
Relativity theory (with diagram), **11** 1949
Speed of sound
Aerodynamics, **1** 24
Bell, Lawrence Dale, **2** 348
Cochran, Jacqueline, **3** 481
Crossfield, Albert Scott, Jr., **4** 594
Mach, Ernst, **8** 1416
Mach number, **8** 1417
Wind tunnels, **13** 2488
Spelterini
Balloons, **2** 317
Sperry, Elmer, Jr.
History of aviation (table), **6** 1119
Instrument panels, **7** 1173
Manufacturing, **8** 1469
Sperry, Lawrence
History of aviation (table), **6** 1119
Spey turbofan
United Kingdom aerospace activities, **13** 2350
Spezio Tuholer (airplane)
Homebuilt aircraft (picture), **6** 1126
Spherical body of matter
Orbits and trajectories, **10** 1743
Spherical features
Lambert projection, **7** 1296
Spherical shell
Astronomy, **2** 242
Spherical simulation chamber
Regional space centers, **11** 1945
Spilhaus, Athelstan
Balloons, **2** 330
Spin, 12 2142
Maneuvers, **8** 1438, (diagram) 1440
Spinoff, 12 2142-44
Aerospace industry, **1** 33
Apollo, **1** 184
Economic implications of aerospace, **4** 672
Political implications of aerospace, **10** 1837
Spinrad, H.
Astronomy, **2** 242
Spin stabilization
Applications Technology Satellites, **2** 189
Guidance and control systems, **6** 1039
Orbiting observatories, **10** 1741
Rockets and rocketry, **11** 1974 (with picture), **11** 1981
Spiral galaxies
Astronomy, **2** 253
Spiral nebulae
Eddington, Arthur S., **4** 673
Spirit of Columbus (airplane)
Mock, Geraldine C., **9** 1623
Women in aerospace, **14** 2496

Spirit of St. Louis (airplane) (with pictures), **12** 2144-45
Commemorative stamps and medals, **3** 495
Corrigan, Douglas, **3** 567
History of aviation, **6** 1109 (picture), 1107
Lindbergh, Charles Augustus, **8** 1359
Spirit of St. Louis, The (autobiography)
Lindbergh, Charles Augustus, **8** 1360
Spirit of St. Louis Medal
Gilruth, Robert Rowe, **6** 981
Spitfire (Vickers Supermarine), **12** 2146
Battle of Britain, **2** 344
Fighter aircraft, **5** 807, 811
History of aviation (picture), **6** 1111
World War II, **14** (pictures) 2511, 2513
Splashdown
Apollo (picture), **1** 166
Recovery, **11** 1928
Split flap
Airplane, **1** 88
Split S
World War I, **14** 2506
Spoilers, 12 2146
Cockpit, **3** 482
Gliders, **6** 985
Gliding, **6** 986, 991
Soaring, **11** 2064
Sport flying, 12 2147-52 (with pictures)
Aero clubs, **1** 18
Balloons, **2** 320
National Aeronautic Association, **9** 1648
Parachutes, **10** 1759
Sport parachuting
Skydiving, **11** 2054
Spot-disc brakes
Brakes, **3** 386
Spot-landing races
Balloons, **2** 323
Spray bar
Crop dusting, **4** 591
Spraying nozzles
Agricultural aviation (picture), **1** 39
Crop dusting, **4** 589
Spring equinox
Equinox, **4** 729
Springfield, Illinois
Airports, **1** 97
Spring steel
Landing gear, **7** 1299-1300
Airplane, 89
Sprint
Antiballistic missile defense, **1** 159
Surface-to-air missiles, **12** 2203-04
SPS, see Service propulsion system
Sputniks (with pictures, table), **12** 2152-54
Astronauts, **2** 217
Explorer satellites, **5** 762
Manned spaceflight (table), **8** 1461
Sputnik 1
Agena rockets, **1** 38-39
Astronautics, **2** 212
Commemorative stamps and medals, **3** 495
Communications satellites, **3** 532
Educational implications of aerospace, **4** 674
Mercury program, **9** 1530
Orbits and trajectories, **10** 1746
Political implications of aerospace, **10** 1836
Rockets and rocketry, **11** 1984
Satellites, **11** 2006
Sputnik 2
Commemorative stamps and medals, **3** 495
Sputnik 5
Animals in space, **1** 155
Sputnik 9
Animals in space **1** 1050
Sputnik 10
Animals in space, **1** 155
Tracking systems and networks, **13** 2300
U.S.S.R. aerospace activities, **13** 2338-39
Weather satellites, **13** 2459
Spy-satellites

Apollo, **1** 184
Squadron Officer School
Air University, **1** 140
Squall lines
Aviation weather, **1** 301-02
Squint angles
Kennedy Space Center, **7** 1267
SRAM, see Short-Range Attack Missile
SR/45 Princess
Flying boats, **5** 861
SR-71, Lockheed and YF-12A, 12 2155-56
SR-71 reconnaissance aircraft (picture, chart, diagram), **12** 2155-56
Government in aerospace (picture), **6** 1005
Jet aircraft (picture), **7** 1234
Johnson, Clarence Leonard, **7** 1242
Reconnaissance aircraft, **11** 1921
Strategic Air Command, **12** 2168
United States Air Force, **13** 2374
SRN-4 (hovercraft)
United Kingdom aerospace activities, **13** 2355
S.S. Twin (airship)
First World War aircraft, **5** 821
S.S. Zero (airship)
First World War aircraft, **5** 821
Stabilator
Empennage, **4** 710
Stability, 12 2156-57
Aerodynamics, **1** 23-24
Aviation weather, **2** 299
Mercury program, **9** 1530
Stabilization and control system
Apollo, **1** 177
Kennedy Space Center, **7** 1267
Stabilized platform
Inertial guidance, **7** 1153
Stabilizers
Airframe, **1** 66
Stack
Apollo, **1** 178-79 (with picture)
Launch vehicles, **7** 1313
Stacking
Airports, **1** 99
Stack, John (1906-   , American aeronautical engineer), **12** 2157
STADAN
Goddard Space Flight Center, **6** 994
Stafford, Thomas P. (1930-   , American astronaut), **12** 2157
Astronauts, **2** 214, 216, 219, 229-30 (with picture)
Gemini, **5** 940-41, 944-45, (picture), 945
Manned spaceflight (table), **8** 1461
Rendezvous and docking, **11** 1956
Stage
Terminology of aerospace (table), **12** 2272
Stage weights
Launch vehicles, **7** 1328
Staggerwing, see Beech 17 Staggerwing
Staging
Launch vehicles, **7** 1317
Stagnation point
Aerodynamics, **1** 22
Stainless steel alloys
Alloys, **1** 144
Steels, **12** 2164-65
X-15 research program, **14** 2532
Stairwell doors
Airplane, **1** 83
Stall, 12 2158
Airplane, **1** 89
Angle of attack, **1** 152
Bird flight, **2** 361
Buffeting, **3** 389
Maneuvers, **8** 1435, 1436, (diagram) 1437
Spin, **12** 2142
Wings, **14** 2492
Stall warning indicator, 12 2158
Stamer, Fredrich
History of aviation (table), **6** 1119
Stamps
Commemorative stamps and medals, **3** 493-95
Objects of art, **10** 1722

Standard (missile)
Surface-to-air missiles, **12** 2203
Standard Aircraft Corp.
Airmail, **1** 71
Caproni, Count Gianni, **3** 405
Standard cruise
Cruising flight, **4** 595
Standard gauges
Precision measurements, **10** 1845
Standard instrument approach
Instrument landing system, **7** 1170
Standardization
Jumbo jets, **7** 1251
Standard Launch Vehicle-3
Atlas missile and launch vehicle, **2** 260
Standard operating procedures, 12 2159
Standards of Certification
Certification procedures, **3** 441
Standard SJ-1 "OX"
Barnstormers, **2** 335
Standard JR-1B
Airmail, **1** 71
Standard target
Resolution (with diagram), **11** 1961
Standby
Redundancy, **11** 1930
Stanley, G. R.
Distance records, **4** 640
Stanton, Charles I.
Airmail, **1** 77
Stanzel, Victor
Model aircraft, **9** 1624
Stapp, John P. (1910-   , American
aeromedical scientist), **12** 2159
Aviation medicine, **2** 296
Escape systems, **4** 733
Star clusters
Astronomy, **2** 238
Star-disks
Planetarium, **10** 1818
Starduster (airplane)
Homebuilt aircraft, **6** 1125
Starfield nuclear experiment
Alouette satellites, **1** 144
Starfield projectors
Planetarium, **10** 1818
Starfighter, see F-104 Starfighter
Starfire, see F-94 Starfire
Stargazer balloon
Ballons, **2** 321
Starlifter, see C-141 Starlifter
Star locations
Planetarium, **10** 1820
Star patterns
Constellations, **3** 561
Stars (with diagrams), **12** 2159-63
Astronomy, **2** 233
Chemical composition
Orbiting observatories, **10** 1740
Extraterrestrial life, **5** 774
Luminosity, **8** 1377
Magnitude, **8** 1420
Milky Way, **9** 1605-07 (with picture and
diagram)
Nebula, **9** 1688-89 (with pictures)
Nova, **9** 1706
Observatories, **10** 1726
Orbiting observatories, **10** 1738
Planetarium, **10** 1818
Quantum theory, **10** 1870
Quasars, **10** 1871
Radiation, **10** 1882
Sun, **12** 2171
Unidentified flying objects, **13** 2324
X-rays, **14** 2533
START, 12 2163
Asset Program, **2** 207
Lifting-body vehicles, **8** 1349-50
Military space program, **9** 1599-1600,
(with picture), (data table) 1604
PRIME, **10** 1852-53
Star tracker assembly
Mariner probes, **8** 1485

Star trackers
Orbiting observatories, **10** 1740
State Aeronautics Commissions
Careers, **3** 417
State and Regional Defense Airlift
National emergency airlift plans, **9** 1663
State, Department of
National Aeronautics and Space Council,
9 1657
State-of-the-art
Terminology of aerospace (table), **12** 2272
Staterooms
Jumbo jets, **7** 1251, 1255
State, Secretary of
Air Commerce Act, **1** 45
Static
Atmospherics, **2** 268
Center of gravity, **3** 435
Inverters
Electrical systems, **4** 682
Pitot-static system, **10** 1816
Static-line parachute
Parachutes, **10** 1756
Static load
Aluminum, **1** 148
Landing gear, **7** 1298
Static noise
Radio, **10** 1887
Radio communication, **10** 1895
Static stability
Aerodynamics, **1** 23-24
Airplane, **1** 86
Static tube
Pitot-static system, **10** 1816
Stationary observer
Relativity theory (with illustration), **11** 1950
Stationary satellite
Applications Technology Satellites, **2** 189
Communications satellites, **3** 536
Station direction finding
Inflight emergency procedures, **7** 1155
Station-keeping radar video presentations
Jumbo jets, **7** 1256
Stator
Brakes, **3** 385
Statute mile
Mile, **9** 1565
Stead, Bill
Air racing, **1** 103
Steady state theory
Astronomy, **2** 253
Space, **11** 2093
Universe, **13** 2391
Steam catapults
Aircraft carriers, **1** 47, 51
Catapult, **3** 423
Steam engines
Aircraft propulsion systems, **1** 56-57
Stearman, Lloyd (1898-   , American
airplane manufacturer), **12** 2163
Stearman PT-17
Agricultural aviation (picture), **1** 39, 40
Crop dusting, **4** 588, (picture) 592
Military aircraft, **9** 1567
Trainer aircraft, **13** 2306
Steel launch pad
Launch facilities, **7** 1307
Steels, 12 2164-65 (with picture)
Boron, **3** 382
High strength
Materials, **8** 1507
Iron, **7** 1216
Metals and metallurgy, **9** 1548-55
Silicon, **11** 2052
Steep glide
Kamikaze, **7** 1262
Steep turns
Maneuvers, **8** 1434, (diagram) 1434
Steerable
Aircraft, **1** 45
Steerable nose wheel
Piloting techniques, **10** 1801
Stefan-Boltzmann Law
Planck's Law, **10** 1817

Stellar astronomy
Astronomy, **2** 249
Classification, **2** 249
Stellar atmosphere
Stars, **12** 2159
Stellar distances
Parsec, **10** 1763
Stellar motion
Astronomy, **2** 251
Stellar objects
Infrared radiation, **7** 1162
Stellar parallax
Parallax, **10** 1760
Stellar populations
Milky Way, **9** 1606
Stellar spectra
Astronomy, **2** 250
Stellar structure
Astrophysics, **2** 257
Stellar television camera
Orbiting observatories, **10** 1740
Stephen, Robert L.
Medals and decorations (table), **8** 1526
Speed and speed records, **12** 2142, (table),
2141
Stereo concept
Photogrammetry, **10** 1780
Stereographic projection
Charts, **3** 455
Maps and mapping, **8** 1478, (table) 1479
Stereo photography
Aerial photography, **1** 9
Sternum
Bird flight, **2** 360
Stevens, R.
Astronomy, **2** 242
Stevenson, W. M.
Distance records, **4** 641
Stewards and stewardesses (with pictures),
12 2165-66
Commercial airlines, **3** 502, (picture) 515
Women in aerospace, **14** 2495
Stick
Parachutes, **10** 1759
Stilwell, General Joseph W.
Chennault, Claire Lee, **3** 457
Stimulated emission
Lasers, **7** 1303
Masers, **8** 1496
Stinson A Trimotor
History of aviation (picture), **6** 1110
Stinson, Katherine
Women in aerospace, **14** 2494
Stinson L-5 (glider)
Gliding (picture), **5** 986
Stinson, Marjorie
Women in aerospace, **14** 2494
Stir the air
Agricultural aviation, **1** 39-41
Stits aircraft
Homebuilt aircraft, **6** 1125, (pictures),
1125, 1126
Stodola, E.
Astronomy, **2** 242
Stoermer, Carl
Van Allen radiation belts, **13** 2399
STOL aircraft (see also V/STOL aircraft)
Autogiros, **2** 286
Canada's aviation, **3** 403
Certification procedures, **3** 445
Fighter aircraft, **5** 810
Helicopters, **6** 1067
International projects (picture), **7** 1200
Jumbo jets, **7** 1255
Langley Research Center, **7** 1302
Rotary-wing aircraft, **11** 1991
U.S.S.R. aerospace activities, **13** 2335
Stone, Elmer F.
Coast Guard aviation, **3** 476
Stoney, G. J.
Electronics, **4** 692
Stony meteorites
Meteors, meteorites, and meteoroids,
9 1561 (with picture)

Stopped rotor
Helicopters, **6** 1069
Storage
Computers, **3** 552
Storage battery
Battery, **2** 339
Stored-data satellites
Weather satellites, **13** 2465
Storing
Oceanographic research, **10** 1732
Stork Squadron
World War I, **14** 2506
Story of a Fabulous Airplane, The
Douglas DC-3, **4** 648
Stout Metal Plane Company
Commercial air transports, **3** 518
Stout Trimotor, see Ford Trimotor
Stout, William Bushnell (1880-1956, American aircraft designer), **12** 2166-67
Aerospace industry, **1** 29
Commercial air transports, **3** 518
Manufacturing, **8** 1468
Stowed rotor
Helicopters, **6** 1069
Strafe, 12 2167
Air raid, **1** 104
Dive, **4** 643
Straight and level flight
Maneuvers, **8** 1433
Straight turbojets
Strain gauges
Data acquisition and processing, **4** 609
Pressure gauges, **10** 1850
Strap-on solid rockets
Launch vehicles, **7** 1323, 1328
Strasser, Pieter
Zeppelins, **14** 2550
Strassman, Fritz
Manhattan Project, **8** 1442
Radiation, **10** 1880
Strategic reconnaissance
Reconnaissance, airborne, **11** 1919
Strategic Air Command, 12 2167-68
Aircraft carriers, **1** 48
Air National Guard, **1** 81
Ballistic Missile Early Warning Systems, **2** 314
Bomber aircraft, **2** 375-76
History of aviation, **6** 1116
LeMay, Curtis Emerson, **7** 1332
McConnell, John Paul, **8** 1517
NATO, **9** 1704
NORAD, **9** 1701
Stratojet, Boeing B-47, **12** 2170
United States Air Force, **13** 2365, 2370
Vandenberg Air Force Base, **13** 2402
Strategic airlift
Airlift, **1** 66-67
Strategic bombardment
Military aviation, **9** 1581-82, 1585
World War II, **14** 2518-19
Stratocruiser, see Boeing 377 Stratocruiser
Stratocumulus clouds
Clouds, **3** 473
Stratoform
Clouds, **3** 471
Stratofortress, see B-52 Stratofortress
Stratojet, see B-47 Stratojet
Stratolab
Balloons, **2** 321
Stratolifter (Boeing) see C-135
Stratopause
Atmosphere, **2** 264
Stratosphere, 12 2170
Aerospace, **1** 27
Aerospace medicine, **1** 34
Atmosphere, **2** 264
Balloons, **2** 325, (picture) 329
Polar flights, **10** 1828
Wind, **13** 2485
Stratosphere flight
Piccard family, **10** 1791
Stratosphere gondola
Balloons (diagram), **2** 325

Strato tanker, see KC-135 Strato tanker
Stratus clouds
Clouds, **3** 473, (pictures) 472-73
Streamlining, 12 2170
Air resistance, **1** 104
Cayley, Sir George, **3** 425
Strelka (dog)
Animals in space, **1** 155
Strength-to-weight ratio
Aluminum, **1** 148
Stress
Lamination, **7** 1297
Stress corrosion
Materials, **8** 1512
Stretch
Launch vehicles, **7** 1322
STRIL/60 (surveillance system)
Sweden's aviation, **12** 2224
Stringfellow, John (1799-1883, British engineer), **12** 2170
Aircraft propulsion systems, **1** 57
History of aviation, **6** 1095, (table) 1119
Strip photography
Photography, **10** 1783, 1784, (diagram) 1783
Strokes
Aircraft propulsion systems, **1** 53
Reciprocating engines, **11** 1916
Strong, John
Telescopes and astronomical instruments, **12** 2250
Structural changes
Jumbo jets, **7** 1253
Structural design
Runways, **11** 1999
Structural integrity
Materials, **8** 1512
Structural materials
Materials, **8** 1501
Military aviation, **9** 1587
Structure
Airships, **1** 105-10
Spacecraft design, **11** 2100
Structure of matter
Matter, **8** 1513
Structure of Matter, The (book)
Teller, Edward, **12** 2264-65
Strughold, Hubertus (1898-   , German-American medical scientist), **12** 2171
Struts, 12 2171
Airplane, **1** 86
Pontoons, **10** 1838
Wings, **14** 2492
Student certificate
Aircraft Owners and Pilots Association, **1** 52
Pilot training, **10** 1811
Student permit
Pilot training, **10** 1809
Studer, Berne
Women in aerospace, **14** 2496
Stuhlinger, Ernst
Electric propulsion, **4** 687
Stuka, see Junkers JU-87 Stuka
Stultz, Wilbur
Earhart, Amelia, **4** 658
Stunt flying maneuvers
Barnstormers, **2** 333
Stunting, see Aerobatic exhibitions
Stunt men
Air shows, **1** 115 (with picture)
Sturtevant engine
Aircraft propulsion systems, **1** 55
SU-7B
Air forces of the world, **1** 65
Attack aircraft, **2** 272
U.S.S.R. aerospace activities (table), **13** 2337
SU-9
U.S.S.R. aerospace activities (table), **13** 2337
Subgravity conditions
Animals in space, **1** 154

Sublimation
Evaporation and condensation, **4** 757
Sublimes
Carbon dioxide, **3** 408
Submarine cables
Oceanographic research, **10** 1731
Submarines
Reconnaissance airborne, **11** 1920
Submersibles
Oceanographic research, **10** 1734
Suborbital launch
Launch vehicles, **7** 1325
Suborbital trajectories
Launch vehicles, **7** 1317
Subroc
Antisubmarine missiles, **1** 161
Missiles (table), **9** 1616
Subsatellites
Environmental research satellites, **4** 723
Lunar exploration (diagram), **8** 1405
Subsidies
Airmail, **1** 75, 77
Subsonic airfoil
Airfoil (diagram), **1** 61
Subsonic commercial transports
Commercial air transports, **3** 530
Subsonic jet
Aircraft carriers, **1** 46
Subsonic missile
Pulsejet engine, **10** 1866
Subsonic speeds
Jumbo jets, **7** 1252
Sonic boom, **11** 2074
Successive apogees
Launch vehicles, **7** 1319 (with diagram)
Sudan
Crop dusting, **4** 587
International Agricultural Aviation Centre, **7** 1187
Sudanese Air Force
Air forces of the world, **1** 64
Sud-Aviation
Commercial air transports, **3** 527
France's aerospace activities, **5** 888
International projects, **7** 1200
Supersonic transports, **12** 2182
Sud-Aviation Caravelle, see Caravelle
Sud-Aviation SA 321F (helicopter) (see also Super Frelon)
V/STOL aircraft (table), **13** 2443
Sud-Aviation SE-210 Caravelle, see Caravelle SE-210
Sudden ionosphere disturbances
Atmosphere, **2** 265
Ionosphere, **7** 1215
Sugden, C. E.
Coast Guard aviation, **3** 476
Sugita, Shaichi
World War II (table), **14** 2517
Suicide air attacks
Kamikaze, **7** 1264
Sukhoi fighters
Africa's aviation, **1** 37
Asia's aviation, **2** 204
U.S.S.R. aerospace activities (table), **12** 2337
Summer flight suits
Personal equipment, **10** 1775
Summer solstice
Ecliptic, **4** 669
Sump
Reciprocating engines, **11** 1916
Sun, 12 2171-75 (with pictures)
Aristarchus of Samos, **2** 193
Astronomy, **2** 233, 240, 242
Celestial mechanics, **3** 427
Corona
Radiation, **10** 1882
Infrared spectrum
Infrared radiation, **7** 1162

(Continued)

Sun (Cont.)
Magnetic storms, **8** 1420
Orbiting observatories, **10** 1738
Orbits and trajectories, **10** 1744-45
Parallax, **10** 1760
Parsec, **10** 1763
Pioneer, **10** 1812-13
Planetarium, **10** 1818
Pluto, **10** 1827
Precession, **10** 1843
Quantum, **10** 1868
Quantum theory, **10** 1870
Radiation, **10** 1882
Solar cells, **11** 2068
Solar system (with diagram), **11** 2070
Space, **11** 2092
Space weather, **12** 2138
spectrum
Astrophysics, **2** 256
Surveyor, **12** 2211, 2213
X-rays, **14** 2533
Sun compass
Polar flights, **10** 1829
Sundogs
Poles, **10** 1834
Sunlight
Jupiter, **7** 1260
Sunrise
Air Almanac, **1** 42
Sun sensors
Mariner probes, **8** 1485
Orbiting observatories, **10** 1740
Sunset
Air Almanac, **1** 42
Sunspots
Astronomy, **2** 241
Sun, **12** 2172, 2174
Sun study
Radio astronomy, **10** 1890
Sun-synchronous orbit
Orbits and trajectories, **10** 1746, 1747
Weather satellites, **13** 2463, 2464
Suomi heat-budget experiment
Weather satellites, **13** 2460
Superalloys
Materials, **8** 1508
Metals and metallurgy, **9** 1551, 1553
Nickel, **9** 1695-96
Steels, **12** 2164
Tensile strength, **12** 2271
Super Arcas
Sounding rockets (with picture), **11** 2083
Superbooster
Launch vehicles, **7** 1318
Super Caravelle
Commercial air transports, **3** 527
Supercharger, 12 2175
Reciprocating engines, **11** 1917
Supercold
Launch vehicles, **7** 1315-16
Superconductivity
Cryogenics, **4** 596
Superconductors
Materials, **8** 1511
Super Constellation, see Lockheed Super
Constellation
Supercooled water
Aviation weather, **2** 301
Precipitation, **10** 1844
Snow, **11** 2061
Superefficient insulation
Launch vehicles, **7** 1317
Superfortress, see B-29 Superfortress
Super Frelon (helicopter)
Air forces of the world (picture), **1** 63
France's aerospace activities (picture),
5 890
Naval aviation, worldwide (France), **9** 1669
Supergiants
Luminosity, **8** 1377

Supergranulation
Sun, **12** 2174
Super Guppy
Outsize cargo aircraft (picture), **10** 1749,
(table, diagram) 1750
Supermarine S6B
Air racing, **1** 102
Super Mystere aircraft
Air forces of the world, **1** 65
Israeli-Arab conflict-1967 (picture), **7** 1218
Superior conjunction
Conjunction, **3** 560
Superior planets
Astronomy, **2** 241
Superior spheres
Astronomy, **2** 235, 242
Supernova
Astronomy, **2** 237
Nova, **9** 1706-07
Super-pressure balloon
Balloons, **2** 331
Super Sabre, see F-100 Super Sabre
Supersonic aerodynamics
Aerodynamics, **1** 24-25, (picture) 19
Supersonic aircraft design
Area rule, **2** 190
Supersonic airfoils
Airfoil, **1** 62
Supersonic combustion ramjet
Hypersonic flight, **6** 1142, 1144
Scramjet, **11** 2022
Supersonic escape
Rocket sled, **11** 1988
Supersonic flight, 12 2177
Supersonic jets
Aircraft carriers, **1** 46
Jet aircraft, **7** 1232-36
Supersonic flight, **12** 2177
Supersonic transports, **12** 2179-99
XB-70, North American Valkyrie, **14** 2528-29
Supersonic open-seat ejection
Rocket sled, **11** 1986
Supersonic pressure disturbances
Sonic boom, **11** 2074
Supersonic speeds
Langley Research Center, **7** 1302
Supersonic transport flight
Circadian rhythm, **3** 461
Supersonic transport program
Lewis Research Center, **7** 1335
Supersonic transports (with pictures),
12 2179-99 (see also Boeing SST,
Concorde)
Aircraft propulsion systems, **1** 59
Airliner, **1** 67
Air traffic control (picture), **1** 136
Aviation medicine, **2** 297
Canada's aviation, **3** 401
Commercial air transports, **3** 530
Control tower, **3** 564
Federal Aviation Administration,
5 797, 801
Flight recorder, **5** 849
France's aerospace activities, **5** 886
Fuel systems, **5** 905
Government in aerospace, **6** 1007
Guidance and control systems, **6** 1040
History of aviation, **6** 1120
Hughes, Howard Robert, **6** 1132
Jumbo jets, **7** 1244
Launch vehicles, **7** 1328
Life-support systems, **8** 1338
Man in flight, **8** 1450
Manufacturing, **8** 1475
Military air transports, **9** 1578
NASA, **9** 1653
Paris Air Shows, **10** 1762
Sonic boom, **11** 2074
Super VC10 (BAC)
Commercial air transports, **3** 497, 526

Supplemental carriers
Commercial airlines, **3** 513
Supplier control
Quality control, **10** 1867
Suppressor grid
Electronics, **4** 697
Supreme Headquarters Allied Powers Europe
Ballistic Missile Early Warning System,
2 314
NATO, **9** 1704
Surface-barrier transistor
Electronics, **4** 703
Surface effect ships
Ground-effect machines, **6** 1023
Surface mobility
Lunar bases, **8** 1391, (drawings) 1393, 1394
Surface of the moon
Moon, **9** 1635-37 (with pictures)
Surface picture
Coast Guard aviation, **3** 479
Surface-to-surface missiles, 12 2204-08 (with
pictures, table)
Air Defense Command, **1** 59
Air defense systems (picture), **1** 61
Air-to-surface missiles, **1** 123
Antiaircraft weapons, **1** 158
Electronic countermeasures, **4** 691
Infrared detection devices, **7** 1161
Missiles, **9** 1610, (pictures) 1613-15, (data
table) 1616
Radar, **10** 1878
Rockets and rocketry, **11** 1980 (with
diagram)
Surface-to-surface missiles, 12 2204-08
(with pictures, table)
Surface transit
High-speed surface transportation, **6** 1089
Surface weather map
Aviation weather, **2** 299 (with picture)
SURPIC, see Surface Picture
Surplus military aircraft
Aerospace industry, **1** 30-31
Agricultural aviation, **1** 39-41
Airmail, **1** 71
Surveillance flights
Photography, **10** 1789
Reconnaissance airborne, **11** 1918-20
Surveillance Room
Semi-Automatic Ground Environment (with
picture), **11** 2040
Surveillance satellite program
Military space program, **9** 1595
Reconnaissance satellites, **11** 1924-27
Survey, aerial
Photography, **10** 1785
Surveying
Azimuth, **2** 308
Surveying by satellite
Implications of aerospace, **7** 1151
Survey markers
Charts, **3** 455
Surveyor, 12 2209-16 (with pictures, table)
Aluminum, **1** 149
Apollo, **1** 169
Astrogeology, **2** 211
Astronomy, **2** 244
Earth science, **4** 666
Jet Propulsion Laboratory, **7** 1240
Lunar bases, **8** 1380
Moon, **9** 1637
NASA, **9** 1653, (drawing) 1651, (table) 1652
Oceanographic research, **10** 1734
Parks, Robert Joseph, **10** 1763
Prospector program, **10** 1863
Radar, **10** 1878
Surveyor 1
Apollo (picture), **1** 170
Centaur, **3** 434
Launch vehicles, **7** 1324
Lewis Research Center, **7** 1334

(Continued)

Surveyor (Cont.)
Surveyor 2
Centaur, **3** 434
Surveyor 3
Centaur, **3** 435
Launch vehicles, **7** 1324
pictures taken by
Apollo, **1** 170
Moon, **9** 1637
surface sampler
Astrogeology (picture), **2** 211
Surveyor 5
Astronomy, **2** 242, 244
Surveyor 7
Lasers, **7** 1304
picture taken by
Moon, **9** 1637
Survival and rescue, 12 2216-20 (with pictures)
Survival equipment
Life-support systems, **8** 1343-44
Recovery, **11** 1928
Survival gear
Bush flying, **3** 392
Survival kits, 12 2200-22 (with picture)
Survival methods
Astronauts, **2** 226
Life raft, **8** 1336
Space flight training, **12** 2114
Survival training
Astronauts, **2** 226
Spaceflight training, **12** 2114
Suspension lines
Parachutes, **10** 1759
Sustainer engine
Aerobee, **1** 17
Sutcliffe, R. C.
Meteorology, **9** 1558
SV-5D
Lifting-body vehicles, **8** 1349, (picture) 1346
Re-entry vehicles (with picture), **11** 1934
Swain, R. D.
Altitude and altitude records, **1** 147
Swallow, see DH-108 Swallow
Swallow Airplane Company
Beech, Walter H., **2** 347
Swann, W. F. G.
Balloons, **2** 325, 327
Swathmaster
Crop dusting, **4** 589, (picture) 590
Swath width
Crop dusting, **4** 590
Sweden's aviation, 12 2222-25 (with pictures)
Air forces of the world, **1** 65
Air-to-air missiles, **1** 120
Air-to-surface missiles, **1** 123
Crop dusting, **4** 587
Demonstration teams, **4** 626
European Space Research Organization,
4 755
Naval aviation, worldwide, **9** 1671
Sweeney, Edward C.
Medals and decorations (table), **8** 1526
Sweepback
Aerodynamics, **1** 24
Sweet, Bill
Air shows, **1** 115
Swigert, John Leonard, Jr. (1931-
American astronaut), **12** 2225
Astronauts, **2** 217, 218, 219 (with picture)
Swingby
Interplanetary travel, **7** 1208
Swing-nose aircraft
Cargo aircraft (picture), **3** 419
Swing-tail cargo transport
Cargo aircraft (picture), **3** 419
Swing-tail Rotoprop (aircraft)
Helicopters, **6** 1069
Swing-wing aircraft
Air forces of the world (U.S.), **1** 65
Variable geometry, **13** 2405
Swissair
Commercial airlines, **3** 506

European aerospace activities, **4** 750
Swiss Air Rescue Guard
European aerospace activities, **4** 750
Switzerland
Air forces of the world, **1** 64
Communications satellites, **3** 538
Crop dusting, **4** 587
European aerospace activities, **4** 750
European Space Research Organization,
4 755
Swivel engines
Atlas missile and launch vehicle, **2** 259
Swordfish, see Fairey Swordfish
Symbols
Maps and mapping, **8** 1478
Symington, Stuart
United States Air Force, **13** 2364
Synchronous orbit
Applications Technology Satellites, **2** 189
Communications satellites, **3** 535-36
Launch vehicles, **7** 1318
Orbits and trajectories, **10** 1746
Synchropter rotors
Helicopters, **6** 1066
Synchrotron radiation
Nova, **9** 1707
Radiation, **10** 1882
Syncom
Active repeater satellite, **1** 6
Communications satellites (picture),
3 535-36
Defense communications satellites,
4 615-16
Delta rocket, **4** 622
International Telecommunications Satellite
Consortium, **7** 1202
Military space program (picture), **9** 1590
NASA, **9** 1653, (table) 1652
Satellites, **11** 2007
Syncom 1
Communications satellites, **3** 536
Syncom 2
Communications satellites, **3** 532, 535-37,
(diagram orbit) 535, (table) 543
Syncom 3
Communications satellites, **3** 543
Synergetic geometry
Geodesics, **6** 970
Synodic periods
Interplanetary travel, **7** 1209 (with data
table)
Synoptic meterology
Meteorology, **9** 1558
Weather maps and charts, **13** 2454
Synthetics
Lubricants, **8** 1375
Rubber, **11** 1997
Syria
Crop dusting, **4** 587
International Agricultural Aviation Centre,
7 1187
Syrtis Major
Mars, **8** 1490
Systems analysis
Aerospace industry, **1** 32
Systems engineering, **12** 2225
Systems approach
Social implications of aerospace, **11** 2067
Systems control
Cockpit, **3** 482
Systems engineering, 12 2225-26
Economic implications of aerospace, **4** 672
Materials, **8** 1500
Systems for Nuclear Auxiliary Power,
see **SNAP**
Systems instruments
Cockpit, **3** 485
Engine instruments, **6** 715
Flight instruments, **5** 843
Systems theories
Lenoir, William B., **7** 1332

T

T, see Tropical air mass
T-1, see Rawdon T-1
T-1A Seastar
Lockheed F80/T33, **8** 1367
T-6 (North American), 13 2314
Asia's aviation, **2** 204, 205
T-28 (North American)
Asia's aviation, **2** 204, 205
Counter-insurgency aircraft, **4** 576
T-32 Condor, see Curtiss Condor
T-33, see F-80 Shooting Star
T-37 (Cessna)
Counter-insurgency aircraft (picture),
4 577
Military aircraft, **9** 1567
T-38 (Northrop)
Aircraft propulsion systems, **1** 58
Astronauts, **2** 225
Military aircraft, **9** 1567
T-39 Sabreliner (North American)
Military air transports, **9** 1575
T-41, see Cessna 172 Skyhawk
T-42 Baron (Beech)
Army aviation, **2** 197
T-64
Asia's aviation, **2** 204
Tabacchi, Ugo
Caproni, Count Gianni, **3** 405
Tabeling, R.A.
Distance and distance records, **4** 640
Tables for Rocket and Comet Orbits
Herrick, Samuel, **6** 1083
TABSO
European aerospace activities, **4** 744
TAC, see Tactical Air Command
TACAN, see Tactical Air Navigation
Tachometer, 12 2227
Engine instruments, **4** 716, 717
Instrument panels, **7** 1176
Reciprocating engines, **11** 1919
Tachometer show pitch
Instrument flight techniques, **7** 1167
Tacomat, see Tactical Communications
Satellite Program
Tactical Air Command, 12 2228-30, (with
pictures)
Air forces of the world, **1** 65
Bobko, Karol J., **2** 369
Invader, Douglas, A-26, B-26, **7** 1214
United Stares Air Force, **13** 2370, 2371
United States Strike Command, **13** 2390
Tactical airlift
Airlift, **1** 67
Tactical air navigation, 12 2231
Automatic direction finder, **2** 287
Avionics, **2** 307
Beacon, radio, **2** 345
Distance Measuring Equipment, **4** 642
Federal airways system, **5** 792
Flight simulators, **5** 855
Invader, Douglas A-26, B-26, **7** 1214
Jumbo jets, **7** 1255
Navigation systems, **9** 1679-80
Omni navigation, **10** 1736
Reconnaissance, airborne, **11** 1919
VORTAC, **13** 2432
Tactical bombing
Bomber aircraft, **2** 376
Tactical Communications Satellite Program
Military space program, **9** 1597
Tactical Communications Systems
Defense communication satellites, **4** 617
Tactical fighter aircraft, USAF
Air forces of the world, **1** 65

TAD, see Thrust Augmented Delta
TAG
  Commuter airlines, **3** 544
Tail
  Comets, **3** 490
Tail assembly
  Airplane, **1** 86
  Elevators, **4** 706
Tailspin, see Spin
Tail surfaces
  Airships, **1** 106, 108
Tail wheel
  Landing gear, **7** 1298
Tail wind, 12, 2231
Tailwind (airplane)
  Homebuilt aircraft, **6** 1125
Taiwan Defense Command
  Nationalist China's aviation, **9** 1664, 1665
Takahashi, F.
  Distance records, **4** 641
Takeoff and climb, 12 3331-32
  Aircraft carriers, **1** 48
  Airfield, **1** 61
  Airships, **1** 110
  Aviation weather, **2** 305
  Distance
    Koch chart, **7** 1282
    Performance charts, **10** 1774
  Instrument Flight Rules, **7** 1165
  Piloting techniques, **10** 1800
  Propeller, **10** 1863
  Torque, **12** 2295, 2296
Takeoff engine
  Apollo, **1** 174
Taliedo, Count of
  Caproni, Count Gianni, **3** 405
Talon, see T-38 Talon
Talos (missile)
  Surface-to-air missiles, **12** 2202 (picture),
    2202 (table), 2204
Tampa International
  Commercial airlines, **3** 503
Tandem arrangement
  Landing gear, **7** 1299
Tanker aircraft, 12 2232-33
  Military aircraft, **9** 1570, (picture) 1566
  Refueling, **11** 1937
Tanks
  Terminology of aerospace (table), **12** 2272
Tantalum
  Materials, **8** 1506
Tape recording, 12 2233-35 (with diagrams)
Target
  Penetration, **10** 1774
Target destruction
  Intercontinental ballistic missiles, **7** 1182
Target docking adaptor
  Rendezvous and docking (with diagram),
    11 1956
Target echo
  Radar, **10** 1875
Target planet
  Orbits and trajectories, **10** 1745
Target plate
  Television, **12** 2258
Target point
  Recovery, **11** 1928
Targets
  United States Air Force, **13** 2371, 2372
TAROM
  European aerospace activities, **4** 749
Tartar (missile)
  Surface-to-air missiles, **12** 2202 (table),
    2204
TAT, see Thrust Augmented Thor
Tarzon
  Air-to-surface missiles, **1** 123
Tau
  Ozma project, **10** 1753
Taube (airplane), (see also Five O'Clock
    Taube)
  First World War aircraft, **5** 823, 824
  World War I, **14** 2501 (picture), 2502
Taurus
  Astronomy, **2** (picture) 248, 252
  Constellations, **3** 562

Taxes
  International Air Transport Association,
    7 1189
Taxiing
  Piloting techniques, **10** 1801 (with
    diagram)
Taxi separation clearances
  Jumbo Jets, **7** 1257
Taxiways
  Airports, **1** 95
  Jumbo Jets, **7** 1257
  Lighting facilities, **8** 1357, (picture) 1353
  Runways, **11** 1998
Taylor, Charles
  Aircraft propulsion systems, **1** 54
  Reciprocating engines, **11** 1913
Taylor, Frederick W.
  Human engineering, **6** 1133
Taylor, George A.
  Australia's aviation, **2** 279
Taylor, James M. (1930- , Aerospace
    research pilot), **12** 2235
  Manned Orbiting Laboratory, **8** 1456
Taylor Monoplane
  Homebuilt aircraft, **6** 1125
T-Bird, see F-80 Shooting Star
Teal (airplane)
  Homebuilt aircraft (picture), **6** 1127
TC, see Telecommunications system
Teamwork
  Rescue and Recovery Service, **11** 1960
Technical institutes
  Educational implications of aerospace,
    4 675
Technicians
  Aerospace medicine, **1** 33
  Careers, **3** 414
  Occupations, **10** 1726
Techniques
  Soaring, **11** 2064
Technological projections, 12 2235-41 (with
    pictures, tables)
Technology utilization program
  Spinoff, **12** 2142
Tee Dee 0.010 engine
  Model aircraft, **9** 1626
Tee hangar
  Hangars, **6** 1048
Teflon
  Ablation, **1** 1
Teisserenc de Bort, Leon
  Balloons, **2** 325, 326
Tektites
  Astrogeology, **2** 212
Telebit
  Explorer satellites, **5** 765
Telecommunications system
  Apollo, **1** 177
Telemetering
  Electronics, **4** 703
  Italy's aerospace activities (picture),
    7 1224
  Space communications, **11** 2096
Telemetering equipment
  Remote control, **11** 1954
Telemetry, 12 2241-44 (with pictures)
  Blockhouse, **2** 368
  Communications satellites, **3** 534
  Data acquisition and processing, **4** 605
  Kennedy Space Center, **7** 1273
  Maneuvering in space, **8** 1430
  Orbiting observatories, **10** 1739, 1741
  Receivers, **10** 1912
  Sensors, **11** 2043
  Surveyor, **12** 2211
Telemetry and Communications Subsystems
  Asteroids (picture), **2** 207
Telephone company
  Information systems, **7** 1156-57
Telescopes and astronomical instruments,
    12 2245-58 (with pictures)
  Astronomy, **2** 237, 242
  Celestial mechanics, **3** 427
  Observatories, **10** 1723
  Orbiting observatories, **10** 1740

  Ozma project, **10** 1753
  Photography, **10** 1789
  Quantum theory, **10** 1870
  Radio astronomy, **10** 1893
Telescope-making
  Planetarium, **10** 1820
Telescope mirror
  Observatories, **10** 1725
Telescope mount
  Apollo Applications Program (picture),
    2 186
Telescopic sight
  Battlefield missile systems, **2** 342
Teletype
  Communications satellites, **3** 534
Teletype Weather Reports
  Aviation weather, **2** 299
Television (with diagram and pictures), **12**
    2258-64
  Communications satellites, **3** 534, 542
  Electronics, **4** 692
  guidance system
    Missiles, **9** 1616
  International projects, **7** 1199
  Radio, **10** 1888
  Resolution, **11** 1961
  Vacuum tubes, **13** 2399
Television and Infrared Observation
  Satellite, see Tiros
Television cameras
  Data acquisition and processing, **4** 606
  Remote control, **11** 1954
Television relay satellites
  Radio, **10** 1888
Television subsystem
  Mariner probes, **8** 1488
Teller, Edward (1908- , Hungarian-
    American physicist), **12** 2264-65
Telstar
  Active repeater satellite, **1** 6
  Communications satellites, **3** 534, 543
  Defense communications satellites, **4** 615
  Delta rocket, **4** 622
  Goddard Space Flight Center, **6** 992
  International Telecommunications Satellite
    Consortium, **7** 1202
  NASA, **9** 1653, (table) 1652
  Satellites, **11** 2007
  Thor rockets, **12** 2286
Tempelhof Airport
  Berlin airlift, **2** 351, (picture) 325
Temperate zone
  Solar system, **11** 2070
Temperature
  Aerospace medicine, **1** 34
  Airports, **1** 95
  Density altitude, **4** 626
  Extraterrestrial life, **5** 776, 777
  Koch chart, **7** 1282
  Man in flight, **8** 1448
  Mars, **8** 1492
  Mercury, **8** 1527
  Meteorology, **9** 1555
  Observatories, **10** 1725
  Oceanographic research, **10** 1732
  Planck's Law, **10** 1817 (with diagram)
  Steels, **12** 2164, 2165
  Temperature gauges, **12** 2269
  Venus, **13** 2408, 2409
  Weather, **13** 2449
Temperature control, 12 2265-69 (with
    pictures)
  Kosmos satellites, **7** 1293
  Observatories, **10** 1723
  Photography, **10** 1789
Temperature extremes
  Radiators, **10** 1884
Temperature gauges, 12 2269-70 (with
    picture)
  Instrument panels, **7** 1176
Temperature-humidity-altitude
  Environmental simulators, **4** 726
Temperature scales, 12 2270-71
Temperature sensors
  Electronics, **4** 704

Tensile strength
 Aluminum, **1** 148
 Boron, **3** 382
 Magnesium, **8** 1419
 Materials, **8** 1502
 Metals and metallurgy (picture), **9** 1554
 Steels, **12** 2164
10th Air Force
 Air Defense Command, **1** 59
Tereshkova, Valentina V.
 Astronauts, **2** 223
 Cosmonauts, **4** 570, 573, 574 (with pictures)
 Bykovsky, Valeri, **3** 397
 Manned spaceflight (table), **8** 1461
 Nikolayev, Andrian G., **9** 1697
 Women in aerospace, **14** 2496,
  (picture) 2495
Terminal ballistics
 Ballistics, **2** 314
Terminal Radar Approach Control
 Control tower, **3** 563
Terminal Visual Omnirange
 Airports, **1** 96
Terminals
 Airmail, **1** 76
 Airports, **1** 93
 Information systems, **7** 1157
 Jumbo Jets, **7** 1256
 Passenger services, **10** 1763
Terminal sterilization chamber
 Spacecraft sterilization (with picture), **11**
  2104
Terminating bars
 Lighting facilities, **8** 1355
Terminator
 Orbits and trajectories, **10** 1747
Terminology of aerospace, 12 2272 (with
  table)
Terraform
 Carbon dioxide, **3** 408
Terrain-avoidance
 Radar, **10** 1875
Terrain charts
 Pilotage, **10** 1794
Terrain-following
 Radar, **10** 1878
Terrain-mapping radar
 Reconnaissance aircraft, **11** 1920
Terrestrial biology
 Mars, **8** 1491
Terrestrial ecology
 Mars, **8** 1493
Terrestrial microorganisms
 Spacecraft sterilization, **11** 2104
Terrestrial planets
 Astronomy, **2** 241
 Planets, **10** 1820
Terrestrial travel
 Implications of aerospace, **7** 1151
Test conductor platform areas
 Kennedy Space Center, **7** 1273
Test cone
 Jupiter rockets, **7** 1261
Test firing
 Aerospace Research Support Program
  (picture), **1** 35
Test flights
 PRIME, **10** 1853
Testing (with pictures), **12** 2272-76
 Materials, **8** 1512
 Precision measurements, **10** 1845
 Preventive maintenance, **10** 1852
 Re-entry, **11** 1931
Test operators' evaluations
 Information systems, **7** 1157
Test pilots and test flying, 12 2277-82 (with
  pictures)
Tethered models
 Model aircraft, **9** 1624, (picture) 1625
Tetrahedral
 Bell, Alexander Graham, **2** 347
Tetrahedral Research Satellite 1
 Environmental research satellites, **4** 723
Tetrahedron
 Airports, **1** 97
 Windsock, **13** 2487

Tetrodes
 Electronics, **4** 696
Tetroon balloon
 Balloons, **2** 330
Texan, see AT-6 Texan
Texas Instruments Inc.
 Air-to-surface missiles, **1** 124
TF-39 (engine)
 Jet engines (picture), **7** 1239
 Jumbo jets (picture), **7** 1247, 1255
TG-180 (turbojet engine)
 X-series aerospace vehicles, **14** 2537
Thaden, Louise
 Women in aerospace, **14** 2494
Thailand
 Asia's aviation, **2** 203, 204
 Crop dusting, **4** 587
Thales
 Astronomy, **2** 234, 235
 Electricity, **4** 683
That's My Story (book)
 Corrigan, Douglas, **3** 568
Thaw, William
 Lafayette Escadrille, **7** 1295
Themis
 Pickering, William Henry, **10** 1791
Theodolite
 Meteorology, **9** 1557
Thermal barrier, 12 2282
Thermal coatings
 Materials, **8** 1510-11
Thermal energy
 Energy, **4** 712
 Mars, **8** 1492
Thermal load
 Quality control, **10** 1868
Thermal maps
 Infrared detection devices, **7** 1159
Thermal meteoroid garment
 Life-support systems, **8** 1343
Thermal motion
 Radiation, **10** 1880
Thermal processes
 Jupiter, **7** 1260
Thermals, 12 2283
 Convection currents, **3** 564
 Gliders, **6** 984
 Gliding, **6** 986
 Man-powered flight, **8** 1465
 Soaring, **11** 2062
Thermal sources
 Soaring, **11** 2065-66
Thermal underwear
 Personal equipment, **10** 1775
Thermionic emission
 Electronics, **4** 694, 695
Thermistor
 Data acquisition and processing, **4** 607
 Temperature gauges, **12** 2270
 Windows and windshields, **13** 2486
Thermocouple
 Temperature gauges, **12** 2270
Thermodynamics, 12 2283
 Aerothermodynamics, **1** 35
 Planck, Max K. E. L., **10** 1816
Thermodynamic scale
 Temperature scales, **12** 2271
Thermometer
 Meteorology, **9** 1556
 Temperature gauges, **12** 2269
Thermonuclear explosion
 Antiballistic missile defense, **1** 159
Thermonuclear process
 Radiation, **10** 1881
Thermonuclear reactions
 Carbon, **3** 406
 Jupiter, **7** 1260
 Matter (picture), **8** 1513
Thermoplastics
 Plastics, **10** 1825
Thermoscope
 Temperature gauges, **12** 2269
Thermoset
 Plastics, **10** 1825
Thermosphere
 Atmosphere, **2** 264

 Ionosphere, **7** 1215
Thetis
 Coast Guard aviation, **3** 479
Thible, Madame
 Balloons, 320, 321
Thieffry, Edmond
 World War I (table, Top Aces), **14** 2507
Thin films
 Data acquisition and processing, **4** 610
Third dimension
 Photogrammetry, **10** 1780
Third level airlines
 Commercial airlines, **3** 499
Third stage
 Apollo (picture), **1** 180
38th parallel
 Korean war, **7** 1283
33rd Tactical Fighter Test Wing
 Eglin Air Force Base, **4** 679
Thius
 Payloads, **10** 1769
Thomas D. White Space Trophy
 Trophies and awards (table), **13** 2312
Thomas-Morse S-6 fighter
 First World War aircraft (picture), **5** 819
Thompson, Milton O.
 X-15 research program (picture), **14** 2531,
  2533
Thompson Trophy
 Air racing, **1** 102, 103
 Doolittle, James Harold, **4** 643
 Trophies and awards (table), **13** 2312
Thomson-Houston Company
 Aircraft propulsion systems, **1** 57
 Jet engines, **7** 1238
Thomson, J. J.
 Atoms, **2** 269
 Electronics, **4** 693
Thomson, William (Lord Kelvin)
 Temperature scales, **12** 2271
Thor-Able
 Delta rocket, **4** 622
 Pioneer, **10** 1812-13
Thor-Agena
 Alouette satellites, **1** 144
 Discoverer Project, **4** 632, 636
 International Satellite for Ionospheric
  Studies, **7** 1201
 Launch vehicles (tables), **7** 1319-20
 NASA, **9** 1653
Thor-Delta
 Biosatellites, **2** 358
 Launch vehicles, **7** 1319-24
 Orbiting observatories, **10** 1738
 Missiles, **9** 1611, (data table) 1616
 United States Air Force, **13** 2369
Thoria dispersed, nickel
 Nickel, **9** 1696
Thorium
 Alpha particle, **1** 145
Thorness, R. B.
 Balloons, **2** 330
Thornton, William E. (1929-   , Scientist-
  astronaut), **12** 2283
 Astronauts, **2** 218, 219 (with picture)
Thoron
 Atmosphere, **2** 263
Thorp T-18 (airplane)
 Homebuilt aircraft, **6** 1125
Thor rockets, 12 2283-86
 Agena rockets, **1** 38-39
 Delta rocket, **4** 622
 Dunn, Louis G., **4** 655
 Edwards Air Force Base, **4** 679
 Explorer satellites, **5** 765
 Geodetic satellites, **6** 972
 Inertial guidance, **7** 1152
 Intermediate range ballistic missiles,
  7 1187
 Military space program, **9** 1601-02,
  (picture) 1599
Three-axis stability
 PILOT, **10** 1794
Three-level maser
 Masers, **8** 1496-97

Three Men on a Flying Trapeze (book)
Chennault, Claire Lee, **3** 457
Three-needle altimeter
Altimeter, **1** 145
Three-point landing
Airplane, **1** 89
Threshold bars
Lighting facilities, **8** 1355
Threshold lights
Airports (picture), **1** 95
Throat
Jet engine, **7** 1239
Throttle
Attitude and attitude control, **2** 275
Power management, **10** 1840
Thrust, 12 2286
Acoustics, **1** 5
Aerodynamics, **1** 20 (with diagram)
Airplane, **1** 90-91
Apollo, **1** 173
Bird flight, **2** 358
Cryogenic propellants, **4** 596
Jet engines, **7** 1237
Launch vehicles, **7** 1314, 1328
Measurement of power, **8** 1519
(diagram)
Piloting techniques, **10** 1802
Propellers, **10** 1862
Reaction engines, **10** 1912
Reciprocating engines, **11** 1918
Rocket propulsion systems, **11** 1968
Rockets and rocketry, **11** 1984
Solid-fuel rockets, **11** 2071
Thrust augmentation
Launch vehicles, **7** 1323
Thrust Augmented Delta
Communications satellites, **3** 536
Delta rocket, **4** 622
Explorer satellites, **5** 773
Launch vehicles, **7** 1323
Pioneer, **10** 1813
Thrust Augmented Thor (TAT)
Thor rockets, **12** 2285
Thrust chamber
Launch vehicles, **7** 1315
Thruster
Maneuvering in space (diagrams), **8** 1431
Reaction control systems, **10** 1911
Thrust kick
Interplanetary travel, **7** 1212
Thrust reversers
Boeing 707, **2** 370
Jumbo jets, **7** 1254
Thrust structure
Launch vehicles, **7** 1316
Thrust variations
Launching, **7** 1309
Thule, Greenland
Ballistic Missile Early Warning System,
1 313
Thunderbirds
Demonstration teams, **4** 623-25 (with
picture)
Formation flying and techniques,
5 883, (picture) 882
Precision flying, **10** 1845
Thunderbolt, see P-47 Thunderbolt
Thunderbolt, see Viggen 37 Thunderbolt
Thunderchief, see F-105 Thunderchief
Thunderjets
Airmail, 78
Thunderstorm
Aviation weather, **2** 301 (diagrams) 302
Soaring, **11** 2062
Thunderstorm cells
Aviation weather, **2** 300
Thunderstreak, see F-84 Thunderstreak
Thyratrons
Electronics, **4** 700
Thyristor
Electronics, **4** 703
Tibbets, Colonel Paul
United States Air Force, **13** 2364
Tiger, see F-11 Tiger

Tiger Moth
Africa's aviation, 36
Australia's aviation, **2** (picture) 282, 283
Tikhov
Mars, **8** 1491
Tiling, Rheinhold
Rockets and rocketry, **11** 1978
Tilting level comparator
Precision measurements, **10** 1845
Time, 12 2286-88
Time-division multiplexing
Telemetry, **12** 2242
Photography, **10** 1783
Quantum theory, **10** 1869
Space communications, **11** 2097
Time changes
Circadian rhythm, **3** 460
Man in flight, **8** 1449
Timekeeping devices
Planetarium, **10** 1820
Time Machine, The
Wells, Herbert George, **13** 2474
Time study
Human engineering, **6** 1132
Tin Goose, Ford Trimotor 4-AT, 12 2288
Tiros
Air masses (map), **1** 81
Command and data acquisition, **3** 493
Delta rocket, **4** 622
Earth science, **4** 667
Goddard Space Flight Center, **6** 992
Guidance and control systems, **6** 1039
Oceanographic research, **10** 1732
RAND Corporation, **10** 1903
Satellites, **11** 2007
Thor rockets, **12** 2286
Weather satellites, **13** 2460, 2462-66,
2468-70 (pictures), 2461, 2470, (table)
2470
Tiros Operational Satellite
Earth science, **4** 667
ESSA spacecraft, **4** 739
NASA, **9** 1653, (table) 1652
National Environmental Satellite Center,
9 1664
Weather satellites, **13** 2459
Tissandier, Albert
Aviation medicine, **2** 293
Tissandier, Gaston
Aviation medicine, **2** 293
Dirigibles, **4** 631
Titan
Astronomy, **2** 246
Titanium, 12 2288
Materials, **8** 1507
Supersonic transports, **12** 2192, 2197
X-15 research program, **14** 2532
Titanium alloys
Alloys, **1** 144
Titanium hot-air ducts
Jumbo jets, **7** 1252
Titan III, 12 2291-93 (with pictures)
Aerospace Research Support Program,
1 35
Manned Orbiting Laboratory, **8** 1452-54,
(picture) 1455
Military space program, **9** 1601,
(picture) 1596
Propellants, **10** 1860
Titan rockets, 12 2289-91 (with pictures)
Blockhouse, **2** 367
Computers (picture), **3** 554
Dunn, Louis G., **4** 655
Edwards Air Force Base, **4** 679
Intercontinental ballistic missiles,
7 1182-83
Launch vehicles, **7** 1317, 1319-24
Military space program, **9** 1601-02
(with picture)
NASA, **9** 1653
Saturn, **11** 2009
Surface-to-surface missiles, **12** 2206
(table), 2208
United States Air Force, **13** 2369
Titan II
Atlas missile and launch vehicle, **2** 260

Dyna-Soar program, **4** 657
Gemini, **5** 927, 931
Inertial guidance, **7** 1152
Launching (picture), **7** 1312
Manned spaceflight, **8** 1460
Military space program (picture), **9** 1602
Missiles, **9** 1612
Silos (with diagrams), **11** 2053
Titov, Gherman Stepanovich (1935-
Cosmonaut) **12** 2293-94
Bykovsky, Valeri, **3** 397
Cosmonauts, **4** 570, 572, 574, (pictures)
570, 573, 575, (table) 574
Korolev, Sergei, **7** 1290
Manned spaceflight (table), **8** 1461
Popovich, Pavel, **10** 1838
U.S.S.R. aerospace activities, **13** 2343
Vostok, **13** 2435
Toe brakes
Airplane, **1** 90
Toepler Schlieren method
Schlieren photography, **11** 2015
Toftoy, Holger Nelson (1902-1967, U.S.
Army Officer), **12** 2294
Tokaido Express
High-speed surface transportation, **6** 1091
Tolerances, 12 2294-95
Precision measurements, **10** 1845
Preventive maintenance, **10** 1852
Tolubko, Vladimir F.
Surface-to-surface missiles; **12** 2205
Tomahawk, see P-40
Tombaugh, Clyde
Astronomy, **2** 242
Mars, **8** 1490
Pluto, **10** 1827
Tondi, Angelo
Distance records, **4** 641
Ton mile, 12 2295
Tooling
Jumbo jets, **7** 1251
Topaze
Launch vehicles, **7** 1327
Topographic features
Charts, **3** 450
Topographic map
Maps and mapping (map), **8** 1477
Topography
Australia's aviation, **2** 279
Top secret
Classified information, **3** 467
Topside Sounder (satellite)
Explorer satellites, **5** 770
Torpedo bombing
Bomber aircraft, **2** 376
Torpedo control
Oceanographic research, **10** 1734
Torpedoes
Bomber aircraft, **2** 372
Oceanographic research, **10** 1734
Torpedo Junction
Coast Guard aviation, **3** 479
Torque, 12 2295-96
Aerodynamics, **1** 23
Guidance and control systems, **6** 1039
Gyroscope, **6** 1044
Landing gear, **7** 1300
Precession, **10** 1843
Torque-free tools
Space tools, **12** 2136
Torque meter
Engine instruments, **4** 716
Power management, **10** 1841
Torque rating
Measurement of power, **8** 1519
Torricelli, Evangelista
Barometer, **2** 336
Meteorology, **9** 1556
TOS, see Tiros Operational Satellite
Toss bombing
Bomber aircraft, **2** 376
Total flying time
Pilot training, **10** 1810
Total vacuums
Pressure gauges, **10** 1849

Touchdown lights
Lighting facilities, **8** 1357, (diagrams) 1355-56
Touchdown point
Landing techniques, **7** 1301
TOW
Battlefield missile systems (picture), **2** 341-42
Surface-to-surface missiles, **12** 2208 (picture), 2208
Tow (gliders)
Gliding, **6** 986, 988
Tower Controller
Air traffic control (picture), **1** 133
Control tower, **3** 564
Towering clouds
Clouds, **3** 473
Tower of Winds
Meteorology, **9** 1556
Towers, John
Curtiss Model D Hydro, **4** 601
Townes, Charles Hard (1915- , American physicist), **12** 2296
Electronics, **4** 693
Toxic fluids
Kennedy Space Center, **7** 1267
Toxic fuels, 12 2296
TRACE
United Kingdom aerospace activities, **13** 2352
Tracers
Radioisotope, **10** 1899
Tracing table
Photogrammetry, **10** 1780
Track, 12 2296
Tracker, see S-2 Tracker
Tracking resolution
Infrared detection devices, **7** 1161
Tracking systems and networks, 13 2297 (with pictures)
Kennedy Space Center, **7** 1273
Launch vehicles, **7** 1316
Mercury program, **9** 1534, (map) 1534
Radar, **10** 1876, 1877
Re-entry vehicles, **11** 1936
Space communications (with sketch), **11** 2097
Transponder, **13** 2309
TRACON, see Terminal Radar Approach Control
Tractor propeller, 13 2305
Tradescantia
Biosatellites, **2** 356
Tradewinds flying boat, see Convair R3Y-1
Traeger, A. H.
Flying doctor services, **5** 862
Traffic analysis
Photography, **10** 1784
Traffic conditions
Plane spotter, **10** 1817
Traffic control
Police and fire services, **10** 1834
Traffic control towers
Air traffic control, **1** 125
Airports, **1** 97
Emergency signals, **4** 709
Traffic pattern
Air traffic control, **1** 125
T-rail
High-speed surface transportation, **6** 1089-90
Trailblazer Series
Sounding rockets, **11** 2083
Trailing edge
Aerodynamics, **1** 21
Airfoil, **1** 61
Fowler flaps
Jumbo jets, **7** 1254
Trailing wire antenna
Airborne antennas (picture), **1** 43
Piper Cub, **10** 1815
Trainer aircraft, 13 2306-07 (with pictures)
T-6, North American, **13** 2314
Trainers
Link, Edwin A., **8** 1361

Military aircraft (with picture), **9** 1567-68
Training
Careers, **3** 416
Cosmonauts, **4** 570-74
Mechanics, **8** 1523-24
Training phases
Pilot's training (with chart), **10** 1811
Training program
Preflight training (with pictures), **10** 1847
Training schedule
Astronauts, **2** 223
Training schools
Commercial airlines, **3** 503
Trains
High-speed surface transportation, **6** 1091
Trajectory
Celestial navigation, **3** 430
Mariner probes (diagram), **8** 1488
Orbits and trajectories, **10** 1742
Terminology of aerospace (table), **12** 2272
Trajectory correction command
Ranger (with diagrams), **10** 1907
Tranquilizers
Drug effects, **4** 653
Transall C-160 (aircraft)
France's aerospace activities (picture), **5** 891
International projects (picture), **7** 1200
Transatlantic airmail service
Airmail, **1** 78
International airmail, **7** 1188
Transatlantic flight
Alock and Brown, 141-42
Balbo, Italo, **2** 311
Transatlantic speed record
Bellanca, Giuseppe, **2** 349
Trans-Canada Airlines
Canada's aviation, **3** 400
Trans Caribbean Airways Inc.
Charter flying, **3** 448
Transceivers, 13 2307-08
Transcontinental Air Transport
Commercial airlines, **3** 510
Transcontinental and Western Air
Commercial airlines, **3** 510
Commercial air transports, **3** 519
Transcontinental routes
Airports, **1** 97
Transcontinental service
Airmail, **1** 72
Transcontinental Travel by Air, 1927-1967
Commercial airlines (table), **3** 513
Transducers
Data acquisition and processing, **4** 605
Radiosonde units, **10** 1899
Sonar, **11** 2073
Transfer aisle
Kennedy Space Center, **7** 1269
Transfer of temperature
Launch vehicles, **7** 1316
Transfer paths
Orbits and trajectories, **10** 1742
Transfer profile
Interplanetary travel, **7** 1209-10
Transformer-coupled circuit
Circuit, **3** 461
Trans-Gabon
Africa's aviation, **1** 36
Transient variations
Earth, **4** 662
Geomagnetic field, **6** 977
Transistor limitations
Solid-state physics, **11** 2073
Transistors, 13 2308
Aerospace industry, **1** 29
Communications satellites, **3** 534
Computers, **3** 557
Electronics, **4** 693
Microcircuitry, **9** 1562
Miniaturization, **9** 1608 (with picture)
Radiation, **10** 1883
Semiconductors, **11** 2041-42
Sensors, **11** 2042
Transceivers, **13** 2307

Transit
Military space program, **9** 1593, (with picture) 1599
Navigation satellites, **9** 1673
Transition area
Electronics, **4** 701
Translation (motion)
Guidance and control systems, **6** 1034
V/STOL aircraft, **13** 2438
Translator service
Passenger services, **10** 1764
Translucent
Light, **8** 1351
Translunar velocity
Launch vehicles, **7** 1314
Transmission
Electromagnetism, **4** 691
Light, **8** 1351
Radio, **10** 1885
Transmitters, 13 2308-09
Radar, **10** 1875
Transceivers, **13** 2307
Transonic aerodynamics
Aerodynamics, **1** 24-25
Transonic flight, 13 2309
Transonic speeds
Korean war, **7** 1287
Transonic wind tunnels
Langley Research Center, **7** 1302
Transpacific Air Mail Service
Airmail, **1** 78
Transparent
Light, **8** 1351
Transparent globe
Lambert projection, **7** 1296
Transpiration cooling
Materials, **8** 1503
Transpolar flight
Polar flights, **10** 1830
Transponder, 13 2309-10
Airborne antennas, **1** 44
Air traffic control, **1** 130
Avionics, **2** 307
Communications satellites, **3** 534
Radar, **10** 1875
Transportable Satellite Communications Earth Station
Television, **12** 2263
Transportation Act of 1966
National Transportation Safety Board, **9** 1667
Transportation, Department of
Aeronautical Center, **1** 25-26
Airports, **1** 98
Air traffic control, **1** 125
Civil Aeronautics Board, **3** 464
Federal Aviation Administration, **5** 795
Transporter erector
Jumbo jets, **7** 1256
Transporter pad
Saturn rockets (with picture), **11** 2011
Transporters
Kennedy Space Center, **7** 1271
Transportes Aeros Portugueses
European aerospace activities, **4** 749
Transports
Commercial air transports, **3** 516
Military air transports, **9** 1574
Military aircraft, **9** 1569-70
Trans-Texas Airlines
Commercial airlines, **3** 513
Transuranium elements
Elements, **4** 705
Transverse G force
Acceleration, **1** 3
Transverse Mercator
Charts, **3** 455
Trans World Airlines
Charter flying, **3** 448
Commercial airlines, **3** 497
Trapped radiation detector
Mariner probes, **8** 1488
Travelair
Crop dusting, **4** 588
Travel Air Company
Cessna, Clyde V., **3** 445

Travel Air Manufacturing Company
Beech, Walter H., **2** 347
Traveling-wave tubes
Electronics, **4** 700
Treatise Upon the Art of Flying (book)
Man-powered flight, **8** 1465
Tremolite
Asbestos, **2** 202
Trenchard, Hugh
Military aviation, **9** 1581
World War II, **14** 2512
Triad
Curtiss Model D Hydro, **4** 601
Triade, see A-1 Triade
Triangular pattern
Emergency signals, **4** 709
Tricycle landing gear
Airplane, **1** 88
Du Temple, Jean-Marie Felix de la Croix,
4 656
Landing gear, **7** 1299
Northrop F-5 Freedom Fighter, **9** 1705
Trident, see Hawker Siddeley Trident
Trigger electrode
Lasers, **7** 1305
Trim control
Instrument flight techniques, **7** 1166
Trim control surfaces
Airplane, **1** 88
Trimotor, see Ford Trimotor
Trimotor 80, see Boeing Trimotor
Trimming devices
Empennage, **4** 709-10
Trim tabs, 13 2310-11
Airplane, **1** 88
Cockpit, **3** 482
Piloting techniques, **10** 1801
Triode
Electronics, **4** 695-96
Miniaturization (picture), **9** 1608
Tri-Pacer, see Piper Tri-Pacer
Trippe, Juan Terry (1899-   , American
aviator, airline executive), **13** 2311
Commercial airlines, **3** 508
Tri-Service V/STOL Program
X-series aerospace vehicles, **14** 2544
Tritium
Triton
Astronomy, **2** 247
Neptune, **9** 1690, (picture) 1689
Radiation, **10** 1881
Trochoidal principle
Rotating combustion engine, **11** 1993
Troop carrier and transport planes
Air forces of the world, **1** 64
Tropical air masses
Air masses, **1** 80-81
Tropical year
Astronomy, **2** 236
Earth, **4** 661
Tropopause
Atmosphere, **2** 264
Weather maps and charts, **13** 2458
Troposphere, 13 2313
Aerospace, **1** 27
Aerospace medicine, **1** 34
Atmosphere, **2** 264
Stratosphere, **12** 2170
Trophies and awards, 13 2311-12 (with
chart)
Truax, Robert Collins (1917-   , American
Naval officer, rocket scientist), **13** 2313
Truculent Turtle
Neptune, Lockheed P2V, **9** 1690
True airspeed
Airspeed, **1** 116
True airspeed indicator
Airspeed indicator, **1** 116-17
True altitude
Altitude and altitude records, **1** 146
True bearings
Bearing, **2** 346
Truly, Richard H. (1937-   , Aerospace
research pilot), **13** 2313
Manned Orbiting Laboratory, **8** 1456

Trunk airlines
Commercial airlines, **3** 497
Truss
Landing gear, **7** 1299-1300
Truss-type fuselage
Airplane, **1** 82
Truxtun (ship)
Nuclear energy, **9** 1713
TRW Systems Group
Environmental research satellites, **4** 722
TSKB- 30
Ilyushin, Sergei Vladimirovich, **7** 1148
TSR.2 (supersonic bomber)
United Kingdom aerospace activities, **13**
2348
Tsiolkovsky, Konstantin Edwardovitch
(1857-1935, Russian schoolteacher,
rocket theorist), **13** 2313-14
Rockets and rocketry, **11** 1975
Sputniks, **12** 2152
U.S.S.R. aerospace activities, **13** 2338
T-Tauri (stars)
Stars, **12** 2161
T-Time
Countdown, **4** 576
Terminology of aerospace (table), **12** 2272
Tu-4 bomber (Tupolev)
Asia's aviation, **2** 203
Tu-16 Badger bomber (Tupolev)
Air-to-surface missiles, **1** 124
Asia's aviation, **2** 205
Naval aviation, worldwide (Russia)
(with picture) **9** 1670
U.S.S.R. aerospace activities (table),
13 2337
Tu-20 (Tu-95) Bear bomber (Tupolev)
Air forces of the world (picture),
1 63, 65
Naval aviation, worldwide (Russia)
(picture), **9** 1670
U.S.S.R. aerospace activities (table),
13 2337
Tu-22 Blinder (Tupolev)
Naval aviation, worldwide, **9** 1670
U.S.S.R. aerospace activities, **13** 2335,
(table) 2337
Tu-95, see Tu-20
Tu-104 (Tupolev)
U.S.S.R. aerospace activities, **13** 2332,
(table) 2337
Commercial air transports, **3** 527
Tu-114 Rossiya transport (Tupolev)
U.S.S.R. aerospace activities, **13** 2332,
(table) 2337
Tu-120 bomber (Tupolev)
Commercial air transports, **3** 527
Tu-134 transport (Tupolev)
Commerical air transports (picture),
3 529, 530
Tu-144 SST (Tupolev)
Commercial air transports, **3** 530
Supersonic transports, **12** 2182, 2190,
(picture) 2179
U.S.S.R. aerospace activities, **13** 2332
Tubeflight system
High-speed surface transportation, **6** 1090
**Tube-launched, Optically-tracked,
Wire-guided,** see TOW
Tumors
Nuclear energy, **9** 1715
Tungsten
Materials, **8** 1507
Tunnel construction
Airlock, **1** 67
Tunnel diode
Electronics, **4** 703
Microcircuitry, **9** 1562
Tupolev, Andrei Nikolaevich (1888-   ,
Russian aircraft designer), **13** 2315
U.S.S.R. aerospace acitivities, **13** 2329
(picture) 2327
Tupolev aircraft, see Tu-4, Tu-16, Tu-20,
Tu-22, Tu-95, Tu-114, Tu-120, Tu-134,
Tu-144, also see U.S.S.R. aerospace
acitivities, **13** 2332 (table), 2337

Tupolev Fiddler
U.S.S.R. aerospace activities
(table), **13** 2337
Medals and decorations (table), **8** 1526
Turbine engine, see Gas turbine engines
Turbine inlet temperatures
Jumbo jets, **7** 1255
Turbine-powered commercial aircraft
Jumbo jet, **7** 1244
Turbine wheel
Pulsejet engine, **10** 1865
Turbo II Commander, see Aero
Commander aircraft
Turbo-Beaver, see DHC-2 Mark III
Turbo-compound
Reciprocating engines, **11** 1913
Turbofan engine
Aircraft propulsion systems, **1** 58
Engines, **4** 717
Gas turbine engines, **5** 923
Jumbo jets, **7** 1249, 1254
Ramjet engines, **10** 1902
Turbojet engine
Aircraft propulsion systems, **1** 57
Engines, **4** 717
Gas turbine engines, **5** 918
Government in aerospace (picture), **6** 1004
High-altitude flight training, **6** 1085
Hypersonic flight, **6** 1142
Jet engines, **7** 1237
Messerschmitt Me-262, **9** 1547
Military aviation, **9** 1587
Power management, **10** 1842
Supersonic transports, **12** 2188
Turboprop engine
Aircraft propulsion systems, **1** 58
Engines, **4** 717
Gas turbine engines, **5** 918, 924
History of aviation, **6** 1116
Jet engines, **7** 1237
Rocket propulsion systems (with picture),
11 1970
Temperature control, **12** 2268
Vickers Viscount, **13** 2413
Turboshaft engine
Aircraft propulsion systems, **1** 58
Gas turbine engines, **5** 924
Turbosuperchargers
Airplane, **1** 84
Reciprocating engines (with diagram),
11 1917
Supercharger, **12** 2175
Turbulence, 13 2315
Airsickness, **1** 115
Aviation weather, **2** 303 (with diagram)
Canopy, airplane, **3** 405
Photography, **10** 1789
Piloting techniques, **10** 1800
Plan position indicator, **10** 1821
Supersonic transports, **12** 2197
Turkey
Crop dusting, **4** 587
International Agricultural Aviation Centre,
7 1187
NATO, **9** 1703-04
Turn
Bank, **2** 332
Maneuvers, **8** 1433
Turn about point
Maneuvers, **8** 1436, (diagram) 1437
Turn-and-bank indicator (see also Turn-and-
slip indicator)
Manufacturing, **8** 1469
Turn-and slip-indicator, 13 2315-16
Attitude indicator, **2** 276
Instrument flight techniques, **7** 1167
Turn-around
Agricultural aviation, **1** 41
Turner, Roscoe (1895-   , American
aviator), **13** 2316
Air racing, **1** 102-03
Barnstormers, **2** 336
Medals and decorations (table), **8** 1526
Turning point
Distance and distance records, **4** 641

Turning requirements
Jumbo Jets, **7** 1257
Runways, turnoffs, **11** 1998
Turns
Piloting techniques, **10** 1801
Turret
Crash trucks, **4** 583
Fighter aircraft, **5** 807
Tuve
Astronomy, **2** 242
TVOR, see Terminal Visual Omnirange
24-hour
Circadian rhythm, **3** 460
Twenty Thousand Leagues Under the Sea
Piccard family, **10** 1790
Twilight
Air Almanac, **1** 42
Twining, Nathan Farragut (1897-   ,
American Air Force officer), **13** 2316
Twin Otter, see DHC-6 Twin Otter
Twiss, L. P.
Medals and decorations (table), **8** 1526
Speed and speed records (table), **12** 2141
Two-minute turn, 13 2316
Two-way radio
Positive control areas, **10** 1839
Tycho Crater
Surveyor, **12** 2215
Tycho's Star
Brahe, Tycho, **3** 385
Tymcsyszyn, Joe
Test pilots and test flying (picture),
12 2277
Type Certificate
Certification procedures, **3** 440
Type Certification Board
Certification procedures, **3** 443
Type design
Certification procedures, **3** 440
Type Inspection Report
Certification procedures, **3** 443
Typhoon, see Hawker Typhoon

U

U-1, see DHC-3 Otter
U-2 (Lockheed), **13** 2396-97
Boost-glide vehicle, **3** 381
Johnson, Clarence Leonard, **7** 1242
Military aircraft (picture), **9** 1568
Reconnaissance aircraft, **11** 1921
World War II (picture), **14** 2513
U-6 aircraft (deHavilland of Canada)
Army aviation, **2** 197
U-8 Seminole (Beech) (see also Beech
Queen Air)
Army aviation, **2** 197
U-9 Aero Commander
Army aviation, **2** 197
U-10 Helio Courier, see Helio H-295
Super Courier
U-21 (Beech)
Army aviation, **2** 197
U-234 atoms
Manhattan Project, **8** 1442
U-238
Nuclear energy, **9** 1711
U-control models
Model aircraft, **9** 1624
Udet, Ernst
Fokker DR-1 triplane, **5** 869

World War I, **14** 2505, 2506, (table) 2507,
2510
UDMH, see Unsymmetrical dimethylhydrazine
UFO, see Unidentified flying objects
UH-1D helicopter units
Police and fire services, **10** 1836
UH-1 Iroquois helicopter (Bell)
Army aviation, **2** 198
Marine Corps Aviation, **8** 1482
UH-19 Chickasaw (Sikorsky)
Army aviation, **2** 197
UHF, see Ultra high frequency
UHF signals
Space communications (with diagram),
11 2099
Ullage rockets
Launch vehicles, **7** 1318
Ultra high-frequency radio, 13 2317
Airborne antennas, **1** 43
Air traffic control, **1** 128
Avionics, **2** 307
radio antennas
Parabola, **10** 1756
Radio communications, **10** 1898
Space communications, **11** 2098
Ultra-high vacuum space chamber facility
Manned Spacecraft Center, **8** 1458
Ultrasonics
Materials, **8** 1512
Ultraviolet light
International Geophysical Year, **7** 1197
Orbiting observatories, **10** 1738
X-rays, **14** 2533
Ultraviolet radiation, 13 2317
Atmosphere, **2** 264, 266
Extraterrestrial life, **5** 777
Light, **8** 1350
Observatories, **10** 1726
Paints, **10** 1754
Radiation, **10** 1880
Spacecraft sterilization, **11** 2104
Umbilical cord, 13 2317
Terminology of aerospace, (table), **12** 2272
Umbilical tower
Kennedy Space Center, **7** 1271
Launch facilities, **7** 1307
Manned Orbiting Laboratory, **8** 1455
Unattended radio transmitters in space
Legal implications of aerospace, **7** 1331
Uncoupling maneuver
Kosmos satellites, **7** 1292
Underbody nozzles
Crash trucks, **4** 583
Undercarriage, 13 2317
Underexposure
Photography, **10** 1785
Underground silos
Launch facilities, **7** 1307
Silo, **11** 2052
Underpasses
Jumbo jets, **7** 1257
Underprocessing
Photography, **10** 1785
Undersea collision warning device
Sonar, **11** 2073
Underwater acoustical technology
Oceanographic research, **10** 1731
Underwater balloon
Balloons, **2** 325
Underwater escape
Escape systems, **4** 735
Underwater training facility
Manned Spacecraft Center, **8** 1458
Underwriting
Insurance, aviation, **7** 1178
Unicom
Airports, **1** 97
Radio communications, **10** 1895
Unidentified flying objects, 13 2318-26,
(with pictures)
Unidirectional composite
Materials, **8** 1504, (diagram) 1504
Unified field theory
Einstein, Albert, **4** 681
Unified S-band antenna system
Apollo (picture), **1** 178

Uniform field rules
Airports, **1** 98
Uniform motion
Motion, **9** 1640
Unions de Transportes Aeriens (UTA)
France's aerospace activities, **5** 886, 887
Unit of measurement
Parsec, **10** 1763
United Aircraft Company
Manned Orbiting Laboratory, **8** 1452
United Air Lines
Air traffic control (picture), **1** 137
Commercial airlines, **3** 498, 502, 510,
(map) 511, (table, transcontinental
travel 1927-67) 513 (table, number of
passengers, 1966) 514
United Kingdom aerospace activities,
13 2346-56 (with pictures)
Air forces of the world, **1** 63, 64-65, 66
Air-to-air missiles, **1** 120-21
Blitzkrieg, **2** 366
Cody, Samuel Franklin, **3** 487
Communications satellites, **3** 538
Crop dusting, **4** 587
European air traffic control, **4** 752
European Launcher Development
Organization, **4** 754
European Space Research Organization,
4 755
International projects (picture), **7** 1198
Launch vehicle, **7** 1322, 1327
International Agricultural Aviation Centre,
7 1187
NATO, **9** 1703-04
Naval aviation, worldwide, **9** 1667-69,
(pictures) 1668
P-40, Curtiss, **10** 1776
United Nations, 13 2357, (with picture)
International aviation and space
agreements, **7** 1189
Korean war, **7** 1283, 1285
Space law, **12** 2119
UNESCO
International Geophysical Year, **7** 1197
United States
Ace, **1** 4
Aerospace industry, **1** 29
Agricultural aviation, **1** 41
Aircraft carriers, **1** 49
Air forces of the world, **1** 63-65
Airlift, **1** 67
Airmail, **1** 68-79
Airman's Information Manual, **1** 80
Airports, **1** 94
Airships, **1** 108, 111-12
Air traffic control, **1** 125-39
Antiballistic missile defense, **1** 158
Antimissile missiles, **1** 159
Apollo, **1** 162-84
Ariel satellites, **2** 191
Astronauts, **2** 217
Atomic bomb, **2** 269
Blimp, **2** 364
Commemorative stamps and medals, **3**
494
Commercial airlines, **3** 507, 509
Commercial air transports, **3** 530
Communications satellites, **3** 538
Crop dusting, **4** 587
First World War aircraft, **5** 815-25
International Satellite for Ionospheric
Studies, **7** 1201
Jet streams, **7** 1241
Launch vehicles, **7** 1315
Satellites, **11** 2006
Second World War aircraft, **11** 2035-38
World War I, **14** 2500-10
World War II, **14** 2512
Women in aerospace, **14** 2494
United States Air Force, 13 2358-74
(with pictures) (see also USAF)
Aerospace research pilot, **1** 34
Agena rockets, **1** 38-39
Air Defense Command, **1** 59
NORAD, **9** 1701-02
Air defense systems, **1** 60

Air Force Historical Foundation, **1** 62
Air forces of the world, **1** 65
Air National Guard, **1** 81
Arnold, Henry Harley, **2** 201
Asset Program, **2** 206
Astronauts, **2** 215-32
Atlas missile and launch vehicle, **2** 259
Attack aircraft, **2** 273
Automatic landing, **2** 287
Bailout, **2** 310
Balchen, Bernt, **2** 312
Boeing 707, **2** 370
Careers, **3** 413
Charts, **3** 455
Civil Air Patrol, **3** 466
Communications satellites, **3** 535
Continental Air Command, **3** 563
Launch vehicle, **7** 1322
Manned Orbiting Laboratory, **8** 1452
McConnell, John Paul, **8** 1516, 1517
Military implications of space, **9** 1588
Office of Aerospace Research, **10** 1735
Pilot and crew wings, **10** 1794
Program management, **10** 1857
X-24
   PILOT, **10** 1793
United States Air Forces in Europe
NATO, **9** 1704-05
United States Air Force, **13** 2371
United States Air-to-Air Missiles
Air-to-Air missiles (table), **1** 120
United States Air-to-Surface Missiles, 1967
Air-to-surface missiles (table), **1** 123
United States Antisubmarine Missiles 1967
Antisubmarine missiles (table), **1** 161
United States Army
Air Defense Command
   NORAD, **9** 1701-02
Airlift, **1** 67
Airmail, **1** 77
Army aviation, **2** 194
Blimps (picture), **2** 364
Communications satellites, **3** 533
World War II, **14** 2512
United States Army Aviation Center
Army aviation, **2** 200
United States Army Ordnance
Bumper Project, **3** 389
United States Army Primary Helicopter School
Army aviation, **2** 200
United States Army Signal Corps
Communications satellites, **3** 532
Materials, **8** 1500
United States Atomic Energy Commission, 13 2375
Aerospace industry, **1** 32
Launch vehicles, **7** 1328
Manhattan Project, **8** 1442
Snapshot payload
   Atlas missile and launch vehicle, **2** 260
United States Balloon Squadron
World War I, **14** 2508
U.S.-Canadian North American Air Defense Command
DEW Line, **4** 628
U.S. Chamber of Commerce Great Living Americans award
Gilruth, Robert Rowe, **6** 981
United States Civil Airlines Table (1949 to 1966)
Commercial airlines, **3** 498
United States Coast and Geodetic Survey
Charts, **3** 455
United States Coast Guard, see also
   Coast Guard Aviation
Police and fire services, **10** 1835
United States Congress
Airmail, **1** 69-79
Civil Aeronautics Board, **3** 462
United States Customs Bureau
National Aviation Trades Association, **9** 1663
United States Deep Space Network
Data acquisition and processing, **4** 606

United States Forest Service
Helicopters, **6** 1071
United States Geodetic Satellite Program
Explorer satellites, **5** 771
United States Geological Survey
Astrogeology, **2** 210
United States Marine Corps
Air forces of the world, **1** 65
Marine Corps Aviation, **8** 1481
United States Naval Air Force
Naval aviation, worldwide, **9** 1667
United States Naval Aviation, 13 2376-90 (with pictures)
United States Naval Observatory
Air Almanac, **1** 42
United States Navy
Aerology, **1** 25
Aerospace industry, **1** 28
Aircraft carriers, **1** 46-51
Air forces of the world, **1** 65
Airships (picture), **1** 112
Antisubmarine missiles, **1** 160
Attack aircraft, **2** 273
Blimps, **2** 365, 366
NORAD, **9** 1701
United States Navy Transit system
Navigation satellites, **9** 1673
United States Strike Command, 13 2390-91
United States Weather Bureau
Aviation weather, **2** 298
Unit of measure
Energy, **4** 712
Measurement of power, **8** 1518
Universal Law of Gravitation
Celestial mechanics, **3** 426, 428
Universal Postal Union
International airmail, **7** 1188
United Nations, **13** 2357
Universe, 13 2391-92
Radio astronomy, **10** 1891
University Aviation Association, 13 2392
National Intercollegiate Flying Association, **9** 1664
Unmanned balloons
Balloons, **2** 324
Unmanned exploration of deep space
Jet Propulsion Laboratory, **7** 1240
Unmanned interplanetary probes
Interplanetary travel, **7** 1208, (table) 1213
Lunar exploration, **8** 1404-05
Unmanned tests
Apollo, **1** 166-67
Unscheduled flights
Air taxis, **1** 117
Unsymmetrical dimethylhydrazine
Apollo, **1** 173
Delta rocket, **4** 622
Upper air research
Piccard family, **10** 1791
Upper atmosphere
Radar, **10** 1879
Sounding rockets (with performance chart), **11** 2082
Upper atmosphere maps
Aviation weather, **2** 299
Upper camber
Airplane, **1** 85
Upper route airway
Airway, **1** 141
Uprated Saturn I booster
Apollo, **1** 164, 169 (with diagram and picture)
Apollo Applications Program, **2** 185
Launch vehicles, **7** 1319-20
Upside-down transfer
Barnstormers (picture), **2** 336
Upson, Ralph
Balloons, **2** 322, 330
Upstairs lounge
Jumbo jets, **7** 1251
Ural-2
Blimps, **2** 366
Uraniborg
Astronomy (picture), **2** 239

Uranium
Nuclear energy, **9** 1710
Piccard family, **10** 1790
Uranium-235
Nuclear energy, **9** 1710-11
Uranus, (planet) **13** 2392
Adams, John Couch, **1** 6
Astronomy, **2** 242, 243, 246
Atmosphere, **2** 265
Bessel, Friedrich Wilhelm, **2** 354
Celestial mechanics, **3** 428
Earth, **4** 663
Extraterrestrial life, **5** 777
Flamsteed, John, **5** 828
Legal implications of aerospace, **7** 1331
Leverrier, Urbain J. J., **7** 1334
Planets, **10** 1820
Pluto, **10** 1827
Urbanowicz, W.
World War II (table), **14** 2517
Urethane
Airships, **1** 108
Paints, **10** 1754
Urey, Harold Clayton (1893-   , American chemist), **13** 2393
Extraterrestrial life, **5** 775
Uruguay
Crop dusting, **4** 587
South and Central America's aviation, **11** 2091
USAF Aeronautical Chart and Information Center, 13 2374
USAF Museum, 13 2374-75
USAF Security Service
United States Air Force, **13** 2371
USAF Southern Command
United States Air Force, **13** 2371
U.S. Air Force Academy
United States Air Force, **13** 2371
USCG, see United States Coast Guard
Useful consciousness
Aviation medicine, **2** 293
Useful load, 13 2394
Piloting techniques, **10** 1801
Weight and balance, **13** 2472
USS, see name of ship
U.S.S.R. aerospace activities, 13 2327-44, (with pictures, tables) (see also Russia)
UTA, see Unions de Transportes Aeriens
Utility Airplane Council, 13 2394
Utility aviation, 13 2394-96 (with pictures)
Utilization of space technology
Implications of aerospace, **7** 1151
Utricle organ
Man in flight, **8** 1447
Uwins, C. F.
Altitude and altitude records, **1** 147

V

V-1 missile
Aircraft propulsion systems, **1** 58-59
Missiles, **9** 1611, (picture) 1612, (data table) 1616
Peenemuende, **10** 1770
Pulsejet engine, **10** 1866
Second World War aircraft, **11** 2038
World War II, **14** 2519-20
V-2 rocket missile, 13 2445-46
Animals in space, **1** 153
Bumper Project, **3** 390

(Continued)

V-2 rocket missile (Cont.)
 Cryogenics, **4** 597
 Dornberger, Walter Robert, **4** 646
 Ehricke, Krafft Arnold, **4** 680
 Inertial guidance, **7** 1152
 Liquid oxygen, **8** 1363
 Military aviation, **9** 1586
 Missiles, **9** 1611, (data table) 1616
 Model rocketry, **9** 1627
 Oberth, Hermann, **10** 1721
 Peenemuende, **10** 1770, (picture) 1771
 Rockets and rocketry, **11** 1979
 Second World War aircraft, **11** 2038
V-12 engine
 Aircraft propulsion systems (picture), **1** 53
VAB, see Vehicle assembly building
Vacuum
 Electronics, **4** 692
 Rockets and rocketry, **11** 1977
Vacuum chamber, 13 2398
 Kerwin, Joseph P., **7** 1276
Vacuum steel
 Steels, **12** 2165
Vacuum tubes, 13 2398-99
 Radio, **10** 1887
 Semiconductors, **11** 2042
Vacuum ultraviolet region
 U.S. Atomic Energy Commission, **13** 2375
Vagabond
 Piper, William T., **10** 1815
Valence electron
 Atoms, **2** 270
 Semiconductors, **11** 2041
Valencia, Eugene
 World War II (table), **14** 2517
Valentine, W. J.
 Distance records, **4** 641
Valier, Max
 Rockets and rocketry, **11** 1978
Valkyrie, see XB-70
Valve-in-head engine
 Aircraft propulsion system **1** 55
Valve, intake
 Reciprocating engines, **11** 1916
Valve rope
 Balloons, **2** 327
Valves, function
 Reciprocating engines, **11** 1916
Vampire T.Mk 5 (de Havilland)
 Asia's aviation, 205
Vampyr (glider)
 Gliders, **6** 985
Van Allen, James Alfred (1914- ,
 American physicist), **13** 2399
 Atmosphere, **2** 265
 Explorer satellites, **5** 761
 Military space program, **9** 1593
Van Allen radiation belts, 13 2399-2402
 Argus project, artificial, **2** 191
 Astronomy, **2** 249
 Atmosphere, **2** 263, 265
 Aurora, **2** 277
 Earth, **4** 662
 Explorer satellites, **5** 761
 International Geophysical Year, **7** 1196
 Jupiter, **7** 1260
 Military space program, **9** 1593
 Radiation, **10** 1883
 Sounding rockets, **11** 2079
 Space, **11** 2093
 Sputnik, **12** 2153, 2154
van de Hulst, H.C.
 Radio astronomy, **10** 1890
Vandenberg Air Force Base, 13 2402
Vandenberg, Hoyt Sanford (1899-1954,
 American Air Force Chief of Staff) **13** 2402
 United States Air Force, **13** 2365
Vander Beek, Pamela
 Worden, Alfred M., **14** 2497
Van der Wal, Franki
 Women in aerospace, **14** 2496
Vanes
 Arrow, **2** 202
 Launch vehicles, **7** 1316
Vanguard (with pictures), **13** 2403-04
 Bumper Project, **3** 389

 Earth science, **4** 666, 667
 Environmental research satellites, **4** 722
 Explorer satellites, **5** 762
 Goddard Space Flight Center, **6** 992
 International Geophysical Year, **7** 1196
 Launch vehicle, **7** 1322, 1326
 Military space program, **9** 1592 (with
  picture)
 NASA, **9** 1650, (table) 1652
 Satellites, **11** 2006
 United Kingdom aerospace activities,
  13 2347
 Weather satellites, **13** 2459-60, (table)
  2470
Vanguard I
 Communications satellites, **3** 532
 Earth, **4** 660
 International Geophysical Year (picture),
  7 1196
Vanguard 3
 Military space program (picture), **9** 1592
Vanguard turboprop aircraft
 Canada's aviation, **3** 401
Van Kirk, Patricia M.
 Musgrave, Franklin Story, **9** 1643
Van Orman
 Balloons, **2** 322
Van Vliet, Cornelius
 World War II (table), **14** 2517
Vapor lock
 Fuels, **5** 901
Vapor pressure
 Oxidizers, **10** 1752
Vapor trails
 Contrail, **3** 563
Variable coast
 Launch vehicles (diagram), **7** 1318
Variable geometry (with picture), **13** 2405
 F-111 variable-wing fighter, **5** 870
 Supersonic flight, **12** 2177
Variable stability system
 X-series aerospace vehicles, **14** 2544
Variable stars
 Astrophysics, **2** 257
Variation
 Compasses, **3** 547
 Isogonic lines, **7** 1216
Variometers, 13 2405
 Gliders, **6** 985
 Soaring, **11** 2062-63
Varney Air Lines
 Commercial airlines, **3** 510
Varney Speed Lines
 Commercial airlines, **3** 509
Varnished silk
 Balloons, **2** 316, 321
Vatican
 Communications satellites, **3** 538
Vaughan, George
 World War I (table, Top Aces), **14** 2507
Vaulx, Count Henri de la
 Balloons, **2** 318
Vauquelin, Louis
 Beryllium, **2** 354
Vautour
 Air forces of the world (France), **1** 65
 Israeli-Arab Conflict (picture), **7** 1218
Vauxhall balloon
 Balloons, **2** 318
VC10, see Super VC10
Vee-Balloon
 Balloons, **2** 324
Vega, see Lockheed Vega
Vehicle assembly building
 Apollo, **1** 178
 Blockhouse, **2** 368
 Kennedy Space Center, **7** 1269 (with
  picture)
 Launch facilities, **7** 1307
 Launching, **7** 1309
 NASA, **9** 1654
Vehicle attitude
 Attitude and attitude control, **2** 275
 Inertial guidance, **7** 1155
Vehicle-borne equipment
 Radar, **10** 1876

Vehicle-configuration research
 Oceanographic research, **10** 1734
Vehicle research spacecraft, 13 2406
Vehicle stability
 Guidance and control systems, **6** 1033
 Launch vehicles, **7** 1316
Veil-like ring
 Astronomy, **2** 246
Vela Hotel
 Nuclear detection satellites, **9** 1707
Vela satellite
 Abrahamson, James A., **1** 2
 Atlas missile and launch vehicle, **2** 260
 Military space program, **9** 1597-98 (with
  picture)
 Nuclear detection satellites, **9** 1707-09
  (with pictures and diagrams)
 U.S. Atomic Energy Commission, **13** 2375
Vela IV
 Microcircuitry (picture), **9** 1562
Vela Sierra
 Nuclear detection satellites, **9** 1707
Vela Uniform
 Nuclear detection satellites, **9** 1707
Velcro
 Terminology of aerospace (table), **12** 2272
Velocity
 Acceleration, **1** 2-3
 Inertial guidance, **7** 1152
 Instrument panels, **7** 1177
 Interplanetary travel, **7** 1210
 Kinetic energy, **7** 1277
 Launch vehicles, **7** 1322
 Light, **8** 1351
 Motion, **9** 1640
 Nozzles, **9** 1707
 Oceanographic research, **10** 1732
 Orbits and trajectories, **10** 1742
 Plasma propulsion, **10** 1823
 Radar, **10** 1872
 Relativity theory, **11** 1949
 Sound (table), **11** 2077
 Spaceflight principles, **12** 2105, 2106,
  (table) 2108
 Speed and speed records, **12** 2140
Velocity microphone
 Microphone, **9** 1563
Venera spacecraft (see Venus spacecraft)
Venezuela
 Crop dusting, **4** 593
 South and Central America's aviation,
  11 2091
Venkaturaman
 Astronomy, **2** 242
Venturi tubes, 13 2406
 Bernoulli's principle, **2** 353
 Carburetion, **3** 408
 Reciprocating engines, **11** 1918
Venus, 13 2406-09 (with pictures)
 Astronomy, **2** 235, 241, 242, 243
 Atmosphere, **2** 265, 266
 Carbon dioxide, **3** 408
 Celestial mechanics, **3** 427, 428
 Conjunction, **3** 560
 Earth, **4** 659, 663, 666
 Extraterrestrial life, **5** 777
 Infrared radiation, **7** 1162
 Interplanetary travel, **7** 1208-09
 Lowell, Percival, **8** 1374
 Mariner probes, **8** 1485-89, (table) 1486
 Orbits and trajectories, **10** 1742, 1747
 Pioneer, **10** 1812
 Planets, **10** 1820
 Quantum theory, **10** 1870
 Radar, **10** 1878
 Solar system, **11** 2070
 U.S.S.R. aerospace activities, **13** 2342-43
Venus (rocket)
 Aerobee, **1** 17
 Agena rockets, **1** 38
Venus (or **Venera**) (spacecraft)
 Astronomy (table), **2** 242, 243
 Interplanetary travel (with picture), **7** 1212
 U.S.S.R. aerospace activities, **13** 2342
 Venus, **13** 2407, 2408

Venusian hydrogen corona
Mariner probes, **8** 1489
Verdin, Lt. Cdr. J. B.
Speed and speed records (table), **12** 2141
Vernal equinox
Astronomy, **2** 240
Equinox, **4** 729
Verne, Jules (1828-1905, French author),
13 2410
Piccard family, **10** 1790
Science fiction, **11** 2017-20
Vernier engines
Surveyor, **12** 2211, 2213-15
Vertical ascent
Orbits and trajectories, **10** 1744
Vertical attitude gyro
Automatic pilot, **2** 288
Vertical axis
Airplane, **1** 87
Attitude and attitude control, **2** 275
Axes of rotation, **2** 308
Yaw, **14** 2547
Vertical circles
Celestial sphere, **3** 431
Vertical fins
Empennage, **4** 709, 710
PILOT, **10** 1794
Rudder, **11** 1998
Vertical flight
Convertiplane, **3** 565
Vertical Flight Foundation
American Helicopter Society, **1** 150
Vertical-lift aircraft
Aerospace industry, **1** 33
Autogiros (picture), **2** 285
Commercial airlines, **3** 515
Helicopters, **6** 1061
V/STOL aircraft, **13** 2439
Vertical movement
Instrument flight techniques, **7** 1167
Vertical needle
Omni navigation, **10** 1737
Vertical probe
Sounding rockets, **11** 2079
Vertical-scale display instruments (with
pictures), **13** 2410-11
Vertical separation
Air traffic control, **1** 127
Vertical speed indicator (picture), **13** 2411-12
Instrument flight techniques, **7** 1167
Pitot-static system, **10** 1816
Vertical stabilizer
Airplane, **1** 86
Jumbo jets, **7** 1249
Vertical takeoff and landing, see VTOL
Vertical visibility
Instrument landing categories, **7** 1169
Vertifan
V/STOL aircraft, **13** 2442
Vertiflite Magazine
American Helicopter Society, **1** 150
Vertijet, see X-13 Vertijet
V/STOL aircraft, **13** 2439
Vertiplane (Ryan)
V/STOL aircraft, **13** 2439
Vertiports
Heliports, **6** 1079
Vertol, see Boeing-Vertol
Verville-Packard
Air racing, **1** 102
Very high frequency omnirange
Omni navigation, **10** 1736
Radio communications, **10** 1894
Very high frequency radio, 13 2412
Airborne antennas, **1** 42-43
Air traffic control, **1** 128, 136
Applications Technology Satellites, **2** 190
Avionics, **2** 307
Beacon, radio, **2** 345
Radio communications, **10** 1894, 1896,
(diagram) 1896
Space communications, **11** 2098
Very long baseline interferometer
Radio astronomy, **10** 1893
Vesta
Asteroids, **2** 207, 208

Astronomy, **2** 245
Vestibular sense
Man in flight, **8** 1446-47, (diagrams)
1447, 1448
Veterans Administration
National Aviation Trades Association,
9 1663
VFR, see Visual Flight Rules
VHF, see Very high frequency
Vibration, 13 2412-13
Environmental simulators, **4** 726
Observatories, **10** 1723
Quality control, **10** 1868
Radar, **10** 1872
Rocket propulsion systems, **11** 1967
Vibration of atoms
Infrared radiation, **7** 1162
Vibration testing
Manned Spacecraft Center, **8** 1459
Vibration-test stands
Cosmonauts, **4** 570
Vibrators
Environmental simulators, **4** 727
Vickers aircraft
First World War aircraft, **5** 816, 820,
(picture) 815
World War I, **14** 2504
Vickers Aircraft Company
Alcock and Brown, **1** 142
Vickers Gunbus
World War I, **14** 2502
Vickers machine gun
World War I (picture), **14** 2508
Vickers-Supermarine, see Sea Eagle
Vickers-Supermarine Spitfire
(see also Spitfire)
Second World War aircraft, **11** 2030
Vickers Super VC10, see Super VC10
Vickers Vanguard
Commercial air transports (picture),
3 524, 526
Vickers-Vimy (with picture)
Alcock and Brown, **1** 142
World War I, **14** 2510
Vickers Viscount, 13 2413
Africa's aviation, **1** 36, 37
Asia's aviation, **2** 204
Canada's aviation, **3** 401
Commercial air transports (picture),
3 524, 525, 526
History of aviation, **6** 1116
Mainland China's aerospace activities,
8 1428
United Kingdom aerospace activities,
13 2347
Vickers Wellington
Wallis, Sir Barnes Neville, **13** 2448
Victa Aircruiser
Australia's aviation (picture), **2** 278
Victor Airways System
Navigation systems, **9** 1675
Victor Mk-2, see Handley Page Victor Mk-2
Victor V-bomber
United Kingdom aerospace activities,
13 2347
Victor, W.
Astronomy, **2** 242
Victory Through Air Power, (book)
De Seversky, Alexander Procofieff, **4** 628
Video cameras
Oceanographic research, **10** 1732
Video signal
Television, **12** 2260, 2263
Vidicon
Electronics, **4** 699
Photography, **10** 1787
Vietnam (with pictures), **13** 2414-23
Army aviation, **2** 196
Asia's aviation, **2** 204
Attack aircraft, **2** 273
Chinook, CH-47, **3** 458
Coast Guard aviation, **3** 479
Helicopters, **6** 1072
History of aviation, **6** 1118

Marine Corps Aviation, **8** 1483, (pictures)
1482-83
Phantom II, McDonnell-Douglas F-4A,
10 1777
Rescue and Recovery Service, **11** 1958
Strategic Air Command, **12** 2168
United States Air Force, **13** 2369
Viet Cong, **13** 2414, 2415, 2419, 2423
Viet Minh, **13** 2415
Vieux Charles
World War I, **14** 2505
Viewfinder
Aerial photography, **1** 9
Viggen 37 Thunderbolt (Saab)
Air forces of the world, **1** 65
Fighter aircraft, **5** 811
Sweden's aviation, **12** 2224
Vigilante, see A-5 Vigilante
Vignoli, Ferrucio
Distance records, **4** 641
Viking (rocket)
American Rocket Society, **1** 151
Explorer satellites, **5** 762
Vikrant
Asia's aviation, **2** 204
Viper 522 engines
Bird flight, **2** 359
Virgo
Astronomy, **2** 253
Constellations, **3** 562
Viscosity, 13 2424
Aerodynamics, **1** 22
Lubricants, **8** 1375
Viscount, see Vickers Viscount
Vishniac, Wolf (1922-
German-American scientist), **13** 2424
Visible light
Infrared radiation, **7** 1162
Light, **8** 1350
Radiation, **10** 1881
X-rays, **14** 2533
Visible radiation
Radiation, **10** 1880
Visibility, 13 2425
Bird flight, **2** 359
Instrument landing categories, **7** 1169
Observatories, **10** 1725
Rain, **10** 1900
Smog, **11** 2059
Snow, **11** 2062
Visual Flight Rules, **13** 2425
Weather, **13** 2450
Vision, loss of
Blackout, **2** 362
Visor nose
Jumbo jets, **7** 1248
Visual binaries
Astrophysics, **2** 257
Visual contrast phenomenon
Mars, **8** 1490
Visual Emergency Signals
Emergency signals (table), **4** 708-09
Visual flight
Bush flying, **3** 393
Charts, **3** 450
Visual Flight Rules, 13 2425-26
Airports, **1** 96
Air traffic control, **1** 126-28, 134-35
Australia's aviation, **2** 284
Aviation weather, **2** 300
Charts, **3** 450
Contact flying, **3** 563
Control tower, **3** 564
Course plotting, **4** 578-79
Federal Aviation Regulations, **5** 802
Flight management, **5** 843
Flight plan, **5** 847
Navigation techniques, **9** 1681-83
Flight service stations, **5** 849
Hemisphere rules, **6** 1081
Inflight emergency procedures, **7** 1155
Radio communications, **10** 1897
Weather, **13** 2450
Visual magnitude
Astronomy, **2** 249
Magnitude, **8** 1420

Visual observation
Reconnaissance aircraft, **11** 1921
Visual omnirange (with pictures), **13** 2426-28
Africa's aviation, **1** 37
Airborne antennas, **1** 43
Air traffic control (picture), **1** 128, 129, 136
Automatic direction finder, **2** 287
Avionics, **2** 307
Distance Measuring Equipment, **4** 642
Federal airways system, **5** 792
Flight director, **5** 840
Ground antennas, **6** 1016
Holding patterns, **6** 1122
Instrument flight techniques, **7** 1166
Navigation systems, **9** 1674-81
Navigation techniques, **9** 1683-85
Omni navigation, **10** 1736
Radio navigation, **10** 1899
Tactical air navigation, **12** 2930
Visual Omnirange/Tactical Air Navigation,
see VORTAC
Visual sense
Man in flight, **8** 1446-47
Visual signals
Panel code, **10** 1755
Vitrification
Ceramics, **3** 439
VLF antennas
Italy's aerospace activities, **7** 1223
Vne
Limiting airspeed, **8** 1358
Vocational high schools
Educational implications of aerospace, **4**
675
Voenno-Vozdushny Sily
Air forces of the world, **1** 64
Voice Communications System
Mission Contol Center, **9** 1618
Space communications, **11** 2098
Voisin aircraft
Delagrange, Leon, **4** 621
First World War aircraft (picture), **5** 823
World War I, **14** 2504
Voisin, Gabriel (1880- , French aircraft
manufacturer), **13** 2428-29
Archdeacon, Ernest, **2** 190
Bleriot, Louis, **2** 363
History of aviation, **6** 1101, (table) 1119
Volk, Julia Ann
Gibson, Edward G., **6** 980
Volant, Vaisseau
Blanchard, Jean Pierre Francois, **2** 363
Volcanoes
International Geophysical Year, **7** 1195
Voltage
Battery, **2** 338
Electricity, **4** 684
Voltage change
Pressure gauges, **10** 1850
Voltmeter
Accelerometer, **1** 3
Volume
Matter, **8** 1515
Von Braun, Wernher (1912- , German-
American aerospace engineer), **13** 2429
Bumper Project, **3** 390
Debus, Kurt Heinrich, **4** 612
Electric propulsion, **4** 685
Explorer satellites, **5** 762
Marshall Space Flight Center, **8** 1494
Medals and decorations (table), **8** 1526
NASA, **9** 1650
Peenemuende, **10** 1770-71
Rockets and rocketry, **11** 1978-79
Second World War aircraft, **11** 2038
World War II, **14** 2519-20
Von Karman, Theodore (1881-1963,
Hungarian-American physicist), **13**
2430-31
Jet-assisted takeoff, **7** 1236
Military aviation, **9** 1586
Program management, **10** 1857
Rockets and rocketry, **11** 1982

Von Neumann, John (1903-1957, Hungarian-
American mathematician), **13** 2431
Computers, **3** 557
Program management, **10** 1857
Von Ohain, Hans-Joachim Pabst (1911-
German-American aeronautical
engineer), **13** 2431
Jet aircraft, **7** 1235
Von Opel, Fritz
Peenemuende, **10** 1770
Rockets and rocketry, **11** 1978
Voodoo, see F-101 Voodoo
VOR, see Visual Omnidirectional range
VOR/ILS navigation system
Navigation systems (diagram), **9** 1676
Voroshilov (dirigible)
Commemorative stamps and medals,
3 494
VORTAC, 13 2432 (with picture)
Africa's aviation, **1** 37
Air traffic control, **1** 128
Avionics, **2** 307
Beacon, radio, **2** 345
Distance Measuring Equipment, **4** 642
Federal airways system, **5** 792
Instrument flight techniques, **7** 1166
Navigation systems, **9** 1679
Omni navigation, **10** 1736-37
Vortex generator, 13 2433
Aerodynamics (picture), **1** 24
Voskhod, 13 2433-34
Belyayev, Pavel, **2** 349
Cosmonauts, **4** 572, (picture) 571, (table)
574
Komarov, Vladimir M., **7** 1282
Launch vehicles, **7** 1326
Manned spaceflight (table), **8** 1461
Soyuz, **11** 2091
U.S.S.R. aerospace activities, **13** 2344
Yegorov, Boris, **14** 2548
Voss, Werner
Fokker DR-1 triplane, **5** 869
World War I, **14** 2506, 2507 (with table)
Vostok (with picture), **13** 2434-35
Bykovsky, Valeri, **3** 397
Cosmonauts (table), **4** 574
Kosmos satellites, **7** 1290
Launch vehicles, **7** 1326
Manned spaceflight (table), **8** 1461
Nikolayev, Andrian G., **9** 1696
Nikolayeva-Tereshkova, Valentina, **9** 1697
Popovich, Pavel, **10** 1838
Soyuz, **11** 2091
Sputniks, **12** 2155
Tracking systems and networks, **13** 2302
U.S.S.R. aerospace activities, **13** 2343
Vought F4U, see F4U Corsair
Voyager (with pictures), **13** 2436-37
Earth science, **4** 666
Interplanetary travel, **7** 1208
Voyager capsule
Spacecraft sterilization (with picture),
11 2104
V/STOL aircraft, 13 2438-44 (with charts,
pictures, diagrams)
Aerodynamics, **1** 25
Airbus, **1** 44
Air forces of the world, **1** 64
Air taxis, **1** 118
Helicopters, **6** 1067
International projects, **7** 1200
NASA, **9** 1653
Rotary-wing aircraft, **11** 1991
Ryan, T. Claude, **11** 1999
United Kingdom aerospace activities,
13 2350, 2352
United States Air Force, **13** 2374
United States Naval Aviation, **13** 2390
Variable geometry, **13** 2405
West Germany's aerospace activities,
13 2478, 2479
X-series aerospace vehicles, **14** 2541, 2542
V-tail
Airplane **1** 87-88
Empennage, **4** 710

VTOL (see also V/STOL aircraft)
Airships, **1** 114
American Helicopter Society, **1** 150
Canada's aviation, **3** 404
Fighter aircraft, **5** 810
Camm, Sir Sydney, **3** 398
Guidance and control systems, **6** 1040
Helicopters, **6** 1067
History of aviation, **6** 1120
Langley Research Center, **7** 1302
V/STOL aircraft, **13** 2438
V-type engine
Aircraft propulsion systems (with
diagram), **1** 55
Levavasseur, Leon, **7** 1333
Reciprocating engines, **11** 1913-14
Vuia, Trajan (1872-1950, Hungarian-French
air pioneer), **13** 2446
Vulcan, see BMk 2 Vulcan
Vulcan
Leverrier, Urbain, J. J., **7** 1334
Vulcan 20mm cannon
Air defense systems, **1** 61
Vulpecula
Astronomy, **2** 248
Vultee BT-13, see BT-13
V-weapons
World War II, **14** 2519-20

W

WAC Corporal rocket
Bumper Project (picture), **3** 389, 390
Waco
Crop dusting, **4** 588
Wade, Lance
World War II (table), **14** 2517
WAFS, see Women's Auxiliary Ferrying
Squadron
Wake
Ballistic Missile Early Warning System,
2 314
Walker, Joseph Albert (1921-66, American
aviator), **13** 2447
Altitude and altitude records, **1** 147, 148
Test pilots and test flying, **12** 2280
X-15 research program, **14** 2530, 2533
Walker, Mary
Garriott, Owen K., **5** 914
Walker, Thomas
Man-powered flight, **8** 1465, (diagrams)
1465
Walk in space, 13 2447
Aldrin, Edwin E., Jr., **1** 142
Astronaut maneuvering unit, **2** 213
Belyayev, Pavel, **2** 349
Cernan, Eugene Andrew, **3** 440
Cosmonauts, **4** 569, 574
Life-support systems, **8** 1341
Wallace, Dwane
Cessna, Clyde V., **3** 445
Walleye
Air-to-surface missiles, **1** 124
Bombs (picture), **3** 378
Wallis, Sir Barnes Neville (1887- .
British aeronautical engineer),
13 2447-48
United Kingdom aerospace activities,
13 2348
Wallops Station
Explorer satellites, **5** 767
NASA, **9** 1657

Walter, Hellmuth
Aircraft propulsion systems, **1** 59
Jet-assisted takeoff, **7** 1236
Wankel engine
Aircraft propulsion systems, **1** 59
Wankel, Felix
Rotating combustion engine, **11** 1993
War Air Service Pattern
Airlift, **1** 67
National emergency airlift plans, **9** 1663
Warfare Systems School
Air University, **1** 140
Warhawk, see P-40
Warhead, 13 2448
Intercontinental ballistic missiles, **7** 1182
Launch vehicles, **7** 1314
Missiles (table), **9** 1616
Radar, **10** 1879
Warm front
Aviation weather, **2** 305
Warner, Ed P.
Medals and decorations (table), **8** 1526
Warner, J. W.
Kingsford-Smith, Charles, **7** 1277
Warning lights
Instrument panels, **7** 1177
War of the Worlds, The (book)
Wells, Herbert George, **13** 2474
War Production Board
Loening, Grover Cleveland, **8** 1369
Wash in
Torque, **12** 2295
Washington, George
Airmail, **1** 69
Blanchard, Jean Pierre Francois, **2** 363
Washington National Airport
Airports, **1** 98
WASP, see War Air Service Pattern
WASP, see Women's Air Force Pilots
Wasp (ship)
Television, **12** 2263
United States Naval Aviation, **13** 2380-81,
(picture), 2387
Wasp Major
Aircraft propulsion systems, **1** 56
Wasserfall
Missiles, **9** 1611
Surface-to-air missiles, **12** 2200,
(picture), 2199
Waste management
Life-support systems, **8** 1343-44
Man in flight, **8** 1451
Water
Air, **1** 42
Environmental control system, **4** 719
Extraterrestrial life, **5** 776
Fuel cells, **5** 894-96
Lunar bases, **8** 1387
Mars, **8** 1492
Water brake
Rocket sled (with picture), **11** 1986
Water deluge system
Kennedy Space Center, **7** 1272
Water desalination plants
Aerospace industry, **1** 33
Water egress training, see Water Survival
Water protection
Personal equipment, **10** 1775
Water survival
Astronauts, **2** 227
Watertight compartments
Pontoons, **10** 1838
Water vapor
Atmosphere, **2** 261
Jupiter, **7** 1260
Watkins, George E.
Altitude and altitude records, **1** 147
Watt
Electricity, **4** 684
Measurement of power, **8** 1519
Wave drag
Aerodynamics, **1** 24
Wavefronts
Lasers, **7** 1306

Wavelength, 13 2448
Electromagnetism, **4** 689
Lasers, **7** 1304
Planck's Law, **10** 1817
Radar, **10** 1872
Television, **12** 2260
Wave motion
Oceanographic research, **10** 1732
Wave of darkening
Mars, **8** 1492
Wave packet
Quantum theory (with diagram), **10** 1869
Wave-particle nature
Light, **8** 1350-51
Wave Propagation Laboratory
Environmental Science Services
Administration, **4** 725
Waves
Radar, **10** 1872
Radio, **10** 1885
Sound (with diagram), **11** 2078
Wave soaring
Soaring, **11** 2062, 2065
Wave theory
Quantum theory (with diagram), **10** 1868
WE (book)
Lindbergh, Charles Augustus, **8** 1360
Weaponry, 13 2448-49 (with pictures)
Weapons delivery
Avionics, **2** 307
Weapons Research Establishment
Woomera rocket range, **14** 2496
Weapons Research Establishment Satellite,
see WRESAT-1
Weapon systems
Air forces of the world, **1** 64
Weather, 13 2449-53 (with pictures)
Air traffic control, **1** 134
American Meteorological Society, **1** 150
Applications Technology Satellites, **2** 189
Aviation weather, **2** 298-306
Bush flying, **3** 392
Pilot training, **10** 1810
Preflight training, **10** 1847
Reconnaissance (airborne), **11** 1920-21
Space weather, **12** 2138
Weather satellites, **13** 2459-71
Weather balloons
Earth science, **4** 666
Meteorology (picture), **9** 1556
Weather briefing
Aviation weather, **2** 298, 305
Briefing, **3** 388
Weather Bureau, 13 2454
Aviation weather, **2** 303
Crash investigation, **4** 581
Electronics, **4** 704
Environmental Science Services
Administration, **4** 724
National Environmental Satellite Center,
9 1664
Plan position indicator, **10** 1822
Preflight training, **10** 1848
Satellites, **11** 2007
Weather forecasting
Aerospace, **1** 27
Apollo, **1** 163
Barometer, **2** 337
Weather information boards
Passenger services, **10** 1765
Weather maps and charts, 13 2454-58
(with charts, maps, pictures)
Aviation weather, **2** 299, 306
Communications satellites, **3** 543
Meteorology (picture), **9** 1558
Weather radar echoes
Aviation weather, **2** 300
Weather reports
Flight service stations, **5** 851
Pilot weather reports, **10** 1812
Weather satellites, 13 2459-71 (with
pictures, table)
Discoverer Project, **4** 634
ESSA spacecraft, **4** 739
Flight recorder, **5** 849
Infrared detection devices, **7** 1159

Legal implications of aerospace, **7** 1331
Meteorology, **9** 1557, 1558
Military implications of space, **9** 1589
NASA, **9** 1653
National Environmental Satellite Center,
9 1664
Satellites, **11** 2006
Weather maps and charts, **13** 2458
Weather ships
Air traffic control, **1** 135
Weather survey
Infrared radiation, **7** 1162
Weather teletype network
Aviation weather, **2** 299
Webb, James E. (1906- , Administrator,
National Aeronautics and Space
Administration), **13** 2471
Orbiting observatories, **10** 1741
Webb, T. H.
Airmail, **1** 70
Weber, Caroline
Henize, Dr. Karl G., **6** 1082
Webster (airplane)
Crop dusting, **4** 589
Wedell, James R.
Speed and speed records (table), **12** 2141
Wedell-Williams Special No. 25
Air racing (picture), **1** 103
Weigel, Erhardt
Planetarium, **10** 1818
Weight and balance, 13 2471-72
Aerodynamics (with diagram), **1** 20
Ballistic trajectory, **2** 314
Center of gravity, **3** 435-37
Estimates
Spacecraft design, **11** 2102
Gravity, **6** 1011
Icing, **7** 1145
Load factor, **8** 1365
Materials, **8** 1501
Paints, **10** 1754
Payload, **10** 1769
Production, **10** 1856
Weight control procedure
Spacecraft design, **11** 2102
Weight factor
Sonic boom, **11** 2075
Weightlessness (with picture), **13** 2472-73
Biosatellites, **2** 358
Centrifugal and centripetal forces, **3** 437
Gravity, **6** 1011-13
Kosmos satellites, **7** 1293
Man in flight, **8** 1447
Space biology, **11** 2094-95
Spaceflight training, **12** 2115
Weight-saving
Propellants, **10** 1861
Weiser, Rene
Distance records, **4** 640
Weitz, Paul J. (1932- , American
astronaut), **13** 2473-74
Astronauts, **2** 217, 218, 219 (with picture)
Wellington bomber, see Vickers Wellington
Wells, Herbert George (1866-1946, English
novelist, historian), **13** 2474
Science fiction, **11** 2017
Welsh, Edward C. (1909- , American
economist, aerospace executive),
13 2474
Economic implications of aerospace, **4** 672
Wendel, Fritz
Speed and speed records (table), **12** 2141
Wenham, F. H.
History of aviation, **6** 1095, (table) 1119
Weninger, Joan
Brand, Vance DeVoe, **3** 388
Werner, Johannes
Copernicus, Nicolaus, **3** 566
West Berlin
Berlin airlift, **2** 351
Westerly patterns
Jet streams, **7** 1241
Western Air Express
Airmail, **1** 77
Commercial airlines, **3** 509, 510

Western Airlines
   Commercial airlines, **3** 497, 498
Western Canada Airways
   Balchen, Bernt, **2** 312
   Bush flying, **3** 392
Western Electric Company
   Antiballistic missile defense, **1** 159
Western Test Range, 13 2474
   International Satellite for Ionospheric
    Studies, **7** 1201
   Military space program, **9** 1602
   Missile test ranges, **9** 1617
   Vandenberg Air Force Base, **13** 2402
West Ford
   Communications satellites, **3** 535
   Space garbage, **12** 2119
Western Indian Aerial Express
   Commercial airlines, **3** 508
West Germany's aerospace activities,
   (with pictures), **13** 2475-80
   Air forces of the world, **1** 63, 66
   Communications satellites, **3** 538
   European Launcher Development
    Organization, **4** 754
   European Space Research Organization,
    4 755
   Italy's aerospace activities, **7** 1222
   NATO, **9** 1703-04
West Germany Federal Ministry for
   Scientific Research
   International projects, **7** 1198
Westinghouse Electric Corporation
   Antisubmarine missiles, **1** 160
Westland Mk-1 Wasp (helicopter)
   Helicopters (table), **6** 1068
Westland Scout (helicopter)
   Helicopters (picture), **6** 1077
Westland Wessex (helicopter)
   Naval aviation, worldwide (United
    Kingdom), **9** 1669, (picture) 1668
   United Kingdom aerospace activities, **13**
    2353, (picture) 2352
Westland Whirlwind (helicopter)
   General aviation aircraft (picture), **6** 965
West longitude
   Latitude and longitude, **7** 1307
West Point
   Service academies, **11** 2044
Wet cell battery, 13 2480
Wetmore, Ray
   World War II (table), **14** 2517
Wheat seedlings
   Biosatellites, **2** 356
Wheeled Rovers
   Lunar exploration, **8** 1403-04
Wheel landing
   Landing techniques, **7** 1301
   Re-entry vehicles, **11** 1935
Wheels, 13 2480
   Airplane, **1** 89
Whipple, Fred J.
   Comets, **3** 490
Whirling arm
   Cayley, Sir George, **3** 425
Whirly Girls, 13 2481
   Women in aerospace, **14** 2495
Whiskers
   Metals and metallurgy, **9** 1554, (picture)
    1549
Whitcomb, Richard T. (1921-   , American
   aeronautical engineer), **13** 2482
   Delta Dagger, **4** 621
White, Alvin S.
   Test pilots and test flying, **12** 2280
White, Barbara V.
   Young, John W., **14** 2548
White dwarf stars
   Astronomy, **2** 251
   Binary stars, **2** 355
   Relativity theory, **11** 1953
   Stars, **12** 2160
White, Edward H., II (1930-   ,
   American astronaut), **13** 2482
   Apollo, (with picture) **1** 168
   Astronauts, **2** 216, 217, 219, (with
    picture) 228

Chaffee, Roger B., **3** 445
Commemorative stamps and medals, **3** 495
Gemini, **5** 935-37, (picture) 936
Life-support systems, **8** 1341
Maneuvering in space, **8** 1429, (picture)
   1429
Manned spaceflight, **8** 1461, (table) 1461
McDivitt, James A., **8** 1517-18
Pressurization, **10** 1852
Re-entry vehicles, **11** 1934
Rendezvous and docking, **11** 1956
Space garbage, **12** 2119
White, H. C.
   Coast Guard aviation, **3** 479
Whiteout
   Bushflying, **3** 393
   Polar flights, **10** 1828
   Poles, **10** 1834
White, Robert M.
   Altitude and altitude records, **1** 147, 148
   X-15 research program, **14** 2530, 2533
White Sands Missile Range, 13 2483-84,
   (with picture)
   Missile test ranges, **9** 1617
   Testing, **12** 2275
White, Thomas Dresser (1901-   ,
   American Air Force officer), **13** 2482-83
Whipple, Fred Lawrence (1906-   ,
   American astronomer), **13** 2481
White Wing (airplane)
   Aerial Experiment Association, **1** 8
Whitefield, Clare G.
   Schweickart, Rullell L., **11** 2017
Whittle engine
   Aircraft propulsion systems, **1** 57-58
Whittle, Sir Frank J. (1907-   , British
   mechanical engineer), **13** 2484
   Aircraft propulsion systems, **1** 57
   Fuels, **5** 901
   History of aviation, (table), **6** 1119
   Jet engines, **7** 1238, 1235
   Medals and decorations (table), **8** 1526
   Patents, **10** 1766
   United Kingdom aerospace activities,
    13 2347
Whitworth, John
   Precision measurements, **10** 1845
Wichita, Kansas
   Careers (table), **3** 414
Wiechert-Gutenberg Discontinuity
   Earth, **4** 660
Wiener, Norbert
   Cybernetics, **4** 603
Wien's Displacement Law
   Planck's Law, **10** 1817
Wijnmalen, Henri
   Altitude and altitude records, **1** 147
Wilbur Wright Field
   Aerospace industry, **1** 29
Wilbur Wright Memorial Lecturer
   Draper, Charles Stark, **4** 651
Wilkes, Charles
   Poles, **10** 1834
Wilkins, George H.
   Polar flights, **10** 1829-30
Willard, Charles F.
   Barnstormers, **2** 332
Williams, Lt. A. J.
   Speed and speed records, (table),
    12 2141
Williams, Clifton C., Jr., (1932-1967,
   American astronaut), **13** 2484-85
   Astronauts, **2** 216, 218, 219, (with
    picture) 222
Williams, J. Newton
   Aircraft propulsion systems (picture), **1** 53
Willinson, Alan M.
   World War I (table, Top Aces), **14** 2507
Wils, Philip A.
   Medals and decorations (table), **8** 1526
Wilson, Captain N.
   Speed and speed records, (table), **12** 2141
Wilson, Woodrow
   Aerospace industry, **1** 29
   Airmail, **1** 68, (picture) 73
   Airports, **1** 98

Winch
   Airships (picture), **1** 110
Wind, 13 2485-86
   Anemometer, **1** 152
   Beaufort scale, **2** 346
   Crosswind landing, **4** 594-95
   GHOST program, **6** 978
   Gusts, **6** 1043
   Soaring, **11** 2062, 2065
   Thermals, **12** 2283
   Weather, **13** 2451-52
Wind direction and velocity
   Air traffic control, **1** 134
   Preflight training, **10** 1848
Wind direction indicators
   Tetrahedron, **12** 2282
   Windsock, **13** 2487
Wind drag deceleration
   Rocket sled, **11** 1986
Wind drift correction
   Dead reckoning, **4** 611-12
   Drift, **4** 651-52
Wind flow field
   Aviation weather, **2** 299
Wind, Hans
   World War II (table), **14** 2517
Windmill plane
   Autogiros, **2** 285
Windows and windshields, 13 2486-87
   Airplane, **1** 83
   Terminology of aerospace (table), **12** 2272
Wind sock, 13 2487
   Airports, **1** 97
Wind triangle problem
   Groundspeed, **6** 1029
Wind tunnels, 13 2487-88, (with pictures)
   Aerodynamics, **1** 21, (picture) 19
   Airfoil, **1** 62
   Italy's aerospace activities (picture), **7** 1222
   NASA (picture), **9** 1656
   Ramjet engines, **10** 1901
   Rockets and rocketry, **11** 1975
   Royal Aeronautical Society, **11** 1994
   Schlieren photography, **11** 2015
   Shock tubes and tunnels, **11** 2048
   Wright brothers, **14** 2524-25
Wind vanes
   Meteorology, **9** 1555-56
Wing design
   Jet aircraft, **7** 1232
   Reciprocating engines, **11** 1918
Wing-down method
   Piloting techniques, **10** 1800
Winged Defense (book)
   Mitchell, William, **9** 1621
Winged Peace (book)
   Bishop, William Avery, **2** 362
Winged Warfare (book)
   Bishop, William Avery, **2** 362
Wing fatigue
   Jumbo jets, **7** 1252
Wing flaps
   X-15 research program, **14** 2532
Wingfoot Lighter-Than-Air Society
   Balloons, **2** 322
Wing lift force
   Maneuvers (diagrams), **8** 1435
Wing loading
   Commercial air transports, **3** 520
Wing-mounted nacelles
   Landing gear, **7** 1299
Wingover
   World War I, **14** 2506
Wing roots
   Aerodynamics, **1** 24
   Airplane, **1** 86
   Wings, **14** 2491
Wings, 14 2489-93
   Airframe, **1** 66
   Airplane, **1** 84-86
   Supersonic flight, **12** 2177
   Variable geometry, **13** 2405
Wings for Life (book)
   Nichols, Ruth Rowland, **9** 1696
Wingspan
   Sailplanes (with picture), **11** 2003-04

Wing spar
Airplane, **1** 85
Wings, **14** 2490
Wingtip
Airplane, **1** 85
Wings, **14** 2491
Wing walkers
Barnstormers, **2** 334, 335
Wing warping controls
Chanute, Octave, **3** 448
Winnie Mae, Lockheed Vega, 14 2493
World records and round-the-world flights, **14** 2497
Winter flight suits
Personal equipment, **10** 1775
Winter solstice
Ecliptic, **4** 669
Wire guidance systems
Battlefield missile systems, **2** 342
Missiles, **9** 1614
Wireless telegraphy
Morse code, **9** 1639
World War I, **14** 2503
Wisconsin Regional Space Center
Regional space centers, **11** 1945
Wise, John (1808-1879, American balloonist and inventor), **14** 2493
Airmail, **1** 69
Balloons, **2** 317, 318
Wittman, Steve
Air races, **1** 103-05
Medals and decorations (table), **8** 1526
Wolf (aircraft carrier)
World War I, **14** 2503
Wolfchen (seaplane)
World War I, **14** 2503
Wolf, Constance
Balloons, **2** 320
Medals and decorations (table), **8** 1526
Woman of the Year in Aviation
Cobb, Geraldyn, **3** 480
Women in aerospace, 14 2493-96
Aero clubs, **1** 18
Balloons, **2** 320
Ninety-Nines, **9** 1697-98
Powder Puff Derby, **10** 1840
Whirly Girls, **13** 2481
World records and round-the-world flights, **14** 2499
Women's Air Force Service Pilots
Cochran, Jacqueline, **3** 481
Women in aerospace, **14** 2495
Women's altitude record
Cobb, Geraldyn, **3** 480
Women's Auxiliary Ferrying Squadron
Women in aerospace, **14** 2495
Wood, 14 2496
Woolams, Jack
X-series aerospace vehicles, **14** 2534
Woodard, V. C.
World War II (table), **14** 2517
Wooldridge, Dean
Program management, **10** 1857
Ramo, Simon, **10** 1902
Woomera rocket range, 14 2496-97
Australia's aviation, **2** 278-84
WRESAT, **14** 2524
Word
Computers, **3** 554
Worden, Alfred M. (1932-   ) **14** 2497
Astronauts, **2** 217, 218, 219 (with picture)
Work
Energy, **4** 712
Working fluid
Launch vehicles, **7** 1328
Work Tower
Launch facilities, **7** 1307
World Aeronautical Chart
Charts, **3** 450
World Agricultural Aircraft and Areas Treated
Crop dusting (table), **4** 587
World Civil Airlines (1919-1966) chart
Commercial airlines, **3** 511

World Class Records
World records and round-the-world flights, **14** 2498
World Meteorological Organization
Meteorology, **9** 1559
United Nations, **13** 2357
World records and round-the-world flights, 14 2497-99
World Soaring Records
Soaring (with table), **11** 2062
World War 1 (with pictures and table), **14** 2500-10
Aerospace industry, **1** 29
Aircraft carriers, **1** 48-49
Aircraft propulsion systems, **1** 53
Air raid, **1** 104
Antiaircraft weapons, **1** 156
Army aviation, **2** 195
Biplane, **2** 358
Blimps, **2** 364
Bomber aircraft, **2** 372
Canada's aviation, **3** 400
Dirigibles, **4** 628-32
Dogfight, **4** 643
First World War aircraft, **5** 815-25
Flying Circus, **5** 861
History of aviation, **6** 1106
Insignia, aircraft, **7** 1163
International airmail, **7** 1188
Italy's aerospace activities, **7** 1220
Jenny, Curtiss JN-4D, **7** 1231-32
Kites, **7** 1279
Lafayette Escadrille, **7** 1295
Manufacturing, **8** 1467
Military aviation, **9** 1580
Missiles, **9** 1611
Naval aviation, worldwide, **9** 1667-72
OX-5 Club, **10** 1751
Parachutes, **10** 1756-57
Paulhan, Louis, **10** 1769
Pegoud, Adolphe, **10** 1773
Plastics, **10** 1823
Pontoons, **10** 1838
Post, Wiley, **10** 1839
Quiet Birdmen, **10** 1871
Reciprocating engines, **11** 1918
Richthofen, Baron Manfred von, **10** 1964
Rickenbacker, Edward Vernon, **10** 1964-65
Royal Air Force, **11** 1994-96
Seaplanes, **11** 2024
Top Aces (table), **14** 2507
Zeppelins, **14** 2549, 2550
World War II, 14 2511-23
Aerial photography, **1** 10, 11
Aerospace industry, **1** 30-31
Aircraft carriers, **1** 49-50
Aircraft propulsion systems, **1** 58-59
Airports, **1** 98
Air raid, **1** 104
Airships, **1** 112, 114
Air-to-surface missiles, **1** 122-23
Antiaircraft weapons, **1** 156-58
Army aviation, **2** 195
Arnold, Henry Harley, **2** 201
Attack aircraft, **2** 273
Autogiros, **2** 286
Aviation medicine, **2** 295
Balloons, **2** 324
Battle of Britain, **2** 343
Berlin airlift, **2** 351-52
Blimps, **2** 365
Blitzkrieg, **2** 366
Boeing, William Edward, **2** 370
Bomber aircraft, **2** 374
Bombs, **3** 377
Brabazon of Tara, Lord, **3** 384
Coast Guard aviation, **3** 475-80
Douglas C-54, **4** 648
Douglas DC-3, **4** 648-49
Fighter aircraft, **5** 807-11
Flying Tigers, **5** 865-66
Government in aerospace, **6** 1002
History of aviation, **6** 1111
Hump airlift, **6** 1136
Inertial guidance, **7** 1152
Infrared radiation, **7** 1162

Intelligence, military, **7** 1180
International Civil Aviation Organization, **7** 1191-92
Invader, Douglas, A-26, B-26, **7** 1214
Italy's aerospace activities, **7** 1220
Japan's aerospace activities, **7** 1227
Jet aircraft, **7** 1232-36
Jet engines, **7** 1238
Kamikaze, **7** 1262
Korolev, Sergei, **7** 1290
Langley Research Center, **7** 1302
LeMay, Curtis Emerson, **7** 1331
Luftwaffe, **8** 1375-77
Manhattan Project, **8** 1442
Manufacturing, **8** 1470
Marine Corps Aviation, **8** 1481-82
Military aviation, **9** 1583-87
Missiles, **9** 1611
Mitchell, North American B-25, **9** 1621
Mitsubishi Zero-Sen, **9** 1622
Mustang, North American P-51, **9** 1643
Naval aviation, worldwide, **9** 1667-72
Outsize cargo aircraft, **10** 1749
P-26, Boeing, **10** 1865
P-40 Curtiss, **10** 1776
Patents, **10** 1766
Pearl Harbor, **10** 1769
Peenemuende, **10** 1770
Phonetic alphabet, **10** 1778
Plastics, **10** 1824
Pontoons, **10** 1838
Program management, **10** 1857
Pulsejet engine, **10** 1866
Quiet Birdmen, **10** 1871
Radar, **10** 1877
Radio, **10** 1888
Radio communications, **10** 1897
Refueling, **11** 1937
Rickenbacker, Edward Vernon, **11** 1965
Rockets and rocketry, **11** 1977
Royal Air Force, **11** 1995
Sabre, North American F-86, **11** 2000
Second World War aircraft, **11** 2027-38
Spaatz, Carl, **11** 2092
Top Aces (table), **14** 2517
United States Air Force, **13** 2358-75
United States Naval Aviation, **13** 2376-90
V-1 missile, **13** 2430
V-2 rocket missile, **13** 2445-46
World Weather Watch system
Meteorology, **9** 1559
Weather satellites, **13** 2471
Worthman, Paul E.
Reconnaissance satellites, **11** 1926
Wren 460 (airplane)
High-lift devices, **6** 1088
WRESAT, 14 2524
Woomera rocket range, **14** 2497
W. R. Grace and Company
Commercial airlines, **3** 508
Wright Aeronautical Corporation
Bellanca, Giuseppe, **2** 348
Wright Air Development Center
Astronauts, **2** 220
Wright Apache
Altitude and altitude records, **1** 148
Wright B-1
United States Naval Aviation (picture), **13** 2377
Wright brothers, 14 2524-26
Aeronautics, **1** 26
Aerospace industry **1** 29
Aircraft propulsion systems, **1** 52, 54, 55
Airfoil, **1** 62
Airplane, **1** 87
Air shows, **1** 115
Aluminum, **1** 148
Aviation, **2** 292
Barnstormers, **2** 332
Bell, Alexander Graham, **2** 347
Cayley glider, **3** 426
Chanute, Octave, **3** 446
Commemorative stamps and medals, **3** 494
Educational implications of aerospace, **4** 673

(Continued)

Gliders, **6** 985
History of aviation, **6** 1097, 1099, 1100, 1101, (table) 1119
Instrument panels, **7** 1173
Kites, **7** 1279
Langley, Samuel Pierpont, **7** 1303
Lefebvre, Eugene, **7** 1330
Manufacturing, **8** 1466
Materials, **8** 1500
Patents, **10** 1766
Reciprocating engines, **11** 1913
Roe, Alliott Verdon, **11** 1989
Short brothers, **22** 2049
United States Air Force, **13** 2359
Wright Brothers Day
National Aerospace Education Council, **9** 1658
Wright Brothers Memorial Trophy
National Aeronautic Association, **9** 1648
Trophies and awards, (table), **13** 2312
Wright Brothers National Memorial
Kitty Hawk, North Carolina, **7** 1280
Wright brothers, **14** 2526
Wright Flyer (airplane), **14** 2527 (with picture, chart, diagram)
Aerial Experiment Association, **1** 8
Government in aerospace, (picture), **6** 1000
History of Aviation, **6** 1100, (picture) 1100
National Air and Space Museum, **9** 1659
Patents, **10** 1767 (with diagram)
Wright brothers, **14** (picture) 2525-26
Wright, Orville (1871-1948, American aviation pioneer), **14** 2524-26
Aircraft propulsion systems, **1** 54
Airmail, **1** 68-69
Altitude and altitude records, **1** 147
Army aviation, **2** 195
Biplane, **2** 358
Kitty Hawk, North Carolina, **7** 1280
Materials, **8** 1499-1500
Wright Patterson Air Force Base
Air University, **1** 140
Wright Turbo Compounds
Aircraft propulsion systems, **1** 56
Wright Whirlwind planes
Coast Guard aviation, **3** 477
Wright, Wilbur (1867-1912, American aviation pioneer), **14** 2424-26, (picture) 2526
Aerial photography, **1** 10
Airmail, **1** 68-69
Biplane, **2** 358
Distance and distance records, **4** 640
Kitty Hawk, North Carolina, **7** 1280
Written examination
Pilot training, **10** 1810
"Wrong Way" Corrigan
Corrigan, Douglas, **3** 567
W-type engines
Reciprocating engines, **11** 1914
Wurster, Herman
Speed and speed records, (table), **12** 2141
Wyld, James H.
American Rocket Society, **1** 151

X

X
Terminology of aerospace (table), **12** 2272
X-1 (Bell)
Altitude and altitude records, **1** 148
Bell, Lawrence Dale, **2** 348
Edwards Air Force Base, **4** 678
Everest, Frank Kendall, Jr., **4** 758
Government in aerospace, **6** 1005
History of aviation, **6** 1118
Rockets and rocketry, **11** 1983
Supersonic flight, **12** 2177
United States Air Force, **12** 2364
X-series aerospace vehicles (picture), **14** 2534-37
Yeager, Charles E., **14** 2547
X-1A and 1B
X-series aerospace vehicles (picture), **14** 2535
X-2 (Bell)
Altitude and altitude records, **1** 148
Rockets and rocketry, **11** 1983
X-series aerospace vehicles, **14** 2537-38, (picture) 2536
X-3 (Douglas)
X-series aerospace vehicles (picture), **14** 2538,
X-4 (guided missile) (Northrop)
Air-to-air missiles, **1** 120
X-series aerospace vehicles, **14** 2538, (picture) 2539
X-5 (Bell)
X-series aerospace vehicles, **14** 2538, 2540 (picture), 2539,
X-6 (Convair)
X-series aerospace vehicles, **14** 2540
X-7 (Lockheed)
X-series aerospace vehicles, **14** 2540, (picture) 2539
X-8 (Aerojet-General)
X-series aerospace vehicles, **14** 2540
X-9 Shrike (Bell)
X-series aerospace vehicles, **14** 2540-41
X-10 (North American)
X-series aerospace vehicles, **14** 2541, (picture) 2539
X-11 and X-12 (Convair)
X-series aerospace vehicles, **14** 2541
X-13 Vertijet (Ryan)
V/stol aircraft, **13** 2439
X-series aerospace vehicles, **14** 2541-42 (picture) 2539
X-14 (Bell)
X-series aerospace vehicles, **14** 2542, (picture) 2539
X-15 research program, **14** 2529-33
rocket engines
Aircraft propulsion systems, **1** 59
Rockets and rocketry, **11** 1983, 1985
Rocket sled, **11** 1986
X-series aerospace vehicles, **14** 2542, (picture) 2539
X-15 rocket plane (North American)
Aerodynamics (picture), **1** 22
Aerospace, **1** 27
Altitude and altitude records, **1** 148
Armstrong, Neil A., **2** 193
Astronauts, **2** 216
Astronaut wings, **2** 232
Crossfield, Albert Scott, Jr., **4** 594
Edwards Air Force Base, **4** 678
Experimental aircraft, **4** 760
Government in aerospace, **6** 1005
Guidance and control systems, **6** 1040
Life-support systems, **8** 1338
Manufacturing, **8** 1472
Mercury program, **9** 1530
National Aeronauitcs and Space Administration, **9** 1653
PILOT, **10** 1793
Reaction control systems (diagram), **10** 1911
Test pilots and test flying, **12** 2278
X-16 (Bell)
X-series aerospace vehicles, **14** 2542
X-17 (Lockheed)
X-series aerospace vehicles, **14** 2542, (picture) 2540
X-18 (Hiller)
X-series aerospace vehicles, **14** 2542-43
X-19 (Curtiss-Wright)
X-series aerospace vehicles, **14** 2543
X-20 Dyna-Soar (Boeing)
Crews, Albert H., Jr., **4** 584
Dynamic soaring, **4** 656
Dyna-Soar program (picture), **4** 657
X-series aerospace vehicles, **14** 2543, (picture) 2540
X-20 Kite (picture)
Kites, **7** 1278
X-21 (Northrop)
X-series aerospace vehicles, **14** 2543-44, (picture) 2541
V/STOL aircraft (table), **13** 2443
X-series aerospace vehicles, **14** 2544, (picture) 2542
X-23 lifting body (Martin-Marietta)
X-series aerospace vehicles, **14** 2544, (picture) 2543
X-24 lifting body (Martin-Marietta)
Lifting-body vehicles, **8** 1349, (picture) 1347, (diagrams) 1374, 1348
X-series aerospace vehicles (picture), **14** 2534
X-258 (engine)
Delta rocket, **4** 622
XAIM-54A
Air-to-air missiles, **1** 121
XB-70 (North American), **14** 2528-29 (with picture, table, and diagram)
Manufacturing, **8** 1472
X-band
Jumbo jets, **7** 1255
XBQM-34E
Drone aircraft, **4** 653
XC-142A (airplane) (LTV-Hiller-Ryan)
V/STOL aircraft, **13** 2442
X-concept
Antiballistic missile defense, **1** 159
Xenon
Air, **1** 42
XH-51N (airplane) (Lockheed)
V/STOL aircraft, **13** 2444
XP-59 (Bell)
Aircraft propulsion systems, **1** 58
Jet aircraft, **7** 1233
Lewis Research Center, **7** 1334
XP6M-1 Seamaster, see Martin XP6M-1 Seamaster
X-pointer
Instrument panels, **7** 1178
X-ray
Antiballistic missile defense, **1** 159
Electronics, **4** 672
Gamma rays, **5** 913
X-ray astronomy
Aerobee, **1** 18
X-ray astronomy explorer
NASA (drawing), **9** 1651
X-ray detector
Nuclear detection satellites, **9** 1709, (picture) 1708
X-rays, 14 2533
Observatories, **10** 1726
Orbiting observatories, **10** 1738
Photography, **10** 1785
Tube **14** 2533
Vacuum tubes, **13** 2398
X-ray star, 14 2533
X-series aerospace vehicles, 14 2534-44
X shape
tail surfaces
Airships, **1** 108
X-type engines
Reciprocating engines, **11** 1914
XV-4B Hummingbird II (Lockheed)
V/STOL aircraft, **13** 2444
XV-5A, see Ryan XV-5A
XV-6A, see P. 1127 Kestrel

Y

Yaeger, Charles Elwood (1923-
American test pilot), **14** 2547-48
Bell, Lawrence Dale, **2** 348
Mach, Ernst, **8** 1416
Manufacturing, **8** 1472
Medals and decorations (table, FAI Gold
Air Medal), **8** 1526
Supersonic flight, **12** 2177
Test pilots and test flying, **12** 2278
United States Air Force, **13** 2365
X-series aerospace vehicles, **14** 2535, 2537
Yager, Frank
Airmail, **1** 73
Yak aircraft, 14 2545 (with pictures)
U.S.S.R. aerospace activities (table),
13 2337
YAK-1 (Yakovlev)
World War II, **14** 2515
Yak-9 (Yakovlev)
Second World War aircraft (picture),
11 2032
World War II, **14** 2515
YAK aircraft (picture), **14** 2545
Yak-18 (Yakovlev)
General aviation aircraft (picture), **6** 964
International competitions (picture),
7 1192
U.S.S.R. aerospace activities (table),
13 2337
YAK aircraft (picture), **14** 2545, 2546
Yak-25 fighter (Yakovlev)
Air forces of the world, **1** 65
U.S.S.R. aerospace activities (table),
13 2337
YAK aircraft, **14** 2545
YAK-28 (Yakovlev)
U.S.S.R. aerospace activities (table),
13 2337
YAK aircraft, **14** 2546
YAK-32 (Yakovlev)
YAK aircraft (picture), **14** 2546
YAK-40 (Yakovlev)
YAK aircraft, **14** 2546
Yakovlev, Aleksander Sergeevich
(1906-   , Russian aircraft designer),
14 2546-47
Medals and decorations (table, FAI Gold
Air Medal), **8** 1526
Yakovlev Mandrake
U.S.S.R. aerospace activities (table),
13 2337
YAK aircraft, **14** 2546
Yalu River
Korean war, **7** 1285
Yankee Clipper (Boeing)
Commercial airlines, **3** 509
YAT-37D
Counter-insurgency aircraft, **4** 576,
(picture) 577
Yaw, 14 2547
Axes of rotation, **2** 308
Bank, **2** 332
Instrument panels, **7** 1177
Maneuvers, **8** 1433
Piloting techniques, **10** 1802
Rudder, **11** 1998
Yaw axis
Aerodynamics, **1** 23
Airplane, **1** 87
Attitude and attitude control, **2** 275
Yaw damper, 14 2547
Year of the Quiet Sun
Astronomy, **2** 249
Yegorov, Boris (1937-   , Russian
cosmonaut), **14** 2548
Cosmonauts, **4** 574, (pictures) 570-71,
(table) 574
Manned spaceflight, **8** 1461 (table)

Medals and decorations (table, FAI Gold
Space Medal), **8** 1524
Spaceflight training (picture), **12** 2117
Voskhod, **13** 2433
Yellow alert, 14 2548
Blue alert, **2** 369
Red alert, **11** 1930
Yemen
Commemorative stamps and medals,
3 495
Yerkes Observatory
Astronomy, **2** 240, 242
Telescopes and astronomical instruments,
12 2247, 2250
Yevstigneev, K. A.
World War II (table), **14** 2517
YF-12A fighter interceptor (Lockheed)
Air forces of the world, **1** 66
Air-to-air missiles, **1** 121
History of aviation, **6** 1120
Johnson, Clarence Leonard, **7** 1242
Yorkshire, England
Ballistic Missile Early Warning System,
2 314
Yorktown (ship)
Aircraft carriers, **1** 49
United States Naval Aviation, **13** 2380,
2382, 2383
Yost, Ed
Balloons (with picture), **2** 318-19
Youmachev, Andre
Distance and distance records, **4** 640
Young, John Watts (1930-   ), **14** 2548
Astronauts, **2** 216-17, 219, 224, 227
Gemini, **5** 931-34, 946-47, (pictures)
933, 947
Manned spaceflight, **8** 1461 (table)
Ranger, **10** 1909
YS-11 (NAMC)
Japan's aerospace activities (picture),
7 1128
Y shape
tail surfaces
Airships, **1** 108
Yugoslavia
Crop dusting, **4** 587
European aerospace activities, **4** 751
World War II, **14** 2515

Z

Zahm, Dr. Albert F.
V/STOL aircraft, **13** 2438
Zaic, Frank
Medals and decorations (table, Paul
Tissandier Diploma), **8** 1526
Zap
Terminology of aerospace (table), **12** 2272
Zeigler, Jean (Skip)
Test pilots and test flying, **12** 2280
Zeke (aircraft) see Mitsubishi Zero-Sen
Zener diode
Electronics, **4** 703
Zenith
Astronomy, **2** 240
Celestial sphere, **3** 431
Zeppelin, 14 2549-52
Aerial photography, **1** 10
Aircraft, **1** 45
Air raid, **1** 104
Airships, **1** 105, 111-13
Alloys, **1** 144
Dirigibles **2** 631

Dirigible sheds
World War I, **14** 2502
First World War aircraft, **5** 817, 823
Flight routes (map), **14** 2551
World War I, **14** 2503, (picture) 2509
Zeppelin Company
Airships, **1** 112
Dirigibles, **4** 631
Zeppelin, Ferdinand von
Aircraft, **1** 45, 105, 111
Balloons, **2** 318
Commemorative stamps and medals,
3 494
History of aviation, **6** 1105
Zeppelin L-49
Airships, **1** 112
Zeppelin Works
Eckener, Hugo, **4** 668
Zero, 14 2552
Zero (airplane), see Mitsubishi
Zero-Sen
Zero altitude drops
Bombs, **3** 378
Zero ceiling
Zero, **14** 2552
Zero defects, 14 2552
Zero Defects Craftsmanship Award
Agena rockets, **1** 39
Zero degree angle
Pitch, **10** 1816
Zero gravity
Biosatellites, **2** 356
Weightlessness, **13** 2473
Zero-gravity simulator
Astronauts, **2** 215
Space biology, **11** 2094
Zero, **14** 2552
Zero-gravity flight
Space biology, **11** 2095
Zero in
Zero, **14** 2552
Zero-length rocket
Zero, **14** 2552
Zero-Sen see Mitsubishi Zero-Sen
Zero visibility
Zero, **14** 2552
Zero-zero weather
Zero, **14** 2552
Zeus
Antiballistic missile defense, **1** 159
Zhukovsky Air Force Academy
Bykovsky, Valeri, **3** 397
Zimenski Observatory
Communications satellites, **3** 533
Zinc
Magnesium, **8** 1419
Zinc plate
Battery, **2** 338
Zip gun
Maneuvering in space, **8** 1429
Z marker
Navigation systems, **9** 1675
Zodiac
Astronomy, **2** 242
Constellations, **3** 562
Zodiac (airship)
First World War aircraft, **5** 823
Zond 3
Astronomy, **2** 243
U.S.S.R. aerospace activities, **13** 2343
Zoning ordinances
Airports, **1** 94
ZPG-2W
Blimps, **2** 365
ZPG-3W
Airships, **1** 114
Blimps, **2** 365-66
ZR-3
Eckener, Hugo, **4** 668
Zuikaku
Aircraft carriers, **1** 49
Zulu time, 14 2552
Zuni
Air-to-surface missiles, **1** 124
Zvezdochka
Animals in space, **1** 155

VOLUME XIV ILLUSTRATIONS COURTESY OF: